RECENT ADVANCES IN CONSERVATION

INTERNATIONAL INSTITUTE FOR CONSERVATION OF HISTORIC AND ARTISTIC WORKS

L'INSTITUT INTERNATIONAL POUR LA CONSERVATION D'OBJETS D'ART ET D'HISTOIRE

The Institute was founded in 1950 to provide a permanent organization to coordinate and improve the knowledge, methods and working standards needed to protect and preserve precious materials of all kinds.

The Institute publishes a specialist journal, *Studies in Conservation*, as well as *Abstracts of the Technical Literature on Archaeology and the Fine Arts*, and a house journal, *IIC News*.

The incorporation of the Institute as a company required the choice of one country for its headquarters and for various practical reasons the Head Office was established in London (address: IIC, c/o National Gallery, Trafalgar Square, London, W.C.2). The Council is, however, international and there are now members of IIC in 52 countries and in most of the major museums of the world.

COUNCIL AND OFFICERS
(at time of conference)

PRESIDENT

A. van Schendel, D.PHIL.

VICE-PRESIDENTS

P. B. Coremans, D.SC.
H. J. Plenderleith, C.B.E., LL.D.(HON), PH.D., F.S.A., F.R.S.E.
F. I. G. Rawlins, C.B.E., M.SC., F.S.A., F.R.S.E., F.INST.P.

SECRETARY-GENERAL

N. S. Brommelle, B.A., A.INST.P.

TREASURER

S. Rees Jones, M.SC., F.S.A., F.INST.P.

ORDINARY MEMBERS

R. J. Gettens, B.S., A.M.
S. Paramasivan, D.SC.
G. L. Stout, A.B., A.M., LITT.D.(HON)
A. E. Werner, D.PHIL.

AMERICAN REPRESENTATIVE

S. Keck, A.B.

MEMBERSHIP COMMITTEE

P. B. Coremans, D.SC.
A. van Schendel, D.PHIL.
Madame M. Hours
S. Keck, A.B.

EDITORS

G. Thomson, M.A. (for *Studies in Conservation* and Technical Publications)
R. J. Gettens, B.S., A.M. (for *IIC Abstracts*)
Miss R. M. Spielman (for *IIC News*)

EDITORIAL ADVISORY COMMITTEE
(for *Studies in Conservation*)

S. Augusti, D.SC.
W. G. Constable, M.A., D.C.L., F.S.A.
P. Coremans, D.SC.
R. J. Gettens, B.S., A.M.
P. Hendy, M.A.
U. Procacci, PH.D.
F. I. G. Rawlins, C.B.E., M.SC., F.S.A., F.R.S.E., F.INST.P.
A. van Schendel, D.PHIL.
G. L. Stout, A.B., A.M., LITT.D.(HON)
B. Marconi, D.SC.
H. Maryon, F.S.A.
H. J. Plenderleith, C.B.E., LL.D.(HON), PH.D., F.S.A., F.R.S.E.
C. Wolters, D.PHIL.
K. Yamasaki

ROME CONFERENCE AND HONORIFIC COMMITTEE

Prof. De Angelis d'Ossat G., *Director of the Institute of History of Architecture, former Director of Fine Arts*
Prof. Vincenzo Arangio-Ruiz, *President of Accademia dei Lincei*
Prof. Giacinto Bosco, *Minister of Public Education*
Prof. Cesare Brandi, *Professor, University of Palermo, former Director of Istituto Centrale del Restauro*
Prof. Foschini, *Professor of Chemistry and Director of the Institute of Merceologia*
Prof. Attilio Fralese, *Director of Library Department, Ministry of Public Education*
Ing. C. M. Lerici, *President of the Societa Italiana Acciai Inossidabili*
Prof. B. Molajoli, *Director of Fine Arts and Chief of the Soprintendenze*

Prof. Giovanni Muzzioli, *Director of Istituto di Patologia del Libro*
Prof. Giovanni Polvani, *President of the National Council of Research*
Prof. Piero Romanelli, *Chairman, Italian Museums Association*
Prof. Pasquale Rotondi, *Director of Istituto Centrale del Restauro*
Prof. Leopoldo Sandri, *Director of Italian Central Archives*
Count Paolo della Torre di Sanguineto, *Director of Pontifical Museums and Galleries*
Prof. Charles Verlinden, *Director of the Accademia Belgica and Current Chairman of the Unione Internazionale degli Istituti di Archeologia, Storia e Storia dell'Arte in Rome*
Count Senator Umberto Zanotti-Bianco, *President of Italia Nostra*

JOINT ORGANIZING COMMITTEE

Mr N. S. Brommelle
Mr S. Rees Jones
Dr A. E. Werner

Dr H. J. Plenderleith
Professor P. Philippot
Mr G. Thomson (Editor of Conference technical literature)

Professor L. Santucci
Professor P. Mora
Mr I. Angle

(a) Taper section through metal and mineral on foot of Chinese bronze Chueh, 11th century B.C. (magnification ×34)

(see p. 108)

(b) Flake of patina from Chinese bronze Li, 9th or 10th century B.C. (magnification ×90)

(see p. 108)

(c) Flake of patina off a bronze from Nimrud (polarized light, magnification ×24)

(see p. 108)

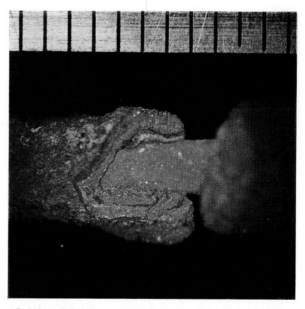

(d) Mineral sheath surrounding remains of copper chisel excavated at Jericho (magnification ×6)—scale in millimetres

(see p. 107)

PLATE I

(a) Algae attack on a restored fresco (Domus Aurea, Rome)
after exposure to light

(see p. 62)

(b) Mosaic plaque made by fusing together bits of six different
coloured glasses (Roman, 1st century B.C. or 1st century A.D.,
possibly made in Alexandria; 1·8 × 1·8 × 0·8 cm)

(see p. 146)

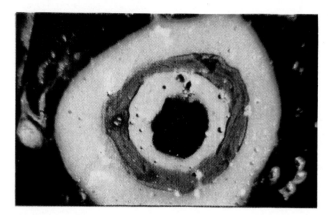

(c) Millefiori fragment (Roman, 1st century B.C. or 1st century
A.D.). Chemical analyses of glasses and of individual particles
of opacifying agents were made with electron microbeam probe

(see p. 146)

(d) Deterioration of a fresco (church of
S. Clemente, Rome) caused by streptomyces, which covered the painting with
a white efflorescence that altered the
colours

(see p. 62)

PLATE II

RECENT ADVANCES

IN

CONSERVATION

CONTRIBUTIONS TO THE IIC ROME
CONFERENCE, 1961

Edited by

G. THOMSON

LONDON

BUTTERWORTHS

1963

England: BUTTERWORTH & CO. (PUBLISHERS) LTD
LONDON: 88 Kingsway, W.C.2

Africa: BUTTERWORTH & CO. (AFRICA) LTD
DURBAN: 33–35 Beach Grove

Australia: BUTTERWORTH & CO. (AUSTRALIA) LTD
SYDNEY: 6–8 O'Connell Street
MELBOURNE: 473 Bourke Street
BRISBANE: 240 Queen Street

Canada: BUTTERWORTH & CO. (CANADA) LTD
TORONTO: 1367 Danforth Avenue, 6

New Zealand: BUTTERWORTH & CO. (NEW ZEALAND) LTD
WELLINGTON: 49–51 Ballance Street
AUCKLAND: 35 High Street

U.S.A.: BUTTERWORTH INC.
WASHINGTON, D.C.: 7235 Wisconsin Avenue, 14

Suggested UDC number: 7·025·3/·4
Suggested additional UDC number: 069·4

Printed in Northern Ireland at The Universities Press, Belfast

FOREWORD

Recent Advances in Conservation is the record of just another international conference of a professional organization—yet with a difference important in this age of specialization. Its topics range from the use of refined electronic techniques to discussions on the esthetic principles of conservation. Here are people who, in the day-to-day course of their profession, must cross and recross the boundaries between what have come to be known as the 'two cultures', art and science. They do not in all cases do this with perfect ease, yet the momentum is such that standards of work and knowledge are steadily increasing, while government funds are being allotted with a better sense of proportion to the proper conservation of priceless antiquities and to the research that must accompany it.

The delegates to this conference represented those who are responsible for the decisions and operations which will safeguard the cultural heritage of twenty-five countries. This book may therefore be taken as representative of the state of the art today.

A. van Schendel
President, IIC

INTRODUCTION

The proposal to hold an international conference on conservation was first considered by the Council of the International Institute for Conservation of Historic and Artistic Works (IIC) in 1959. It was agreed that the Conference should deal with subjects which were of particular interest at the time to professional conservators, i.e. subjects in which positive progress had recently been made, in research or practice.

The subjects for discussion, drawn up by a committee of IIC members in London and Rome, encompassed the whole field of conservation. The present volume contains the 47 papers which were circulated as preprints before the Conference.

The practical arrangements for the Conference were greatly helped by the International Centre for the Study of the Preservation and the Restoration of Cultural Property (the Rome Centre), whose Director, Dr. H. J. Plenderleith, is a Vice-President of IIC.

Two other conservation centres in Rome made important contributions to the organization: the Istituto Centrale del Restauro and the Istituto di Patologia del Libro. Through the courtesy of the late Prof. Giovanni Muzzioli and of Prof. Gustavo Bonaventura, the latter Institute provided the Conference with appropriate and distinguished headquarters. The delegates received with great sorrow the news that Prof. Muzzioli had been killed in an automobile accident a week before the Conference began.

IIC, through its publications and meetings, is a focal point for world technical and professional advances in the field of conservation, and the present publication forms to some extent a summary of the highlights of the rapid progress which has taken place in the subject since the foundation of the Institute in 1950. It is a book which will be widely consulted, and referred to in the technical literature, for a generation to come.

The Conference itself was made financially possible by the generous action of the Calouste Gulbenkian Foundation Lisbon, in releasing for this purpose a sum of money which the Foundation had been holding for the Institute out of an earlier grant.

NORMAN BROMMELLE
Secretary-General, IIC

Note by the Editor. Long abstracts of the papers printed in this book, together with reports of discussions, have been published in *Studies in Conservation*, 6, No. 4 (1961) (complete issue).

CONTENTS

Foreword v

Introduction vii

List of Contributors xiii

MUSEUM CLIMATE

Evaluation of Spectral Radiation Hazards in Window-lighted Galleries
   Laurence S. Harrison 1
The Influence of Light on Museum Objects
   J. Lodewijks 7
Some studies on the Protection of Works of Art during Travel
   Nathan Stolow 9
Relative Humidity in a Closed Package
   Kenzo Toishi 13
Methods of Packing in the Victoria and Albert Museum
   Hugh Wakefield 16

PHYSICAL AND CHEMICAL METHODS OF ANALYSIS

Les Méthodes d'Analyse Appliquées aux Oeuvres d'Art et aux Antiquités
   Selim Augusti 19
Proposal for a Handbook on Analysis of Materials of Paintings
   Rutherford J. Gettens 26
Methods of Analysis (Physical and Microchemical) applied to Paintings and Antiquities
   E. T. Hall 29
Application of the Electron Microbeam Probe and Micro X-rays in Non-destructive Analysis
   W. J. Young 33

FUNGICIDES AND INSECTICIDES

The Application of Chemical and Physical Methods to Conservation of Archival Materials
   Ludovico Santucci 39
Problems in the Use of Insecticides on Occupied Premises
   Piero Gallo 48
Biological Agents which Damage Paper Materials in Libraries and Archives
   Fausta Gallo 55
Microbiological Changes on Frescoes
   Antonio Tonolo and *Clelia Giacobini* 62
Etude de la Résistance biologique des Procédés de Renforcement des Documents graphiques
   F. Flieder 65
Lutte contre les Moisissures des Matériaux constitutifs des Documents graphiques
   F. Flieder 70
The Conservation of Works of Art in Tropical and Sub-tropical Zones
   W. Boustead 73

APPLICATION OF SCIENCE TO CLEANING METHODS

The Effect of Aging and Re-forming on the Ease of Solubility of Certain Resins
   Elizabeth H. Jones 79
Application of Science to Cleaning Methods: Solvent Action Studies on Pigmented and Unpigmented Linseed Oil Films
   Nathan Stolow 84

EXAMINATION AND TREATMENT OF METALLIC OBJECTS

Mineral Alteration Products on Ancient Metal Objects
Rutherford J. Gettens 89

Le Problème de la Conservation des Antiquités métalliques en France
Albert France-Lanord 93

La Restauration et la Conservation de grands Objets de Bronze
Albert France-Lanord 97

Advanced Methods for the Metallurgical Examination of Archaeological Metal Objects
C. Panseri and *M. Leoni* 101

The Examination and Treatment of Bronze Antiquities
R. M. Organ 104

Application à l'Etude des Pièces de Collection en Métal de quelques Méthodes non destructives Utilisées en Métallurgie
Adrienne R. Weill 111

ITALIAN METHODS OF FRESCO TRANSFER

Methods used in Italy for detaching Murals
Leonetto Tintori 118

Some Observations on Mural Paintings
Paolo Mora 123

CONSOLIDATION OF FRAGILE OBJECTS

Consolidation of Fragile Objects
A. E. Werner 125

The Consolidation of Fragile Metallic Objects
R. M. Organ 128

Some New Experiments in the Conservation of Ancient Bronzes
Hanna Jedrzejewska 135

New Methods for the Consolidation of Fragile Objects
Anna M. Rosenqvist 140

EXAMINATION AND CONSERVATION OF GLASS

The Electron-Beam Probe Microanalysis of Ancient Glass
Robert H. Brill and *Sheldon Moll* 145

Repair and Reproduction of Ancient Glass
Rolf Wihr 152

REINFORCING AND TRANSFER OF WOOD PANEL PAINTINGS

Some Applications of Mechanics to the Treatment of Panel Paintings
Richard D. Buck 156

Treatment of Warped Wood Panels by Plastic Deformation; Moisture Barriers; and Elastic Support
Christian Wolters 163

The Transfer of Easel Paintings
A. W. Lucas 165

La Conservation des Peintures sur Panneaux
G. Urbani 169

NEW PICTURE VARNISHES

New Solvent-type Varnishes
R. L. Feller 171

New Picture Varnishes
Garry Thomson 176

TREATMENT AND REPAIR OF TEXTILES AND TAPESTRIES

The Preservation of Textile Objects
    Agnes Geijer 185
Restoration and Preservation of Ancient Textiles, and Natural Science
    Jentina E. Leene 190
Basic Habits of Textile Fibres
    Louisa Bellinger 192
Reinforcing Weakened Textiles with Synthetic-Fibre Net
    E. R. Beecher 195

EDUCATION AND TRAINING OF CONSERVATORS AND RESTORERS

La Formation des Conservateurs et des Restaurateurs
    P. Rotondi 197
Training for Engineers in Conservation
    Sheldon Keck 199
The Training of Restorers
    Helmut Ruhemann 202
Programme of the Faculty of Conservation at the Academy of Fine Arts in Warsaw
    Bohdan Marconi 206
An *ab initio* Course in the Conservation of Antiquities
    Henry Hodges 211

Index 215

LIST OF CONTRIBUTORS

AUGUSTI, SELIM
Director of the Laboratory,
Museo di Capodimonte,
Naples (Italy)

BEECHER, E. R.
Researcher,
Conservation Department,
Victoria and Albert Museum,
London, S.W.7 (Great Britain)

BELLINGER, LOUISA
Curator-Analyst,
Textile Museum,
Washington 8, D.C. (USA)

BOUSTEAD, WILLIAM
Conservator,
National Art Gallery of New South Wales,
Sydney, N.S.W. (Australia)

BRILL, ROBERT H.
Administrator,
Scientific Research,
The Corning Museum of Glass,
Corning Glass Center,
Corning, N.Y. (USA)

BUCK, RICHARD D.
Director,
Intermuseum Laboratory,
Allen Art Building, Oberlin,
Ohio (USA)

FELLER, R. L.
Fellow in Research,
National Gallery of Art Research Project,
Mellon Institute,
Pittsburgh 13, Pa. (USA)

FLIEDER, FRANÇOISE
Attachée de Recherches au C.N.R.S.,
Museum d'Histoire Naturelle,
Laboratoire de Cryptogamie,
12 rue Buffon,
Paris 5 (France)

FRANCE-LANORD, ALBERT
Directeur,
Laboratoire de Recherches Archéologiques,
Musée Historique Lorrain,
Nancy (France)

GALLO, FAUSTA
Biologist,
Istituto di Patologia del Libro,
Via Milano 76,
Rome (Italy)

GALLO, PIERO
Biochemist,
Istituto di Patologia del Libro,
Via Milano 76,
Rome (Italy)

GEIJER, AGNES
Curator in Charge,
Laboratory for Textile Conservation,
Museum of National Antiquities,
Storgatan 41,
Stockholm Ö (Sweden)

GETTENS, RUTHERFORD J.
Head Curator,
Technical Research,
Freer Gallery of Art,
Smithsonian Institution,
Washington 25, D.C. (USA)

GIACOBINI, CLELIA
In charge of microbiological research,
Istituto Centrale del Restauro,
Piazza S. Francesco di Paola 9,
Rome (Italy)

HALL, E. T.
Director,
Research Laboratory for Archaeology
and the History of Art,
6 Keble Road,
Oxford (Great Britain)

HARRISON, LAWRENCE S.
Consulting Engineer,
P.O. Box 628,
Scarsdale, N.Y. (USA)

HODGES, HENRY
Lecturer in Archaeological Technology,
Institute of Archaeology,
31 Gordon Square,
London, W.C.1 (Great Britain)

JEDRZEJEWSKA, HANNA
Head of the Research Laboratory,
Department of Antiquities,
National Museum,
Warsaw (Poland)

JONES, ELIZABETH H.
Chief Conservator,
Fogg Art Museum, Harvard University,
Cambridge 38,
Mass. (USA)

KECK, SHELDON
    Director,
    Conservation Center of the Institute of Fine Arts,
    New York University,
    1 East 78th Street,
    New York 21, N.Y. (USA)

LEENE, JENTINA E.
    Lecturer in Fibre Technology,
    University of Delft,
    Laboratorium voor Textieltechniek en Vezeltechnologie,
    Prof.-Mekelweg 2,
    Delft (Netherlands)

LEONI, M.
    Research Metallurgist,
    Istituto Sperimentale dei Metalli Leggeri,
    C.p. 129,
    Novara (Italy)

LODEWIJKS, J.
    Chemical Engineer,
    University of Delft,
    Laboratorium voor Textieltechniek en Vezeltechnologie,
    Prof.-Mekelweg 2,
    Delft (Netherlands)

LUCAS, A. W.
    Chief Restorer,
    National Gallery,
    London, W.C.2 (Great Britain)

MARCONI, BOHDAN
    Professor and Dean of the Faculty of Conservation,
    Academy of Fine Arts,
    Krakowskie Przedmieście 5,
    Warsaw (Poland)

MOLL, SHELDON
    Laboratory Manager,
    Advanced Metals Research Corporation,
    625 McGrath Highway,
    Somerville,
    Mass. (USA)

MORA, PAOLO
    Restorer, Istituto Centrale del Restauro,
    Piazza S. Francesco di Paola 9,
    Rome (Italy)

ORGAN, R. M.
    Chief Experimental Officer,
    British Museum Research Laboratory,
    London, W.C.1 (Great Britain)

PANSERI, C.
    Director,
    Istituto Sperimentale dei Metalli Leggeri,
    C.p. 129,
    Novara (Italy)

PLESTERS, JOYCE
    Experimental Officer,
    Scientific Department,
    National Gallery,
    London, W.C.2 (Great Britain)

ROSENQVIST, ANNA M.
    Curator of the Technical Department,
    Universitetets Oldsaksamling,
    Frederiks Gate 2,
    Oslo (Norway)

ROTONDI, P.
    Director,
    Istituto Centrale del Restauro,
    Piazza S. Francesco di Paola 9,
    Rome (Italy)

RUHEMANN, HELMUT
    Restorer,
    37 Queens Grove,
    London, N.W.8 (Great Britain)

SANTUCCI, LUDOVICO
    Chemist,
    Istituto di Patologia del Libro,
    Via Milano 76,
    Rome (Italy)

STOLOW, NATHAN
    Chief,
    Conservation and Scientific Research Division,
    National Gallery of Canada,
    Ottawa,
    Ontario (Canada)

THOMSON, GARRY
    Head of the Scientific Department,
    National Gallery,
    London, W.C.2 (Great Britain)

TINTORI, LEONETTO
    Director,
    Fresco Laboratories for Florentine Galleries,
    Via della Ninna 5,
    Florence (Italy)

TOISHI, KENZO
    Chief of the Physical Research Section,
    National Research Institute of Cultural Properties,
    Ueno Park,
    Tokyo (Japan)

TONOLO, ANTONIO
    Professor,
    Istituto Centrale del Restauro
    Piazza S. Francesco di Paola 9,
    Rome (Italy)

URBANI, GIOVANNI
    Inspector,
    Istituto Centrale del Restauro,
    Piazza S. Francesco di Paola 9,
    Rome (Italy)

WAKEFIELD, HUGH
    Keeper of Circulation,
    Victoria and Albert Museum,
    London, S.W.7 (Great Britain)

WEILL, ADRIENNE R.
    Conseiller Scientifique du Laboratoire du Musée du Louvre,
    56–60 rue de l'Amiral Mouchez,
    Paris 14 (France)

WERNER, A. E.
    Keeper,
    British Museum Research Laboratory,
    London, W.C.1 (Great Britain)

WIHR, ROLF
    Restorer,
    Rheinisches Landesmuseum,
    Trier (Germany)

WOLTERS, CHRISTIAN
    Keeper,
    Doerner Institut,
    Meiserstrasse 10,
    Munich (Germany)

YOUNG, W. J.
    Head of Research Laboratory,
    Museum of Fine Arts,
    Boston 15,
    Mass. (USA)

Laurence S. Harrison

EVALUATION OF SPECTRAL RADIATION HAZARDS IN WINDOW-LIGHTED GALLERIES

General aspects

The interest among those working in the museum field of photochemical damage appears quite justly to have been directed chiefly towards the effects of artificial light sources. One reason perhaps is because this is more easily controlled than is natural light. The purpose of this paper is to describe (a) the problem of controlling daylight to be used partly for illuminating exhibits and partly for the visiting public viewing the exhibits against and as part of the exterior landscape, and (b) the solution proposed.

The locale of the problem is a museum building under construction in a substantially broad area of handsome public buildings, wide avenues, drives and lawns. The long dimension of the building is oriented east and west. It is designed to accommodate visitors expected to number more than 5,000,000 persons annually. Architectural and esthetic considerations required the provision of large windows, 16 ft. high by 30 ft. wide, on three floors of the east and west façades. This provision posed the problem of regulating their use by curtains in order to 'protect any museum materials which might be exhibited near them in the lifetime of the building . . . the problem of old costumes being probably the most severe that can be anticipated'—the alternative being the blocking up of window openings.

Survey steps

The first step was an investigation of two factors, it being clearly understood that direct sunlight would, under no circumstances, be admitted into the exhibition area with susceptible material on display. One factor is the ratio between overcast illumination from an unobstructed area of sky and the illumination from the same source incident on a vertical window in a similar environment to that of the new building.

The illumination on such a window represents a field of brightness considerably less than a theoretical 180° horizontal and 90° vertical. External, window-glass reflections both within and beyond critical angles contribute substantially to the reduction of available light. Field measurements, later confirmed by a wooden 'mock-up' tested near the building site, indicated that with cut-off of building structure, the incidence of trees, neighbouring buildings and widely varying brightnesses of ground surface, the ratio was between 2 and 3 to 1, or an average of about 0·40 (a 60 per cent light cut-off).

The second factor was the determination of an acceptably low brightness of sky and external surround which would present good visibility through a clear glass window on an overcast day. These tests (from six suburban school buildings with six persons) averaged an incident 120 ft. cd on the window, measured at an angle of 45° from the horizontal. Although an effort was made to select conditions tending toward minimum values of daylight, judgment ranged from 85 to 168 ft. cd for clear visibility.

These two basic factors, then, were:

1. A 60 per cent daylight cut-off representing the ratio of unobstructed sky light to integrated outside illumination on a vertical window.
2. A 120 ft. cd permissible maximum from which an assumed average of 60 ft. cd of incident sunless illumination, annually on a clear glass window measured 45° from horizontal, was established.

The above two factors provided the models for analysing local conditions of spectral radiation and of determining the number of daylight hours during which curtains could be opened.

Two features of the installation were determined before the first analysis. One-quarter inch thick plate glass, known as 'Solar Gray', was specified by the architects in the weather sashes for reducing solar heat load on the air-conditioning. This glass has an external transmittance in the visible spectrum of about 0·42, admitting a relatively high level of ultra-violet.

The second feature was the specified use of $\frac{1}{4}$ in. thick panels of clear Plexiglas IIUF acrylic filter or equivalent in an inner sash. This decision resulted in practically eliminating ultra-violet radiation, thus limiting the scope of analysis to within the visible spectrum. In this regard it cannot be too strongly emphasized that the substantial damage hazard shown here is attributable practically to the visible spectrum alone, a fact which appears to be widely ignored in view of the quite frequently, if justly, emphasized fears of ultra-violet. The combined transmittance of both sashes is then 0·41.

We were thus enabled to raise the permissible maximum of incident outside illumination on the window to 292 ft. cd, keeping the maximum directly inside the window at 120 ft. cd as a criterion for the setting of a light-sensitive controller.

Tests and calculations

Working backwards through Judd's formula and the methods used in the writer's 1954 report[1], it was determined that utilization of the window (open curtains) would probably be about 35 per cent of available daylight. This figure was deemed sufficient by the museum authorities to justify keeping the windows as specified. However, preliminary calculations showed that the hazard was of an order which predicted a probable museum life for exposed material in excess of the life of the building, thus complying with specifications—the actual exhibition of any individual item is taken for half of any total period as expressing maximum possible exposure.

Efforts were made, however, to find or develop new or improved filters. These resulted in testing and evaluating three additional types. *Table 1* shows the characteristics of all four filters so derived, the last column showing those of the filter finally adopted. The latter provides a probable utilization of 54 per cent. Since 71 per cent represents the average total available sunless daylight hours on either of the two façades, the adopted filter will accommodate open curtains for 76 per cent of them, owing to its low value of damage per foot-candle.

Filter II, Kodak 2B Laminate—consisting of an experimental 'sandwich' of Kodak 2B, commercial acetate, colour-printing filter between two layers of clear plate glass, 6 mm in total thickness—proved to be second best. However, because of its thinness, this acetate film may well be used alone behind protection glasses for prints, water colours, Chinese paintings, etc. It is manufactured on special order in 30 in. width and to any length in rolls.

Table 1

Comparative characteristics of filters tested and evaluated for use with ($\frac{1}{4}$ in.) P.P.G. Solar Gray plate glass

	I Plexiglas $\frac{1}{4}$ in. IIUF	II Kodak 2B $\frac{1}{4}$ in. glass laminate	III Plexiglas $\frac{1}{4}$ in. G911A	IV Plexiglas $\frac{1}{4}$ in. G911B
D/fc Zenith sky	0·385	0·301	0·391	0·245
Overcast sky	0·266	0·188	0·237	0·159
Annual average 'sunless' illumination on window (in ft. cd)	399	399	399	399
Total external transmittance of both sashes	0·41	0·36	0·35	0·35
Permissible annual average illumination inside window due to value of D/fc (in ft. cd)	60	69	59	75
Permissible maximum outside illumination incident on window (open curtains) (in ft. cd)	292	383	337	416
Permissible maximum illumination inside window (open curtains) (in ft. cd)	120	138	118	150
Indicated use of window in percentage of daylight hours (annual average)	36	48	42	54

Filters III and IV were made experimentally. The formula finally adopted (IV), to be known commercially as IIUF-3, was developed with special observance of previous results (I, II and III). The characteristics in Column I for the use of Plexiglas IIUF were the criteria used for subsequent filters evaluated.

In explaining how the data of *Table 1* were derived, it may be well briefly to review the factors of the original ratio in the 1954 report[1], viz.

$$D/fc = \frac{\sum_{0}^{\infty} H_\lambda D_\lambda \, \Delta\lambda}{\sum_{0}^{\infty} H_\lambda \bar{y}_\lambda \, \Delta\lambda}$$

(These symbols are recommended by the American Optical Society.)

Because the above equation applies only to bare light sources, both numerator and denominator must be modified by the spectral internal transmittances (specific to wavelength), T_λ, of any interposed media through which such energy is passed. This ratio may be expressed in language, rather than symbols, as follows:

PROBABLE DAMAGE
PER FOOT CANDLE

equals

TOTAL HAZARDOUS RADIATION
THROUGH ANY TRANSLUCENT MEDIA

divided by

TOTAL LUMINOUS RADIATION
THROUGH SAME TRANSLUCENT MEDIA

Hazardous radiation may be defined as: spectral irradiance (H_λ) modified by a probable damage factor (D_λ) for each wavelength concerned in a given problem.

Luminous radiation may be defined as: spectral irradiance (H_λ) modified by the efficiency of the human eye (standard observer) ($\bar{y}_\lambda$) for each wavelength concerned in a given problem.

This ratio, therefore, means that when such values are applied to reasonably sized increments ($\Delta\lambda$)—say, ten or twenty millimicrons of spectral distribution—and added together in both numerator and denominator, the result provides the condition for dealing with light sources, meters and filters in this problem. *Tables 2* and *3* show the basic data for this project. The calculations are tiresome but not abstruse. A portable printing calculator was rented at negligible cost for a few days, producing a proof record for checking.

Table 2

Hazardous radiation as the product of H_λ and D_λ, and luminous radiation as the product of H_λ and $\bar{y}_\lambda$ for overcast and zenith sky

Wavelength (mμ)	Overcast sky ($H_{\lambda_o} . D_\lambda$)	($H_{\lambda_o} . \bar{y}_\lambda$)	Zenith sky ($H_{\lambda_z} . D_\lambda$)	($H_{\lambda_z} . \bar{y}_\lambda$)
400	58·2	0·04	117·6	0·07
420	38·4	0·42	68·6	0·74
440	21·7	2·5	34·6	4·0
460	13·8	6·9	20·2	10·0
480	7·1	15·1	9·4	20·1
500	3·9	34·4	4·8	42·1
520	2·2	74·1	2·5	83·1
540	1·2	96·1	1·3	101·3
560	0·69	97·6	0·69	97·7
580	0·38	82·9	0·36	79·3
600	0·18	58·1	0·17	53·5
620	0·09	33·8	0·08	30·0
640	0·04	14·9	0·04	12·8
660	0·00	5·0	0·00	4·2
680	0·00	1·3	0·00	1·1
700	0·00	0·31	0·00	0·25
720	0·00	0·07	0·00	0·06
740	0·00	0·02	0·00	0·02

Table 3

Spectral internal[a] transmittance of the filters tested and evaluated

Wave-length (mμ)	Solar gray ¼ in. plate glass	I—Plexi-glas[b] ¼ in.[c] IIUF	II—Kodak 2B ¼ in. glass[d] laminate	III—Plexi-glas ¼ in.[d] G911A	IV—Plexi-glas ¼ in.[e] G911B
400	0·550	0·403	0·200	0·339	0·020
420	0·490	0·925	0·670	0·819	0·641
440	0·447	0·978	0·820	0·837	0·845
460	0·440	0·984	0·864	0·839	0·879
480	0·423	0·990	0·892	0·837	0·882
500	0·410	0·994	0·900	0·845	0·889
520	0·401	0·996	0·905	0·845	0·893
540	0·430	0·998	0·910	0·845	0·897
560	0·480	1·000	0·910	0·845	0·900
580	0·424	1·000	0·910	0·845	0·904
600	0·402	1·000	0·910	0·854	0·906
620	0·418	1·000	0·910	0·845	0·904
640	0·406	1·000	0·909	0·850	0·907
660	0·430	1·000	0·907	0·846	0·912
680	0·518	1·000	0·905	0·846	0·911
700	0·600	1·000	0·903	0·846	0·911
720	0·610	1·000	0·900	0·846	0·911
740	0·580	1·000	0·898	0·846	0·911

[a] External transmittance equals 0·91 times respective average.
[b] Extrapolated from *Table 3*, 1954 report, which covered ⅛ in. thickness.
[c] Ultra-violet cut-off at 370 mμ; [d] Ultra-violet cut-off at 390 mμ; [e] Ultra-violet cut-off at 395 mμ.

The formula for this project, therefore, was

$$D/fc = \frac{\sum\limits_{740}^{400} (H_\lambda . D_\lambda)(T_{\lambda_p} . T_{\lambda_f}) \text{ (for 20 m}\mu \text{ increments)}}{\sum\limits_{740}^{400} (H_\lambda . \bar{y}_\lambda)(T_{\lambda_p} . T_{\lambda_f}) \text{ (for 20 m}\mu \text{ increments)}}$$

separate summations being required for irradiance (H_{λ_o}) from overcast sky and (H_{λ_z}) for zenith sky. Grouping of calculations in this way provides easier proof and more accurate placing of decimals.

T_{λ_p} represents distributed transmittance for Solar Gray plate glass, and T_{λ_f} the transmittances for the particular filter being evaluated. H_λ expresses radiant power in microwatts per square centimetre per millimicron[3]. Both D_λ and $\bar{y}_\lambda$ are arbitrary units—D_λ fixing unity at 390 mμ, the point of transition from ultra-violet to visible energy, and $\bar{y}_\lambda$, of course, fixing unity at 554 mμ, the wavelength at the point of maximum daytime visual efficiency.

Evaluations

With the foregoing information at hand, an analysis of local daylight conditions was necessary. Information supplied by the United States Weather Bureau and other sources follows:

1. Percentage of possible hours of sunshine, annually ... 58
2. Average level of sunlight from June to October (unattenuated by clouds) ... 4500 ft. cd
3. Average level of overcast sky (unobstructed) ... 884 ft. cd
4. Average level of clear sky (unobstructed) ... 1080 ft. cd

At this point it became apparent than many of the data being accumulated were subject to considerable discount. For example, the level of sunlight represented the incidence of the sun mainly in its northerly declination and the figure might be lower if averaged for the year. Other data developed of the same character: lacking any cues by which such figures could

be properly modified, the discounts remain unapplied as factors of safety.

As previously indicated, the building is oriented east and west, so that the east and west façades are each under direct sunlight one half of 58 per cent, or 29 per cent each. The respective exhibition areas would therefore be in an average sunless environment for 71 per cent of daylight hours if curtains are kept closed only under direct sunlight. The average levels of overcast and clear sky illumination are, as previously stated, subject to the 60 per cent cut-off for outside illumination incident on the windows. The local 'sunless' conditions, consequently, evaluate as given in *Table 4*.

Table 4

Local 'sunless' conditions*

	Unobstructed illumination (ft. cd)	Incident on window (40%) (ft. cd)	Percentage of daylight hours
Average annual overcast sky	884	354	42
Average annual clear sky	1080	432	58
Average annual daylight	998	399	100

* The word 'sunless' expresses conditions similar to north sky illumination for 100 per cent of the time.

The relationship, in the case of the Solar-Gray/IIUF combination, between the average annual level incident outside on the window and the permissible average level with open curtains is in the ratio 146/399. The numerator is determined by dividing the 'model' average inside the window of 60 ft. cd by the transmittance of the Solar-Gray/IIUF combination, i.e. 41 per cent. This ratio obviously equals the utilization of open curtains, or 36 per cent of available daylight.

Two more considerations operate to reduce damage. One is the attenuation of light over the interior exhibition area. The second, as stated earlier, is the extreme improbability of any susceptible material being exhibited without substantial withdrawal, as a matter of ordinary curatorial housekeeping, during the life of the building*. To ignore both of these factors would quite logically distort any estimate of the museum life of the objects concerned.

Accordingly, for purposes only of predicting the probable life of exhibited material, we should estimate the average illumination to be expected over the exhibition area. Using handbook methods[2], we can rely on a reduction of 20 per cent of the model 60 ft. cd permissible average at the window to 48 ft. cd for the Solar-Gray/IIUF criterion.

To allow also for changes, rearrangement and maintenance of exhibit space, material and equipment, an exposure-time percentage of half of the pertinent values in *Table 4* is used, which results in an incidence of 21 per cent of overcast sky radiation and 14·5 per cent of clear sky radiation in terms of probable exposure of material. However, these values of *Table 4* represent a maximum of 71 per cent available daylight when, in fact, we propose to keep curtains opened only 36 per cent of the time.

This being the case, a proportionate distribution results in a net exposure of exhibited material to overcast sky for 10·6 per

---

* The museum states that the normal life of an exhibition gallery arrangement is from 10 to 15 years.

Figure 1. Light controller with cover removed. Photocell can be recognized by zig-zag metallic strip over cadmium sulphide surface. Cover has window onto which neutral-density filter may be cemented to adjust light-level setting. Further adjustment is provided by adjustable curved shutter in front of photocell.

(By courtesy of General Electric Company)

cent, and to clear sky for 7·4 per cent of the time. The index of exposure for our Solar-Gray/IIUF criterion can then be calculated following the method of the 1954 report[1]

$$IX = \frac{(48) \cdot (0\cdot385) \cdot (0\cdot074) + (48) \cdot (0\cdot226) \cdot (0\cdot106)}{107\cdot31} = 0\cdot023$$

By using D/fc values in *Table 1*, and if $(0\cdot80)X$ be the average illumination expected over the exhibition area, the net exposure in percentage of daylight hours may be calculated as a function of X. Thus, the remaining characteristics of each filter may be calculated based on a uniform IX of $0\cdot023$.

The projection of the index of exposure into a prediction of probable museum life of exhibits (PL) is shown, as set forth in the 1954 report, by inverse proportion of $IX(0\cdot023)$ to $IX(15\cdot5)$ and $0\cdot425$ years derived from the results of experiments in Sweden, as follows

$$\frac{(IX)15\cdot5}{(IX)0\cdot023} = \frac{PL}{0\cdot425}$$

and $PL = 286$ years

Equipment to be installed

The primary control consists of photosensitive controllers mounted directly behind the weather sashes (*Figures 1* and *2*). They are recently developed units widely employed in street and highway lighting for turning on the lamps at dusk and turning them off at dawn. Because the cell is normally arranged to operate at very low levels of illumination, it must be modified

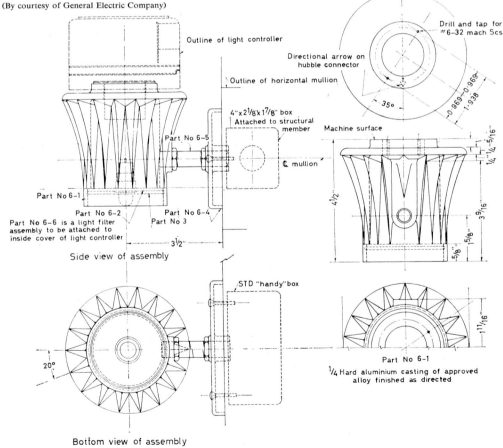

Figure 2. Cast-aluminium bracket for controller. Bright red neon indicator lamp at bottom lights up to show 'curtain opened' condition of circuit.

(By courtesy of General Electric Company)

by cementing a Wratten neutral filter to the inside surface of its window aperture, of sufficient density to bring the cell within the desired range. An adjustable shutter provides accuracy. The entire device is 4 in. in diameter and $2\frac{3}{4}$ in. high.

The photocell is of cadmium sulphide sealed in a vacuum tube and mounted at an angle of 45° from the horizontal. This cell has sufficient output to actuate directly a small but rugged relay through a half-wave rectifier. *Figure 5* shows the internal connections.

The operation is as follows. With the controller always at line potential, the system circuitry maintains curtains normally in the closed position. Should reversal take place during an operating cycle, the curtains will automatically 'home' to the

closed position before responding to a changed call. Cadmium sulphide cells are photoconductive and not photoelectric in the usual sense. At the higher designed values of incident light, the cell's electrical resistance is relatively low. As the light value decreases, the cell's resistance increases.

This characteristic is used here to pass d.c. line current in the sensing relay coil so that it will not operate at the higher light levels. When the cell's resistance has thus increased to the adjusted level, the relay contact is held open, causing the curtains to close.

The system circuitry is energized through a master control panel which operates the individual curtain motors (*Figure 3*). Green and red signal lamps indicate the position of any curtain

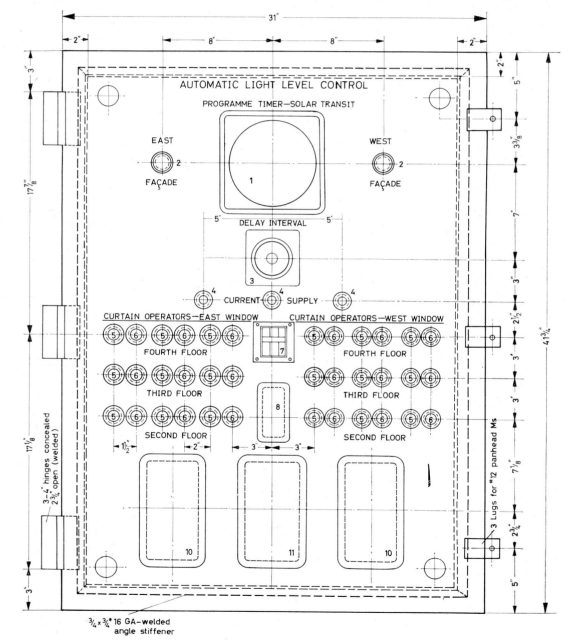

Figure 3. Master control panel (16-gauge steel, weight 65 lb.): 1—main panel, medium grey, 2—engraved lettering, 3—all instruments, indicator bodies, relay bases, etc., black, 4—enclosing cabinet interior, black crackle-baked, 5—bezel and black light fixtures, black cracklebaked.

(By courtesy of General Electric Company)

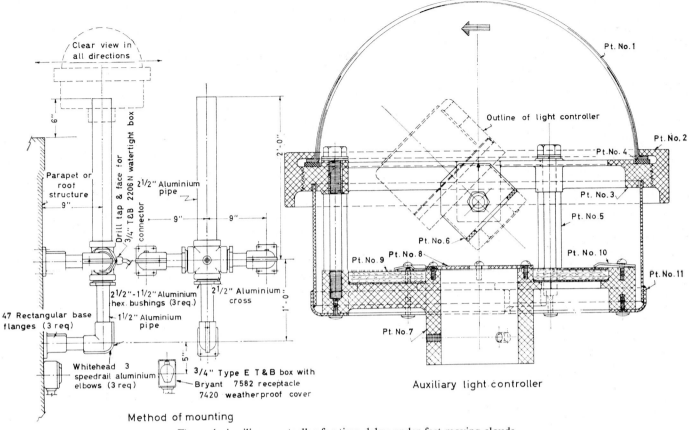

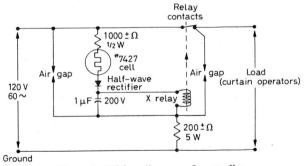

Figure 4. Auxiliary controller for time delay under fast-moving clouds.
(By courtesy of General Electric Company)

on the system through co-operating relays at each motor-operator. The photocontrollers have an 'on–off' differential of 1 to 1·10.

Figure 5. Wiring diagram of controller.

An important matter revealed itself when experiments were made at the Metropolitan Museum in 1951 on automatic sun control for louvers above gallery laylights. Fast-moving clouds frequently accelerated the operation of the louvers, sometimes to a frequency of ten seconds between opening and closing. This was not objectionable for louvers fully concealed by obscure ceiling glass. For large, decorative curtains moving in full view of visitors, the speed limitations owing to inertia as well as possibly ridiculously frequent opening and closing makes a provision for time delay mandatory.

The master control panel provides for an auxiliary photocell controller (*Figure 4*) on the roof which functions with a 10-minute cycle interval timer to introduce the required delay of any local window controller's operation whenever sky brightness exceeds an adjustable 1500 lumens per square foot. This feature is necessarily programmed so that it applies only to the east façade in the morning and to the west in the afternoon.

Conclusion and acknowledgements

This paper is technically the engineering appraisal of a risk. It demonstrates no guarantee other than that each factor has been ascertained, developed and analysed with care. It re-emphasizes the hope expressed in 1954 that research work in this area be encouraged along as broad a line as possible so that future estimates may have fewer probabilities and more facts on which to rely.

Grateful appreciation is expressed to members of the U.S. National Bureau of Standards; namely, to Dr D. B. Judd, for advice and counsel, to Mr L. E. Barbrow, Chief of the Photometry and Colorimetry Section, for his suggestions, to Messrs H. J. Keegan, J. C. Schleter and V. R. Weidner for the laboratory work involved, and to Mr Frank A. Taylor, Director of the Museum of History and Technology, Smithsonian Institution, for his review of the text and helpful criticisms.

References

[1] HARRISON, L. S., *Report on the deteriorating effects of modern light sources*, Metropolitan Museum of Art, New York, 1954.
[2] Illuminating Engineering Society, *Lighting Handbook*, pp. 9.29 and 9.30, 1959.
[3] MOON, P., Proposed standard solar radiation curves for engineering use, *J. Franklin Inst.*, 230 (1940) 595.

J. Lodewijks

THE INFLUENCE OF LIGHT ON MUSEUM OBJECTS

One of the most important problems we have to deal with in the museums is the problem of aging of materials. As it is, the life of an object of art is directly dependent on the measure to which it is exposed to aging factors, and as one of the main tasks of the museum staff consists of retaining the works of art entrusted to them, it is of the greatest importance to know what aging consists of and in what way this process may be retarded as much as possible.

Aging may be explained as the degradation of a material taking place at a more or less rapid pace and leading in the end to a total destruction of the object consisting of this material. Aging can be brought under three headings:

1. Natural aging,
2. Mechanical aging,
3. Biochemical and microbiological aging.

Natural aging is the degradation of a solid material taking place under the influence of light in combination with environment. This form of aging generally leads to a slow, total degradation of the matter.

Mechanical aging is brought about by mechanical forces to which the material is subjected for varying periods; for example, the flying of a flag in the wind or the wear seen in chair-covers. Attack by insects is also a form of mechanical aging. This aging is characterized by a disintegration—generally very quick—of the matter at those spots. Mechanical aging need not play any part in a museum, as both wear and attack by insects can be practically excluded.

Biochemical and microbiological aging are caused by bacteria and fungi. This kind of aging too, which is characterized by a degradation of the matter in those spots where the bacteria or fungi manifest themselves, can be almost entirely excluded by using fungicides and antibiotics.

Since natural aging plays the main part in the degradation of objects of art in our museums, we shall restrict ourselves to the discussion of this type.

The factors determining natural aging are light and temperature and composition of the environment. The surroundings are formed by air, to which is added water vapour, solid material, such as particles of quartz and metal, soot, heavy hydrocarbons, and industrial pollutions, such as mercaptans, organic nitrogen compounds, sulphur dioxide, hydrogen sulphide, etc. All these factors determine the degree of natural aging of matter. However, they work not separately but in combination with each other. This renders the entire process of natural aging an extremely complicated business. In order to gain an insight into this process it is essential to examine individually the factors mentioned above in connection with their contribution to natural aging.

A highly important factor in aging is the influence of light. A constant watch on its effect is necessary in museums, more especially since other causative factors can often be simply eliminated. However, light is, of course, necessary to make exhibitions of works of art possible.

Light

To be able to understand the behaviour of matter under the influence of light it is at first necessary to know what light really is. Light, treated energetically, is made up of radiation of varying wavelength and intensity. Light becomes richer in energy as the wavelength is shortened. This energy is composed of certain units, the so-called light quanta, the energy of which is equal to the product of a constant (the constant of Planck) and the frequency of light v ($E = hv$). The frequency of light v is equal to the quotient of the velocity of light, c, and the wavelength, λ

$$v = \frac{c}{\lambda}$$

It appears from this that the energy of the radiated light quanta, or photons, is inversely proportional to the wavelength.

Matter

The objects in the museums with which we are concerned can be roughly divided into two groups with respect to molecular structure, namely:

1. Substances consisting of monomer molecules, e.g. metals, inorganic and many organic dyestuffs.
2. Substances consisting of large polymer molecules.

A polymer arises from linking various numbers of basic molecules, called units. When this linking, polymerization, takes place in one direction we speak of linear or chain polymers; if it takes place in several directions, then three-dimensional structures are obtained. Many substances consist wholly of chain polymers—namely, all textiles—while paper, wood and leather consist mainly of these kinds of polymer.

Materials belonging to the first group generally do not present great problems in connection with natural aging. On the whole they are structurally very stable, and certain chemical or physico-chemical changes which may take place in these substances, such as oxidation of metals or a change of one form of crystal into another (as in tin) or a crystallization from the amorphous phase (e.g. glass), can easily be explained and in many cases can be prevented by certain protective measures.

The natural aging of polymer substances, however, is a much more extensive and complicated matter. Natural aging in these cases is manifest as a decay or depolymerization of the polymer material. Contrary to the aging of materials in the first-mentioned group, this aging does not become apparent until it has been going on for a long time and depolymerization has advanced to such a degree that a decline in the strength of the material becomes evident. There need not be any change in outward appearance.

If we now consider the material of any chain polymer, which we can represent schematically as –A–B–A–B–A–B–, then it can be said that only energies equal to or larger than the energy required to break up the connection –A–B– in the molecule will be able to bring about a break of the chain, and so a depolymerization. We have seen that the energy of a light photon is equal to

$$\varepsilon = \frac{hc}{\lambda}$$

If now the construction of the chain molecule of a certain material is known, as is the case with cellulose, then it can be easily calculated what wavelength is detrimental to a certain material, without taking into account other factors. For example, we shall consider what wavelength of light is able to break a carbon–carbon bond.

The value of ε will lie between $58{\cdot}6 \times 10^3$ cal/mol (the energy needed to break a simple C–C bond) and 80×10^3 cal/mol (the energy needed to break a straightforward saturated chain)

$$h = 6{\cdot}6 \times 10^{-27} \text{ erg-sec}$$

$$c = 3 \times 10^{10} \text{ cm/sec}$$

$$M \text{ (Avogadro number)} = 6{\cdot}03 \times 10^{23}$$

$$1 \text{ erg} = 2{\cdot}4 \times 10^{-8} \text{ cal}$$

$$\lambda = \frac{6{\cdot}6 \times 10^{-27} \times 2{\cdot}4 \times 10^{-8} \times 3 \times 10^{10} \times 6{\cdot}03 \times 10^{23}}{\varepsilon}$$

Therefore λ lies between 4860 and 3580 Å.

In the case of a cellulose molecule, the energy necessary to break the chain directly is not known, though we can expect it to lie between the values given above.

All wavelengths of light shorter than 4860 Å can break a C—C bond and consequently be detrimental to many organic materials. This sort of decay in which light alone is the disintegrating medium is called photolysis.

In fact we are always concerned with light in combination with the environment of the material. The environment contains, as already mentioned, numbers of compounds— among others, water vapour and oxygen. These two compounds can, under the influence of light, form substances that have a detrimental effect on the aging of material. Under influence of the substances present in the polymer material, such as dirt, pigments and the like, the oxygen from the air can take an active form under the influence of light and bring about an oxidative decay of the polymer material. This active oxygen together with water vapour can at the same time form hydrogen peroxide, which in this case is responsible for the oxidative decay of the polymer material.

The energies necessary to enable the above-mentioned reactions to take place can be much lower than those for photolysis. The above-mentioned decay mechanisms manifest themselves in visible light and, according to Kansky, even to wavelengths over 12,000 Å, far into the infra-red spectrum. The oxidative decay described here forms part of a photochemical degradation and is called photo-oxidation.

Little is known as yet about the influence of temperature on these processes, though it may be expected that these reactions advance more quickly as the temperature increases.

Besides photolysis and photochemical decay, we can also distinguish pure chemical and physical decay. Chemical decay is caused by harmful compounds present in the atmosphere, of which sulphur dioxide is an important example. This substance, with water, produces sulphuric acid which, even without the influence of light, may contribute to the depolymerization of the material.

Physical decay is brought about by solid particles present in the atmosphere, e.g. quartz. Particles possessing sharp edges gradually penetrate into the material and exercise a cutting and scouring influence on it. This is easy to see under the microscope in old, soiled textiles. The dirt often clings to the material in such a way that it cannot be removed by washing.

As we have seen above, concerning the influence of light on polymer materials, we can distinguish two types of decay: photolytic and photochemical. We can entirely exclude photolysis as an aging factor if we take care to eliminate all radiation below a certain wavelength. In museums glass windows remove most of the damaging radiation. Other harmful radiation can be removed by using ultra-violet absorbing material. These materials are coated on the inside of the windows after being dissolved in a transparent lacquer or varnish. Depending on the type of ultra-violet absorber chosen, a smaller or greater part of shortwave light may be absorbed. Visible light, however, is not obstructed. This light too can be absorbed if necessary, but then colour filters, generally undesirable in museums, must be used.

It is better to reduce the effect of photochemical decay in exhibition spaces to a minimum by reducing the total intensity of light to the permissible minimum. The human eye is able to adapt to a large extent and, a certain time for accommodation being allowed, one can see distinctly and without exertion at a very low intensity of light. For good lighting of museums it is of the greatest importance, apart from filtering the radiation causing photolysis, to reduce the remaining light to the permissible minimum intensity, taking care to maintain all rooms at about the same light intensity.

From the above it appears that not only ultra-violet radiation can bring about photolytic decay, as is often supposed, but also that a part of the visible light may bring about photolysis. It is a matter of the greatest moment, therefore, to be most careful with any form of artificial lighting which contains shortwave light, as is the case with certain types of T.L. tubes (the blue T.L. tubes contain a considerable amount of shortwave radiation). As it is of the highest importance to reduce to a minimum the aging processes of material in museums, investigation in this direction will have to be continued energetically. Aging processes, however, are generally so complicated that if a fundamental scientific result is to be reached, there will have to be adequate cooperation between the various laboratories. Only after a thorough knowledge of the aging mechanisms of various materials has been gained will it be possible to take the most effective steps to retard them or even to eliminate them entirely. This knowledge will only be obtained by serious cooperation and by efficient planning of the experiments to be made.

Nathan Stolow

SOME STUDIES ON THE PROTECTION OF WORKS OF ART DURING TRAVEL

Museum statistics show that during the last decade there has been an upward trend in the circulation of travelling exhibitions of works of art and museum objects. It seems impossible to reverse this trend; especially in the face of the increasing popularization of museums and the extension of the educational arm of the museum far afield. Many museum directors, curators, scientists and conservators are rather disturbed with the greater frequency of travelling exhibitions and the obvious increased danger to the safety of works of art. Ideally it would be best for exhibits if they never left their original homes, at least they can then be constantly observed and cared for by trained personnel, and preserved under proper environmental conditions.

Much has been written on the desirable museum environment[1,2] for the effective conservation of humidity- and temperature-sensitive art objects. Certain progress has been made, and several major art museums have stabilized, temperature- and humidity-controlled atmospheres. Unfortunately little effort has hitherto been spent on research into desirable environments for such objects during transit conditions. Some notable studies have, however, been made[3,4]; these indicate that it is now possible to ship panel paintings overseas if strict attention is paid to environmental control of humidity and temperature at all stages of the trip—that is, from 'museum to museum'. To do so requires a major effort on the part of senior museum officials, scientists, travel agents and customs personnel at border crossing points. Not least in the effort is the requirement of suitable packing against the possible effects of shock, vibration and condensation.

The museum scientist and conservator can no longer afford to be indifferent to the needs for better preservation of works of art during travel. In his particular museum there may be an active circulating exhibition programme. It is encumbent upon the scientifically or technically trained museum employee to offer advice, perform research and be otherwise helpful in ensuring the safety of the exhibits in transit. Newer methods of packing must be devised (in this respect much can be learned from the packaging industry[5,6]) and personnel responsible for packing procedures must receive newer and more extended training.

The purpose of this report is to indicate briefly the results of certain procedures which have been successfully used at the National Gallery of Canada, in a country which has a very difficult climate. Some trial experiments with an environmental chamber will be reviewed, and general comments will be made on particularly difficult travel situations.

Shipment of canvas paintings during the winter

In 1960 the Dutch authorities lent Canada a very valuable collection of paintings and drawings by Van Gogh. It was intended to circulate this extensive exhibition through several large cities, extending into the winter period of that year. Thus at the end of December it was to travel from Ottawa to Winnipeg

(in the interior of the country), a distance of approximately 3000 kilometres, with outside temperatures as low as $-30°C$ and correspondingly dry atmospheres. Some of the paintings were wax-relined, but most were not; these were, therefore, in the moisture-sensitive category, whence great attention had to be paid to conditions of relative humidity in transit. Likewise the prints and drawings required protection to avoid desiccation. While these works of art had been shipped mainly by air from Holland in light containers it was considered essential to repack the entire exhibition for winter travel. Consultations were arranged with the scientific staff, the packing and handling staff and officials of the National Railroad system to ensure that maximum safety would result. Cases were constructed of top-quality white pine, painted on the outside and carefully lined with a fibre-board material (compressed de-fibred wood pulp) to serve as a heat-insulating and moisture-retentive envelope to surround the painting and graphic art works. All construction materials had been stored inside the National Gallery at the conditions prevailing there; that is, at a relative humidity of 48 per cent and a temperature of 21°C. Under such conditions the equilibrium moisture content (oven-dry basis) for the wood is 10 per cent and that of the fibre-board is approximately 8 per cent. The works themselves were pre-packed in kraft paper to afford additional protection.

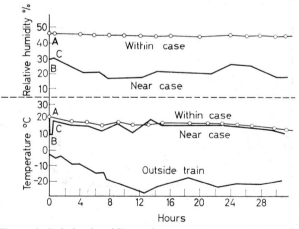

Figure 1. Relative humidity and temperature record of shipment of Van Gogh exhibition, Ottawa to Winnipeg, December 19–20, 1960.

The temperature and relative humidity behaviour of the shipment is recorded in *Figure 1.* One of the cases was packed with a recording hair thermohygrograph which recorded the relative humidity and temperature within and another instrument was placed near the outside of the case to record ambient conditions. The initial conditions within the cases were 48 per cent relative humidity and 21°C (A in the figure). The shipment was transported to the railway depot in a large van and immediately transferred to a waiting freightcar, heated to approximately 19°C. The outside temperature at this time was −3°C with a relative humidity of 30 per cent. Shortly afterwards the freightcar was coupled to the passenger train, and the trip to Winnipeg commenced (C in figure).

Approximately 31 hours later the shipment arrived at Winnipeg. Two responsible officials accompanied the shipment

Figure 2. Picture packing case showing arrangement of fibre-board, polyethylene film and wooden case construction. Picture 'trays' are also shown in layer arrangement.

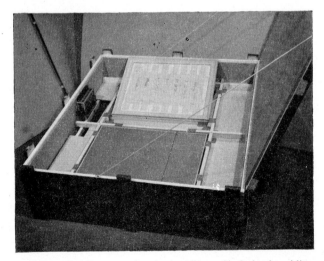

Figure 3. Packing case showing position of relative-humidity and temperature-recording instrument on the left.

and kept check on arrangements, handling, temperatures, recorders, etc. One was a conservator and the other was head of the packing and handling staff of the National Gallery. As the graphs indicate, the relative humidity within the cases remained remarkably constant, never falling below 44 per cent. This represents a drop of 4 per cent in relative humidity. The relative humidity in the car was very low throughout, in the range of 18–30 per cent, while the temperature varied from 20° to 10°C. It is of interest to record that the outside weather during this trip was quite severe, with temperatures varying

from −3° to −27°C. At no point during the transit of the paintings did the interior of the cases reach the dew-point, which would cause condensation of moisture. (The dew-point for the initial conditions of 48 per cent relative humidity and 21°C is close to 11°C.) It is quite obvious from these results that the wood and fibre-board components acted as very efficient buffers in maintaining a constant relative humidity and offset any sudden external changes. Upon arrival at the destination the cases were 12° below room temperature, and were left unopened for 24 hours to permit equalization of temperatures. No damage that might be attributed to variation in humidity or temperature was observed.

Figure 2 shows a section of a typical case, while *Figure 3* shows a packed case with the recording instrument installed.

Protection of paintings for shipment to tropical countries

A year and a half ago the National Gallery of Canada received a return shipment of Canadian contemporary paintings from an international exhibition which took place in São Paulo. Examination of these paintings showed that they were covered with mould. This was identified as *Aspergillus niger* and *Rhizopus nigricans*[7]. Apparently the cases had remained closed for a long period, approximately two months, owing to transit and storage arrangements, and the conditions of temperature and humidity built up to a level where mould growth could be readily supported. The conditions for rapid growth of mould are considered to be 15–30°C at 90–95 per cent relative humidity, although growth may commence at any temperature above freezing point (up to 50°C) so long as the relative humidity is above 70 per cent. As a result of this experience it was decided to revise the methods of packing for shipments to tropical countries or shipments that pass through belts of tropical climate.

A method which is now in use, on an experimental basis, is as follows. The cases are preferably made of plywood, and after being conditioned to a relative humidity of approximately 50 per cent at 21°C they are lined with polyethylene sheeting. Over this is placed fibre-board, in order to form a moisture buffer next to the paintings. Before packing, all of the interior wood and fibre-board is sprayed with a solution of pentachlorophenol in carbon tetrachloride. In the case of canvas paintings, the backs are also sprayed with this material. The solvent is allowed to evaporate, and packing is continued as speedily as possible. The polyethylene outer envelope is sealed with pressure-sensitive cloth tape, and the lid of the case is tightly fastened. By such means, all live spores packed with the paintings are killed, and the residual deposits of pentachlorophenol within the wooden and fibre-board members of the case, as well as on the back of the canvas of the paintings, would ensure a moderately toxic atmosphere for the return voyage. This method of packing is also shown in *Figure 2*.

Misuse of polyethylene in shipping works of art

Two years ago the National Gallery of Canada received a very important shipment of old-master canvas paintings from Europe. This was arranged on a high governmental level and an important museum official accompanied the shipment. The shipment crossed the Atlantic in the early winter period and reached New York, where it was transferred by train to Ottawa. The security arrangements and the care in handling were excellent. Double casing was used throughout to enable the moisture content within to remain as stable as possible under the wide variations of external conditions during the trans-Atlantic crossing and subsequent overland trips. On opening the cases in the gallery it was noted that each painting was wrapped in a polyethylene envelope, and that considerable condensation of moisture was evident on the inside of the polyethylene plastic and on the painting surface. Thus the effect of the buffering action of the double wooden casing was completely lost. When the shipment went below the dew-point, the moisture between the polyethylene film and the painting was trapped and had to condense on the nearest cold surface.

This is a classic case of misapplication of a potentially useful material. If the shippers from the museum in question were properly advised by experts they would either have avoided the use of polyethylene or have used it as an interleaving tissue well removed from the picture surface, as in *Figure 2*.

Environmental chamber studies

Some studies have already commenced on the efficiency of established methods of packing to retain constant levels of relative humidity within an enclosed package. The environmental chamber (*Figures 4* and *5*) presently in use has a capacity of 5 cubic metres, and is of the 'walk-in' type. It is possible to control the temperature within the range of 0° to 40°C and the relative humidity from 15 to 95 per cent by means of a recorder-controller circuit and a humidifying and dehumidifying system. The latter system is a dual-bed silica-gel dehumidifier which is self-reactivating. Changes in chamber conditions can be made to duplicate very closely those which may exist in an actual shipment.

Figure 4. Environmental chamber of 'walk-in' dimensions, capable of control of relative humidity and temperature. Case under test is shown within the chamber.

A case was constructed similar to those currently in use (with fibre-board insulation) and placed in the chamber after installing relative-humidity and temperature-sensing devices which would read on an external two-point recorder. These devices were of the temperature-resistance type. Once the case was in the chamber, it was possible to follow the variations of relative humidity and temperature (dry bulb) within and compare these readings with those which existed in the chamber proper (recording console is shown in *Figure 5*).

Figure 5. Environmental chamber with automatic recorder and ten-point automatic selector switch for recording multiple readings.

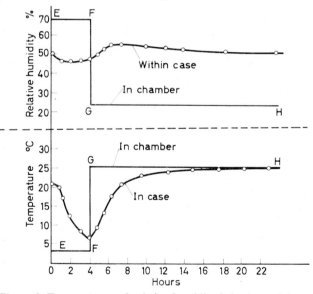

Figure 6. Temperature and relative humidity behaviour of insulated case in the environmental chamber.

A typical experiment is graphically presented in *Figure 6*. The case was initially stored for several weeks at 50 per cent relative humidity and 21°C (E), and was then placed in the chamber where the temperature was set to 3·5°C with the relative humidity at 60 per cent. The lower curve shows how the temperature falls, reaching a value of 6·5°C after about 4 hours. The upper curve of relative humidity shows how the relative humidity falls initially, within the first hour, then stabilizes at a level of 45 per cent, and finally rises slowly to 47 per cent (F). Apparently when the case is cooling down, the wood and fibre-board construction is no longer at equilibrium with the interior, enclosed air. The equilibrium moisture content for these materials increases with drop in temperature. As a result of this, moisture is absorbed from within the enclosed space at such a rate that an increase in relative humidity is not obtained. (This would be expected in a non-absorbing system, e.g. one of metal or glass construction, where the dew-point would be attained before long.) If the case were permitted to remain in the chamber beyond F, then the relative humidity on the inside would eventually climb to 69 per cent as the temperature levelled off. This would take many hours. At F the case was subjected to a higher temperature, 25°C, and a relative humidity of 23 per cent. This change would correspond to the transfer of a case of paintings from a cold train or truck to the interior of a centrally heated building in the winter time. As the temperature within the case rises, the relative humidity also rises. During this interval moisture is being emitted by the wood and fibre-board, and at a sufficient rate to increase the relative humidity. After 2 or 3 hours the relative humidity falls, as moisture diffuses out of the crate in the direction of low exterior relative humidity. It is therefore concluded that this type of insulation and case construction is quite suitable for buffering changes of temperature and relative humidity in the surrounding environment, at least for several hours.

Further experiments on different systems of insulation, and the application of silica gel or other 'humidity-storing' salts, need to be carried out. There are, of course, certain practical difficulties in retaining a substance like conditioned silica gel in a case containing paintings. How is the diffusion of moisture in such a system to be made uniform? Perhaps a material can be found which will be in board or sheet form, which will have the 'correct' humidity-restoring properties, and which will be easy to use as a packing material.

Acknowledgements

Acknowledgement is made to Mr Ruggles and Mr DeCoste for recording the data of the Winnipeg trip, and to the Director of the National Gallery, Dr C. F. Comfort, for his support of this work.

References

[1] LEWIS, L., Air-conditioning in museums, *Museum, Unesco*, 10 (1957) 132–147.

[2] PLENDERLEITH, H. J. and PHILIPPOT, P., *Climatology and Conservation in Museums*, Rome Centre Publication No. 3, 1960 (reprinted from *Museum, Unesco*, 13, No. 4 (1960) 202–289).

[3] TOISHI, K., Humidity control in a closed package, *Stud. Conservation*, 4, No. 4 (1959) 81–87.

[4] BUCK, R. D., *Some observations on the care of panel paintings during trans-atlantic shipment*, lecture given at the Annual Meeting of the Art Technical Section of the American Association of Museums, Detroit, Michigan, May 24, 1961 (unpublished).

[5] BROWN, K., *Package Design Engineering*, Wiley and Sons, New York, 1959, pp. 139–160.

[6] BARAIL, L. C., *Packaging Engineering*, Reinhold Publishing Corp., New York, 1954.

[7] FLORIAN, M. L., *Investigation of Mold Material*, Special Report No. E544, National Gallery of Canada, October 7, 1960.

Kenzo Toishi

RELATIVE HUMIDITY IN A CLOSED PACKAGE

Problems of packaging which have received attention up to now are mainly connected with weight and mechanical strength. Materials for packaging have been studied fairly well, and many advances have been made in this field. Only of late has moisture in the package been taken into consideration, and it has become common practice to insert some drying agent into a package accommodating iron goods or groceries.

Art objects are, in general, fragile and may lose much of their value through damage occurring in transport. The exchange of art objects in the past took place mainly within limited domains —for instance, in Europe or at most between Europe and America—and mostly between districts of similar climate. We have had many opportunities recently, however, of sending art objects from one temperate district to another through a tropical zone or a cold zone, or from a temperate zone to a tropical zone, and so on. If a Japanese art exhibition is held in Europe, for example, the articles must pass through hot or cold climatic regions, whether they are sent by sea or by air. Because of this, various failures have been experienced. A bronze Buddha which was sent from Japan to America was damaged by surface corrosion caused by condensation, losing its lustre at the places affected. This is thought to have been caused when the ship went through a cold zone following the great circle route. Conversely, the same result might have taken place with a bronze statue sent from Japan to a tropical zone. In fact, a bronze Buddha which was sent last year from Japan to Thailand was damaged on its surface by condensation just like the one mentioned above. We know of many other accidents caused in travel, including increased flaking of paint and tearing of surface paper on sliding doors, etc. In 1959 the Matsukata collection was sent to Japan from France; one painting in this collection, 'Douleur au pays de la mer' painted by Cottet, has lost much of its value from deformation of the wooden box and consequent generation of mould, as I reported in *IIC News*, Vol. 1, No. 2, pp. 18, 19.

I think we Japanese have more experience of such events caused by humidity changes than most in the world for we are accustomed to great temperature variations during relatively short journeys. A temperature variation generally gives rise to a great change in relative humidity in a closed package, but this form of package is adopted in Japan as a general rule for art objects. I believe that warnings against such events are necessary not only for Japanese people, but for all in charge of travelling art objects, especially since there are likely to be more travelling exhibitions in the future.

Now we must consider the 'humidity' which acts on art objects. As is known, there are two kinds of expression for humidity. Absolute humidity is expressed by the water vapour contained in a given quantity of air, whilst relative humidity means the percentage ratio of the weight of water vapour in the air to the weight which would be contained in the same volume of saturated air at the same temperature. The effect of humidity on an art object is related to relative humidity, not absolute. As can be seen from the above definition, air of a definite absolute humidity—for instance, of 8 g/m³—can have different relative humidities at different temperatures. This air will have a relative humidity of about 85 per cent at 10°C because a little over 9 g of water vapour is the most that can be contained in air at that temperature, while at 20°C, at which the maximum quantity is about 17 g, a relative humidity of about 47 per cent is realized. From this it is easily understood that air of a certain absolute humidity and enclosed in a closed vessel varies its relative humidity greatly if the vessel is made to travel through districts of various temperatures.

Consider now the reactions of materials in the closed package when temperature and relative humidity vary in this way. Wood has been used as a packing material since ancient times. It is also a common material for art objects themselves. The reactions of wood to temperature and relative humidity changes are, however, very complicated and those in charge of packing must know the nature of wood. We can attribute many failures to ignorance of the nature of wood. The following concept about wood has become a commonplace, though it is responsible for the failures. If we put wood in air of a definite temperature and relative humidity for a sufficiently long time, it reaches a condition in which no water is emitted from or absorbed into the wood—namely, an equilibrium between the wood and the air is created. We then put this wood in a box made of a material that has no reaction against humidity, and seal the box. Of course, some of the air in equilibrium with the wood will be sealed in the box. Let us then make the air in the box drier by some means (this can be accomplished by making the temperature of the whole system rise, as mentioned above). When the air in the box thus becomes drier, water contained in the wood gradually evaporates into the air. Soon a new state of equilibrium is reached and the transposition of water stops. By this reaction the humidity change of the air in the box is mitigated, and the actual humidity variation of the air is smaller than when the box contains no wood. This fact indicates the effectiveness of the presence of wood in a box as a means of mitigating relative humidity variations when the box contains, say, art objects, for which large humidity changes are unfavourable.

Everyone has these concepts in mind, and they are true in one way. But, as there are few who take the other properties of wood into consideration, failures often do take place. The cause of transposition of water from or into wood does not lie only in relative humidity change. Variation of temperature is another very effective cause. By this I do not mean the indirect action of temperature in which the temperature change invokes a change in relative humidity of the enclosed air which, in turn, causes transference of water. Water contained in wood is driven out from the wood directly by a rise of temperature, and the reverse transference takes place also by a drop of temperature. If we try to keep the air enclosed in a wood package at a constant relative humidity by raising the temperature of the package as mentioned before, this rise makes the water contained in the wood evaporate into the air, and the air generally becomes more humid than before. This increase in humidity is, of course, related to the quantity of wood, and it can generally

13

be said to be unexpectedly great. From this fact, the mitigating action of the wood in this case operates in the direction of absorption of water vapour, except when the quantity of wood is very small.

This analytical explanation might not be too easily understood. Let us now look at the same phenomenon from another aspect. *Figure 1* shows how much water (referring to the dry weight of cypress wood) can be contained in the wood at various temperatures under constant relative humidity of the surrounding air. If we allow cypress wood to stand in air of 5°C and 30 per cent relative humidity for a long period, a water quantity of about 10 per cent of the weight of the wood will be contained in the wood. This condition is expressed by point **A**. After enclosing this wood in a package with some of this air we make the temperature rise suddenly to 60°C (point **B**). We find this point **B** is situated on the line of 70 per cent relative humidity; that is to say, at this state the wood can remain in equilibrium with surrounding air of 70 per cent relative humidity. Actually

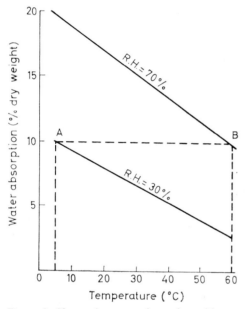

Figure 1. Change in water absorption with temperature (Japanese cypress in air of 30 per cent and 70 per cent relative humidities)[1].

the surrounding air becomes very dry with the sudden change of temperature from 5°C to 60°C, the resultant relative humidity being estimated at only a few per cent. This unbalance is mitigated gradually by the evaporation of water from the wood into the air. However, if the quantity of the wood is not very small, a small change of the contained water effects a large change in the relative humidity of the air, and the stable point of equilibrium is expected to be a little below 70 per cent. This humidity would be quite unexpected by the common theory mentioned above, the new equilibrium point being more humid than the original state.

In a very special case, the drop of relative humidity of the air and the vapour given off from the wood cancel out, and relative humidity is kept constant while temperature changes. But this condition is calculated to be satisfied only when about one kilogram of wood is sealed in one cubic metre, which seldom occurs in an actual package. A package containing less wood becomes drier with a rise of temperature. However, enclosed air in a package containing wood generally becomes very humid

with a rise of temperature, and a subsequent drop of temperature, if it takes place, causes a very dangerous condition in the air. Such a drop may occur if the temperature drops at night or if the package enters a colder climate. With this drop in temperature the relative humidity of the enclosed air rises, and, of course, the wood begins to mitigate this rise. But as this speed of absorption is in general very low (we have not as yet measured the speed) it cannot follow the rise of humidity, and the air may become saturated, causing condensation in the package.

With the above-mentioned painting, 'Douleur au pays de la mer', which was sent to Japan in the spring of 1959, we recognized signs of this phenomenon. The size of this painting was 263 × 346 cm, and the box for it had no large dead spaces. This case was made of wood and the inside surface was covered with waxed paper. It was made to stand in the hold in such a way as to keep the plane of the painting vertical to prevent other packages from pressing against the walls of the box. When unpacking, we found that the centre of the painting was pressed against the sides of the box (which were parallel to the painting) and mould grew at this point, leaving strange coloured secretions. We found much condensation on the back of the waxed paper, and drops were also found on the inside surface of the waxed-paper pads used for packing (fine wood shavings lapped with waxed paper). From these data the condition during travel can be imagined as follows: As the ship advanced from Europe through the Near East and to the Indian Ocean, the temperature rose gradually, inducing evaporation of water from the wooden walls of the box. Whilst on the outside of the box the vapour diffused away freely, it was stopped by the waxed paper on the inside, and the thin space between the paper and the wood became very humid. As a result of this, the outside surfaces of the box contracted and the inside ones expanded, and consequently the walls of the box curved so as to be convex to the inside. The deformation must naturally be greatest in the two large planes parallel to the painting. Finally they came in contact with the painting. The air in the box must have been fairly humid to have caused generation of mould. The above explanation might be surprising to some, but I think it is important to bear these facts in mind when making packages for distant destinations.

Most of the common packing materials have the same nature as wood—paper, cotton, cloth, etc.—and not only react against the relative humidity of the surrounding air but also change their contained water directly with changes of temperature, though the extent is not as great as with wood. There are materials which have no such properties: metals and glass are sensible to neither temperature nor humidity from the viewpoint of water transfer, because these materials contain no moisture.

I recently encountered a material whose water content is determined almost entirely by relative humidity, independently of temperature. Furthermore, its absorption and desorption curves were found almost to coincide in the relation between relative humidity of surrounding air and contained water. This material is called 'Kaken gel', and resembles silica gel. Although it is thought to have no effect on art objects if it comes into contact with them (since it is chemically almost neutral) it is preferable to use it indirectly. To use this gel as a mitigator, we first season it, putting it in air of the relative humidity which we wish to maintain in the package. If we insert the correct quantity of this seasoned gel in the closed package it mitigates large changes of relative humidity. As the water content in this gel is almost unaffected by temperature, the gel absorbs vapour if the enclosed air becomes more humid, and emits vapour if the air is dried, regardless of the cause of the humidity changes; thus it keeps the enclosed air at a humidity near to the original state.

Although this gel is very useful, as mentioned above and for reasons which will be given below, I am not recommending it as the best among other materials, which I have not yet studied widely. I believe that in every country in the world materials may be found with properties similar to Kaken gel. For example, among the silica gels there are some which are comparable to Kaken gel in absorbing ability and absorbing speed. But it must be remembered that some silica gels have lower absorption speeds and some hysteresis. This hysteresis phenomenon is very unfavourable for our purposes, especially if the difference between the absorption and desorption curves is great. Such materials as bentonite and active clay are also thought to be promising. I think it is necessary for every country to look for suitable materials among its most readily available products.

The quantity of Kaken gel or others needed to mitigate humidity changes in a closed package depends upon the dimensions of the package, quantity and quality of art objects contained and the permissible variation limit of relative humidity. I have published a rough calculation about these relations in *Studies in Conservation*, Vol. IV, No. 3, pp. 81–87. The theoretical expectation mentioned above that Kaken gel is useful for humidity control was also verified by experiment. When we enclose some wood and Kaken gel in a glass vessel and make the temperature vary, the humidity change of the air in the vessel is small, as predicted by the theory. We applied this scheme to packages for the Japanese art exhibitions held in Europe (1958–1959). On the way to Europe it was not very successful, because (unknown to us) imperfectly dried wood was used in the packages. But I can report that the packages were unpacked in a very satisfactory condition after their return to Japan.

This method can, of course, also be applied to showcases in a museum.

We have found another useful property in Kaken gel, which may be expected to be common to others such as silica gel. The ability of these to contain vapour seems to be an adsorption phenomenon, which is also effective for other polluting gases. For instance, air containing a small quantity of hydrogen sulphide, sulphur dioxide, ammonia, carbon dioxide or gasoline is rapidly purified by Kaken gel. The package made for an art object is as a rule waterproof, but by no means airtight. Hence, if such a gas is generated in the hold, it might penetrate into the package. Though the speed of entry is thought to be very low, since the action takes place by diffusion, the package is never thought to be safe from the gas. In such a case an adsorber in the package can be said to promise safety of art objects.

Kaken gel which has adsorbed such a gas can be revived by raising the temperature to about 50–60°C in clean air. Too high a temperature, such as 100°C, makes the gel coloured and seems to cause chemical change in the impurities contained in it.

Transportation by air is expected to cause the changes mentioned above very rapidly and repeatedly. I intend to study whether the above method is useful in such cases or whether some more effective mitigator is needed.

Reference

[1] MIYABE, H., *Kenchikugaku-Taikei* (Outline of Architectural Engineering), p. 494, Vol. 22, Shōkokusha Co., Tokyo, 1957.

Hugh Wakefield

METHODS OF PACKING IN THE VICTORIA AND ALBERT MUSEUM

I must explain first of all that I am not in any sense an expert in packing. I am the head of the department in the Victoria and Albert Museum which uses the greater part of the services of the museum's packing staff; and to that extent I am perhaps a consumer of packing services rather than a practitioner.

This department, called the Circulation Department, is one of the oldest in the museum, and its activities may be said to have started as early as 1844 when decorative art objects were bought from the Paris exhibition of that year in order to be shown in the Government School of Design in London, and subsequently to be circulated around the other Schools of

Figure 1. Making a two-ply wad.
(By courtesy of Central Office of Information)

Design which had by that time been set up in a number of provincial cities. In the fifties and early sixties of the last century two large 'circulating museums' were formed and sent around the country. A regular system of loans to provincial museums dates from 1880; and for a long period before the Second World War these consisted mainly of small collections of objects such as pottery, glass or silver, which were changed annually. More recently, since the war, the department has concentrated upon the provision of temporary exhibitions which are sent around the country on circuit and are moved from place to place by our own packing staff after comparatively short periods of showing.

I have mentioned these historical details in order to show the background of our experience. It is obviously a very long experience; but it will be noticed that the fruits of that experience are adapted to our main problem of moving frequently a great number of decorative art objects, many of which are as fragile as prehistoric pottery or paper-thin Roman glass. It may be noticed, too, that most of our activities are carried out within a relatively small country and under circumstances which enable us to use the same staff for both packing and unpacking at each successive point, although these factors may not in themselves have any bearing on the methods used. Our experience naturally includes the frequent packing and moving of large stone sculptures and large oil and tempera paintings; but it is with the relatively small and fragile decorative art objects that we have been most concerned, and it is for the packing of these that we have evolved an effective method which is little known and is worthy of description. When during the last hundred years or so the method was worked out we do not know. No doubt refinements were incorporated from time to time, but substantially its use in the museum packing room stretches back as far as memory and hearsay can recall.

Like most packing methods it is basically simple, and it is more easily demonstrated than described. It is based on the use of paper wads as packing material which are of a size and consistency designed to ensure ease of handling and the correct degree of elasticity. Each individual wad is made in the following manner. A sheet of medium thick brown paper 30 × 19 in. (76 × 48 cm), a size known in Britain as 'Double Small Hand', is placed against a sheet of tissue paper of the same size. Held initially in the right hand and then wrapped around the left hand, the two-ply sheet is turned inward around its edges, so that a loose wad is formed roughly oval in shape about 8 in. long, 6 in. wide and 2 in. deep (20 × 15 × 5 cm) with the tissue paper on the outside. Made in this way, one side of the wad is relatively smooth while the other is rumpled inwards (*Figure 1*). As a packing material the virtue of these wads is that whilst absorbing a considerable degree of vibration they do not show any appreciable tendency to reassert their previous shape after they have been tucked around the object to be protected.

Many hundreds of wads are, of course, needed to fill a packing case such as might hold twenty or thirty pieces of pottery; but they can be used many times over and they are only rejected when eventually the outer tissue paper begins to get torn. A packing case in use will normally be kept full of wads; on any particular packing operation one would not expect to have to replace more than, say, 5 per cent of them.

In filling a packing case the bottom of the case is first covered with a layer of closely packed wads. The first group of heavier objects is packed on this foundation, each object being carefully separated from the side of the box and from its neighbours by wads which are firmly packed around it. Each of these is covered by further wads, and progressively lighter objects are packed above. Flat objects such as plates and dishes are packed edgewise, and not flat, since the main movement within

Figure 2. A packer ensuring that the objects in the lower layer
are evenly bedded.
(By courtesy of Central Office of Information)

the case is likely to be vertical rather than horizontal. Over the
top level of objects further wads are packed, usually several
layers, so that the contents protrude a little above the top of
the sides of the case, and the whole is slightly compressed when
the top of the case is fixed in position. When the case is
subsequently unpacked it will be found that each object is
removed from a matrix of wads which closely reproduces its
shape (*Figures 2* and *3*).

The degree of pressure used in placing the wads in position
around the objects is the critical feature of this method of
packing. If the wads are unduly flattened there will be proportionately less protection against shock; on the other hand,
if the wads are too loose the objects may move within the case.
In practice the use of this method implies a wide margin of
safety. It is, however, sensible to place the heavier objects at
the bottom level of the case as a protection against extreme
conditions of shock, especially when lettering and signs on the
case and the position of handles are likely to ensure that the
top does travel topmost.

It is assumed that all of the objects packed within a particular
case are in a similar category of size and material. It would be
reasonable to pack in the same case a collection of pots which
varied in size by, say, 100 per cent. It would obviously not be
reasonable to pack only with wads a group of glasses down the
side of a wooden cabinet; in this instance it would be necessary
to limit the maximum movement of the cabinet with internal
battens across the case. At the opposite extreme the inclusion
of some small objects would call for special measures. Small
objects can often travel safely with larger ones if they are placed
in hollows formed in the smooth sides of wads and if the person
unpacking the case knows to expect such objects under the top
layers of wads. When all of the objects are relatively small the
wads can be made wholly of sheets of tissue paper used either

singly or two-ply. On the other hand, when the packing is
wholly of large objects, such as furniture or sculpture, it is wise
to use wads of a larger size and a more resilient nature. These
are formed of wood-wool rolled in sheets of brown paper with
the ends tucked in to make 'sausages' about 15 in. (38 cm) long
and 4 in. (10 cm) in diameter.

One point that should be noticed is that the objects themselves are not wrapped in any material before being packed.
Indeed, the wrapping of objects should be deliberately avoided,
since it is most important that the person unpacking should
sight an object as soon as it begins to be exposed and that he
should be able to see immediately the sort of object it is and the
way it should be handled. Exceptions are, however, made to this
rule when dealing with very large or very small objects. A
piece of furniture within a packing case should be wrapped
with resilient material where, with its relatively great weight, it
might penetrate to the inner surface of the case; and it might be
necessary to pack some very small objects such as jewellery in a
small container, which could then be packed in the usual way
with wads among medium-sized objects in a packing case.
Exceptional treatment may also be necessary to prevent either
wads or wrapping from touching a delicate surface which must
be protected from the least degree of rubbing.

The efficacy of packing decorative art objects in paper wads
can best be determined by a consideration of the alternatives.
A moulded foam-rubber bed, fitting precisely the form of each
object, could no doubt be designed to provide the most effective
possible protection against vibration and shock; but in our
experience this method could only be provided for quite
exceptionally precious and fragile objects, or else perhaps for
collections of objects which are to be repacked frequently by
unprofessional hands. At the other end of the scale the loose
packing materials, such as sawdust, straw and wood-wool, do

Figure 3. A small object being packed in the hollow of a
wad.
(By courtesy of Central Office of Information)

not provide a satisfactory bedding, and in varying degrees allow the objects packed in them to creep within the case or else to penetrate the packing too easily on receipt of a blow. The use of such packings represents a calculable risk, which may be acceptable, for instance, to the makers of industrial pottery, but not to those who are conveying museum objects. On the other hand, the method of packing by wads has been used almost exclusively by the Victoria and Albert Museum for the packing of its three-dimensional decorative art objects, and in spite of a continuous activity of packing and repacking, especially for the Circulation Department, there is scarcely a single remembered instance when the method has failed.

Selim Augusti

LES MÉTHODES D'ANALYSE APPLIQUÉES AUX NEUVRES D'ART ET AUX ANTIQUITÉS

Partie générale

Empirisme et science

Tout ce qui concerne l'examen d'une oeuvre d'art (désignant sous ce terme toutes ces oeuvres et ces objets qui aient intérêt du point de vue historique, artistique ou archéologique) soit aux fins de sa connaissance structurale et technique, de sa datation, de son attribution, et soit aux fins de sa conservation, était, jusqu'à une époque qui n'est pas lointaine, conduit sur une base purement empirique (avec toutes les erreurs et tous les horreurs auquels l'empirisme conduit) et était confié uniquement à la culture et à la sensibilité d'un connaisseur ou d'un amateur d'art. Aujourd'hui cette conception empirique est complètement, ou presque complètement, abandonnée et l'examen de l'oeuvre d'art, avec tous les problèmes qu'ils s'y rattachent, est conduit sur une base purement scientifique. Il est évident qu'après les premiers et pénibles pas, confiés seulement à la compétence et à la passion de quelques hommes d'étude isolés, de nos jours l'examen scientifique d'une oeuvre d'art est réalisé par des techniciens qualifiés, qui ont à leur disposition des méthodes et des moyens toujours plus perfectionnés et qui se servent d'organisations non seulement locales, tels que les laboratoires annexés aux musées et aux ateliers de restauration, mais aussi de grands centres d'études, à caractère national ou international.

Le but de l'analyse scientifique

L'examen scientifique d'une oeuvre d'art peut avoir comme but: (1) l'étude de la nature et de la composition d'une oeuvre d'art, visant à la connaissance de la «matière première» ou des «matières premières» qui forment l'objet, dans son ensemble ou dans ses parties, et par conséquent des «matériaux» employés par l'artisan ou par l'artiste pour sa préparation, et visant à la connaissance de la «technique» ou des «techniques» mises en oeuvre, dans les différents lieux et dans les différentes époques; (2) la datation et l'attribution de l'oeuvre d'art, par rapport à la nature, à la qualité et à la quantité de ses composants, et par rapport à la technique de sa préparation; (3) la détermination de l'authenticité ou de la falsification de l'oeuvre d'art, par rapport à la nature de ses composants et à la technique employée pour sa préparation; (4) l'examen de la nature, de l'état et des conditions d'une oeuvre d'art, aux fins de sa conservation, soit comme conservation «à l'état» et dans «le milieu» où il se trouve, et soit pour les opérations de restauration.

L'examen des oeuvres d'art

L'examen des oeuvres d'art, n'importe à quel but il soit réalisé, doit être basé sur des points axiomatiques fondamentaux: (a) il n'existe aucune méthode analytique qui puisse donner un jugement absolu sur la nature, la composition et la structure d'une oeuvre d'art—le jugement peut et doit prendre naissance de la rationnelle élaboration des données analytiques obtenues par l'application des différentes méthodes d'analyse; (b) l'examen scientifique d'une oeuvre d'art ne peut et ne doit pas être fin à soi même—il doit représenter le recueil d'un ensemble de données, dont l'élaboration doit constituer la base d'une collaboration avec un expert qualifié du point de vue artistique ou archéologique (critic d'art, directeur de musée, conservateur ou simple amateur). Le jugement final doit être le résultat de cette collaboration (ce qui doit toujours être, non seulement dans le cas spécifique d'une étude particulière ou d'une recherche, mais aussi pendant le normal travail de touts les jours pour la garde et la conservation des oeuvres d'art).

La collaboration entre science et art

La conception de cette collaboration s'affirme de nos jours toujours de plus en plus: tandis-que pendant les années passées un directeur de musée ou un conservateur était l'arbitre, plus ou moins absolu, de ce qui lui était confié, et ne faisait recours que de temps en temps à un homme de science pour lui demander quelques données analytiques, qu'en thèse finale il gardait pour soi même, ou bien un homme de science, simplement pour la curiosité ou pour sa propre satisfaction, faisait quelque analyse, dans l'espace fermé de son laboratoire, qui généralement n'était que fin à soi même, sans aucune utilité pratique dans la domaine des beaux arts ou de l'archéologie, de nos jours on sent toujours plus la nécessité et l'indispensabilité de cette collaboration entre la science et l'art. L'obstacle causé par le fait que les hommes qui cultivaient l'art étaient absolument dépourvus de toute connaissance scientifique, arrivant jusqu'au point d'ignorer ou de mépriser la science et ces applications, et autant de leur part étaient dépourvus de connaissances artistiques, historiques ou philologiques les hommes de science, qui examinaient un objet d'art avec le même désinvolture et froideur d'un n'importe quel «échantillon» de laboratoire, sans en apercevoir ou même en imaginer sa vitalité et sa valeur sociale et humaine, cet obstacle, s'il n'est pas encore complètement tombé, il est au moins fortement atténué, car il a été aperçu et on cherche de l'éliminer. Ceux qui cultivent l'art n'ignorent plus la science, mais ils en apprécient les applications et cherchent à se pourvoir d'un ensemble de connaissances scientifiques, qui puisse les mettre en condition de savoir ce qu'ils peuvent demander et ce qu'il doivent prétendre d'un analyste scientifique, ainsi qu'aujourd'hui il n'y a pas un chimiste, qui veuille se dédier à cette activité, qui ne sente pas la nécessité de se pourvoir d'une culture, soit même superficielle, de tout ce qu'il lui puisse être utile et nécessaire de savoir, du point de vue artistique et archéologique, pour entreprendre une recherche scientifique sur des bases sérieuses et profitables.

Les méthodes d'analyse

L'examen d'une oeuvre d'art exige le relèvement en détail, et aussi possible complet, de tous ces éléments qui composent l'oeuvre et que l'on peut grouper en deux groupes de nature très différents, savoir les éléments artistiques et les éléments matériels. Les «éléments artistiques» indiquent la manière par laquelle les matériaux composants ont été rangés, et par conséquence «la facture» de l'oeuvre d'art et sa «collocation» dans le temps et dans le lieu, par rapport au style, à l'école, à «la personnalité» de l'artiste et à ses «prérogatives de métier», c'est à dire tous ces éléments qui prennent origine de la littérature, de l'histoire de l'humanité et de l'histoire de l'art, et dont le relèvement est la prérogative absolue de l'homme qui cultive l'art. Les «éléments matériels» indiquent, au contraire, la nature, la qualité et la quantité des «matières premières» qui composent l'oeuvre d'art, «l'ordre» par lequel elles sont groupées et rangées, c'est à dire «la structure intime» de l'oeuvre et «le procédé» par lequel on est parvenu à sa réalisation, ou bien «la technique» de sa préparation, et dont le relèvement est la prérogative absolue de l'homme de science et de ses méthodes et instruments d'analyse. Il est pourtant bien évident que l'examen vraiment complet d'une oeuvre d'art peut résulter seulement de l'addition et de la fusion de ces deux groups d'éléments, c'est à dire de la collaboration entre la science et l'art, puisque les résultats de «l'examen artistique» et les resultats de «l'examen scientifique» s'intègrent et se complètent réciproquement.

Les méthodes scientifiques pour l'étude et l'examen d'une oeuvre d'art, comme d'autre part toutes celles qui sont employées pour l'examen technico-scientifique de n'importe quelle substance naturelle ou artificielle, sont de nature purement physique ou de nature purement chimique, ou bien de nature physico-chimique (jusqu'à la limite à laquelle nos actuelles connaissances scientifiques nous empêchent de différencier ultérieurement la physique et la chimie). De nos jours l'examen scientifique des oeuvres d'art appelle en cause la physique théorique et la physique expérimentale, dans toutes leurs applications, et la chimie, dans toutes ses branches (chimie générale, inorganique, organique, analytique et appliquée, éléctrochimie, etc.) et la chimie-physique, dans toutes ses applications, même les plus récentes; il appelle en outre à son aide toutes les branches des sciences naturelles, telles que la minéralogie, la géologie, la biologie (botanique, zoologie, microbiologie), la géographie générale et la géographie humaine, etc., et se sert aussi de toutes les connaissances pratiques rélatives à l'usinage artisan et aux procédés industriels de fabrications, dans les domaines de la métallurgie, de l'art céramique, de la verrerie, etc.

Aujourd'hui nous préférons de grouper toutes les méthodes d'analyse appliquées à l'examen des oeuvres d'art en deux groups, savoir les méthodes d'analyse «destructives» et les méthodes d'analyse «non destructives». Les méthodes d'analyse non destructives, qui demandent l'emploi de moyens de nature purement physique, sont employées pour l'examen direct d'une oeuvre d'art, aux fins de la connaissance de sa nature et structure et de son état et conditions, dans son ensemble ou dans ses parties, sans qu'elle soit en aucune manière altérée ou modifiée. Les méthodes destructives d'analyse, qui sont employées pour l'examen de matériaux isolés ou de fragments prélevés d'une oeuvre d'art, aux fins de la connaissance de la composition chimique, qualitative et quantitative, des matières premières qui la composent, et de leurs quantités proportionnelles, important, par conséquence, la modification et la destruction des substances examinées. Naturellement ces méthodes d'analyse, destructives ou non destructives, peuvent, et doivent souvent, s'intégrer et se compléter réciproquement.

Au delà de l'examen, en soi et pour soi, de l'oeuvre d'art, il est souvent important, aux fins de sa conservation *in situ* ou de la connaissance des lieux où l'oeuvre a vecu ou a été découverte, d'étudier les facteurs climatiques du milieu et leur influence sur l'oeuvre d'art (température, humidité, ventilation, poussière, salinité de l'air auprès de la mer, action de la lumière, présence de parasites animaux ou végétaux, etc.) ce qui fait part de la tâche d'un analyste chimique, moyennant l'aide eventuelle d'un spécialiste (physicien, biologiste, géologue, etc.) et que l'on peut réaliser par les moyens des communes méthodes d'analyse.

Aperçu historique

Il n'est pas facile de préciser quand, pour la première fois, on a appliqué des méthodes scientifiques à l'examen des oeuvres d'art, mais il est evident qu'à telles applications on soit arrivé par degrés. De nos jours il semble tout naturel et spontané que l'on doive commencer l'examen d'une oeuvre d'art par les moyens d'investigation de nature physique et par une bonne et détaillée documentation photographique. Mais des siècles ont dû s'écouler, et il faut parvenir à une époque qui est bien proche de nous, avant que la photographie et ces moyens physiques, qu'aujourd'hui nous semblent si élémentaires, aient fait leur entrée et se soient affirmés dans la domaine de l'analyse appliqué aux oeuvres d'art. En définitive, je pense que l'on puisse distinguer trois périodes historico-chronologiques : (1) une première période, que débute de l'antiquité classique (avec Pline, Vitruve, etc.) et qui a durée pendant des siècles, dans laquelle on n'a que des essais isolés, au premier moment empiriques puis scientifiques et basés sur l'analyse chimique, appliquée aux matériaux et aux objets d'intérêt archéologique; (2) une deuxième période, qui date de la deuxième moitié du XIX siècle jusqu'aux premières années du XX siècle, pendant laquelle l'échange d'informations et la collaboration entre les hommes de sciences et les hommes de lettres et d'art commence à jeter des bases toujours plus solides, et pendant laquelle à l'analyse chimique viennent s'ajouter les méthodes et les moyens de nature physique; (3) une troisième période, qui date du début du XX siècle, en particulier de cette dernière trentaine d'années, pendant laquelle les méthodes scientifiques sont appliquées aussi à l'examen direct des oeuvres d'art, et la collaboration entre la science et l'art devient un fait accompli. De l'homme de science isolé, qui, même de haute valeur scientifique, ne s'occupait que seulement par hasard de recherches dans la domaine des beaux arts, on passe à des «groupes de savants» qui se dédient exclusivement aux recherches et aux études appliqués à l'examen des oeuvres d'art, avec l'organisation de laboratoires, lesquels, à partir du premier fondé en Allemagne in 1888, deviennent toujours plus nombreux dans le monde entier, et toujours mieux équipés. Des premiers travaux scientifiques, qui ont trouvé hospitalité dans les périodiques de recueil général des travaux de physique, de chimie et de sciences naturelles, nous sommes passés à toute une littérature spécialisée, avec des publications toujours plus nombreuses et importantes, sous forme de livres ou de périodiques, lesquels sont particulièrement dédiés à l'étude et à l'examen des oeuvres d'art.

A cet égard, je désire faire ici une considération : il est nécessaire, à mon avis, qu'aux publications de caractère strictement scientifique, rélatives aux perfectionnement de méthodes connues d'analyse et à l'élaboration de nouvelles méthodes, et qui sont réservées aux seuls spécialistes, viennent s'ajouter de plus en plus des «oeuvres de vulgarisation», lesquelles puissent illustrer au gros public l'apport de la science à l'art, et surtout puissent donner aux non spécialistes (amateurs d'art, conservateurs, restaurateurs, etc.) une bonne connaissance des méthodes scientifiques, de leur importance et de leurs applications, et puissent réveiller en eux le désir de s'en renseigner et de les considérer comme des compagnons nécessaires et indispensables de leur travail quotidien.

Les méthodes scientifiques pour l'examen des oeuvres d'art

Les méthodes d'analyse, comme je viens de l'indiquer, se divisent en deux groupes: méthodes non destructives et méthodes destructives. Je commence ma description par ces dernières car elles ont été les premières et pendant longtemps les seules à être usées, tandis-que les non destructives sont une acquisition beaucoup plus récente dans la domaine des analyses appliquées aux oeuvres d'art.

Les méthodes destructives d'analyse

Après les «essais empiriques» de l'antiquité, la première à paraître a été sans doute l'analyse chimique, appliquée aux matériaux isolés ou aux objets d'intérêt archéologique, retrouvés pendant les excavations. L'analyse chimique appliquée à l'examen des oeuvres d'art s'est pratiquement servie des communes méthodes et moyens de la chimie analytique, qualitative et quantitative, et pourtant l'évolution chronologique des méthodes appliquées aux oeuvres d'art marche au pas et s'identifie avec l'évolution des méthodes générales, qualitatives et quantitatives.

Mais ces méthodes n'ont plus étées utilisables et suffisantes quand on a commencé à procéder à l'analyse de toutes petites quantités de substances et surtout quand on a commencé à prélever ces substances directement de l'oeuvre d'art. Voilà donc la nécessité de recourir aux «microtechniques», soit comme technique de prélèvement des specimens pour l'analyse (dont je parlerai tout à l'heure) soit pour l'analyse elle-même. L'analyse microchimique, qui a pris sa naissance du perfectionnement des méthodes chimiques d'analyse et surtout de l'emploi du microscope au laboratoire, s'est servie au début des réactions microchimiques générales, «au microscope» et puis «à la touche», auxquelles successivement sont venues s'ajouter des réactions particulières, étudiées à dessein pour l'analyse des oeuvres d'art. De nos jours, dans cette domaine, quand on parle d'analyse chimique on se rapporte à l'analyse microchimique (sauf des cas particuliers).

La microscopie s'est de plus en plus perfectionnée, par la construction d'appareils et dispositifs toujours plus parfaits, de précision croissante, qui permettent soit l'examen direct d'une oeuvre d'art (dont je parlerai à propos des méthodes non destructives) et soit l'analyse microscopique de fragments et de sections, soit par transparence que par réflexion, soit en lumière normale qu'en lumière polarisée, et soit par l'application des radiations invisibles (ultraviolet, infrarouge) qui permet d'en tirer des données analytiques importantes sur la nature et la structure des substances cristallines (en outre naturellement des applications du microscope pour l'analyse microchimique). L'application de la photographie, soit par des macro- que par des micro-photographies (photomicrographies), a constitué un énorme progrès pour l'analyse, permettant de fournir une documentation stable des résultats, soit de l'examen microscopique direct, soit de l'examen de fragments et de sections (coupes) soit de l'analyse microchimique et des réactions qui s'ensuivent.

En aide à l'analyse microchimique, la détermination de l'index de réfraction constitue une bonne méthode d'analyse et de différentiation (par exemple entre substances naturelles et substances artificielles) qui peut être réalisée au moyen d'un réfractomètre, ou plus simplement par la détermination de la «ligne de Becke» (examen, au microscope, d'un fragment de la substance à examiner plongé dans un liquide à l'index de réfraction connu).

Aux communes méthodes de la chimie analytique classique viennent s'ajouter toutes les méthodes modernes d'analyse, savoir l'analyse électrolytique et l'analyse polarographique, qui permettent de doser les composants métalliques d'un mélange, l'analyse chromatographique, qui permet de séparer et doser les composants d'un mélange, etc.

Une méthode analytique vraiment précieuse, quand on dispose de quantités minimes de substances à analyser, ce qui représente le cas le plus fréquent dans la domaine de l'analyse appliquée aux oeuvres d'art, est représentée par l'analyse spectrale, laquelle de nos jours présente des applications si nombreuses et importantes qu'elle vient à constituer une vraie branche de la chimie: la spectrochimie. L'examen spectroscopique, c'est à dire l'examen du «spectre» caractéristique de chaque élément, constitué par des couleurs et des raies colorées produit par le passage au travers d'un prisme des radiations émises par un corps lumineux ou rendu lumineux (par exemple en le brûlant dans un arc électrique), est un moyen des plus importants, au point de vue analytique, surtout si le spectre d'émission vient photographié, au moyen de l'analyse spectrographique, fournissant des spectrogrammes, qui permettent de caractériser les composants d'une substance minérale (par exemple un pigment de couleur) ce qui rend possible d'identifier la substance. Cette identification est rendue possible aussi par la spectrographie de fluorescence, qui fournit la courbe spectrale caractéristique des radiations lumineuses émises par la substance (par exemple un pigment) sous l'excitation de la lumière ultraviolette. Le même service rendu dans la domaine de la chimie inorganique par les spectres d'émission est rendu dans la domaine de la chimie organique par les spectres d'absorption, qui viennent analysés et fixés photographiquement par un spectrophotomètre. Le spectrophotogramme obtenu peut caractériser les composants d'une substance organique (par exemple une matière colorante) ce qui rend possible son identification. Dans la domaine des radiations invisibles, la spectrographie infrarouge permet l'identification de n'importe quelle substance organique, ce qui vient de nos jours appliqué avec grand profit à l'analyse des matières colorantes, des laques, des résines, etc.

Les rayons X, au delà de leur emploi direct pour l'examen des oeuvres d'art (dont je parlerai tout à l'heure, à propos des méthodes non destructives) fournissent une méthode importante d'analyse pour caractériser les substances cristallines, se basant sur la diffraction des rayons X. Les composants cristallins d'un spécimen à analyser dévient les rayons X selon des angles bien spécifiés: le modèle de taches et de lignes ainsi formé, dont l'image vient fixée photographiquement (debyegramme), est caractéristique de chaque type de cristal et peur servir à l'identifier.

La domaine des applications des méthodes analytiques à l'examen des oeuvres d'art s'est de plus en plus étendue pendant ces dernières années et les horizons se sont enlargis: à partir des premières simples requêtes aux analystes de connaître «la qualité» et «la quantité» des composants d'un corps, nous sommes aujourd'hui passés à des requêtes toujours plus engageantes, qui demandent non seulement l'analyste spécialisé mais aussi «l'analyste spécialisé dans la spécialisation» et la disposition d'équipements de laboratoire bien particuliers. On sait de nos jours que les isotopes radioactifs, dont on a tant parlé après la découverte de la radioactivité artificielle, peuvent être employés avec profit comme moyens d'analyse, mais leur emploi dans la domaine des beaux arts est encore reservé à bien peu de spécialistes et à bien peu de laboratoires. Ainsi, par exemple, la datation des objets archéologiques est rendue possible par la détermination quantitative du carbone radioactif, isotope ^{14}C, du carbone normal ^{12}C, la formation quantitative duquel, en nature, est en rapport direct à l'âge de la substance organique.

Les méthodes non destructives d'analyse

Les méthodes non destructives d'analyse, appliquées à l'examen direct d'une oeuvre d'art, sont basées sur l'emploi de «radiations», soient-elles des radiations lumineuses, visibles ou invisibles à l'oeil humain (les méthodes optiques) que des radiations d'autre nature.

Le premier pas pour l'examen d'une oeuvre d'art est une observation très soigneuse à l'oeil nu, suivie d'une observation par les moyens de grossissement, qui vont de la simple loupe, à main ou fixée sur un support, aux systèmes binoculaires, tels que la lorgnette à visière et les jumelles, fixées sur un casque ou sur un support à bras dénouables (systèmes généralement usés par les restaurateurs) jusqu'au microscope mono- et binoculaire. L'image de l'oeuvre et son état de conservation sont fixés et documentés par la photographie (en lumière naturelle ou artificielle; en lumière frontale, oblique ou rasante, etc.).

La photographie a pris de nos jours une très grande importance comme méthode d'analyse, car nous avons là non seulement un moyen subsidiaire de documentation mais aussi un moyen direct d'examen, puisque l'image photographique, reprise dans les plus différentes conditions d'illumination et d'agrandissement, permet d'apercevoir ces détails qui échappent à l'observation directe. Il faut encore penser que la photographie représente le moyen absolument nécessaire et indispensable pour l'utilisation et l'interprétation de toutes les méthodes analytiques.

Parmi les méthodes optiques sont à rappeler celles basées sur l'emploi des radiations monochromatiques, de longueur d'onde déterminée, qui sont obtenues par filtration de la lumière artificielle au travers de filtres colorés ou par l'emploi de sources lumineuses monochromatiques particulières, qui permettent l'examen de la surface d'une oeuvre d'art, créant des contrastes de nuances, qui mettent en évidence des points particuliers de cette surface, qui ne sont point apercevables en lumière normale polychromatique. La projection par des faisceaux de rayons monochromatiques peut être substituée par l'examen par écrans analyseurs colorés, en utilisant des filtres monochromatiques combinés, qui permettent d'obtenir certains caractères colorimétriques particuliers des pigments. De la simple observation par rayons monochromatiques, on peut passer à l'examen colorimétrique d'une surface colorée, aux moyens de colorimètres et photocolorimètres, à l'examen par la cellule photoélectrique, etc.

Mais les moyens les plus importants et indispensables pour l'examen des oeuvres d'art sont aujourd'hui fournis par les méthodes basées sur l'emploi des radiations invisibles à l'oeil humain.

Les rayons infrarouge, formés par des «rayons calorifiques», accordent aux substances qu'ils traversent une «intensité calorifique», qui est fonction de la constitution atomique de la matière traversée, de son épaisseur, etc., et qui est enregistrée et fixée par des émulsions photographiques, particulièrement préparées et sensibilisées. L'examen à l'infrarouge, qui s'identifie avec la photographie infrarouge, peut rendre de très grands services car il dévoile des particularités d'une surface ou d'une image, qui ne sont absolument perceptibles à l'oeil nu ou même à la photographie normale (j'ai déjà parlé de l'emploi des rayons infrarouges pour la microscopie et pour la spectrographie). Comme source de rayons infrarouge on utilise des lampes à incandescence, mais aujourd'hui on trouve en commerce aussi des lampes aux radiations riches de rayons infrarouges, mais sans émission de lumière visible (et par des écrans convenables on peut réaliser des dispositifs de laboratoire) qui se démontrent de vraie grande utilité pour obtenir des photos plus parfaites et bien détaillées.

Les rayons ultraviolets ont la propriété d'exciter la fluorescence de particulières substances: en projetant un faisceau de rayons ultraviolets sur un corps on en relève des fluorescences différentes en fonction de la composition chimique de la substance ou des substances qui le constituent. Les rayons ultraviolets, qui doivent être le plus possible monochromatiques et exempts de rayons visibles, viennent généralement produits par une lampe à vapeur de mercure et viennent filtrés par des filtres à l'oxyde de nickel, obtenant ainsi un faisceau de rayons ultraviolets filtrés, qui prennent le nom de «lumière de Wood». On réalise l'examen d'une oeuvre d'art directement à la lumière de Wood, par l'observation à l'oeil nu des fluorescences produites sur les divers points de la surface de l'objet examiné et qui consistent en émissions de rayons visibles sous l'excitation des rayons ultraviolets. L'image photographique constitue la photographie de fluorescence sous ultraviolet que d'habitude on désigne erronément sous le nom de «photographie ultraviolette». Il faut en effet préciser que nous avons ici une photographie de radiations lumineuses visibles à l'oeil humain et qui sera d'autant plus complète et parfaite plus on en élimine les rayons ultraviolets, tandis-que pour obtenir une vraie photographie ultraviolette il faut procéder exactement en sens contraire, c'est à dire éliminer, par des filtres convenables, tous les rayonnements visibles, fixant, sur un matériel photographique sensibilisé, les seules images produites par les rayons ultraviolets, invisibles à l'oeil humain.

Les rayons X, qui ont la propriété de traverser les corps, en fonction de l'épaisseur de la substance examinée et du poids atomique des éléments qui la composent, peuvent fournir des indications vraiment précieuses sur leur structure. Les images produites peuvent être recueillies sur un écran et observées à l'oeil nu (radioscopie) ou fixées sur un film photographique (radiographie). Dans la domaine de l'examen des oeuvres d'art, la radiographie est devenue tellement importante quelle constitue, avec la photographie et l'examen de la fluorescence sous ultraviolet, une des opérations analytiques fondamentales et d'usage commun. Pour la radiographie des oeuvres d'art on trouve en commerce des appareils qui ont été étudiés et réalisés exclusivement pour l'examen des oeuvres d'art. La radiographie des oeuvres d'art, qui emploie de préférence des «rayons moux» doués d'un grand pouvoir de pénétration, est réalisée soit comme radiographie normale, par image sur un plan perpendiculaire, soit comme radiographie stratigraphique, qui est réalisée par l'appareil en rotation et permet de séparer et mettre en évidence, chaque fois séparément, les différentes couches qui intéressent l'analyste, et soit comme stéréoradiographie, prise en deux radiographies sur les points diamétralement opposés, et qui présente, au stéréoscope, une image à trois dimensions. Pour ces dernières plusieurs laboratoires viennent de présenter des résultats vraiment excellents. De ma part je suis en train de mettre au point un système de projection des stéréoradiographies, sur un écran spécial, qui permet la stéréovision simultanée de la part de n'importe quel nombre de personnes.

Au delà de la radiographie conventionnelle, dont je viens de parler, les rayons X nous présentent d'autres importantes applications à l'examen des oeuvres d'art, savoir: la radiographie par émission d'électrons, basée sur le fait que, sous l'irradiation des rayons X, les éléments constituants d'un spécimen en examen émettent des différents intensités d'électrons qui, enregistrés photographiquement, fournissent une image qui est caractéristique de la substance examinée; et l'analyse de la fluorescence aux rayons X, basée sur le fait que, sous l'irradiation des rayons X, les éléments émettent des radiations de fluorescence, de longueur d'onde déterminée, qui, analysées, permettent d'identifier quelques-uns des éléments présents et donnent une indication de leur concentration.

Une méthode moderne de radiographie est représentée par la gammagraphie, qui, pour l'examen de corps fortement opaques, utilise les rayons gamma, émis spontanément par les corps radioactifs, naturels ou artificiels, qui ont un pouvoir de pénétration supérieur à celui des rayons X. L'absorption des rayons gamma est fonction de la densité des objets (par égalité d'épaisseur) et peut permettre la détermination quantitative indirecte de ces composants, la présence desquels est déjà connue du point de vue qualitative.

Méthodes modernes d'analyse des oeuvres d'art ont pour base l'emploi des neutrons et des rayons beta. Les neutrons, fournis par une pile atomique, communiquent à une proportion minime des atomes de la plupart des éléments des propriétés radioactives qui sont caractéristiques de chaque élément: l'irradiation d'un objet par les neutrons et l'étude de la radioactivité ainsi induite peuvent fournir l'indication des éléments contenus dans l'objet, et parfois une appréciation de leur proportion (mais la méthode est très délicate et n'est pas à la portée de tous). Les rayons beta, émis par des isotopes radioactifs (tels que ^{32}P ou ^{35}S) qui frappent la surface d'un corps, viennent en partie absorbés par le corps et en partie repoussés. Le nombre des rayons beta repoussés est proportionnel au nombre atomique de l'élément qui les repousse: la détermination de ce nombre, soit la quantité des rayons repoussés, permet d'identifier les éléments qui composent le corps examiné.

Autres méthodes d'analyse

En outre des méthodes que je viens de décrire, il est evident que l'on a utilisé, et que l'on puisse toujours les mettre en oeuvre, n'importe quelle méthode physique ou chimique, appliquée à l'examen des matériaux les plus divers (par exemple la flexométrie, applicable aux huiles et aux vernis, etc.). Pour dater les objets provenants des fouilles archéologiques, plusieures sont les méthodes auxquelles on peut faire appel, à partir des plus simples méthodes physiques (par exemple la détermination du degré d'aimantation d'un objet en fer, en fonction de l'âge de l'objet) à celles basées sur la physique atomique (du type, par exemple, de la méthode au radiocarbone ^{14}C) à celles purement chimiques (par exemple la détermination du rapport fluor/phosphore dans les ossements, en fonction de l'âge) ou bien à celles basées sur les autres branches des sciences naturelles (par exemple la dendrochronologie, l'analyse pollinique, etc.).

L'examen des oeuvres d'art

Le cours de l'analyse et le choix des méthodes

Posé que: (1) l'analyste doit connaître le but de l'analyse qu'on lui confie, afin de choisir les méthodes les plus convenables au cas; (2) n'importe quel analyste et n'importe quel laboratoire peuvent réaliser l'analyse de substances sans réelle valeur artistique ou dont on dispose de quantités plus que suffisantes (pigments, résines, vernis, etc.) tandis que, au contraire, on demande un analyste spécialisé, doué d'une culture suffisante au point de vue des beaux arts et de l'archéologie et un laboratoire particulièrement équipé, lorsqu'il s'agit de procéder sur des substances de valeur artistique ou directement sur des oeuvres d'art; (3) le fait d'établir si l'examen doit être réalisé sur l'oeuvre entière ou sur une ou plus de ses parties est le résultat d'une décision prise d'accord avec le compétent du point de vue artistique, et subordonné à la nature de l'oeuvre à

examiner et au but de l'analyse; (4) le choix des méthodes et le cours de l'analyse varient selon l'objet de l'analyse, et pourtant je pense que le cours de l'analyse doit être choisi et décrit en fonction de la nature de l'oeuvre à examiner, savoir: analyse des peintures, analyse des objets métalliques, analyse des céramiques, etc.

Mais il est nécessaire, et il ne faut jamais l'oublier, que, quel que soit le but de l'analyse et quelle que soit la nature de l'oeuvre à examiner, toute analyse soit toujours précédée par une opération commune et indispensable, c'est-à-dire l'examen préliminaire de l'oeuvre d'art, qui puisse donner des indications sommaires, mais précises, de sa structure et de son état de conservation et surtout qui puisse garantir que, sous peine d'en perdre ou d'en fausser les résultats, l'analyse soit sûrement et strictement conduite sur l'oeuvre originale et non sur des parties modifiées ou refaites.

Quant au choix des essais nécessaires pour un examen préliminaire, il n'y a pas de règles fixes: le choix est entièrement confié à la compétence et à l'esprit d'observation de l'analyste.

Examen des peintures

Les peintures varient selon la nature du support (mur, panneau, toile, etc.) et selon la nature de la peinture et sa technique de préparation (fresques, détrempes, à huile, à la cire, etc.). Aux fins de l'examen, je pense que les peintures peuvent se diviser en deux groupes, selon la nature du support (étant en effet aussi la technique en relation à la nature du support), savoir: peintures sur support immobile (peintures murales) et peintures sur support mobile (sur panneau et sur toile; sur autres supports). Le cours de l'analyse peut ainsi se décrire:

Peintures	Cours de l'analyse
(1) Sur support immobile (peintures murales)	Examen, sur place, à l'oeil nu et par les méthodes non destructives; documentation photographique (en lumière frontale et rasante, sous infrarouge, etc.); prélèvement de fragments et analyse (comme pour les peintures sur support mobile)
	Examen physico-chimique du mur; examen minéralogique ou géologique (pour les peintures sur pierre ou rocher)
	Détermination des facteurs climatiques
	Sur une peinture détachée du mur: analyse (comme pour les peintures sur support mobile)
(2) Sur support mobile	(a) Examen du support:
	Panneau: examen à l'oeil nu et par les moyens optiques; radiographie (stratigraphique); détermination du type et de l'âge du bois (à l'aide d'un naturaliste ou d'un artisan); documentation photographique.
	Toile: examen à l'oeil nu et par les moyens optiques; analyse microscopique et microchimique (recherche de substances étrangères); documentation photographique (et microphotographique)
	Autres: examen selon la nature du support (papier, métal, céramique, etc.)
	(b) Examen de la peinture
	Examen à l'oeil nu et par les moyens de grossissement (loupe, microscope, pinacoscope) à la lumière de Wood et aux rayons x, documenté par la photographie et la radiographie; complètement éventuel de l'analyse par les autres méthodes non destructives
	Examen du vernis, par des essais physiques (examen des craquelures, etc.) et par des essais chimiques

Peintures	Cours de l'analyse
	Examen de la couche picturale et de l'imprimure: analyse microscopique et microchimique des pigments et des mediums sur les fragments prélevés, au moyen de microtechniques de prélèvement et de préparation de couches microscopiques; examen spectrographique et par les autres méthodes destructives d'analyse; documentation macro- et microphotographique

Examen des objets en bois

Le bois forme le support des peintures sur panneaux et constitue la matière première de sculptures, meubles, objets divers, ainsi que de grandes constructions (navires, bâtiments divers, temples, etc.). L'examen du bois peut être réalisé comme suit:

Objet de l'analyse	Cours de l'analyse
(1) Support de peintures (panneaux)	Voir: examen des peintures
(2) Sculptures, meubles, objets divers	Examen par méthodes d'analyse non destructives; analyse microscopique de coupes et de fragments; détermination du type et de l'âge du bois (à l'aide d'un naturaliste ou d'un artisan); documentation photographique
(3) Fragments de navires ou de bâtiments; objets de fouilles	Essais physiques et chimiques; documentation photographique; datation par détermination du radiocarbone ^{14}C

Examen du papier et du parchemin

Le papier et le parchemin forment le support des écritures et de l'imprimerie (manuscrits, documents, livres, etc.) ainsi que le support de peintures et desseins; le papier est aussi le support des billets de banque, des effets bancaires, des timbres-poste, etc. L'analyse est réalisée comme suit:

Objet de l'analyse	Cours de l'analyse
(1) Papier et parchemin	Examen par les méthodes optiques: essais physiques (poids, épaisseur, etc.); étude microscopique et analyse chimique des composants de la pâte
(2) Peintures sur papier ou sur parchemin	Examen de la peinture: par les méthodes non destructives indiquées; examen du papier ou du parchemin: comme ci-dessus
(3) Écriture à la main, desseins	Examen de l'encre: par les méthodes non destructives (loupe, microscope, lumière de Wood, etc.) avec documentation macro- et microphotographique; analyse microchimique et spectrophotométrique Examen du papier: comme ci-dessus
(4) Documents divers, billets de banque, timbres-poste, etc.	Examen par les méthodes non destructives (optiques); documentation macro- et microphotographique Examen du papier: comme ci-dessus

Examen des objets métalliques

Les objets métalliques, très importants du point de vue archéologique, sont toujours constitués par des alliages, parmi lesquels les plus importants sont les bronzes. Le cours de l'analyse peut être indiqué comme suit:

Objet de l'analyse	Cours de l'analyse
(1) Tout objet métallique	Examen optique et documentation macro- et microphotographique de la surface, des incrustations et de la corrosion (altérations, maladies); analyse chimique ou microchimique des incrustations et des produits de la corrosion; examen au microscope métallographique; détermination des composants de l'alliage et de leur proportion par l'analyse électrochimique ou par la spectrographie ou par la diffraction de rayons X par les méthodes les plus récentes, telles que la radiographie par rayons gamma (gammagraphie), etc.
(2) Bronzes, cuivres	Analyse comme ci-dessus
(3) Objets en fer	Analyse comme ci-dessus; datation par la détermination du degré d'aimantation, etc.
(4) Objets en or et en argent	Détermination du titre de l'alliage par les méthodes communes; analyse quantitative par diffraction de rayons X, etc.

Examen des céramiques

Les céramiques, produites par l'empâtement et la cuite de matériaux argileux (argile, caolin), comprennent une gamme assez variée de produits divers, à partir des plus simples et communs (briques, terres cuites) jusqu'aux majoliques et aux plus fines porcelaines, etc. L'analyse en peut être réalisée comme suit:

Objet de l'analyse	Cours de l'analyse
(1) Briques, tuiles, terres cuites	Analyse chimique, qualitative et quantitative; détermination des lieux de provenance par diffraction de rayons X ou par analyse de la fluorescence sous l'excitation des rayons X; gammagraphie; datation par la détermination du degré de magnétisation des argiles, etc.
(2) Faïences, majoliques, porcelaines	Analyse microchimique de l'empâtement et analyse par les méthodes ci-dessus indiquées; examen des couleurs et des surfaces vitrifiées (vernis, glaçures) comme pour les verres et les émails (voir)
(3) Scories et déchets de fabrication	Analyse comme pour les verres et les émails (voir)

Examen des verres, vitraux, émails

Les verres (verrerie et vitrerie), les vitraux, les émaux, etc., sont chimiquement des silicates insolubles: l'analyse en peut être réalisée suivant les méthodes communes d'analyse, qualitative et quantitative, des silicates, ou bien par l'analyse spectrographique. L'analyse microscopique et microchimique peut venir en aide pour caractériser les pigments (comme pour les peintures) (voir).

Examen d'objets de différente nature et composition

L'analyste peut avoir occasion de voir présenter à l'analyse des objets de différentes natures, qui ont rapport à l'art ou à l'archéologie, tels que des objets en os, en ivoire, des pierres précieuses, etc. Voici le cours de l'analyse des plus communs de ces objets:

Objet de l'analyse	Cours de l'analyse
(1) Objets en ivoire ou en os	Différentiation microscopique et chimique entre os et ivoire, ou entre des produits naturels et des produits artificiels
(2) Ossements (de fouille)	Détermination des caractères anatomiques (à l'aide d'un naturaliste spécialisé); datation par analyse chimique du rapport fluor/phosphore
(3) Pierres précieuses, perles	Analyse à la lumière de Wood et photographie de la fluorescence sous ultraviolet; radiographie
(4) Ambre	Propriétés électriques par frottement; spectrographie infrarouge
(5) Tissus, étoffes, tapisseries	Examen et différentiation microscopiques et microchimiques des fibres; spectrophotométrie ou spectrographie infrarouge pour la détermination des matières colorantes des teintures
(6) Autres, divers	Analyse par méthodes destructives ou non destructives, auxquelles l'analyste peut faire appel, selon la nature des substances, leur quantité, leur valeur, etc.

Un laboratoire moderne pour l'analyse des oeuvres d'art

Un laboratoire pour l'examen des oeuvres d'art demande de l'air (comme n'importe quel laboratoire d'analyse) et surtout de la lumière et de l'espace: de la lumière, car l'observation directe d'une oeuvre d'art est toujours indispensable et demande beaucoup de lumière naturelle, ainsi que de moyens d'éclairage; de l'espace, avec des moyens d'accès faciles et commodes, car des grands tableaux, des grandes sculptures, etc., doivent pouvoir y circuler facilement et librement.

Un laboratoire pour l'examen des oeuvres d'art peut constituer un centre à soi-même ou peut être annexé à un atelier de restauration d'un musée, et peut avoir un but d'études et de recherches scientifiques, ou d'aide et de contrôlement au travail de restauration, ou bien des deux ensemble.

L'équipement d'un laboratoire varie naturellement beaucoup selon ce qu'on lui demande, mais on peut fixer des installations qui sont fondamentales et indispensables, savoir: (1) une section chimique, (2) une section physico-technique, (3) une section photographique.

Le laboratoire chimique élémentaire doit être doué des installations fixes et des appareils nécessaires à la réalisation d'une analyse chimique complète, qualitative et quantitative; le laboratoire physico-technique des moyens d'observation et de grossissement (loupes, microscopes, etc.) et d'examen aux radiations invisibles (rayons X, lumière de Wood, infrarouge, etc.); le laboratoire photographique des moyens de prise photographique, de développement, de tirage des copies, etc.

Cette installation constitue le noyau fondamental d'un laboratoire et naturellement son équipement s'enlargit et se spécialise au fur et à mesure que le laboratoire croît d'importance. Ainsi le laboratoire chimique s'enrichit de tous ces dispositifs et appareils qui sont nécessaires aux microtechniques, à l'analyse microscopique et microchimique, à l'analyse électrolytique, à l'analyse polarographique, à l'analyse spectrographique, etc.; les moyens physiques et physicochimiques d'analyse deviennent toujours plus nombreux et complexes, pour toutes les applications des rayons X, des rayons ultraviolets, des rayons infrarouges, etc.; les laboratoires et les équipements se spécialisent de plus en plus. Ainsi on arrive aux méthodes d'analyse les plus modernes, dont les moyens sont fournis par la physique atomique (isotopes, rayons gamma et beta, neutrons, etc.) et qui constituent, comme je l'ai dit auparavant, «une spécialisation dans la spécialisation». Alors voilà qu'un laboratoire de musée ne peut plus soutenir son pas et qu'il doit recourir aux laboratoires scientifiques des universités ou des grandes institutions.

Est-ce un bien ou est-ce un mal? Je pense que ce soit un bien: il faut encourager cette «spécialisation spécifique», et non seulement pour ces dernières méthodes. Il est inutile qu'un laboratoire déjà installé ou qu'un laboratoire de nouvelle installation veuille faire «tout» dans la domaine de la science et de l'analyse. Il est nécessaire, naturellement, qu'un laboratoire soit en conditions de faire tous ces essais et toutes ces analyses physiques, chimiques ou physicochimiques, qui sont indispensables à l'examen le plus complet des oeuvres d'art, ainsi pu'aux études et recherches d'ordre général sur les métaux, ou sur les pigments, ou sur les vernis, etc., et d'autre part il vaut mieux qu'il se spécialise dans une branche particulière de l'analyse. Ce qui est nécessaire c'est qu'il y ait un échange fréquent, plus intense et continu, d'information entre les analystes et les laboratoires spécialisés dans les différentes branches, dans le monde entier, et que les spécialistes soient à la disposition de tous les laboratoires non spécialisés dans leur branche particulière. Tout cela peut très bien se réaliser par le moyen d'un centre de coordination, qui peut bien être le Centre International pour la Conservation et la Restauration des Biens Culturels de Rome, avec un avantage réel et indiscutable de tous les laboratoires et de tous les analystes, même des spécialistes, qui auront toujours besoin des spécialistes dans une autre branche, et qui pourront ainsi dédier plus de temps et plus d'attention à leurs recherches, sans des inutiles répétitions et pertes de temps.

Rutherford J. Gettens

PROPOSAL FOR A HANDBOOK ON ANALYSIS OF MATERIALS OF PAINTINGS

Interest in the analysis and identification of the materials of painting began in the early part of the nineteenth century with two short publications, first a paper by Chaptal[1] of France and a little later one by the eminent English scientist Sir Humphrey Davy[2]; these both dealt with pigments and inerts on wall paintings found at Pompeii. Really serious study of the materials of early painting had to wait nearly another hundred years, when they were again taken up about the turn of this century by the late Arthur Pillans Laurie of England; Dr Laurie's chemical and microscopic studies on materials of art covered half a century, during which he issued a long series of papers and books on the scientific aspects of artists' paints and painting. They are still worthwhile reading. His book, *The Pigments and Mediums of the Old Masters*, which was published in 1914, was his most important contribution to analytical studies. Several short papers dealing with the microchemical identification of pigments were issued in the 1930s. Dr A. Martin de Wild of Holland, on the basis of his technical studies on the Dutch Masters, published in 1929 a short book entitled *The Scientific Examination of Paintings*. This excellent monograph is still the standard work on the subject. Eibner, of Munich, who carried on research in paint chemistry at the Technische Hochschule in that city, applied his methods of scientific research to ancient paintings, especially to wall paintings, and he published papers on the application of microchemistry to picture examination in the 1930s in both *Mouseion*[3] and in *Angewandte Chemie*[4]. The first was a report read at the Rome Conference in 1930. Dr Scheffer, professor at the Technical High School in Delft, and teacher of Dr de Wild, read a paper at that conference on picture examination[5]. At about the same time H. Hetterich, a pupil of Eibner, published three important papers on microchemical methods for identifying pigments and mediums in paintings in *Mikrochemie*. Hetterich, unfortunately, did not continue these studies but turned his talents to industry. In the 1930s Dr Selim Augusti of Naples began publishing a notable series of papers on the microchemical identification of pigments, mostly in Italian journals but also in English, French, German and Spanish. Dr Augusti is still producing and contributing to the increase of knowledge on Pompeian paintings, on which he is an expert. The author of this paper, also in the 1930s, issued a series of articles in *Technical Studies* on the identification of materials in painting, mainly in the Far Eastern field.

The 1930s seem to have been the golden decade in the analysis of painting materials. Then the war intervened and it was not until the 1950s that interest in paint materials study was revived. From the Institut Royal du Patrimoine Artistique de Belgique, Dr Paul Coremans and his colleagues commenced publication of microchemical studies of materials on the Van Eyck 'Mystic Lamb' and other Flemish Primitive paintings. Miss Joyce Plesters of the National Gallery in London in 1956 issued her well-known paper in *Studies in Conservation* on 'Cross-sections and chemical analysis of paint samples'.

These books and articles on the examination of painting materials, which were produced in the last half century, contain a wealth of information and they constitute the beginnings of a new branch of chemical art. The information, however, is widely scattered in several languages, in little-known journals or out-of-print books. Most of the analytical methods that relate to paintings are micro methods, either chemical microscopy or microchemistry. Chemical microscopy is the observation of chemical reactions on specimens directly under the compound microscope; microchemistry is the handling and manipulation of small amounts of materials by classical procedures on a microscale. The latter includes what are sometimes referred to as 'spot tests'.

In all of these methods applied to the identification of pigments and inerts it appears that insufficient use is made of physical and optical methods of identification, especially in the initial study of the sample. Also, too little consideration is given to the adjunct methods of analysis like x-ray diffraction, spectrographic analysis and others. The reason is simple: microchemical methods require relatively inexpensive equipment. These adjunct methods require costly apparatus and it is only in recent years that they have become available to museum workers.

In 1958 the author, in a short paper entitled 'The identification of pigments and inerts in paintings and other museum objects'[6], outlined a proposal for a modern handbook or manual on identification of materials of painting which could serve chemists, conservators, curators and collectors in the field of art. In making this proposal it was fully realized that the creation of such a handbook would be a large undertaking; much too large for any single person to embark upon unless he had a lifetime ahead of him or a corps of assistants to help with the job. The speaker suggested that the preparation of the handbook be handled as a cooperative venture which would be shared by several laboratories. This proposal met rather favourable reception in America and abroad, and soon after Mr Norman Brommelle, of London, suggested that the handbook might be sponsored by the International Institute for the Conservation of Historic and Artistic Works. Miss Joyce Plesters of the National Gallery expressed interest and she was gradually drawn into the project as a collaborator. Miss Plesters and I are attempting here to present this proposal in greater detail and to discuss it with colleagues who are now gathered here. The handbook should perhaps initially cover the 50–75 pigments and inert materials that are commonly found in both ancient and modern paintings. The pigments, arranged by colour groups, would be treated individually. The data for each pigment would comprise:

Chemical composition,
History of the early period of use or discovery,
Geographical distribution and occurrence of the pigments used in ancient times,

Methods of manufacture and preparation of modern pigments,

Particle characteristics,

Optical properties,

Chemical properties,

Microchemical tests for principal elements,

Criteria considered necessary for certain identification,

Illustrations (mostly photomicrographs preferably in colour showing particle characteristics); also photomicrographs showing microchemical tests,

X-ray diffraction data for crystalline pigments,

Spectrographic data for inorganic pigments,

Spectrophotometric curves for organic dye pigments,

List of occurrences showing earliest known use, or termination of use on important paintings or objects,

Selected bibliography.

In order to give substance to the proposal and to inform others of our intentions, Miss Plesters and I have each chosen three pigments to serve as examples of how the data can be selected and presented. Miss Plesters has chosen zinc white, natural ultramarine and orpiment; I have taken white lead, azurite and viridian. We are presenting separately for each of these pigments the pertinent data following more or less the plan outlined above, using tables, charts or photomicrographs according to the needs of each pigment. We hope that this presentation will precipitate lively discussion and provoke constructive criticism. After Rome it is proposed that initial drafts of the 'trial data' on each pigment species be sent to other qualified museum laboratories for independent study, and for checking, testing and evaluation. After at least three museum laboratories have given approval, the trial data may be considered to be officially accepted. Some procedure or acceptance similar to that used by the American Society for Testing Materials might be adopted for setting up test methods. After formal acceptance these trial data on pigment testing methods could be offered for publication serially in *Studies in Conservation*. Furthermore, after data of 40–50 pigments have accumulated, plans could be started to bring these data sheets together in book form, much like 'Trial Data on Painting Materials', which was first published serially in the old *Technical Studies* and was later brought together to form the *Short Encyclopedia on Painting Materials* (Gettens and Stout).

This body of data, gathered according to the plan outlined, would form Part II of the Handbook. Part I, to be prepared later, would consist of several sections or chapters covering such introductory materials as (1) microscopes and accessory equipment for pigment analysis, (2) sampling procedure and sample preparation, (3) classes and general properties of pigments, (4) microchemical tests for anions and cations.

A Part III would be necessary. It would include: (1) a table of physical properties of pigments covering name and composition, particle or crystal characteristics, specific gravity, refractive indices and others; (2) tables of chronology of pigments; (3) methods for the identification of paint mediums; (4) preparation and interpretation of cross-sections of paint films; (5) notes on adjunct methods of identification covering x-ray diffraction, spectrochemistry and spectrophotometry of organic dyestuffs; (6) schemes for the systematic identification of pigments.

Already several of these schemes have been published, including those by Augusti[7], Gettens and Stout[8] and Miss Plesters[9]. In these schemes pigments are classified by colour and differentiation is based on chemical behaviour. In applying the schemes it is more or less assumed that pigment samples are pure and uncontaminated and little consideration is given to the complexity of pigment mixtures and to the presence of interfering substances like mediums. They also mostly ignore microscopic and optical methods of identification. The form and usefulness of systematic analytical schemes for pigment identification and their place in the handbook will have to be carefully considered.

There is no good reason to stop with pigments; after all, they form only a small part of art materials. Eventually the handbook might be extended to cover the full range of materials of art and archaeology, including metals and alloys, corrosion products of metals, ceramic materials, wood, textile fibres, paper fibres, animal products and others. All of these could be made part of the same handbook, or they might be set up as separate monographs.

This handbook would be useful. It could bring a whole new body of criteria of service to art connoisseurship and to art conservation. It could well become a classic which would take its place along with A. Lucas' *Ancient Egyptian Materials and Industries*, A. M. de Wild's *Scientific Examination of Paintings* and H. J. Plenderleith's *Conservation of Antiquities and Works of Art*. It seems more and more apparent that the project outlined above is too large for one person to undertake and expect to complete within a reasonable time. If present readers want to enjoy the fruits of such a work the preparation of a handbook should be set up as an inter-museum or inter-institutional enterprise. Research and editorial costs could be provided by existing institutions, but the professional approach and atmosphere necessary to assure that the job is well done can only be provided by such an independent organization as is embodied in IIC. Publishing costs might be assumed by IIC. In Rome we can provide the interest and leadership to get it started.

References

[1] CHAPTAL, M., Sur quelques couleurs trouvées à Pompeia, *Ann. Chim.*, 10 (1809) 21–31.

[2] DAVY, SIR HUMPHREY, Some experiments on the colours used in painting by the ancients, *Phil. Trans.*, 105 (1815) 97–124.

[3] EIBNER, A., L'examen microchimique des tableaux et décorations murales, *Mouseion*, 13–14 (1931) 70–92: *also* L'examen microchimique des agglutinants, *ibid.*, 20 (1932) 5–22.

[4] EIBNER, A., Zum gegenwärtigen Stand des naturwissenschaftlichen Bilderuntersuchung, *Angew. Chem.*, 45 (1932) 301–307.

[5] SCHEFFER, F. E. C., L'examen chimique des tableaux, *Mouseion*, 13–14 (1931) 93–103.

[6] Read at a seminar on *Application of Science for the Examination of Works of Art*, at the Museum of Fine Arts in Boston, 1958, under the chairmanship of Mr W. J. YOUNG.

[7] AUGUSTI, S., Metodo systematico per il riconoscimento microchimico dei colori minerali, I-II, *Mikrochemie*, 17 (1935) 1–10, 344–355 and others.

[8] GETTENS, R. J. and STOUT, G. L., The stage microscope in the routine examination of paintings, *Tech. Stud.*, 4 (1936) 207–233.

[9] PLESTERS, JOYCE, Cross-sections and chemical analysis of paint samples, *Stud. Conservation*, 2 (1956) 110–157.

Editor's Note

The paper above formed part of a joint contribution by R. J. Gettens and Miss J. Plesters. A very important part of this contribution cannot, however, be printed here. It consisted of a first draft of six sections of their proposed handbook:

J. PLESTERS, on: zinc white
                    natural ultramarine
                    orpiment

R. J. GETTENS, on: white lead
                    azurite
                    viridian

This draft was on display at the Conference. It contained numerous illustrations, many in colour, and a great deal of compressed information.

As explained by Mr Gettens, it is planned that these sections will first be printed in final form in *Studies in Conservation*, to be followed by others, as they are completed. Finally, of course, all sections will be published together as a handbook.

E. T. Hall

METHODS OF ANALYSIS (PHYSICAL AND MICROCHEMICAL) APPLIED TO PAINTINGS AND ANTIQUITIES

Synopsis

It is my intention in this paper to present a résumé of our experience at Oxford of the comparative merits of various types of analytical procedure and to show why it is necessary to choose the method of analysis to suit the problem. If a museum laboratory is to deal with all types of objects their arsenal of weapons to tackle these problems must be comprehensive, and since many of the techniques involve large and complicated apparatus the outlay in both money and competent personnel is, of necessity, considerable.

Perhaps it would not be out of place to emphasize this point of personnel and the correct apparatus for the problem. Since the scientist who specializes in developing apparatus is seldom keen on using it in a routine fashion, it is necessary that the 'using' type of scientist is also present in a laboratory. Moreover, the idea that the 'arts' side of the museum staff should use the apparatus under the supervision of the scientist just does not work out in practice. We are left with two alternatives. Either the laboratory must be well equipped in apparatus and staff, or it must specialize. It is so easy to bring the use of scientific techniques in archaeology and art history into disrepute; although there may be excellent 'scientific' reasons (or excuses) why one's results are not correct, the museum man is only interested in the fact that he was given the wrong answer. Moreover, he may have been given the answer as dictated by the particular apparatus being used, when, for instance, because he was only analysing the surface, the average result for the whole object should have been quite different. Therefore not only must the most suitable apparatus be used, but also a knowledge of the nature of the object being analysed is almost essential.

For various reasons we have during the last five years been changing our ideas about the most suitable equipment to use on the widely differing materials that have been involved in analytical projects during this time. Before we consider these problems in detail a very superficial description of the methods employed may be helpful. More comprehensive descriptions of the apparatus, particularly as applied to art objects, may be found in the literature.

Standard wet macro- or micro-chemistry

For a small laboratory where funds are limited and where some damage is tolerable, the classical chemical methods have much to recommend them. Little apparatus is necessary. However, in quantitative work the procedures are slow, and in many instances where only small quantities are available the minor constituents are missed. In Oxford we have not concentrated on this type of work since it is already covered by other laboratories.

Optical emission spectrometry

Here the artifact must be sampled by drilling and the material so removed is placed in an electric arc and a photographic plate

obtained of the resultant spectrum. The position of the lines on the photographic plate, together with their intensity, reveals the concentration of the different elements present.

X-ray fluorescent spectrometry

The whole object to be examined is irradiated by x-rays, and the fluorescent x-rays which are thereby excited from the specimen are found to be characteristic of the elements in the sample. By analysing these characteristic x-rays in wavelength and intensity we can tell the composition of the object. The

Figure 1. X-ray fluorescent spectrometer.

incident as well as the resultant characteristic x-rays have small penetrating power, and, as we shall see, this limits the use of the technique in quantitative work. *Figure 1* illustrates the apparatus used.

X-ray diffraction

In this instance we are examining the crystal structure of the sample (which must be scraped or drilled from the object). Generally, when using this technique we are not so much interested in chemical analysis as in a determination of the crystal form in which a chemical compound exists. This may be

Figure 2. Gamma-ray spectrometer.

useful for identification purposes, although generally we can tell more about the manufacturing technique used by such studies.

X-ray spectrometry

This is perhaps the most powerful tool we have available where completely non-destructive analysis is required, and

where a value which is representative of the whole object is essential. After irradiation in a neutron pile (we use BEPO at Harwell) the object, which is now radioactive, will give off gamma rays. By investigation of these rays the chemical composition can be deduced. *Figure 2* illustrates a gamma-ray spectrometer.

The electron-probe microanalyser

Since this technique will be new to most people working in our field I would like to devote a little more space to describing it. *Figure 3* illustrates the apparatus used.

The principle depends on the fact that it is possible to focus electromagnetically a beam of accelerated electrons to a very small spot, and when these electrons strike the specimen they will cause x-rays to be given off which will be characteristic of the elements present, and these may be measured in a fashion similar to fluorescent x-ray analysis. In our apparatus the electrons are generated at a potential of up to 50,000 volts, and two lenses focus these on to a spot one thousandth of a milli-metre in diameter (1 micron). The x-rays generated are analysed by a bent lithium fluoride crystal and focused again into a scintillation counter or gas-flow proportional counter. We can summarize some of the advantages of the technique:

(a) Sensitivity: Concentrations down to 0·01 per cent can be detected quantitatively and, since the analytical volume is only 1 cubic micron, quantities of material of the order of 10^{-16} g can be estimated.

(b) The state of chemical combination is not important; therefore, besides metals, ceramics and glasses can be examined. The surface exposed to the beam of electrons must be a conductor, and therefore insulators must have a very thin conducting surface evaporated on to them before examination. This does not cause any serious difficulty.

(c) It might be thought that poor conductors of heat would be melted by the incident radiation, particularly since the wattage per square centimetre can amount to several megawatts. However, owing to the very small areas involved conduction of

Figure 3. Electron-probe microanalyser.

heat away from the target is very efficient and no damage results.

(d) Electrons may be deflected by electrostatic voltages. This is what occurs in our television sets to build up a picture. In the microanalyser we also have two sets of deflection plates at right angles to each other. By applying voltages to these we can scan a certain area of the specimen. At the same time we can scan a cathode-ray tube (again similar to our television tube) in synchronism with the electron spot impinging on our specimen.

Let us assume we have set our spectrometer to register a certain element in the sample; as we scan the electron beam across the sample we can obtain output pulses whose number will be a measure of the concentration of that element at each point. Now we can use these output pulses to modulate the cathode-ray tube, which is running in synchronism with the electron probe. In this way we will have built up on the cathode-ray tube a 'picture' of the sample scan area in terms of the concentration of the element to which the spectrometer is set.

For instance, we may wish to investigate a picture pigment. Say we have a copper-based pigment, interspersed in a titanium matrix. We can set the spectrometer to copper: the small grains of copper compound will be magnified several hundred times and will appear on the cathode-ray tube as white patches on a black ground. If we set to titanium the reverse will occur, i.e. black magnified grains on a white ground.

Practical considerations

When a series of objects is to be analysed there are certain questions which must be asked before we decide on the method of analysis to be used:

(1) How much damage is permissible?
(2) Is a quantitative, semi-quantitative or purely qualitative analysis required?
(3) Are we interested in the main constituents, the traces or both?
(4) Are we able to obtain a truly representative analysis?
(5) Are we interested in the original composition or only its corrosion products?

Metals

Coins and precious metal, jewellery, etc.

The numismatists are perhaps the most persistent in not allowing any damage to their material; therefore any emission spectrometry is not allowed. There have been occasional attempts to use a Tesla coil to excite the spectrum with long exposures. When we consider the comments below on surface enrichment we can see that this method is quite valueless.

Many coins which are presented for analysis appear to be in almost mint condition, and it would seem reasonable to suppose that an analysis of the surface of the coin would suffice to represent the original composition. On investigation this is found to be very far from the truth. The surface composition of a silver–copper or gold–silver coin may differ by a factor of five from the composition at the centre. Since x-ray fluorescence, which seems the obvious technique to use, only 'looks at' the exterior few hundredths of a millimetre the results will mean very little except for purely qualitative investigation. We in this laboratory and other workers elsewhere have given results based on x-ray fluorescence and these will unfortunately be misleading if too much weight is put on the conclusions which have been drawn. Fortunately little of this work has been published.

Our suspicions concerning x-ray results were first aroused by a large programme of analyses using gamma-ray spectrometry. This method is particularly valuable where quantitative estimation of small traces of 'unintentional' elements is required. We found that the results differed widely from checks made with the x-ray spectrometer. After some full chemical analyses had been made of complete coins the gamma-ray results were found to be reliable. Moreover, when cross-sections were analysed on the electron-probe microanalyser the variable composition with distance from the surface became completely apparent. Of course, using the microanalyser in a routine fashion is out of the question, since at least a small notch must be made in the coin to obtain a suitable cross-section.

For reliable quantitative non-destructive analysis we are left, therefore, with the gamma-ray spectrometer. This equipment is not particularly expensive, but it does need a physicist to operate it, and also the accessibility of a neutron source. Most countries now have research reactors which might be used for these purposes. Moreover, portable neutron generators are becoming available commercially (in particular in the USA and France). One word of warning should be given: during our first irradiation, owing to a misunderstanding, the coins, luckily only two of them, were given an irradiation several thousands of times greater than was required. This meant that the silver coins involved have become so radioactive that they cannot be returned to the museum for several thousand years!

Bronze weapons, ornamental bronzes, etc.

Here again the surface, which is likely to be corroded to a greater or less extent, will make x-ray fluorescence of little value except for a qualitative examination. The extent of any actual separation towards the surface of one element more than another is unknown at the moment, but will be unimportant compared with the effects of corrosion.

Gamma-ray spectrometry will not be convenient, since the objects would in most cases be of an awkward shape for irradiation in a pile. This leaves us with little alternative but to use emission spectrometry. This entails a small drilling being made in the object, but this is generally not objectionable—although vague talk about 'upsetting the stability' of Chinese bronzes has been heard. We, after sampling several hundred such objects, have never seen any resulting deterioration.

The investigation of the corrosion products themselves is, of course, important and may tell us more than the analysis of the bronze itself; our work to date on the composition of Chinese bronzes would seem to confirm this. X-ray diffraction should be a powerful tool for such studies.

The use of emission spectrometry on bronzes is very convenient, since generally we are interested in trace elements, the amounts of which may be indicative of date or provenance.

In this context I would like to discourage archaeologists from asking for unnecessary information. This applies not only to those who are interested in bronzes but in all spheres where a chemical analysis is required. We often find that, although the archaeologist has good reason to want certain information, he is inclined to ask for additional elements which will add nothing to the archaeological conclusions but which have been estimated by other workers and he therefore feels he ought to add that information. The result of this tendency is twofold. The work for the scientist will be increased and for awkward elements may present a real problem; and it might avoid those columns of results all showing N.D.* It should be the archaeologist's

---

* Not detected

job to find out first what is significant even if a pilot experiment is necessary to determine this.

Ceramics, glazes and glass

Many of the considerations given above for metals are applicable when ceramics are studied. However, surface enrichment and surface contamination problems would seem to be much less severe. Many useful results have been obtained with emission and gamma-ray spectrometry on ceramic sherds and glass fragments. However, obtaining samples for the emission spectrograph is difficult from whole pieces, whereas such objects are again inconvenient for gamma-ray work. We therefore require a non-destructive method of analysis for ceramics and glass. X-ray fluorescence provides such an answer, and we have found this a very useful tool where the concentrations to be expected are above the 0·1 per cent level. Recently a vacuum instrument with a large sample chamber has been constructed, and this has enabled us to tackle such elements as potassium, silicon, sodium, calcium, titanium (in low concentrations), phosphorus and sulphur, which have previously been too low in the periodic table. A great deal more work is waiting to be done in this field.

The examination of ceramic glazes with the microanalyser may prove fruitful. We shall be able to examine glazes in cross-section and in this way discover something of the techniques used in manufacture as well as their actual chemical composition.

Picture pigments

Our experience in this field is very limited and we have made few contributions compared with other speakers at this conference. We are, however, hoping that in the near future two new pieces of apparatus—one already operating and the other only conjectured—will help people working on the analysis of pigments. The electron-probe microanalyser will enable mixed pigments to be identified: the individual pigment grains can be differentiated from one another. When several layers of paint are present the different chemical compositions can be identified since the thickness of a layer of paint is large compared with the resolution of the instrument.

The method of examination is as follows. After removal of a small flake of paint—of microscopic dimensions if necessary—this is mounted in the usual way in a resin and polished to expose the paint cross-section. This is now mounted in a vacuum deposition apparatus and a few Ångström units of aluminium metal are deposited. The sample is then mounted in the microanalyser. Point-to-point analyses may be made or scanned displays may be built up of areas from 5 microns square to ½ mm square. All elements between carbon and uranium may be estimated. Unfortunately, of course, different pigments containing the same element are indistinguishable unless the crystal form can give us a clue. The shape of the crystals will be shown on the scanned image. We believe we have a powerful instrument for these and allied studies.

In situ x-ray fluorescent analysis of pictures would seem to be an avenue of research which might yield useful results. We hope that we shall soon be in a position to construct such an apparatus. The idea would be to bombard the picture, which would be mounted in a suitable frame and movable in two directions at right angles, with a fine beam of x-rays and look at the fluorescent x-rays produced with a curved-crystal spectrometer. A curved-crystal instrument would be necessary since only a small area (perhaps 1 mm square) would be irradiated at a time, and the sensitivity would be increased in this way. By a suitable optical system incorporating a low-power microscope one could arrange things in such a way that the precise point of analysis could be determined by crosswires in an eyepiece. In this way no sample of paint would have to be removed.

W. J. Young

APPLICATION OF THE ELECTRON MICROBEAM PROBE AND MICRO X-RAYS IN NON-DESTRUCTIVE ANALYSIS

During the last decade the most powerful analytical methods to be applied to archaeological research have been optical spectroscopy, x-ray fluorescence and x-ray diffraction. For the last seven years the Research Laboratory at the Boston Museum of Fine Arts has concentrated on non-destructive methods of analysis.

Röntgen, who discovered x-rays in November 1895, made every effort in his experiments with cathode rays to produce a spectrum of a beam of x-rays, assuming that these invisible rays belonged to the same electromagnetic spectrum as visible light. His logical experiments designed to disperse the beam by reflection by prisms and diffraction by ruled gratings were unsuccessful.

These early experiments indicated that x-rays were essentially different from light, an erroneous conclusion based upon the failure to observe regular reflection, refraction or diffraction. We now know that this failure was due to the extremely short wavelength of the rays, the range of which extends from the ultra-violet into the gamma-ray region; that is, from 10^{-7} to 10^{-9} cm.

The experiments in 1912 by von Laue and his associates proved that all crystals are three-dimensional diffraction gratings for x-rays, which brought about a subsequent derivation of Bragg's law

$$-n\lambda = 2d \sin \theta$$

where λ is the wavelength, n is the order of the reflection, d is the known distance between the parallel planes in the crystal and θ is the measured angle of incidence.

Although von Laue's experiment proved the electromagnetic nature of x-rays, it was not until after 1920 that refraction by prisms and diffraction by ruled gratings were successfully used, which opened the way for construction of a crystal spectrometer. This new approach was soon put to use by the Braggs, Mosely, Siegbahn and others, whose experiments proved that it was possible to resolve x-ray beams into spectra with emission lines characteristic of the chemical element serving as the target in the x-ray tube.

It was soon understood that when a target was bombarded by a stream of electrons in an evacuated bulb, the electrons were stopped by the target atoms and a kinetic energy transformed, by a process involving the inner electrons in the atoms, into x-ray radiation.

The use of the x-ray spectrograph for chemical analysis of archaeological material has gained rapid recognition. The speed, sensitivity and precision of x-ray fluorescent analysis for substances of varied composition and physical structure place this technique in the forefront of modern methods of instrumental analysis. The fact that the technique is essentially non-destructive and does not deface the specimen lends it attractiveness in instances where specialized analysis is needed.

The relative simplicity of the fluorescent spectrum, as contrasted, for example, with the optical emission, provides distinct advantages in its interpretation.

The fluorescent x-rays emitted by a material and used for its analysis are generated by directing a primary beam of high-energy x-rays against it. The x-ray photons of the high-energy beam are absorbed by the material. Using the Bohr concept of atomic structure, when an atom in a material is given sufficient energy by absorbing these photons, an electron may be ejected from one or more of its inner shells.

The place of the electron is immediately filled by an electron from an outer shell, whose position in turn will be filled by an electron even further out. In this manner the atom returns to its normal energy state by a series of steps in electron transitions. For each of these steps an x-ray photon is emitted. Since each of these steps is characteristic, the energy or wavelength for each photon may, therefore, be used as a means of characterizing the element in the material. After the first primary spectra of beams excited by electrons in an x-ray tube were observed with the spectrometer, it was found that secondary fluorescent x-rays were excited in any material irradiated with beams of primary x-rays and that the spectra of these fluorescent x-rays were identical in wavelength and relative intensities with those excited when the specimen is bombarded with electrons. Hence the characteristic spectrum is generated either by electrons or x-ray photon excitation.

In x-ray fluorescent analysis the primary radiation from the x-ray tube strikes the specimen or object being analysed, which emits characteristic x-ray spectra of the elements contained in the specimen, which may be in a solid, liquid or gaseous form (*Figures 1* and *2*).

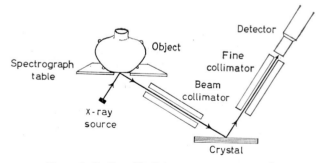

Figure 1. Optics of bulk-type x-ray spectrograph.

The fluorescent radiation is then collimated so that only a parallel beam of polychromatic radiation strikes the analysing crystal (lithium fluoride, $d = 4 \cdot 0276$ Å) of the Geiger-counter spectrometer. The crystal then separates the rays into their component wavelengths in the x-ray spectrum representing the constituent elements. These invisible rays are detected by the Geiger-Müller tube, which can be made to travel automatically along a quadrant at the same rate of speed at which the paper chart of the electronic recorder unfolds.

As the Geiger-Müller tube encounters the various diffracted x-ray beams (according to the Bragg equation) it furnishes to

33

the recorder electrical energy proportional to the intensity of the x-ray beam, and a series of peaks is recorded on the chart. A comparison of the intensities of the beam or spectra lines of the elements will then permit a quantitative analysis of their concentrations.

Figure 2. Apparatus for x-ray diffraction (*left*) and x-ray fluorescence (*right*).

Quantitative limits and precision

Many elements can be analysed by the x-ray spectrograph to levels as low as 0·001 per cent or to the maximum of 100 per cent. As higher-energy x-ray source tubes are invented and detecting systems become more sensitive, the minimum limit of detection moves toward smaller decimal figures. Trace elements generally cannot be considered for fluorescent analyses. It is wiser to use the emission spectrograph and wet chemistry.

The quantitative limits of any element are directly related to the wavelength and absorption characteristics of the element and to the quality of the standards.

Standards for routine analysis should cover a range of 5 to 60 per cent for major elements and 0·5 to 5 per cent for minor elements. Normally four or more standards are made for the analysis of one alloy.

Size of sample

The qualitative analysis of a sample does not demand uniform surface or uniform size. A one-degree per minute scan of the two theta angles usually constitutes a qualitative analysis. However, for precise quantitative results, it is necessary to expose a constant area of the specimen in a constant manner.

Bulk specimen holder

This instrument is designed for x-ray fluorescent analysis of large specimens and can accommodate samples ranging up to 2 in. in depth and 10 in. square. To this basic design a lead-covered steel container was made to accommodate larger objects such as figures, silver tankards, etc., which enables an analysis to be made directly from the object without previous preparation. The specimen chamber is completely ray-proofed. The cover incorporates a springloaded beam shutter to cut off automatically the x-ray beam when the cover is opened.

Exciting K radiation

Lines in the x-ray spectrum result when the exciting x-ray quantum knocks out an electron from the innermost K shell of the atom or the adjacent shell, which is known as the L shell.

The lines characteristic of the material being bombarded are called K lines when they result from an electron falling into a K shell vacancy and L lines when they result from an electron falling into an L shell vacancy. The K lines are fewer and much more intense than the L lines because there are normally only two electrons in the K shell and eight in the lower-energy L shell.

The most efficient excitation of a particular K or L line requires that the exciting x-ray radiation has a maximum energy of the order of three to five times the energy required just barely to excite the line. A 50 or 60 kV unit can satisfy that condition for excitation voltages of the order of only 20 kV or less. This includes elements up to molybdenum (atomic number 42). Therefore, by increasing the voltage of the exciting x-ray tube to 100 kV, it would open up the possibility of working with K lines in the higher atomic numbers and of working very efficiently with K radiations up to the middle of the rare earth series.

Prediction of inter-element effects

Quantitative analysis of a sample by x-ray spectrography is facilitated by prior qualitative examination for its major constituents. Knowledge of the sample matrix allows general prediction of the absorption effects that will occur. Intelligent selection of the appropriate method for inter-element effect correction, and choice of analytical lines subject to a minimum absorption are then possible. Inter-element effects can be predicted by a study of mass absorption coefficients and the relative positions of x-ray lines and element absorption edges. Tabulations of absorption-edge and emission-line wavelengths are readily available[1]. The effects fall into two categories:

1. General absorption of the element fluorescence radiated by the matrix.
2. Specific absorption or enhancement of the radiation by the matrix.

A light element emitting long-wavelength radiation in a heavy-element matrix is strongly absorbed and its intensity is low at low concentrations. Generally, the absorption of the

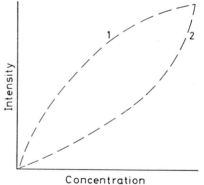

Figure 3. Typical intensity *vs.* concentration calibration curves. Curve 1 represents a heavy element in a light matrix: curve 2 a light element in a heavy matrix.

radiation from a heavy element by a light matrix is small, and its intensity is high at low concentrations[2] (*Figure 3*).

If it were not for these absorption effects, the intensity of the fluorescent radiation from an element in an alloy would be proportional to the atomic density of that element and a quantitative analysis could be made from the ratio of the intensity of the alloy to a pure element. Absorption effects arise because the incident x-rays penetrate a significant distance below the specimen surface. A sample which is of unlimited thickness (i.e. absorbs all the exciting radiation) will exhibit the maximum disturbing effects; for an infinitesimally thin sample, the absorption effects would be at a minimum.

In most applications, the fluorescent intensity is not directly proportional to the concentration of the element. This non-linear property can be attributed to fundamental x-ray matter interaction effects which take place in a substance between the component elements themselves.

The effects of interaction, variously called absorption and enhancement, matrix, self-absorption or inter-elemental effects, are well known. The interaction between copper and iron in the same specimen provides a good example. The absorption edge of iron is at 1·739 Å and the Kα emission line of copper is at 1·537 Å. The 1·537 Å copper radiation occurring on the short-wavelength side of the iron absorption edge will be strongly absorbed by iron. This absorbed radiation will excite and further enhance the characteristic radiation of iron over that generated by the primary exciting beam. When an element such as manganese rather than copper co-exists with iron, the interaction effects are much less pronounced. The manganese Kα line occurs at 2·098 Å on the long-wavelength side of the iron absorption edge, and therefore is not strongly absorbed.

Dr Susan Schur's thesis, in partial fulfilment of the requirements for the degree of Master of Science at Massachusetts Institute of Technology, undertook to determine the variation in fluorescent intensity as a function of composition in the binary systems of Cu–Pb and of Cu–Sn and the ternary systems of Cu–Pb–Sn. With these relationships, the composition of bronze art objects could be established by x-ray fluorescent techniques. Standards were prepared and calibration curves were set up by plotting relative intensity versus composition. Dr Schur proved that a linear relationship was not obtained owing to absorption effects and mutual fluorescence effects. She found, for example, that an alloy of 10 per cent Fe and 90 per cent Cr will absorb the iron fluorescent rays more strongly than an alloy of 10 per cent Fe and 90 per cent Ni. Thus, the intensity value of Fe in the Fe–Cr system will be lower than the intensity value of Fe in the Fe–Ni system, even though the Fe content is the same in both of these alloys. The excitation effect is of a second order, but it can be important. Mutual fluorescence will occur if the wavelength of the fluorescent x-rays of one element in the specimen is less than the absorption edge value of another element in the specimen. These fluorescent x-rays will be absorbed by the second element, which will then emit its characteristic radiation. Thus, the total emitted intensity will be composed of fluorescent intensities from two elements if a third element is present and its line occurs between the absorption edges of the two elements to be compared. In such a case, the third element will emit rays which will excite the element with the longer absorption edge but not the one with the shorter edge. Therefore, the presence of this element will shift the intensity ratio of the other two elements in favour of the one having the longer edge.

Standard specimens were prepared by compressing chemically pure powders of Cu, Pb and Sn. These samples were then homogenized by shaking them in the 'Wig-L-Bug' Amalgamator for five minutes. The powders were then compacted in a Buehler mould press for 20 minutes at 150°C and 13,000 lb./in.². The resultant samples had a diameter of 1 in. and a minimum depth of 0·1725 in. This depth was adequate to produce maximum fluorescent yield.

During specimen preparation all the powders were screened through 400-mesh screens before mixing and compressing. As the compacted specimens did not approach 100 per cent theoretical density, therefore, it was desirable to see if differences in density would affect the fluorescent intensity recorded. Scans were made with powder specimens and metal sheet.

Comparison of the intensities showed no significant difference in the intensity value of the fluoresced metal sheet and the less dense powder samples. Therefore, the compacting method of preparing standards was thought to be satisfactory.

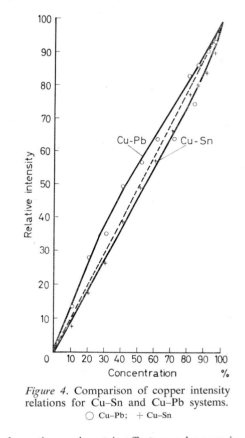

Figure 4. Comparison of copper intensity relations for Cu–Sn and Cu–Pb systems.
○ Cu–Pb; + Cu–Sn

The absorption and matrix effects can be seen in *Figure 4*, where the relative intensity of Cu is plotted as a function of composition for the binary systems of Cu–Pb and Cu–Sn. The mass absorption coefficients of Cu (49·7) and Sn (33·3) (with Mo radiation) are quite close to one another; therefore only slight deviations from linearity are to be expected. Lead, however, has a larger mass absorption coefficient (141·0) in comparison with Cu, and deviations are more pronounced. It was found that Cu in a Cu–Sn system showed a positive deviation while Cu in a Cu–Pb system showed negative deviations (*Figure 5*). Greater accuracy can be obtained by first making a scan of the unknown, which will give the composition and a rough quantitative analysis without altering the potential excitation. Standards, similar in composition, were then inserted in the x-ray beam and comparisons of the counts per second made, which resulted in an accurate quantitative analysis.

Curved-crystal optics

Curved crystals may be used in x-ray spectroscopy to diffract and focus radiation diverging from a line or point source (*Figures 6* and *7*).

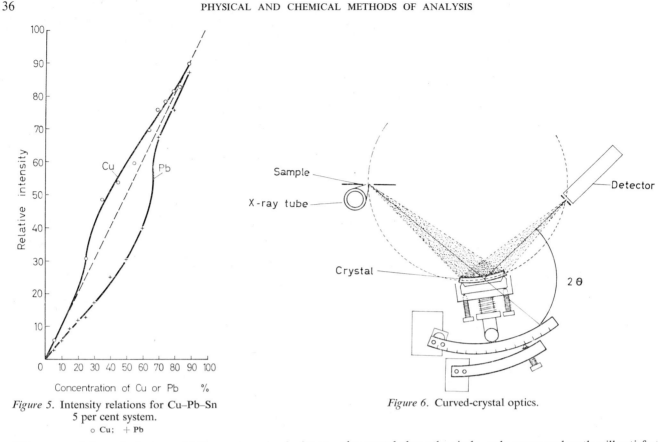

Figure 5. Intensity relations for Cu–Pb–Sn 5 per cent system.
o Cu; + Pb

Figure 6. Curved-crystal optics.

This approach is particularly useful if a specimen is of minute physical dimensions, as curved-crystal optics will yield 100 times the intensity of flat-crystal optics. The factor of 100 is brought about because in flat-crystal optics the radiation from the specimen is limited by the collimator and reaches a very small section of the analysing crystal, whereas in curved-crystal optics the radiation can reach the entire crystal, which is usually a minimum of one inch in length.

For best resolution, the crystal is first curved to a radius which is equal to the diameter of the focusing circle (the Rowland circle in light optics) by the aid of a specially designed bending device which curves the crystal as it is made to travel along an arc. The crystal is then bent so that the surface of the crystal lies exactly on the focusing circle. For each position of

the crystal along the circle, only one wavelength will satisfy the Bragg condition and be diffracted ($n\lambda = 2d \sin \theta$). The primary radiation is masked down to a pin-hole in size so that only 0·5 mm of the specimen is irradiated at one time. The specimen can be made to traverse past the primary beam, exciting different areas.

These areas of interest emit characteristic x-ray spectra of the elements contained in the specimen. The crystal then separates the rays into their component wavelengths in the x-ray spectrum representing the constituent elements (in similar fashion to flat-crystal optics). These x-rays are detected by the Geiger-Müller tube and the analysis recorded on the chart of the electronic recorder.

For this work lithium fluoride and mica have been used as analysing crystals.

During the last six months research has been carried out by this approach. It was found a particularly useful analytical tool in the study of ancient metals, in the analysis of corrosion bands, metallic enrichments and in the identification of segregated areas.

Analysis of pigments can be carried out by adhering a minute sample to a glass capillary tube which is then placed in the primary x-ray beam. It is a non-destructive method which makes it possible to carry out an analysis *in situ*. The minimum detectable quantity for curved-crystal optics is 10^{-8} g, thus a 1 mg specimen may be considered as a full-sized sample.

The electron microbeam probe

The electron microbeam probe, first developed by Costaing and Guinier in 1950, provided a new dimension in x-ray spectrochemical analysis. The focal spot may be made as small as one or two microns in diameter. In this instrument the sample itself serves as the target against which a needle-like stream of

Figure 7. Crystal-bending device placed on x-ray spectrograph.

electrons impinges to generate the fluorescent x-rays. A point-by-point analysis may be made in which the composition of one cubic micron can be determined (*Figure 8*).

The electron probe combines the fine-focus electron optics of the x-ray microscope with the goniometer of the x-ray spectrograph. Using focused electrons and curved-crystal optics, the instrument enables rapid microanalysis of elements in exceedingly small inclusions and analysis of crystals too small to analyse by chemical methods. It is possible to determine composition gradients as they occur in alloy phases or

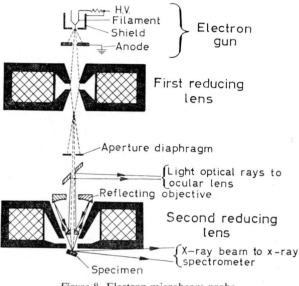

Figure 8. Electron microbeam probe.

corrosion layers. Glass, faience and glazes have been successfully subjected to the electron beam for analysis. Finally, it was found a most practical method of analysis of cross-sections of painting strata.

The electron microbeam probe uses an electron-type gun, electromagnetic lenses and a specimen chamber. An optical microscope system is built into the instrument for direct observation of the area undergoing analysis (see *Figure 8*).

Electrons originating from the hot filament pass through two electromagnetic lens coils, which act to collimate a one-micron beam of electrons on the specimen. Characteristic x-rays generated in the specimen emerge through a mylar window. This beam of x-rays originates essentially from a point source. The specimen can then be made to travel so that any desired area may be brought into position for analysis.

In the analysis of painting strata the finest hypodermic needle that it was possible to purchase (#27) was inserted through the painting to include surface varnish down to the ground of the painting. The hypodermic needle was then mounted in plastic and polished down longitudinally, revealing the paint layers, from the varnish to the ground of the painting, in cross-section (*Figures 9* and *10*).

In order to avoid boiling-out effects of the paint medium by preventing a charge from being built up in the sample, a very thin layer of aluminium was evaporated onto the cross-section.

The cross-section was then positioned in the specimen chamber and the electron beam focused on each paint layer. The produced fluorescent x-rays were analysed by a crystal of known *d* spacing. Since every element has its own characteristic wavelength, it was possible to identify peaks of 2θ values by

running a scan whereby the elements in the pigments of each paint layer were identified.

The electron microbeam demands such a small sample (2 microns) that a hollow needle the size of a human hair (80–100 microns) would obtain a more than adequate sample.

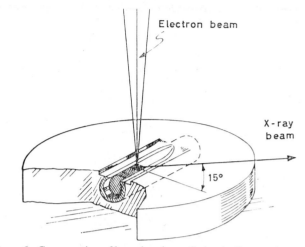

Figure 9. Cross-section of hypodermic needle in plastic mount.

The method has been found satisfactory in authenticating artists' signatures on paintings where a pigment sample of the signatures can be compared with similar paint from other parts of the painting.

Analyses have been made by the microbeam probe on pigment strata containing oil as a medium; and also on

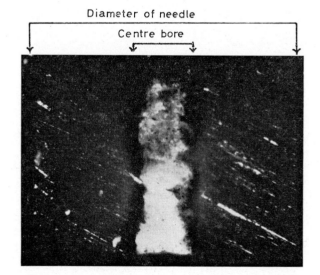

Figure 10. Cross-section of pigment sample in hypodermic needle.

pigment strata containing tempera as a medium. With the aid of hypodermic needles, samples have satisfactorily been obtained both from canvas and wood panel supports.

The minute hole left by the entrance of the needle into the paint strata is only detected with difficulty by the unaided eye.

The electron microbeam probe extends the limit of analysis far beyond the possibilities of fluorescent x-ray excitation. The minimum detectable quantity is 10^{-14} g.

Acknowledgement

The author gratefully acknowledges the assistance given by Dr Robert Ogilvie and Dr Norman Peterson, of the Department of Metallurgy at Massachusetts Institute of Technology, who built the electron microbeam probe, without which the research in the above article would have been impossible.

References

[1] COMPTON, A. H. and ALLISON, S. K., *X-rays in Theory and Experiment*, Van Nostrand, New York, 1935.

[2] CAUCHOIS, Y. L. and HULUBEI, H., *Tables de constantes et données numériques, longueurs d'onde des émissions X et des discontinuités d'absorption X*, Hermann, Paris, 1947.

Bibliography

AITKEN, M. J., *Physics and Archaeology*, Interscience, New York, 1961.

BIRKS, L. S., *X-ray Spectrochemical Analysis*, Interscience, New York, 1960.

CAUCHOIS, Y. L. and HULUBEI, H., *Tables de constantes et données numériques, longueurs d'onde des émissions X et des discontinuités d'absorption X*, Hermann, Paris, 1947.

COMPTON, A. H. and ALLISON, S. K., *X-rays in Theory and Experiment*, Van Nostrand, New York, 1935.

CLARK, G. L., *Applied X-Rays*, McGraw-Hill, New York, 1955.

COSTAING, R. and GUINIER, A., *Analyt. Chem.*, 25 (1953) 724.

HALL, E. T., *Archaeometry*, 3 (1960) 29.

MITCHELL, B. J., *Analyt. Chem.*, 30 (1958) 1894.

SCHUR, S. E., *The Use of X-Ray Fluorescence in Analyzing Bronzes*, Massachusetts Institute of Technology, 1960.

PAINE, R. T. and YOUNG, W. J., Sub-surface structure of Kuan-type wares, *Far east. ceram. Bull.*, 5, 3 (1953) 2.

YOUNG, W. J. and WHITMORE, F. E., Analysis of oriental ceramic wares by non-destructive x-ray methods, *Far east. ceram. Bull.*, 9 1–2 (1957) 1.

YOUNG, W. J. and WHITMORE, F. E., Examination of a group of mortuary objects—Warring States period, *Far east. ceram. Bull.*, 6, 1 (1954) 8.

Application of Science in Examination of Works of Art (compiled papers), Museum of Fine Arts Seminar, 1959.

Ludovico Santucci

THE APPLICATION OF CHEMICAL AND PHYSICAL METHODS TO CONSERVATION OF ARCHIVAL MATERIALS

The problems

The participation of science in the struggle for the rescue and conservation of written records was brought about by the observation of certain facts and the consequent necessity of action with which archivists and librarians could not cope satisfactorily by themselves. This does not mean, I wish to point out, that scientists can replace keepers and literary men, even in such kinds of activity: it means that scientists have a better knowledge of matter, and this knowledge is necessary in a complementary way to solve problems of this type.

The facts referred to above concern the decay of matter; that is, such things as embrittlement and discoloration of paper and parchment, decay of bindings, fading of inks and other pigments, agglomeration of pages, rusting of metal parts, mechanical wear through use and all kinds of damage of biological origin. This alone is quite an impressive list, even without mentioning supplementary causes of deterioration or complete loss, such as the infinite variety of possible accidents (fires, war, etc.).

If we want to retain our past and present records, action must be taken to avoid, or at least reduce, decay. This originates three orders of problem.

Restoration of damaged materials

This may involve mechanical repair, removal of dirt and stains, strengthening, restoration of legibility (permanent or not), application of antiparasite agents (temporary or permanent); that is, in general, any safe treatment to restore appearance and usability, and, above all, to remove any factors of further deterioration. It is worth mentioning that another important point is the choice of the proper materials to be employed in restoration. Finally, there are problems of quantity and organization.

Conservation

Restoration work, even when carried out according to the best criteria, is by no means sufficient to ensure good durability of the objects treated. Experience can prove this. As a consequence, the need was felt to establish directions for proper conservation. This is quite a frightening proposition, because it involves anticipating answers which only the future can yield unmistakably.

New records

The observation of decayed records unavoidably leads to the question of whether or not more permanent materials could be used for this purpose. This is not a new question, either, and substantial consideration has been given to it.

Early attempts at preservation

Preservation of written records has certainly been a concern for learned people ever since the origins of culture. The fact that durable materials were usually employed for important records is significant in this connection.

Of course, as a result of the first efforts to translate thought into writing, it became impracticable to engrave long records on stone, brick or bronze, so that scholars were soon to face the problem of preserving such materials as papyrus, bark, parchment and leather. They had a keen feeling of the importance of documents. Readers may recall a letter of Cicero to a friend, where he expressed the hope that his friend would not erase Cicero's letters to write upon them himself. Titus Livius wrote that a Roman scribe who had found some old books in a buried case complained to the Senate when their destruction was ordered for religious reasons. It is interesting to note that these papyri were said to be flavoured with cedarwood oil, and their good state of preservation was ascribed to this treatment (see Pliny). We know also from other sources that inserting aromatic flowers or leaves between pages of books to protect them from insects was widespread practice, even now not quite extinct.

Those who have visited the Museum of the Istituto di Patologia del Libro might remember an Arabian manuscript containing an invocation aimed at obtaining protection of books from moths. The importance of the location of libraries, in order to obtain the best conservation of books, was also considered by the Romans, who recommended they should face east (Vitruvius).

There is some mention in medieval manuscripts about the danger of insect attack and ways to prevent it, but, owing to the limited number of records in use and the good quality of materials, their preservation was probably not a great problem during the Middle Ages. The real difficulties arose later, when the introduction of paper, and subsequently of cheaper paper, allowed a much greater use of (less permanent) written records, and at the same time the ancient parchment manuscripts grew older and older and began to deteriorate.

This is when keepers and scholars started worrying, and the age began of empirical remedies (only a few examples of older works are known). We can say that the resulting craftsmanship of restoration, which was the only source of remedy up to the end of the 18th century, did develop some sound practices and criteria, still in use for the most part, but also introduced very harmful methods that produced serious damages in the past and have not yet been completely abandoned today. As typical instances, we need mention only the widespread practice of bleaching paper with hypochlorites or permanganate, to which some early chemical experiments were probably contributed by Chaptal (reported to the Academy of Sciences of Paris in 1787) on using oxygenated hydrochloric acid (hypochlorous acid?); then some disastrous attempts to unroll the Herculaneum papyri, where all sorts of solvents, glues and varnishes were experimented with, including baths in mercury; and, in the field of ink revival, the application of tannins or sulphides to parchment manuscripts[59]. However, with respect to the latter problem, we could perhaps mention the results of Cristoforo Marino, a Neapolitan restorer of the last century[59,110]; he revived faded writing on parchment by immersion in an infusion of certain flowers. Although very empirical in nature, this procedure is said to have been remarkably effective and not harmful to manuscripts, but Marino never revealed the secret of his recipe. Anyway, the danger of applying empirical methods to valuable materials is shown by the fact that some manuscripts mechanically restored according to another special procedure of that same Marino are now in a poor condition.

True scientific advice and applications were initially limited to isolated cases. It seems that the first contributions came from biologists early in the 17th century, but this is outside the scope of the present paper. We shall quote, instead, Davy's experiments in 1826 for unrolling the Herculaneum papyri[59]. After having analysed them, he was able to separate some sheets by the effect of heat and different types of fumigation, although he was not completely successful because in some instances the writing disappeared. Actually, this is not yet a case where science defeated empiricism, since neither Davy nor other scientists were able to improve on the results of the mechanical method devised by Father Piaggio in 1753[59]. This should only be considered one of the first scientific attempts to solve the difficult problem of restoration.

As an early contribution of physics, if we may say so, we note in 1905 the photographic double-negative method of Pringsheim and Gradewiss[59] for deciphering palimpsests, and in 1908 the application to the same effect of ultra-violet rays by Father Kögel[99].

Important and pioneer studies were carried out in 1877 by Church and by Davis[40] and in 1888 by Woodward[181] on the damage caused by gas lights on leather book bindings. Finally, it is worth mentioning the first comprehensive attempts to merge practical experience with scientific knowledge, which are the well-known Bonnardot books of 1846 and 1858[21].

It was not until the turn of the 19th century that substantial action was taken to organize the potential contribution of science to restoration and conservation of record materials. A pioneer in this field was Cardinal Ehrle[43,59,110], keeper of the Vatican Library and promoter of the International Conference of St Gallo in 1898, where the importance of coordination between various branches of knowledge was recognized. This coincided with the first report of the Committee on the Deterioration of Paper, named by the Society for the Encouragement of Arts, Manufactures and Commerce, in London[47]. Shortly afterwards there followed the Archivists' Conference of Dresden, in 1899, and the International Congress of Librarians in Paris, 1900. In that same year, the Society for the Encouragement of Arts, Manufactures and Commerce also appointed a scientific committee for the study of decay of leather book bindings[1]; a similar step was taken in Germany in 1911[2], at the same time as the foundation of the restoration laboratory of the Archivio centrale dello Stato, in Rome[110]. The spreading of such initiatives was very important, since it resulted in a number of important investigations and further cooperation, as we shall see later.

More historical data may be found under references 20, 59, 88, 110.

Application of modern science

Isolation of deterioration factors

When the scientific method was first applied to the study of deterioration of record materials, the necessity for a break-down of the problem into the individual factors promoting every alteration was recognized, in order to establish its cause and thus treat it properly. We have already reviewed the kinds of observable decay a document may suffer, to which we might add deterioration not observable without special laboratory determinations. The causes of decay may be grouped into three broad classes, i.e. biological, physicochemical and mechanical; they may act concurrently on a single document—their effects are closely dependent upon each other. Therefore, in order to understand why a document is in a certain condition, it is often necessary to separate different causes and possibly to study their interrelations.

For instance, take a sheet of paper which is yellowed and brittle. Its appearance is altered and its use impaired, since it does not withstand folding and can easily be torn. It does not take much scientific knowledge to suppose that this sheet, perhaps of poor quality, has been exposed to sunlight too long. Similarly, anyone with some experience in restoration might guess that its appearance would be improved by a good bleaching and its strength increased by sizing. But systematic investigations have shown this kind of deterioration to be present also in papers that have not been exposed to sunlight unduly, and to be particularly frequent in documents stored in industrial areas. Furthermore, such papers usually have a high degree of acidity, expressed by their pH, which is not measurable without the aid of special laboratory equipment or removable without specific treatment. Also, their condition depends greatly on composition. So this is a case where visual examination and current knowledge are not sufficient for correct diagnosis, and classical restoration treatments would not remove the cause of alteration. This is why it is necessary to go back to the origins.

Hence, in short, scientific research has shown that paper deterioration is brought about by any one of the following physicochemical factors, or a combination of them:

(a) Heat;

(b) Moisture (dangerous for its hydrolytic power, in addition to favouring biological attack);

(c) Frequent and pronounced changes in temperature and relative humidity;

(d) Exposure to light and, in general, radiations, those of high frequency being the most dangerous;

(e) Acidic compounds, such as those contained in the atmosphere of industrial areas, in dust, etc. (strong alkalis are no less injurious);

(f) Oxidizing agents (oxygen included), which often occur in bleaching compounds;

(g) Presence even of traces of heavy metals, because they catalyse oxidative degradation and the formation of sulphuric acid from the sulphur dioxide of the atmosphere;

(h) Presence of acidic sizes, such as alum, rosin, etc., or acidic inks;

(i) Presence of non-cellulose materials of the lignin type, since they are often acidic in nature or yield acidic derivatives upon decomposition, and are particularly sensitive to deteriorative agents such as light.

It should be further noted that it is not sufficient to ascertain the presence of one or more of the factors listed above in order to conclude that the deterioration observed is due to them. What researchers actually attempt is to reproduce experimentally the conditions which are thought to cause deterioration and compare their effects with those originally observed, since experimentation is an essential step for any hypothesis to lead to a theory.

In this way, step by step, the adverse factors to the stability of documents can be identified individually and, of great importance, their effect can be determined quantitatively. This allows them to be classified as more or less dangerous, so that action may be taken accordingly. It may be necessary, while studying the effects of certain agents on sample documents, to employ experimental conditions quite different from the ones naturally occurring, such as very high concentrations of obnoxious gases or high temperatures; but this is part of the accepted methods of science, which only takes into account typified events. In the cases mentioned above, for instance, this is justified by the fact that chemical reactions, including degradations, are accelerated by reagent concentrations and high temperatures. In any case, this is the only way to extrapolate present results into the future, about which we all are very much concerned.

The most significant studies on factors affecting the permanence of paper are quoted in references 6, 7, 13, 24, 25, 28–30, 47, 50, 53, 54, 57, 58, 65, 67, 69–75, 77, 86, 89, 91–95, 102, 104, 105, 114, 121, 123, 127, 135–138, 141, 142, 144, 155, 157, 158, 160–162, 169, 173, 179, 182. It should be noted, though, that reference 74 is a general treatise dealing with many other topics, and that references 29, 121, 136, 138, 142, 173 and 179 are more specifically concerned with the technique for investigating decay. References 1, 2, 16, 27, 32, 35, 44, 55, 56, 65, 79, 80–83, 85, 101, 109, 118, 156, 168, 177 and 178 deal with deterioration of leather for bookbinding. References 11, 22 and 106 are concerned with the effect of nuclear radiations on documents.

As a more detailed record of a few important investigations, it may be noted that the Committee on Leather for Bookbinding, appointed by the Society for the Encouragement of Arts, Manufactures and Commerce, was able to isolate several causes of the decay of leather[1]; these studies were further pursued by Faraday Innes, who could eventually give effective directions for the protection of bookbindings[79]. His researches were also supported by the British Leather Manufacturers' Research Association, who are now carrying out an interesting long-term test in order to compare the durability of bookbindings in industrial and country areas[80–82]. Herzberg[69] was able grossly to establish the degree of permanence of paper according to its constituent materials, a study later resumed and exhaustively dealt with by the U.S. National Bureau of Standards[135,137,157,158]. Other activities of the National Bureau of Standards, as early as 1931, are those of Kimberly and Hicks[92], who classified the causes of deterioration of paper as intrinsic and extrinsic, grouping the latter as follows: (a) sunlight, (b) moisture and air pollution, (c) atmospheric changes and (d) insects and micro-organisms. Several important methods of investigation were developed there, notably the one of artificial aging by heat[136,138,155,173,179]. One of the latest N.B.S. projects is the work of Wilson on materials for lamination[180].

Development of restoration and conservation

Once the cause or causes of alteration are known, the search is possible for means to prevent them and means to check and possibly repair the damage. This implies that when it comes to deciding about the restoration of a document and the best way to keep it, one should know (a) how to identify the nature and causes of that particular alteration, and (b) how to treat it and prevent the same alteration from occurring again or other alterations taking place.

Much has been done already with respect to point (b), to the extent that the chances of success in keeping records are now much greater than in the past. But there is still a great deal to be done about point (a). In other words, no matter how extensively these problems have been studied, we still lack a systematic arrangement of procedures to apply confidently in any individual case. This is so largely because almost any decayed document presents a different problem, especially concerning its ability to withstand restoration treatment and its long-term consequences. Also, it would often take a long and difficult investigation to establish exactly what happened to the object, this being impracticable to do in many cases. Finally, a scientific investigation often requires more than negligible sample amounts of the document under examination, which is out of the question for valuable objects.

Therefore, in the domain of restoration much is still entrusted to the personal judgment and intuition of the restorer or the consultant scientist. This, however skilled they may be, is certainly unfortunate.

Perhaps the only physicochemical test that is now coming into use, or at least being generally recommended[12,103,130,175], is the measurement of the pH of paper. This was greatly facilitated by the recent discovery of the possibility of measuring pH by contact with special electrodes, without mutilating the document. This problem, which had been under study for some time[151,176], was solved by Hudson and Milner[76], and the news was spread in the world of archivists and librarians by Werner[175]. This method has a great advantage over the extractive one, not requiring any withdrawal of samples from the document, and is much more precise than the 'spot' method. Incidentally, it may be of value to point out two inconveniences I personally observed; namely, the amount of water required to ensure contact still seems dangerous for valuable documents not requiring further aqueous treatment, and there is difficulty when examining rather porous paper. Anyway, if a low pH value is found, one may classify, to some extent, the deterioration of the document as being originated by excessive acidity. This, coupled with a few more observations[130,165] and the results of biological examination (in which there exists a much broader possibility of diagnosis by withdrawal of insect or micro-organism specimen), does yield some information on the nature of decay.

An attempt has been made at the Istituto di Patologia del Libro to coordinate all the information obtainable on the decay of every document and the treatments required. To this end, since 1957, forms were adopted which accompany every document received through the various departments of the institute. These forms are divided into several sections. First come diagnostic sections, i.e. technological, biological and chemical ones. Each section is divided in turn into a descriptive subsection containing signed and dated observations of restorers, biologists and chemists on the condition of the document and the possible causes of its decay, while in another subsection they advise about provisions to be taken for restoration. The latter are ultimately decided upon in a final consultation between people in charge, taking into account the whole of the diagnosis and other elements such as the historical and philological implications of the operations to be executed, the value of the document, the cost of restoration and so on. The last page of the form includes reports of the departments of chemistry, biology, photography and restoration on the operations actually carried out. An archive is maintained of these forms.

Point (b) of the beginning of this section is actually manifold, in that we have to consider how to repair the damage, how to prevent future damage and how to make sure we are doing the right thing in either case.

Concerning the first two of the above propositions, space does not allow a detailed treatment: these subjects were recently reviewed thoroughly at the International Conference of Archivists in Stockholm, 1960 (see, for example, reference 125), but the bibliography includes the studies of some outstanding contributors (12, 13, 19, 42, 45, 46, 59–61, 63–65, 79, 90, 103, 108, 115–117, 124, 128–132, 145, 154, 155, 174, 175). Here we shall confine our interest mostly to general principles, as we shall further explain later.

The third problem is worthy of a broader discussion, because it has not been greatly pursued up to now and its vital importance still calls for further emphasis. As a matter of fact, we have become suspicious about nearly any treatment documents might undergo in the course of restoration, and even of some protective provisions; this is good, provided exaggeration is avoided. In his recent review, Papritz[125] has expressed this situation well, remarking that the responsible restorer is at present deprived of his principal tools, so many are the doubts aroused about current procedures. It is true that several empirical methods have now passed the test of time satisfactorily, but we know of many dangerous ones, and others keep coming into use now and then. Hence the need is felt for rigorous control of present and distant effects of all procedures being practised[98,148]. This is our major responsibility as curators of the historical patrimony, and this is one thing that science must contribute to the art of restoration.

In the case of paper, for instance, this control is possible because the material can be characterized by a number of measurable properties, i.e. mechanical, chemical and optical characteristics. Mechanical properties are measured by instruments devised to simulate the main types of strain paper may undergo when in use, such as folding, tearing, pulling, etc.; the effort required to break the sample is usually taken as the significant value. These determinations are, of course, generalized; that is, if a paper withstands 24 machine-folds before breaking, this does not mean one can turn a page of a book made of that paper 24 times only. However, the test certainly has a high practical value when, for instance, it predicts that one paper will withstand use longer than another of a lower folding endurance as measured by the instrument. Chemical properties concern composition, fibre quality, etc. They are very important because the dependence of paper durability upon composition has been definitely established. Also, some are important in that they are related to mechanical strength: this is explained by the fact that mechanical strength depends upon such things as the length of cellulose chains, which can be determined chemically. One of the effects of deteriorating agents is the breakdown of the large cellulose molecules, reducing their length. Optical properties are also related to chemical changes (see, for instance, reference 121), although this has not yet been satisfactorily established, and they are important for esthetic reasons.

Now, in order to pronounce a treatment to be harmless to paper, it should be shown not to alter the values of any measurable property of the sample. At least, there should not be significant changes in the characteristics that are important from the standpoint of appearance, use and durability. Therefore, in order to establish this, the important variables of paper are measured before and after the treatment, and matched for possible changes. Still, this does not yield a final answer, especially if the treatment consists of the permanent application of foreign materials, because changes might occur in time. If the expected action is of a chemical nature (with, naturally, mechanical and other consequences), the only way to anticipate this is to apply a concentrated dosage of factors known to favour chemical decay, such as moisture, oxygen, ultra-violet rays, etc., or to apply the physicochemical principle that all chemical reactions are accelerated by a rise in temperature (the speed being approximately doubled every 10–15 °C temperature rise). After this artificial aging, treated and untreated samples are examined again to detect any possible differences.

There are objections to the latter procedures for aging, especially when the paper is treated with volatile substances, and also because of the possibility of side reactions with different thermal coefficients. It is certainly not scientific to draw definite conclusions on the length of time a treated paper will last. But the method definitely has a great comparative value and, while there is no evidence so far that its predictions should be considered unreliable, we have been given some positive evidence by Wilson[179], who, comparing the folding endurance of some papers stored for 26 years with the folding endurance measured on the fresh paper by Rasch after accelerated aging at 105 °C, showed that there was remarkable agreement between natural and artificial aging. For this reason, then, Papritz's[125] recent remark that no paper should be assigned any definite life expectancy might have been unduly pessimistic. Anyway, our descendants will know better than we do, because several laboratories (mine included) are storing samples for future reference, thus following Rasch's wise precaution.

Perhaps the first systematic investigation of this kind is that of the National Bureau of Standards on the effect of sizing on the durability of paper, carried out in the thirties by Kimberly, Hicks, Shaw and O'Leary[91,158]. They were actually more concerned with the size employed in manufacture, but their findings certainly provided conservators with valuable information. The effect of fumigants on paper was also investigated by the N.B.S. in 1935[172]. Then Barrow followed[12,13] with his well-known studies on the stability of de-acidified and laminated documents. And I should like to point out here that his most recent study, in my opinion, provides the answer to another of Papritz's questions[125], i.e. whether or not every document in archives should be previously de-acidified; Barrow[13,14] has actually shown that the durability of sound, average-quality paper is improved also by the addition of calcium and magnesium carbonates. Hence, also considering Werner's inquiry[175] into the ability of weak documents to withstand the treatment, it is now only a matter of expense—an argument not discussed by Papritz in this connection.

Gammexane smokes for disinfestation were found to be harmful to paper by Chakravorti[35], whose study has been taken up by the Istituto di Patologia del Libro[150] and again by the National Archives of India[66]. Recently, the effect of sizing was again studied in the USSR[160], and it is now the object of another study in this country[151]. Kathpalia and Gear[90] reported on the excellent folding endurance of paper sheets hand-laminated by the Indian technique[63]. The consequences of applying fixatives for pencil writing were investigated by Kishore and Goel[96], who were able to suggest some harmless materials. Kishore and Kathpalia[97] studied the deterioration of dextrine for silking and recommended a formulation containing lead carbonate (but this, being liable to be blackened by the hydrogen sulphide in the atmosphere, seems somewhat questionable). The effect of some fungicides on leather was recently examined by Dahl[39].

When Gettens[61] in 1952 advised the replacement of hypochlorites with chlorites for cleaning paper, he attempted a demonstration of the greater safety of chlorites[121] by means of tear tests. In 1960 Mrs Flieder's experiments[52] essentially confirmed Gettens' conclusions, although her results do not seem to indicate sodium chlorite to be a very safe reagent in itself. This problem is now also being examined at the Istituto di Patologia del Libro[151]. In this connection, it is noteworthy to mention that we have found Chloramine-T, a reagent advocated by Plenderleith[128] since 1937, to be a very useful bleacher in a number of cases. Mrs Flieder did not test its effect on paper because she did not find it effective in removing some experimental mould stains; we also observed this in some cases, but in our opinion Chloramine-T deserves more investigation. This also seems important from the standpoint of gradual intervention, of which I am a supporter. I have actually observed that in many cases fox marks can be removed, or at least greatly reduced, by mere water washing, and that those which survive this seldom require more drastic reagents than Chloramine[147].

Another group of investigations coming within this category is that directed to establish whether or not a given material is suitable and durable in itself for restoration purposes, to develop new materials for such applications and to establish specifications for them all. A very exhaustive study is that of Wilson on materials for lamination[180]: this is a real milestone in the field. Barrow's search for a stable and cheap paper suitable for average books and records, and easily produced on a commercial scale, also seems to be another admirable development[14]. Interesting studies were carried out by Brecht[25] on the stability of Japanese paper and 'Pergamin', and a concerted research programme of the Marburg Archivschule and the Bundesinstitut für Materialprüfung in Berlin was set up for the development of the best plastic material for lamination[125]. In Marburg, irradiation tests with ultra-violet light on Japanese paper and silk were also carried out[125]. The National Committee of Archivists of India recently published their specifications for tissue paper[120], and the National Archives of India developed some formulations for dextrine paste[97,119]. In the field of insecticides and fungicides there are also wide possibilities of development, either as application of known compounds in formulations for conservation purposes[51] or as research for new compounds that might be suitable for archival materials[149].

While wishing to provide this section with some additional bibliography, I should like to point out that the role of science in restoration departments was properly described, although focusing mainly on a different field, by Coremans[38] and more recently by Rawlins[139]. For some general information on the constituent materials of paper, leather, etc., references 5, 8, 9, 33, 41, 62, 134 and 170 may be consulted. The books under references 49 and 112 contain many data about air pollution. Some isolated studies or reviews on restoration and conservation which deserve mention may be found under references 4, 31, 56, 68, 78, 87, 96, 122, 153 and 159. Finally, some recent applications of optical decipherment of writing are entered under references 15 and 48.

General principles

The results of scientific research, as was to be expected, were applied in practice and came to form the basis on the one hand of modern methods of restoration and, on the other hand, of modern library and archival architecture and organization. Such things can only be further improved through more research.

However, it should be noted here that the science of restoration by no means depends entirely on the application of scientific criteria, even though it could not dispense with them. It is something much more complex, where scholarly knowledge, skill and technological experience also merge. I cannot deal in detail with all these other aspects, but here I wish to point out briefly that industrial technology, which is ultimately a derivative of pure science, is making an important and independent contribution. We need only recall, as an example, the development of plastic films for lamination, and we hope to get an equal cooperation from the manufacture of stable brands of paper.

We may now summarize in general principles the acquisitions of scientific research. In the first place, the necessity was recognized for the following information:

(1) Knowledge of the constituent materials of the objects concerned.

(2) Isolation of deterioration factors, in order to have a starting point in the study of their effects and of the way to prevent them.

(3) Identification of the type of alteration and examination of the condition of the individual specimen, before applying any remedy.

(4) Control over the harmlessness of restoration and prevention procedures in use and of those being developed prior to their introduction into practice.

(5) Use of more permanent materials for future records.

(6) Establishment of specifications for materials to be employed, and, within the limits allowed by the nature of such work, standardization of restoration procedures.

(7) Avoidance as far as possible of the use of commercial products of unknown composition (pure substances should be preferred).

This is based upon the contribution of science, and future contributions are likely to derive from these developments. These requirements, combined with those of scholars and keepers of records, permit us to formulate some important general criteria, which should be complied with in the present state of our knowledge:

(1) Restoration is not always either necessary or desirable. Anyway, its extent should at least be carefully decided.

(2) Extreme caution is advisable in deciding upon any treatment for important documents, at least until more is known about their consequences. Only procedures and materials of established reliability should be employed, and the work should be entrusted exclusively to competent and responsible personnel, always under the supervision of persons with humanistic sensitivity if the object is of artistic value.

(3) Hopeless cases must, however, be dealt with: it is possible that this will prevent the total loss of irreplaceable documents fated to destruction and at least will provide valuable information about the effect of treatments used.

(4) Whenever possible, proceed gradually in restoration, trying the least drastic methods first (this applies specially to cleaning).

(5) Records should be stored according to the best available criteria of conservation.

(6) Whenever possible, facsimiles of important documents in a bad condition should be used for consultation in place of the originals.

(7) A record should be kept of provisions and observations made in the course of time on material being cared for.

Present situation and prospects

A general consideration that imposes itself as an urgent requirement for the present time and for the future is the necessity of definite specifications for materials to be employed in restoration and in manufacturing new records, and of controlled standardized procedures in restoration. Such a need has been increasingly felt, and expressed often recently[98,125,148]. As Papritz neatly put it, now that suspicion has been thrown on all materials and procedures, something must be given in exchange to restorers and manufacturers to work with[125,167]. However, it should be borne in mind that specifications ought to be commensurate with the purpose to be attained without unduly restrictive requirements. Furthermore, vague specifications should be avoided; it is of no use stating, say, that paper for record purposes should have the highest possible degree of polymerization. The archivist must know exactly what degree of polymerization is acceptable, and consequently require as much from the manufacturers.

We are all working to this end, and it is desirable that there should be more studies like those mentioned in the previous section. Also, more reviews and books must be made accessible to archivists and librarians, to refer to data of practical use; some recent ones may be found under references 13, 37, 100, 116, 117, 124, 125, 130 and 175.

Present and future studies

I know of a few works in progress in various laboratories, and these I can list here. The subjects being investigated include the effects on paper of cleaning methods, insecticides and repeated changes of temperature; the non-aqueous deacidification of delicate documents; the permanence of documents laminated with silk and various plastic films; the testing of materials for repair work; the consolidation of miniatures on parchment manuscripts and the strengthening of parchment itself. Lamination and its application to large amounts of material are, of course, a major concern of many laboratories, including industrial ones. This suggests indirectly that problems of organization must be another important preoccupation of every laboratory, although the subject has scarcely been dealt with hitherto[59,125,130,139,164]. As far as the chemical laboratory of the Istituto di Patologia del Libro is concerned, work in progress includes the comparison of gelatine with other sizing materials, the synthesis of potential new fungicides and insecticides (and the determination of their effect on paper), and the perfection of writing revival.

As a final instance of our activities, I wish to describe briefly a concept that may turn out to be a criterion of practical interest. We are now studying[151] the possibility of expressing, by one number only, the effect of a treatment and the effect of subsequent aging on single properties of any given paper, thus perhaps eliminating the need to refer to tables of individual experimental data in order to discover what happened. In other words, any treatment would be characterized by an index relating it quantitatively, as a function of aging time, to each variable of a sample paper, thus allowing a very simple selection of the best out of several treatments. Such an index would be an arbitrary quantity, but related to physical reality. Experimental work is under way to ascertain its actual applicability, and I hope to be able to describe it soon in a more detailed report.

As to other problems that might be worth investigation, I may mention the microanalysis of ink in writing in order to establish its composition without appreciably altering the document: work has been done to this effect (references 10, 23, 26, 36, 84, 107, 111, 133, 140, 163, 171), but in my opinion this is far from being sufficient. Further study, I think, should be devoted to the imparting of water resistance (hydrophobization) to paper by treatment with suitable polymers. There are a number of suggested applications[17], mostly of industrial origin, but apparently no comprehensive effort has been made in the field of conservation to bring together all of these scattered data for critical examination and specific experimentation. Another interesting application which does not seem to have been further pursued is that of using metallic oxides as a barrier against the attack of light on cellulose[126]. One industrial application which I encountered while scanning the literature has impressed me as being potentially very interesting for our field. This is a new compound for bleaching paper pulps—a complex obtained from sodium perborate and chlorine dioxide that is said to be non-explosive, non-toxic to humans and a powerful fungicide[3]. In view of such properties, it seems worthwhile to find how effective it is for cleaning documents (it would not be suitable for permanent protection from moulds, of course) and what its effect on finished paper is, considering the known disadvantages of the use of plain chlorine dioxide or sodium chlorite in a restoration laboratory.

Then there is the problem of the restoration of coated papers. Doubts are also expressed now and then about the permanency of microfilms. In archives, the problem of preventing rust in metal clips and other metal parts is important, and it is still to be established whether or not plastic substitutes are to be used. It should be realized that paper itself sometimes favours rust formation[152,166]. We shall not mention specific problems of repair, because they are more strictly a manual part of restoration, but let us recall once more the necessity that every single procedure be tested with regard to its durability and effect on the original materials.

International cooperation

One factor that will probably facilitate the solution of all these problems is that scientific research is being increasingly organized on an international basis. The International Institute for Conservation is an example of this tendency. We should also be grateful to the Rome Centre, for its remarkable work of coordination among so many institutions and individuals: an outstanding example of its activity is the recent Répertoire of scientific and restoration laboratories[143]. Not to mention other international organizations, I finally wish to draw attention to the useful role of the ICOM Committee for Museum Laboratories, which is in turn subdivided into smaller subcommittees for the study of specific problems. Much credit should go to UNESCO for its initiatives in this field, the creation of the Rome Centre being one.

Conclusions

We have reviewed the potential and, at times, real danger of empirical procedures and quoted some instances of damage caused to documents by inadequate treatment. On the other hand, scientists have often been accused by curators of careless experimentation or at least insensibility to the humanistic aspects of the problem. Such curators have probably spared many a valuable document from considerable alteration. In effect, the scientist should not be content with solving his problem from a technical point of view; he should also take into account historical, esthetic and even legal considerations. I have experienced this additional difficulty myself to some extent, noticing how little credit was given to my method of ink revival by in situ substitution of iron gallotannate by lead sulphide[18,146], even when the iron pigment had degenerated almost entirely to yellow iron oxide. However, this is stimulating me towards further improvement and verification, which is always desirable.

The major conclusion therefore is that the closest cooperation should be established between scholars, keepers and scientists; and finally, it is necessary that governments and persons in charge of public administration realize the importance of record conservation, and that this cannot be achieved without a great deal of effort and expense.

It is encouraging to note that such ideas are spreading more and more, which allows better hopes for the future.

References

1 *J. R. Soc. Arts*, 49 (1900–01) and 53 (1905).

2 *Gerber*, 37 (1911).

3 *Paper Maker*, 138, No. 1 (1959) 43.

4 ICOM—Comité pour les laboratoires de musées, Groupe de travail pour l'étude de la conservation des matériaux constitutifs des documents graphiques (Paris, Bibliothèque Nationale, May 19–21, 1960), Pièce jointe No. 3 (unpublished report).

5 ALLEGRINI, R. and DE PISAPIA, N., *Cuoio*, 34 (1958) 379.

6 AMBLER, H. R. and FINNEY, C. F., *Nature*, 179 (1957) 1141.

7 ARIBERT and BOUVIER, *Papeterie*, 42 (1920).

8 ARMITAGE, F. D., *An Atlas of the Common Paper-Making Fibres*, Guildhall, London.

9 B.L.M.R.A., *Hides, Skins and Leather under Microscope*, British Leather Manufacturers' Research Association, Egham, Surrey, 1957.

10 BAILEY, C. R. and CASEY, R. F., *Industr. Engng Chem. (Anal.)*, 19 (1947) 1020–22.

11 BARCAN, A. and BASCOM, R. J., *Dun's Rev. mod. Ind.*, 67 (1956) 52–53.

12 BARROW, W. J., *Manuscripts and Documents: Their Deterioration and Restoration*, University of Virginia Press, Charlottesville (Va.), 1955.

13 BARROW, W. J. and CHURCH, R. W., *Deterioration of book stock: causes and remedies*, Virginia State Library Publication No. 10, 1959.

14 BARROW, W. J. and CHURCH, R. W., *The manufacture and testing of durable book papers*, Virginia State Library Publication No. 13, 1960.

15 BASSI, S., *Boll. I.P.L.*, 16 (1957) 1–2, 38,

16 BEEBE, C. W., FREY, R. W. and HENNIGAN, M. V., *J. Amer. Leath. Chem. Ass.*, 51 (1956) 20–31.

17 BELEN'KAYA, N. G., VORONKOV, M. G. and DOLGOV, B. N., *Zh. prikl. Khim.*, 28 (1955) 886–98; *Chem. Abstr.*, 49 (1955) 16430.

18 BENETTI, E. and SANTUCCI, L., *Boll. I.P.L.*, 14 (1955) 3–4, 45.

19 BLAAS, R., *Mitt. öst. Staatsarch.*, 6 (1953) 3500392; *Miscellanea di scritti in memoria di Alfonso Gallo*, Olschki, Florence, 1956, p. 187.

20 BONAVENTURA, G., *Boll. I.P.L.*, 18 (1959) 93.

21 BONNARDOT, A., *Essai sur l'art de restaurer les estampes et les livres*, or *Traité sur les meilleurs procédés pour blanchir, détacher, décolorer, réparer, et conserver les estampes, livres et dessins*, Castel, Paris, 1858.

22 BOPP, C. D. and SISMAN, O., *Nucleonics*, 13, No. 7 (1955) 28–33.

23 BRACKETT, J. W. and BRADFORD, L. W., *J. crim. Law, Crim. Police Sci.*, 43 (1952) 530.

24 BRECHT, W., *Das Papier*, 13 (1959) 130–7, 201–7.

25 BRECHT, W., *Archivar*, 13 (1960) 491–8.

26 BROWN, C. and KIRK, P. L., *J. crim. Law, Crim. Police Sci.*, 45 (1954) 334.

27 BUETTNER, H., *Z. Leder- u. GerbChem.*, 2 (1922–23).

28 BURTON, J. O., *J. Res. nat. Bur. Stand.*, 7 (1931) 429.

29 BURTON, J. O. and RASCH, R., *J. Res. nat. Bur. Stand.*, 6 (1931) 603.

30 CARSON, F., *Nat. Bur. Stand. Circ.*, C. 445, Govt. Printing Office, Washington, 1944.

31 CASAMASSIMA, E., *Notiz. A.I.B.*, 3, No. 1–2 (1957) 13–21.

32 CASSEL, J. M., *J. Amer. Leath. Chem. Ass.*, 53 (1958) 507.

33 CENTOLA, G., *Melliand Textilber.*, 40 (1959) 769–72.

34 CHESHIRE, A., *J. Int. Soc. Leath. Chem.*, 30 (1946) 134.

35 CHAKRAVORTI, S., *Nature*, 163 (1949) 607.

36 COLDWELL, B. B., *Analyst*, 80 (1955) 68.

37 COLLIS, I. P. and ROOK, C. L., *Soc. Loc. Arch. Bull.*, 6 (1949) 6.

38 COREMANS, P., *Alumni*, 19, No. 3–4 (1950) 292.

39 DAHL, S., *J. Soc. Leath. Tr. Chem.*, 41 (1957) 611.

40 DAVIS, G. E., *Chem. News*, 36 (1877) 227.

41 DOLL, H., *Allg. PapRdsch.* (1955) 930–2, 985–6.

42 DURYE, P., *Gaz. Arch.*, 17–18 (1955) 48–57.

43 EHRLE, F., *Riv. Bibl. Arch.*, 9 (1898) and 22 (1911).

44 EITNER, W., *Gerber*, 33 (1907) 267, 281, 296, 309.

45 ELLIS, R., *The Principles of Archive Repair*, London, 1951.

46 ELLIS, R., *J. Soc. Archiv.*, 1, No. 9 (1959) 252.

47 EVANS, J., *J. R. Soc. Arts*, 46 (1898).

48 FABIANI, M. L., *Boll. I.P.L.*, 15 (1956) 212.

49 FAITH, W. L., *Air Pollution Control*, Wiley and Sons, New York, 1959.

50 FAULHABER, M. and PIETRZYK, K., *Wbl. Papierfabr.*, 84 (1956) 75–82, 111–7, 147–53 and 183–7.

51 FLIEDER, F., *Bull. bibliogr. Fr.*, 2, No. 1 (1957) 48–51; French Patent 747–632, 19/9/1957.

52 FLIEDER, F., *Bull. A.T.I.P.*, No. 4 (1960) 173–184.

53 FLYNN, J. H., WILSON, W. K. and MORROW, W. L., *J. Res. nat. Bur. Stand.*, 60 (1958) 229–33.

54 FOSCHINI, A., *Boll. I.P.L.*, 12 (1953) 91.

55 FREY, R. W. and CLARKE, I. D., *J. Amer. Leath. Chem. Ass.*, 26 (1931) 461.

56 FREY, R. W. and BEEBE, C. W., *J. Amer. Leath. Chem. Ass.*, 29 (1934) 528.

57 FROHBERG, A., *Wbl. Papierfabr.*, 44 (1913) 3599.

58 FYNN, P. J., SANDS, J. E. and CAMPBELL, K. S., *Nat. Synth. Fibers*, 4 (1948) 779.

59 GALLO, A., *Patologia e terapia del libro*, Raggio, Rome, 1951.

60 GEAR, J. L., *Amer. Archiv.*, 22 (1959) 322.

61 GETTENS, R. J., *Museum*, 5, No. 2 (1952) 116.

62 GIERER, J., *Holz a. Roh- u. Werkst.*, 18 (1958) 251.

63 GOEL, O. P., *Indian Arch.*, 7, No. 2 (1953) 162.

64 GRANT, J., *Books and Documents*, Grafton and Co., London, 1937.

65 GREATHOUSE, G. A. and WESSEL, C. J., *Deterioration of Materials*, Reinhold, New York, 1954.

66 GUPTA, R. C., private communication.

67 HALL, A. J., *Paper Tr. J.*, 82 (1926).

68 HEILAND, H., *Allg. Anz. Buchbind.*, 73 (1960) 486–8.

69 HERZBERG, W., *Chem. Ind.*, 18 (1895); *Kgl. Materialprüfungsanst. Mitteil.*, 25 (1907), 26 (1908); *Paper Tr. J.*, 76 (1923) 176.

70 HIGGINS, H. G., *J. Polym. Sci.*, 28 (1958) 645–8; *J. Aust. Pulp Paper Ind. Tech. Ass.*, 11, No. 4 (1958) 84.

71 HILL, F. P., *Bull. Amer. Libr. Ass.*, 4 (1910); 6 (1912).

72 HITCHINS, A. B., *Paper Monthly J.*, 56 (1918) 11.

73 HOFFMAN, W. F., *Paper Tr. J.*, 86 (1928).

74 HONEYMAN, J., *Recent Advances in the Chemistry of Cellulose and Starch*, Heywood, London, 1959.

75 HUDSON, F. L. and MILNER, W. D., *Paper Mkr.*, 133 (1957) 210.

76 HUDSON, F. L. and MILNER, W. D., *Svensk PappTidn.*, 62 (1959) 83–4.

77 HUDSON, F. L. and HEINSIUS, H. J., *Brit. Paper Board Mkrs Ass., Proc. Tech. Sect.*, 40 (1959) 31–47 (discussion 48–51).

78 IBSCHER, R., *Allg. Anzeig. f. Buchbinder.*, 73 (1960) 486.

79 INNES, R. F., *B.L.M.R.A. Lab. Rep.*, 12 (1933) 228; *Libr. Ass. Rec.*, 1 (1934).

80 INNES, R. F., *B.L.M.R.A. Lab. Rep.*, 11 (1932) 276; 24 (1945) 104.

81 INNES, R. F., PLENDERLEITH, H. J. and MOSS, A. A., *B.L.M.R.A. Lab. Rep.*, 31 (1952) 380.

82 INNES, R. F., PLENDERLEITH, H. J. and WERNER, A. E. A., *B.L.M.R.A. Lab. Rep.*, 33 (1954) 208,

83 INNES, R. F. and MITTON, R. G., *J. Soc. Leath. Tr. Chem.*, 39 (1955) 225–35.

84 IWASAKI, S., *Sci. Crime Detect.* (*Japan*), 8, No. 3 (1955) 36; *Chem. Abstr.*, 50 (1956) 6810.

85 JALADE, E., *Cuir*, 12 (1923).

86 JARRELL, T. D., HANKINS, J. M. and VEITCH, F. P., *U.S. Dept. Agr. Tech. Bull.*, 334 (1932), 541 (1936), 605 (1938).

87 JENKINSON, H., *Archivum*, 2 (1952) 31–44.

88 JUSTINIJANOVIĆ, N., *Bibliotekar* (*Belgrade*), No. 2–3 (1958) 122132.

89 KANTROWITZ, M. S., SPENCER, E. W. and SIMMONS, R. H., *Permanence and Durability of Paper* (containing annotated bibliography of the technical literature, 1855–1939), U. S. Govt. Printing Office, Washington, 1940.

90 KATHPALIA, J. P., and GEAR, J. L., *Amer. Archiv.*, 21 (1958) 271–6.

91 KIMBERLY, A. E. and HICKS, J. F. C., *J. Res. nat. Bur. Stand.* 6 (1931) 603.

[92] KIMBERLY, A. E. and HICKS, J. F. C., *A survey of storage conditions in libraries relative to the preservation of records*, Nat. Bur. Standards Misc. Pubs., Washington, 1931.

[93] KIMBERLY, A. E., *J. Res. nat. Bur. Stand.*, 8 (1932) 159.

[94] KIMBERLY, A. E. and EMLEY, A. L., *U.S. Nat. Bur. Stand. Misc. Pubs.*, 140 (1933).

[95] KIMBERLY, A. E. and SCRIBNER, B. W., *U.S. Nat. Bur. Stand. Misc. Pubs.*, 154 (1937).

[96] KISHORE, R. and GOEL, O. P., *Indian Archiv.*, 6, No. 1–2 (1952) 34.

[97] KISHORE, R. and KATHFALIA, J. P., *Proc. Nat. Com. Archiv. India*, 1 (1956) 35–44.

[98] KLEINDIENST, T., *Bull. Bibl. France*, 5, No. 8 (1960) 309–310.

[99] KOEGEL, R., *Die Photographie historischer Documente nebst Grundzügen der Reproduktionverfahren*, Leipzig, 1914.

[100] KUBILIUS, W., *Libr. Binder*, 4, No. 2 (1956) 8–11.

[101] LAMB, M. C., *J. Soc. Dy. Col.*, 24 (1908).

[102] LANGWELL, W. H., *Libr. Ass. Rec.*, 55 (1953) 212–5; *Archives*, 2, No. 2 (1954) 136–137; *Tech. Bull. Brit. Paper & Board Mkrs. Ass.*, 29 (1952) 21, 29 (1952) 52, 30 (1953) 2; *Proc. Tech. Sec., Paper Mkrs. Ass. G. Brit. & Ireland*, 36 (1955) 199; *J. Soc. Archiv.*, 1, No. 6 (1957) 172–174.

[103] LANGWELL, W. H., *The Conservation of Books and Documents*, Pitman, London, 1957.

[104] LANIGAN, H., *Nat. synth. Fibers*, 5 (1949) 779.

[105] LAUNER, H. F. and WILSON, J. A., *J. Res. nat. Bur. Stand.*, 30 (1943) 55; *J. Amer. Chem. Soc.*, 71 (1949) 958.

[106] LAVACHERY, H. and NOBLECOURT, A., *Musées et Monuments: VIII. Les techniques de protection des biens culturels en cas de conflit armé*, UNESCO, Paris, 1954.

[108] LE GEAR, C., *Maps: Their Care, Repair and Preservation*, Library of Congress, Washington, D. C., 1949.

[109] LITTLE, A. D., *J. Amer. Leath. Chem. Ass.*, 4 (1909).

[110] LODOLINI, A., *Miscellanea di scritti vari in memoria di Alfonso Gallo*, Olschki, Florence, 1956, p. 519.

[111] MACRIS, C. G. and RIGANEZIS, M. D., *Anal. Chim. Acta*, 13 (1955) 129–34.

[112] MAGILL, L., HOLDEN, F. R. and ACKLEY, C., *Air Pollution Handbook*, McGraw-Hill, New York, 1956.

[113] MARCONI, B., Report to the Vth conference of the ICOM Committee for Scientific Laboratories, Copenhagen, 1959.

[114] MARTENS, A., *Kgl. Materialprüfungsanst. Mitteil.*, 25 (1907).

[115] MINOGUE, A., The repair and preservation of records, *Bull. Nat. Arch.*, No. 5, Washington, 1943.

[116] MINOGUE, A., *Libr. Trends*, 5, No. 3 (1957) 344–51.

[117] MIZIN, P. J. and CEREVITINOV, N. A., *Tehnologia Hranenija dokumental'nyh materialov. Učebuoe posobie*, Moscow, 1950.

[118] MOELLER, W., *Z. Leder- u. GerbChem.*, 2 (1922–23).

[119] National Archives of India, *Tech. Bull.*, 1 (1955) 5.

[120] National Committee of Archivists of India, *Proc. Nat. Com. Archiv. India*, 2 (1959) 46.

[121] NEDERVEEN, G. and VAN ROYEN, A. H. H., *Papier*, 9 (1955) 463–8.

[122] NOBÉCOURT, P., and BARNOUD, F., *Mus. Collect. publ. France*, 4 (1955) 153–161, 5 (1955) 211–20.

[123] NORDMAN, L. S., *Tappi*, 41 (1958) 23.

[124] PAPRITZ, J., *Erfahrungen und Verhandlungsbericht*, Die Archivtechnische Woche der Archivschule Marburg, Marburg, 1957.

[125] PAPRITZ, J., *Allg. Anzeig. f. Buchbinder*, 74 (1961) 136.

[126] PERTI, S. L., RANGANATHAN, S. K., SUBRAMANIAN, T. S. and SUD, L. R., *Nature*, 163 (1949) 877.

[127] PIMONT, B., *Papier, carton, cellulose*, 6, No. 2 (1957) 109.

[128] PLENDERLEITH, H. J., *The Conservation of Prints, Drawings, and Manuscripts*, British Museum, London, 1937.

[129] PLENDERLEITH, H. J., *The Preservation of Leather Bookbindings*, British Museum, London, 1947.

[130] PLENDERLEITH, H. J., *The Conservation of Antiques and Works of Art*, Oxford University Press, London, 1956.

[131] PLENDERLEITH, H. J. and WERNER, A. E. A., *J. Soc. Archiv.*, 1, No. 7 (1958) 198.

[132] PORCHER, J., FLIEDER, F. and GUICHARD, R., ICOM—Comité pour les laboratoires de musées. Groupe de travail pour l'étude de la conservation des matériaux constitutifs des documents graphiques (Paris, Bibliothèque Nationale, 19–21 mai 1960), Pièce jointe No. 1 (see also Copenhagen Report, 1959).

[133] PUPIL, F., *Bull. Lab. Mus. Louvre*, 1 (1956) 10.

[134] RAPSON, W. H. and HAKIM, K. A., *Pulp. Pap. Mag. Can.*, 58, No. 8 (1957) 151.

[135] RASCH, R. H., *J. Res. nat. Bur. Stand.*, 3 (1929) 469–506.

[136] RASCH, R. H., *J. Res. nat. Bur. Stand.*, 7 (1931) 465.

[137] RASCH, R. H., SHAW, H. B. and BICKING, J. V., *J. Res. nat. Bur. Stand.*, 7 (1931) 765.

[138] RASCH, R. H. and STONE, G. O., *Paper Tr. J.*, 95, No. 4 (1932) 28.

[139] RAWLINS, F. I. C., Report to ICOM Laboratories Committee, Copenhagen, 1959.

[140] RAWLINS, F.I. C. and WERNER, A. E. A., *Endeavour*, 13 (1954) 140.

[141] RICHTER, G. A., *Ind. Engng Chem.*, 27 (1935) 177, 432.

[142] RICHTER, G. A. and WELLS, F. L., *Tappi*, 39 (1956) 603–8.

[143] Rome Centre, *Répertoire des laboratoires de musée et ateliers de restauration*, International Centre for the Study of the Preservation and the Restoration of Cultural Property, Rome, 1960.

[144] ROOS, J. O., *Svensk Kem. Tidskr.*, 24 (1912) 110.

[145] RYPALLA, H., *Archivmitt.*, 7, No. 3 (1957) 105–109.

[146] SANTUCCI, L., *Boll. I.P.L.*, 12, No. 3–4 (1953) 69.

[147] SANTUCCI, L., *Boll. I.P.L.*, 18 (1959) 146.

[148] SANTUCCI, L., *Boll. I.P.L.*, 19 (1960) 77.

[149] SANTUCCI, L., *Boll. I.P.L.*, 19 (1960) 82.

[150] SANTUCCI, L., *Boll. I.P.L.*, 19 (1960) 162.

[151] SANTUCCI, L., unpublished studies.

[152] SCHIKORR, G. and VOLTZ, K., *Papier*, 8 (1954) 431–4.

[153] SCHOMANN, H. O., *Allg. Anzeig. f. Buchbinder.*, 74 (1961) 29.

[154] SCHWEIDLER, M., *Die Instandsetzung von Kupferstichen, Zeichnungen, Büchern usw. Alte Fehler und neue Methoden bei der Beseitigung von Altersschäden an graphischem Kulturgut*, Buchbinderverlag, Stuttgart, 1949.

[155] SCRIBNER, B. W., *Nat. Bur. Stand. Misc. Publs.*, 145 (1934); *J. Res. nat. Bur. Stand.*, 25 (1939) 405.

[156] SEYMOUR JONES, A., *Libr. Ass. Rec.*, 8 (1906) 641.

[157] SHAW, M. B., BICKING, J. W. and O'LEARY, M. J., *J. Res. nat. Bur. Stand.*, 14 (1935) 649.

[158] SHAW, M. B. and O'LEARY, M. J., *J. Res. nat. Bur. Stand.*, 21 (1938) 71.

[159] SIEVERS, K. and WELZEL, F., *Archivar*, 2 (1956) 93–98.

[160] SIMIONESCU, C., POPPEL, E. and ASANDREI, N., *Bumazh. Prom.*, 30, No. 11 (1955) 5–10; *Chem. Abstr.*, 50 (1956) 4501.

[161] SINDALL, R. W., *Paper Technology*, Griffin & Co., London, 1920.

[162] SOLECHNIK, N. Y. and TRUKHTENKOVA, N. E., *Zh. Prikl. Khim.*, 29 (1956) 416–24; *Chem. Abstr.*, 50 (1956) 9737.

[163] SOMEFORD, A. W., *J. crim. Law, Criminol., Police Sci.*, 43 (1952) 124.

[164] STOLOW, N., *Application of Science in Examination of Works of Art*, Res. Lab., Museum of Fine Arts, Boston (Proc. of the Seminar, Sept. 15–18), 1958, p.1.

[165] T.A.P.P.I., Suggested Method T. 445 sm-57; Standard T437 m-43,

[166] TOKER, B., *Przegl. papiern.*, 14 (1958) 161.

[167] TURNER, R. W. S., *Amer. Archiv.*, 20, No. 4 (1957) 319–29; cf. GEAR, J. L., *Amer. Archiv.*, 20, No. 4 (1957) 329–334.

[168] VEITCH, F. P., *J. Amer. Leath. Chem. Ass.*, 21 (1926).

[169] VERNON, W. H. J., *Bibliography of Metallic Corrosion to Papers*, London, 1928.

[170] VILLARS, J., *Bull. A.T.I.P.*, 2 (1956) 50–55.

[171] VITOLO, A. E., FORNARI, A. and VENTURA, R., *Med. leg. e assicurazione*, 1 (1953) 330–66; *Chem. Abstr.*, 50 (1956) 16948.

[172] WEBER, C. G., SHAW, M. B. and BACK, M. A., *J. Res. nat. Bur. Stand.*, 15 (1935) 271–5.

[173] WEHMER, P. F., *Paper Tr. J.*, 94, No. 3 (1932) 37.

[174] WERNER, A. E. A., *Chron. Egypt*, 32, No. 66 (1958) 277; ICOM-Comité pour les laboratoires de musées. Groupe de travail pour l'étude de la conservation des matériaux constitutifs des documents graphiques (Paris, Bibliothèque Nationale, 19–21 mai 1960), Pièce jointe No. 2 (unpublished report).

[175] WERNER, A. E. A., *J. Soc. Archiv.*, 1, No. 10 (1959) 280.

[176] WERNER, A. E. A., private communication.

[177] WILSON, J. A. and LINES, G. O., *J. Amer. Leath. Chem. Ass.*, 21 (1926).

[178] WILSON, J. A. and KERN, E. J., *Ind. Engng Chem.*, 29 (1927) 115.

[179] WILSON, W. K., HARVEY, J. L., HANDEL, J. and WORKSMAN, T., *Tappi*, 38 (1955) 543.

[180] WILSON, W. K. and FORSHEE, B. W., *Preservation of Documents by Lamination*, Nat. Bur. Standards Monograph 5, Washington, 1959.

[181] WOODWARD, C. J., *Libr. Chron.*, 5 (1888) 25.

[182] ZIMMERMAN, E. W., WEBER, C. G., and KIMBERLY, A. E., *J. Res. nat. Bur. Stand.*, 14 (1935) 463.

Piero Gallo

PROBLEMS IN THE USE OF INSECTICIDES ON OCCUPIED PREMISES

In this paper recent advances in the use of insecticides are described. This field includes such aspects as the use of poisoning during disinfestation processes, the problem of 'toxic residues' and the prevention of poisoning caused by insecticides. Finally, a brief summary is made of the research being carried out at the Istituto di Patologia del Libro and at the Centre of Studies for Termite Control in Rome.

Recent advances in the field of insecticides

The field of insecticides has undergone a profound transformation in the last few years as a result of the progress in the production of a great number of synthetic compounds capable of exercising a lasting toxic action against the majority of insect species. A wide range and long persistence of action are two of the most important properties of modern insecticidal substances[1].

In the expansion of researches in this field the resistance which the parasites gradually acquire towards the new insecticides plays an important role because, on the one hand, it makes such compounds almost or absolutely ineffective and, on the other hand, it acts as an incentive for the discovery of others[2]. Thus a contest is established between the chemist and the insects, and the resistance of the latter provides one of the most serious challenges facing man, a challenge which is a true race against time[3]. In fact, insects, says Schoof[4], successfully adapt themselves to coexistence with pesticides almost as fast as the poisons are produced, and Schoof[5] also records that the number of species of resistant parasites had mounted from two to 46 between 1946 and 1958. Numerous other species of insects have become resistant in the years 1958 and 1959[6]. Such data, which refer to the carriers of infectious illnesses, clearly show the severity of the problem of insect resistance.

The number of antiparasitic compounds* existing today is considerable and even more so if one adds to insecticides in the strict sense all those fungicides and repellents which display a toxic action towards insects. Moreover, new compounds are synthesized every year in the universities and in the research departments of industrial concerns. The research carried out in this field is aimed at discovering insecticides which can not only replace those which have become ineffective but which also possess a selective toxicity; that is to say, a high potential toxicity against insects and scarcely any for human beings[7]. Such research has led in recent years to important advances and has produced new means of control against insects, some chemical, others physical, which are capable of vast and interesting development; these we shall describe together with some essential bibliographical references.

(a) Microbial insecticides are, as Palmer[9] stated, a category of pathogenic organisms used to combat insects. At the

---

* Fabre[26] divides insecticides into three groups, depending on their mode of absorption: (1) respiratory insecticides; (2) insecticides of ingestion; (3) contact insecticides (to this group belong the organic phosphorus and halogen compounds).

present time there are only two or three examples of this class, comprising Thuricide[10,11], Agritol and Biotrol. The active agent of Thuricide is spores of *Bacillus thurigensis* (see also the work of Hall[12]).

(b) Amongst the new fumigants, we would point out sulphuryl fluoride[13–15], which is judged better than methyl bromide since it has a greater power of penetration, is more toxic for many species of insects and does not damage paper, rubber, plastic materials, metals and leather (Kenaga[15]).

(c) Silica aerogels are inert powders which cause the death of the insect by removing the waxy protective layer which covers the body of the parasite, bringing about a process of dehydration. They have been used with success against cockroaches[4] and drywood termites and have the advantage of a very low toxic potential for human beings[8,16,17].

(d) Radioactive isotopes: cobalt-60, phosphorus-32 and carbon-14 have been used in the agricultural field for sterilizing insects and so preventing their reproduction. The use of such isotopes could be extended to other fields[4,18,19].

(e) Among the new fungicides we bring to notice the antibiotics, which are already extensively employed in the agricultural field and which have the advantage of being less toxic than the old fungicides[20]. We have mentioned fungicides in this review, dedicated to insecticides, because these substances find wide use in the control of moulds on paper, leather, varnishes, etc., in libraries, archives and museums.

(f) The less toxic organo-phosphorus compounds, as far as human beings are concerned, are another important recent development[21,22].

In the following paragraphs we shall deal with some of the more important health problems relating to the use of insecticides in public buildings (libraries, museums, archives, schools). We shall deal with such problems from a general point of view, giving for each of them those references which will allow the reader to widen his knowledge, and we shall attempt to make clear the importance of the risks resulting from the use of modern antiparasitic substances and some elementary principles on which one can base the prevention of poisonings, accidental and occupational, which can occur during the disinfestation processes.

Poisonings by insecticides are classified, by the majority of health workers[3], into three groups, in connection with (a) the manufacture of such materials, (b) their use in public buildings and (c) the residues which can pollute the materials and surroundings disinfested. The poisonings which occur during manufacture are obviously outside our terms of reference and therefore we shall examine only the health problems relating to the use of these insecticides and their residues.

Barnes[3] writes: 'The handling of insecticides . . . is inevitably accompanied by a great risk of poisoning. Pesticides are employed in different ways with all types of apparatus by persons differing greatly amongst themselves in experience and intelligence.' Consequently one is dealing with problems extremely interesting from both the scientific and practical points of view.

The risk of poisoning during disinfestation

Before illustrating the risks connected with the use of insecticides, we take the opportunity to recall the fundamental difference between the concept of risk and that of toxicity. 'The toxicity of a compound is the total of its physical and chemical properties dangerous to health, while the risk which it represents is the probability of the realization of this potential danger.'[23]

The toxicity of modern insecticides, which is amply documented by an imposing number of experimental works, is much greater for some compounds than for others[22]. All the same, all insecticides, in different ways, to different extents and by different mechanisms, can cause functional or anatomical damage to the human organism whenever those conditions are realized which make possible the manifestation of the toxic potentialities of such substances. These conditions can be summarized in the following ways:

Toxic potential of commercial insecticide preparations

Firstly we shall see how insecticides are available commercially.

There are two groups of products: *concentrated materials*, which must be diluted with water or other solvents and mixed with additives, and *mixtures* (indicated in the technical literature by the term 'formulation'), which, besides the insecticide, consist of particular solvents and the additives. The latter substances are subdivided into the following[21] three groups; (a) wetting agents, which favour and make more durable the adhesion of the insecticide onto the materials treated; (b) surface-active agents, which facilitate the adhesion and the homogeneous dispersion of the disinfestant on the surfaces to which it is applied; (c) emulsifiers, which are added to non-water-soluble disinfestants, making it easier to mix them with water in the preparation of antiparasitic emulsions. (In the last few years, successful experiments have been carried out with resin insecticides—insecticides incorporated into resins—which have a long persistence, protecting the material treated for many years against the attack of insects[24,25].)

The number of mixtures actually available is overwhelming—it amounts to several thousands.

We shall now consider the risks resulting from the use of these two groups of products.

Concentrated materials: These are the most risky to handle and are those which have most frequently caused severe poisoning and, in a few cases, death, amongst people carrying out disinfestation work. The dilution of these insecticides must, therefore, be carried out with extreme caution because the splashing of small drops and of powders can expose the operator to a poisonous or lethal dose of the pesticide. The high potential toxicity of some of these substances is seen from *Table 1*, in which are recorded the LD50 for single skin applications of these insecticides. We have reported these data,

relating to poisoning through the skin, with the definite aim of calling the attention of the reader to its importance, because 'contamination of the skin is actually the most important way of absorption in the field of work with pesticides' (Barnes[3]).

Table 1

LD50 for single skin application of some insecticides

Insecticide	Solvent	Dose (mg/kg)	Animal	Reference
Dieldrin	Dimethyl phthalate	150	Rabbit	26
Lindane	Dimethyl phthalate	188	Rabbit	26
DDT	Kerosene	300	Rabbit	22, 27
DDT	Dimethyl phthalate	2820	Rabbit	26
Malathion		4000	Rat	22
TEPP	TEPP technical	5	Rabbit	26
Demeton	Oily solvents	24	Rabbit	22

The cutaneous absorption of disinfestants dissolved in solvents is rapid and high and occurs not only directly through contact of the toxic materials with the skin but also indirectly in all those cases in which the working clothes contaminated with the insecticides are not replaced immediately. Relative to this, Barnes[3], who affirms that the protective value of rubber gloves is, in many cases, limited because some insecticidal materials penetrate the rubber, observed that it is not easy to obtain thoroughly protective clothing. It is essential, therefore, that workers handle these materials with great caution and wash themselves thoroughly after work.

Below is a list of the more important insecticides, fungicides and repellents, subdivided into three groups: low, intermediate and high toxicity. This classification is the work of the English hygienist, Butterwood, and it is also reported by Edson[20].

Insecticides

    Low toxicity: gammexane, chlordane, DDD, DDT, dipterex, malathion, methoxychlor, mineral oils, pyrethrine, rotenone, chlorbenzide.

    Intermediate toxicity: aldrin, chlorthion, diazinon, dieldrin, heptachlor, lead arsenate, phenkoptone, toxaphene.

    Very toxic: demeton, dimefox, dinitrobutylphenol, dinitrocresol (DNC), endrin, fluoroacetamide, guthion, methylparathion, phosdrin, schradan, sulphodex, TEPP.

Fungicides

    Low toxicity: antibiotics, copper compounds, dithiocarbamates, TMTD.

    Very toxic: concentrated organic mercury compounds.

Repellents

    Low toxicity: naphthalene, paradichlorbenzene.

Mixture or formulation insecticides: These are less hazardous to handle than the concentrated products but they present other difficulties to which we call the attention of the reader. They are formed, as we have said, from insecticide, solvent and additives. Consequently their toxicity is not equal, both from a qualitative and quantitative point of view, to that of the insecticide which is the active agent, but is the sum of the factors which are summarized in *Table 2*.

Table 2

Toxicity of mixture or formulation insecticides

Impurity of the component insecticides ⟍
                  → Toxicity of the insecticidal formulation ← Toxicity of the component insecticides
Toxicity of the solvents and the additives ⟋
                                         ⟍ Physical (ultra-violet rays, humidity, etc.) and chemical factors which alter components of formulation

Hence a simple qualitative indication of the principal insecticidal components of the mixture, although of undoubted practical importance, is not sufficient. But not even this information is given in many cases (we shall return to this later) and a large number of mixtures is available commercially in many countries without any information regarding toxicity and chemical composition; and the resulting poisonings, whether occupational or accidental, cannot be effectively treated when one lacks the basis for imposing adequate therapeutic provisions.

Characteristics of the working surroundings

The operations of disinfestation carried out in the open air or in well-ventilated surroundings are obviously much less risky than those carried out in confined places that are badly ventilated and of small area. Barnes[3] records a noticeable lowering of the rate of cholinesterase in the blood of workers accustomed to spraying diazinon (one of the less toxic organo-phosphorus compounds) in enclosed areas, while other research has shown that persons handling parathion (an organo-phosphorus compound much more poisonous than diazinon) in the open air very seldom inhale toxic doses of this insecticide.

These investigations show that a disinfestant such as diazinon becomes more dangerous in closed areas than parathion used in the open air, because it is easier to obtain a high atmospheric concentration of the poison in the working area. The danger is obviously much greater when the disinfestant is more poisonous and its rate of evaporation is greater.

In *Table 3* are recorded the maximum concentrations in air tolerable by man of some of the more important insecticides.

Table 3

Maximum atmospheric concentrations of insecticide tolerable by man

Insecticide	Concentration (mg/m³)
Aldrin	0·25
Dieldrin	0·25
Lindane	0·50
DDT	2
Chlordane	2
Methoxychlor	15
TEPP	0·05
Malathion	15
Parathion	0·10

The data relating to parathion have been taken from Barnes[3]. All others are given by Fabre [26,28].

Health education of workers

The probability of cases of poisoning is much greater when there is a lack of technical and hygienic education of workers using the disinfestants. We shall return to this problem, which is so important from the point of view of work hygiene, in later paragraphs.

Documentation of composition and toxic properties

In all countries there exist health regulations which control the manufacture and sale of insecticidal products. All the same, legislation on disinfestants varies widely, being very strict in some countries and very slack in others, so that, in the latter case, one frequently comes across commercially available materials, even very poisonous ones, without any information about their chemical composition and toxicity. In some cases the manufacturers give only incomplete information on the composition of the mixtures or else note only the insecticidal part of the mixture and do not indicate the solvents and any additives they have used.

Unfortunately, too, even in those countries whose health regulations are very progressive, one can see infringements of the laws controlling the sale of insecticides. Lack of precise information, as well as being inconvenient, considerably increases the risk of poisoning, makes prevention and cure of poisoning difficult and deserves to be called to the attention of (and seriously considered by) all those concerned with disinfestation and, in particular, by the health authorities.

The problem of the 'toxic residue'

The danger of poisoning does not end with the actual process of disinfestation but frequently lasts for some time in those cases where the surroundings of the materials treated are polluted by the residue of the toxic materials which have been used. There are many ways in which this can happen, and we cannot list them all without exceeding the limits of this work, which has a general character. All the same, it would be useful to list briefly the following aspects.

Toxic residues from fumigants

Dangerous atmospheric pollution can persist for several days after the cessation of fumigation in all those cases in which the elimination of the gas from the surroundings or from the material treated takes longer than usual. The causes of this slower elimination are many[13,29,30] and are principally sought for in a particular relationship established between the materials being treated and the fumigant, or else in a particular location or disposition of the disinfested surroundings.

The first occurs when (a) gases soluble in water are absorbed to a considerable extent in damp materials and those soluble in oils dissolve easily and in conspicuous quantities in materials rich in oils; and (b) the gas is adsorbed or absorbed by the materials treated, either simply dissolving in the adsorbent body or combining with it and giving rise to the formation of toxic compounds.

In both these cases there is a slow evaporation from the objects treated, with consequent atmospheric pollution which persists for several days, as long as the poison has not been eliminated. Consequently one must forbid access to areas treated with toxic gases until sufficient time has elapsed for the complete elimination of the fumigant (several days).

The second arises when one employs a gas heavier than air (for example, methyl bromide) in surroundings communicating with the exterior through openings placed in the vicinity of the ceiling. Under such conditions, the fumigant stratifies close to the floor and so its elimination at the end of the fumigation will present considerable difficulties and take place particularly slowly.

Evaporation of insecticide mixtures

Insecticide mixtures applied to wood inside public buildings evaporate very slowly from the surface treated, polluting the air, in the first days after treatment, to an extent which should not be neglected. Sometimes atmospheric concentration of the poison is such as to cause subjective or objective disturbance to people working in the area for several hours a day, above all if the area is small and ill-ventilated.

Prevention of poisoning by insecticides

The prevention of the poisonings derived from the use of the numerous insecticides existing today obviously cannot be dealt with in a few pages; moreover, since such treatment goes beyond the scope of the present work, we shall try to explain only the basic work which will allow the reader to see what he is about when faced with this important problem. Therefore it seems useful to us to indicate some standards of general character whose application can contribute to the reduction of the risk of poisoning.

Preparation and training

The technical preparation of those who carry out the disinfestation is of fundamental importance; many cases of poisoning have been caused by ignorance on the part of the sufferers concerning the dangers of such insecticides. It is therefore imperative that the people accustomed to such operations should know of the risks that they run, should be regularly instructed, should know how to adopt the measures which will effectively prevent poisoning and should know how to carry out immediately the most important first-aid measures when necessary (see p. 52). If the technical preparation of the workers is important, even more so is the scientific preparation of those who organize and direct the disinfestation, whose success and risk depend on the methods by which the processes are carried out—methods which will be correct if founded on a knowledge of the biology of the insects, the chemistry of the insecticides and on the pathology of the poisonings. Therefore, the task of organizing the fight against the parasites which infest libraries, archives and museums must not be left to a person destitute of biological, chemical and medical preparation but must be entrusted to specialized staff who have had specific training in the various problems connected with the use of disinfestants.

Since we cannot illustrate in detail all the necessary measures for the prevention of poisoning by insecticides, which vary from compound to compound, we refer the reader to works which deal specifically with this problem (references 21–23, 26, 28–36). Nevertheless, we consider it useful to cite as an illustration some of the general principles (supplemented with specific precautions) which must be adopted in vacuum fumigations with methyl bromide and in the spraying of mixed insecticides. The reader will thus be made aware of the multiplicity of practical problems which must be solved.

In vacuum fumigations* with methyl bromide, in order to prevent the escape of toxic gas, it is necessary that closure of the door of the cell should be effected by exerting an equal pressure on all the screws, because if some of the screws are tight and others are loose, there will be an escape of methyl bromide. The introduction of gas into the cell (that is, after the vacuum has been produced) should be effected in such a way that the pressure inside the cell remains below atmospheric pressure. After introducing the gas the operator must close the cylinder completely so that the gas does not (as has happened in many cases) continue to escape, so building up the pressure inside the cell which could cause a leak if the cell is not completely closed. Methyl bromide should be used which contains a warning substance, since it is odourless and so, without such a substance, escaping gas could not be detected. In such a case,

---

* The material to be disinfested must be placed in the cell 12–24 hours before the process if it comes from surroundings whose temperature is below 12°C. Below this temperature the respiratory activity of the insects is much reduced and does not increase unless the same insects have been at a temperature between 12° and 38°C for several hours. These are the optimum temperatures for the fumigations. Above 38°C and below 12°C the insects (which are heterothermal organisms) show, as we have said, a considerable reduction in respiratory activity and thus the absorption of the fumigant into their bodies diminishes considerably and the fumigation cannot succeed.

the workers, unaware of the peril, could remain for a long time in the vicinity of the cell and inhale a toxic or fatal quantity of the gas. The risk of poisoning would be aggravated by the fact that the first symptoms appear several hours after inhaling the gas, so that the victims would not be induced to leave the place of peril even by particular disorders or by a general sensation of ill-being. The tubes connecting the cylinder with the cell must be made of metal and not rubber, which is permeable to methyl bromide. The workers must always have at hand gas-masks which they can use either when, approaching the cell, they become aware of the warning substance (sign of a leak) or when opening the cell, because residual methyl bromide can remain for some time around the material being treated, from which it evaporates slowly. The mask filters have a limited life and must be changed frequently. The materials disinfested with methyl bromide must be kept for several days in well-ventilated unused places so that the air can circulate freely around them and any gas which is left can evaporate freely.

This information on fumigation has been based on the work given in references 13, 29 and 30.

W.H.O. regulations: For aerosol sprays and mixed insecticides the World Health Organization[23] has fixed the following general safety measures:

(a) All persons destined to manipulate pesticides must be informed of the risks they run and receive instructions which will allow them to work with safety.

(b) It is necessary to provide either medical supervision of the workers or the necessary means for the treatment of all accidents.

(c) Whatever the pesticide, whoever applies it must wear a protective impermeable hood which should be washed as frequently as possible.

(d) If the product is sprinkled, the workers must have facilities for washing themselves and their clothing.

(e) There must not be more than eight hours' work a day. This is particularly important when the same workers use pesticides for long periods of time.

(f) The workers must wear washable clothing which must be changed and washed as frequently as possible.

(g) The workers must neither smoke nor eat without previously washing their hands and must observe other simple precautions in the places where pesticides are handled.

(h) In consideration of the fact that the most dangerous phase is always the manipulation of the concentrated material, a group of studies calling attention to this and putting forward safety recommendations is indicated in section 9 of the sixth report of the Committee of Experts on Insecticides[35].

(i) The material of pulverization must conform to the general standards concerning the construction and maintenance of the material and particular specifications which have been laid down in the same report[35].

(j) All containers for pesticides must carry a label giving the contents and must indicate in a manner intelligible to the operator the nature of the product and the necessary precautions to be observed.

Knowledge of composition and properties

A knowledge of the chemical composition and the toxic properties of commercial mixtures of insecticides is extremely important with regard to the prevention of poisoning. It is essential that in the disinfestation of public buildings only those mixtures should be used whose chemical composition and toxicity are known. About this, the conclusions reached by the Committee of the World Health Organization[23] can be given: 'The Committee recommends that the labels (on commercially prepared insecticides) should provide the following information: (a) maker's name; (b) ordinary description recommended by the competent International Standards Organization; (c) type of preparation with the concentration of the component substances; (d) recommended uses and, if necessary, when it should not be used; (e) principal precautions to be observed; (f) clear indications of the risks, and a particular graphic symbol for the most toxic materials; (g) treatment recommended in cases of poisoning.'

It is evident that by using insecticides which carry these indications one considerably reduces the risk of poisoning and in cases of accidental poisoning one can apply the treatments described below.

The problem of toxic residues

On p. 50 we have listed the risks of poisoning resulting from pollution of material and surroundings disinfested with toxic gases or contact insecticides. Dangerous pollution caused by the liberation of fumigant from the material treated occurs when the latter is brought into working surroundings immediately after fumigation and can be avoided by applying the safety precautions indicated either in the publications referred to[13,22,29,30] or in the present work (cf. p. 51). The general principles to be adopted for avoiding atmospheric pollution through evaporation of mixed insecticides applied to wood or other substances inside public buildings can be summarized as follows:

The evaporation of the mixtures from the material treated (generally of wood) is characterized by two phases. In the first phase, which generally lasts for several weeks or months, the major part of the solvent evaporates, while during the second phase, which can last as much as several years, the other constituents of the formulation slowly evaporate. Therefore the surroundings in which the insecticides have been applied must not be used during the first weeks, but could be used in the second period of time; that is to say, when the evaporation of the residues remaining on the wood is at a minimum. Such residues are not so dangerous to those breathing them if the aerial concentration is very low and below the safety level. In order to carry out these principles it is necessary to know the composition of the mixture used and its rate of evaporation, which naturally varies with the temperature and humidity of the air.

Progress during the last few years (cf. p. 48) raises the hope that the use of protective materials on wood inside public buildings will become easier and safer, thanks to some new insecticides (silica aerogels[4,8,16,17]) and resin insecticides[24,25], which may apparently be applied without carrying out all the safety measures we have just mentioned.

Urgent measures to be taken after poisoning

During disinfestation processes it can happen that workers run a grave risk of poisoning through having accidentally swallowed a mixed insecticide or inhaled aerosol compounds, or had their skin or clothing contaminated by toxic materials dissolved in oily solvents. The latter compounds are absorbed through the skin extremely rapidly (in a few minutes). When this happens, it is necessary to help the unfortunate person immediately, without losing even a minute, since rapid and sensible aid can save a human life. It is essential, therefore, that all who deal with insecticides should know how to apply certain essential first-aid measures. The Public Health Service of the United States published[37] in 1955 a circular in which are clearly explained elementary first-aid principles, which we

shall now summarize, adding some information drawn from our own experiences:

(a) In all cases of poisoning or absorption of insecticides (through the skin, by inhalation or by swallowing) a doctor must be called immediately and shown *Table 4*, with the relevant explanations, and the container for the disinfestant, on which should be shown the chemical composition and toxicity of the disinfestant. Above we have advocated the use of only those commercial preparations which give this information.

(b) While waiting for the doctor, follow the following procedure:

(i) If the poison has been inhaled, move patient to open air and, if breathing has stopped, apply artificial respiration.

(ii) If the insecticide has fallen onto skin or clothing, change the latter as quickly as possible and carry out careful washing of the skin with water (if possible, hot water) and synthetic detergent (Kop type or similar). Washing should be carried out not by immersion but by showers so that the water and detergent run over the contaminated skin. Immediately after washing, shake talc over the surfaces so that it can adsorb any residues left after washing.

(iii) If drops of insecticide have entered the eye, wash immediately.

(iv) If the insecticide has been swallowed, cause the patient to vomit. One should try to empty the stomach completely, and therefore the action of vomiting should be repeatedly provoked until the patient only emits clear stomach fluid. When the stomach has been emptied, give white of egg mixed with water or milk or flour and water.

(v) Try to calm the patient.

(vi) If unconscious, give nothing to eat or drink.

Table 4

Treatment after insecticide poisoning

Poison	Insecticide		Medicine administered
	on the skin	swallowed	
Aldrin	1	3, 4	5a
Gammexane	1	3, 4	5, 5a, 6
Chlordane	1	3, 4	5, 5a
DDT	1	3, 4	5, 5a, 6
Demeton	1	2, 3	7, 8, 9
Dieldrin	1	3, 4	5a
Dilan	1	3, 4	5a
Dinitrophenol	1	3	8
Parathion	1	2, 3	7, 8, 9
Tetraethylpyro-phosphate	1	2, 3	7, 8, 9
Toxaphene	1	3, 4	5, 5a

1—Carry out washing as directed in paragraph (ii) above.
2—Induce vomiting.
3—Wash out the stomach.
4—Do not administer oily laxatives.
5—Administer pentobarbital.
5a—Administer phenobarbital.
6—Administer calcium gluconate intravenally.
7—Administer atropine (atropine sulphate), 1–2 mg subcutaneously every hour as far as a maximum daily dose of 10–20 mg. Do not administer morphine, theophylline or aminophylline.
8—Administer oxygen.
9—Carry out artificial respiration if breathing has stopped.

This table has been elaborated on the basis of that given by the United States Public Health Service[37].

Research at Istituto di Patologia del Libro and Centre of Studies for Termite Control

The Istituto and the Centre* started work on the health and toxicological problems connected with the use of insecticides many years ago when the scientific and practical importance of these problems, now recognized by all, passed unnoticed by many[38]. A great deal of experimental work† already published and widely known in Italy and abroad gives the results of our work, which have allowed anti-termite control in Italy to be placed on a scientific basis and to make rational and safe the insecticides which are employed against termites[13,39—44,50]. In our laboratory we have studied for the first time some biochemical alterations caused by specific insecticides[46] and have produced a new method of histological examination for locating ATP in the tissues of animals treated with toxic substances[47,48].

These researches were encouraged between 1953 and 1956 by Dr Grillo and Professor Bonaventura[38] and afterwards by Professor Muzzioli, present head of the Istituto, who has given new and vigorous purpose to our studies and equipped our laboratory with the most modern apparatus.

Dr Grillo, Professor Muzzioli and Professor Bonaventura created the conditions which allowed the development of research so real and so interesting as that concerning insecticides, which has not only practical significance but which also occupies a prominent place in the scientific world.

References

1 BROWN, A. W., *Insect Control by Chemicals*, Wiley and Sons, New York; Chapman and Hall, London, 1951.
2 CHADWICK, L. E., Progress in physiological studies of insecticide resistance, *Bull. World Hlth Org.*, 16 (1957) 1203–1218.
3 BARNES, J. M., Control of health hazards associated with the use of pesticides, in METCALF, R. L., *Advances in Pest Control Research*, Interscience Publishers, New York, London, 1957.
4 SCHOOF, H. F., Recent developments in pesticides, *Amer. J. publ. Hlth*, 50 (1960) 632–636.
5 SCHOOF, H. F., Resistance in arthropods of medical and veterinary importance, 1946–1958, *Misc. Pub. Ent. Soc. Amer.*, 1 (1959) 3.
6 MICKS, D. W., Insecticide resistance, *Bull. World Hlth Org.*, 22 (1960) 514–529.
7 MARTIN, H., Trends in insecticidal chemicals: a summary, in Symposium on metabolism of insecticides, *Canad. J. Biochem. Physiol.*, 37 (1959) 1089–1151.
8 EBELING, W. and WAGNER, R., Rapid desiccation of drywood termites with inert sorptive dusts and other substances, *J. econ. Ent.*, 52 (1959) 190–212.
9 PALMER, A. K., Biological warfare, *Pest Technol.*, 2 (1959) 4–6.
10 FISHER, R. and ROSSIER, L., Toxicology of the microbial insecticide Thuricide, *J. Agric. Food Chem.*, 7 (1959) 686–8.
11 HEIMPEL, A. M., Bacterial insecticides, *Bact. Rev.*, 24 (1960) 266–288.

12 HALL, I. N., Microbial control of insects, *Agric. Chemic.*, 14 (1959) 45–112.
13 GALLO, P., Conni sui fattori fisici e chimici che influenzano o condizionano la tossicità e l'azione insetticida dei fumiganti adoperabili nella disinfestazione di edifici pubblici, *Boll. Ist. Pat. Libro*, 17 (1958) 21–37.
14 GRAY, H. E., Vikane—a new fumigant for control of drywood termites, *Pest Contr.*, 28 (1960) 43–46.
15 KENAGA, E. E., Some biological, chemical and physical properties of sulphuryl fluoride as an insecticidal fumigant, *J. econ. Ent.*, 50 (1957) 1–6.
16 EBELING, W. and WAGNER, R., Control of drywood termites infestation or reinfestation with inert dusts nontoxic to humans and animals, *Calif. Agric.*, 13 (1959) 3–5.
17 TARSHIS, B., UCLA tests with desiccant for roach control, *Pest Contr. Mag.*, 27 (1959) 14, 16, 18, 20, 22, 24, 26, 28, 30, 32.
18 BAUMHOVER, A. H. et al., *J. econ. Ent.*, 48 (1955) 462–466.
19 CHIN PIAO LU, Effects of atomic energy on silkworm and mulberry tree, *J. Agric. Ass. China*, 15 (1956) 99–103.
20 EDSON, E. F., Applied toxicology of pesticides, *Pharm. J.*, 185 (1960) 361–367.
21 FISCHETTI, B., *Il parathion e gli esteri organofosforici*, E.S.I., Naples, 1958.
22 NEGHERBON, W. O., *Handbook of Toxicology*, Vol. III (Insecticides), Saunders, Philadelphia, London, 1959.
23 World Health Organization, *Toxicité des pesticides pour l'homme*, Study group report in the technical report series, No. 114, Geneva, 1956.
24 DYTE, C. E., Preliminary tests of an insecticidal lacquer containing malathion, *Pest Technol.*, 2 (1960) 98, 99.
25 PRICE, M. D., Insecticidal resins—a new concept in residual insect control, *Pest Contr.*, 28 (1960) 47–58.
26 FABRE, R. and TRUHAUT, R., *Toxicité des produits phytopharmaceutiques*, S.E.D.E.S., Paris, 1954.
27 CAMERON, G. and BURGESS, F., The toxicity of 2,2-bis(p-chlorophenyl-1,1,1-trichlorethane (DDT), *Brit. med. J.*, 1 (1945) 865–871.
28 *American Conference of Governmental Industrial Hygienists*, Chicago, April 1954 (given by FABRE, R. and TRUHAUT, R.[26]).
29 LEPIGRE, A. L., *Technique de la désinsectisation*, Lechevalier, Paris, 1947.
30 LEPIGRE, A. L., *La desinsectisation par fumigation avec vide préalable*, Document phytosanitaire No. 9 du Ministère de l'Agriculture, Alger, 1949.
31 BARNES, J. M., Toxic hazards of certain pesticides to man, *Bull. World Hlth Org.*, 8 (1953) 419–490.
32 HAYES, W. J., The toxicity of dieldrin to man, *Bull. World Hlth. Org.*, 20 (1959) 891–912.
33 VAN OETTINGEN, W. F., *The toxicity and potential danger of methyl bromide with special reference to its use in the chemical industry, in fire extinguishers and in fumigation*, United States Government Printing Office, Washington, 1946.
34 World Health Organization, Select bibliography on the toxicity of pesticides to man and animals, 1953–1955, *Bull. World Hlth Org.*, 16 (1957) 1219–41.
35 World Health Organization, Comité d'experts des insecticides (1956), Technical report series, No. 110.
36 World Health Organization, *Normes pour les pesticides*, Geneva, 1957.
37 *Entoma: A directory of pesticides, materials, equipment, services* (FISHER), Dept. of Entomology, University of Wisconsin, 1957.
38 BONAVENTURA, G., Ventennio, *Boll. Ist. Pat. Libro*, 18 (1959) 93–125.
39 ANGELUCCI, L. and GALLO, P., Contributo sperimentale alla tossicologia di una formulazione a base di cloronaftaleni, *Boll. Ist. Pat. Libro*, 13 (1954) 93–109.
40 BENETTI, E. and GALLO, P., Indagini chimiche e farmacologiche sull'impiego di una formulazione di cloronaftaleni e gammaesano (xylamon) in ambienti confinati, *Boll. Ist. Pat. Libro*, 14 (1955) 49–59.
41 GALLO, F., Gli agenti biologici nemici delle biblioteche e degli archivii, *Boll. Ist. Pat. Libro*, 16 (1957) 141–199.

---

* The work of Gallo[49] illustrates the principles which inspired the formation of the Interministerial Commission and the Centre, the scientific and practical purposes of the institutions and the work they developed in their first years.

† In the library of the Istituto the reader can find a complete collection of the many works (ca. 60), almost all experimental, carried out by the Interministerial Commission for Termite Control on insecticides and termites. Some of this research is of a toxicological nature (that given in the present work) and the rest of a biological and chemical nature. Amongst these we recommend that by Gallo[42] on the toxicity of residual films and that of Santucci[45], which describes the synthesis of a new organoboron compound whose possible insecticidal properties will be studied.

54

FUNGICIDES AND INSECTICIDES

⁴² GALLO, F., Ricerche sulla tossicità dei films residui. I saggi sulla relazione concentrazione tempo mortalità di quattro miscele insetticide, *Boll. Ist. Pat. Libro*, 18 (1959) 65–77.

⁴³ GALLO, P., Ricerche sperimentali sulla tossicità di un insetticida (Termiten Basileum) a base di parathion, *Boll. Ist. Pat. Libro*, 15 (1956) 175–190.

⁴⁴ GALLO, P., Ricerche sperimentali sulla tossicità di tre miscele insetticide (Piroxyl H.N.C. colloidale; Cobra Impratox; Icromit), *Boll. Ist. Pat. Libro*, 17 (1958) 112–132.

⁴⁵ SANTUCCI, L., Un nuovo composto boro-organico: l'acido 2-metossi-5-cloro-benzenboronico, *Boll. Ist. Pat. Libro*, 19 (1960) 82–83.

⁴⁶ GALLO, P., Il consumo di ossigeno del tessuto epatico di animali sottoposti ad applicazione cutanee di DDT, *Boll. Ist. Pat. Libro*, 19 (1960) 26–39.

⁴⁷ GALLO, P., Un nuovo metodo di indagine biochimica applicabile alle ricerche tossicologiche sugli insetticidi, *Boll. Ist. Pat. Libro*, 18 (1959) 47–61.

⁴⁸ GALLO, P., *Il significato biochimico dei quadri istologici del rigor mortis del miocardio, in condizioni normali e nell'intossicazione sperimentale da gammaesano*, Centro di Studi per la lotta anti-termitica, Rome, 1959.

⁴⁹ GALLO, A., La lotta antitermitica in Italia, *Boll. Ist. Pat. Libro*, 11 (1952) 3–34.

⁵⁰ SANTUCCI, L., Il contributo della chimica alla lotta antitermitica, *Boll. Ist. Pat. Libro*, 13 (1954) 15–77.

Fausta Gallo

BIOLOGICAL AGENTS WHICH DAMAGE PAPER MATERIALS IN LIBRARIES AND ARCHIVES

Introduction

The problem of the deterioration of books and archival material caused by biological agents assumes serious proportions in many countries. Frequently precious collections of books and documents suffer damage which cannot be repaired even with the help of the most modern restoration techniques. The grave damage suffered by valuable historical and artistic antiquities in several countries has forced many scholars to apply themselves to the problem. It is now possible to identify the entomological and microbial species responsible for alterations to paper and to verify that their vigorous development and rapid reproduction is frequently helped by erroneous methods of preservation.

These investigations, with the aid of the most recent research techniques, have been following for years the many problems concerning the conservation of books and documents.

The rapid progress of the last years has placed at the disposal of scientists and technicians a range of products among which some find a wide and easy application in the struggle against insects and paper micro-organisms.

Of necessity I shall be obliged to deal with the vast subject of this report in general terms only. Nevertheless, I hope that even such an exposition can attract the attention of research workers to some subjects of general interest which deserve deeper investigation.

Insects: morphological and functional characteristics

Back, in his interesting monograph on the fauna of libraries, writes: 'When one enters the most modern buildings of concrete and steel, such as some American libraries, one is so overwhelmed by a sense of beauty and solidity that it is difficult to believe in the oft-repeated phrase that insects have destroyed more books and papers than have fire and water. Insects are in the front ranks of the enemies of books.'

From the beginning of the eighteenth century, the problem of the damage done to books and documents by insects has been the subject of numerous studies (Blades, Quatrefages, Hagen) and since then a rich bibliography on the subject has accumulated, collected by Houlbert in his book *Les insectes ennemis des livres.*

The interesting work carried out later by Back, Weiss and Carruthers, Feytaud, Perotin, Lepesme and others, and by the Italians Bonaventura, Illuminati and Saccà of the Istituto di Patologia del Libro, has suggested the division of entomological fauna of libraries and archives into two groups: habitual visitors and occasional visitors.

Habitual visitors: About 70 species belong to this group, living on, and therefore destroying, paper, parchment, leather, etc.

Occasional visitors: These are the insects which live in the supports or wooden furnishings, in foodstuffs and in fabrics, and which occasionally can infest the books, producing atypical damage.

For brevity I shall limit myself to describing the morphological and functional characteristics of some of the habitual visitors belonging to the following orders: *Thysanura, Isoptera, Coleoptera, Blattodea, Corrodentia.*

Some representatives of the entomological fauna of paper materials are cosmopolitan; some, on the other hand, are found only in specific regions. Above all, *Coleoptera*, cockroaches, termites, *Thysanura* (without reference to a single species) are destroyers of books more or less widespread throughout the world.

Thysanura

Amongst the insects belonging to this order, one must record some belonging to the family *Lepismatidae* (*Lepisma saccharina, Ctenolepisma targionii*, etc.), known commonly as 'silverfish', 8–10 mm long, light-avoiding, silver or pearly-grey in colour. Frequently found in libraries and archives, they show a particular predilection for bleached wood-pulp paper (although not disdaining mechanical wood-pulp paper as well), for flour-glue, photographic gelatine and for some textile fibres. Generally they penetrate books through the back, which offers them flour-glue as food. The life-cycle is 2–3 years. Silverfish find ideal conditions for growth and reproduction in places where the temperature varies between 16°C and 24°C, and the humidity is greater than 55 per cent. On paper they produce superficial erosions of irregular shape, and when their presence assumes large proportions they cause considerable damage.

Isoptera

The *Isoptera* live in communities which are subdivided into castes of sexed adults, who are responsible for reproduction, and sterile soldiers and workers, who are responsible, among other things, for the defence of the colony, the feeding of the queens and the rearing of the young.

Termites belonging to various classes represent a marvellous example of social organization in which every individual or class of individuals has a well-defined function as if it were a complementary part of a single organism.

In our part of the world, termites are represented by the species *Reticulitermes lucifugus* and *Calotermes flavicollis.*

Reticulitermes lucifugus lives in complicated nests in the subsoil or in the depths of walls, from which it comes out through often imperceptible discontinuities (i.e. breaks in the wall) in endless columns, which proceed in search of food, constructing galleries covered with material produced by the mastication of wood, paper, etc., when they have no other way of hiding themselves. They devour rapidly and silently all that is composed of cellulose, digging out intricate communication trenches, and in some cases causing the almost total destruction of the material attacked, leaving intact an external skin which hides the devastation underneath. Their insidious activity can remain unnoticed for a long time and is often only identified when it has caused irreparable damage. Colonies which have infested beams or bookshelves in libraries soon invade books and documents, generally commencing their devastating work with the surfaces which are in contact with the shelves. These surfaces then assume a felty aspect and show generally characteristic small entry holes of funnel-shaped appearance, which extend to tortuous communication trenches of irregular course strewn with pellets and all kinds of faecal deposits. Sometimes all that remains intact of the books are the spines.

Calotermes flavicollis generally lives in the wood of dead trees or in the dead parts of still living trees. It seldom infests buildings.

Termites in all mediterranean countries, and particularly in Italy, where in the last eight years there has been a rapid spread of *Reticulitermes* in all regions, constitute a grave and continuing menace to the national heritage of libraries and archives. The struggle against them must be carried out by all rational means, both by preventing their attack with technical devices (anti-termite constructions) and by subsequent extermination (elimination of infested material, fighting by chemical means, etc.) when an infestation of even modest proportions is discovered.

In Italy, in order to check the rapid and worrying spread of these insects and to save precious historical and artistic relics, an interministerial Committee for Termite Control has been set up, composed of experienced research workers who are studying the scientific and technical aspects of the problem and putting the disinfestation processes on a national footing.

Coleoptera

Amongst the coleopteroids which damage the parts of books of vegetable origin, and, in particular, paper, a prominent position is occupied by numerous species belonging to the *Anobidae* and *Lyctidae* families.

The anobids deposit their eggs in small hollows in the wood of bookshelves and in the edges and especially the backs of books. The whitish, worm-like larva which comes out of the egg excavates galleries perfectly circular in section, having a diameter which varies between 2 and 5 mm (characteristic for each species) and a winding and irregular course. The larva, after having undergone a certain number of changes, constructs, with the destruction of the paper or wood, a small cocoon in which it changes first to a nymph and then into the adult insect. This breaks the thin wall separating it from the outside world (the back and sides of the book), it then escapes, leaving as traces of its exit those characteristic round holes which one very often sees in wood and books, makes a brief flight, lays its eggs and, after a few days, dies.

The life-cycle of anobids lasts 1–3 years, and in some cases even more than 4 years. In warm surroundings more than one generation a year may occur. These insects develop best at temperatures of 24–28°C but can resist temperatures as low as 8–9°C and as high as 40°C. Among the species of paper anobids are *Anobium striatum*, *Nicobium castaneum*, *Sidotrepa panicea* and *Gastrallus immarginatus*.

The *Lyctidae* deposit eggs in sheltered or concealed places from which, after several days, the young whitish worm-like larva emerges, very similar to that of the anobids, to excavate galleries of oval section in wood, paper, etc. After a series of changes, the larva first becomes a nymph and then an adult which emerges, makes a brief flight, deposits its eggs and dies. Its life-cycle is one year. Natural enemies of the lictids and anobids, also found frequently in library and archival material, are some species of Betilidi and Braconidi.

Blattodea

These insects deposit their eggs in small cracks in walls in dark, warm and damp places. The life-cycle lasts for a period of time varying with the different species (from a minimum of 5–6 months for *Blatta germanica* to a maximum of several years for *Blatta orientalis*).

The species most frequently encountered in our regions are *Blatta germanica*, *Blatta orientalis* and *Blatta americana*. In library and archival material they do not excavate galleries but produce superficial erosion of irregular shape. It is good practice when carrying out the annual cleaning to pay particular attention to the walls in order to reveal the presence of possible cracks in which these insects could nest.

Corrodentia

Belonging to this order are the Liposcelidi, small (2–3 mm length) insects which are commonly known as book-lice. The species of *Corrodentiae* which most frequently attack paper materials are *Liposcelis divinatorius*, *Psocus domesticus*, *Psocus venosus* and *Atropos pulsatorium*. They feed on flour-glue, paper, etc. The changes caused by these insects are minute corrosions limited mainly to the parts of the binding close to the spine where the adhesive is more abundant. Generally book-lice do not cause outstanding damage. They rarely occur in well-lit and ventilated surroundings or in books used daily.

Summary

The table below summarizes the scientific and common names, the diet and type of damage characteristic of the

Scientific name	Common name	Main diet	Type of damage
Ord. *Thysanura* fam. *Lepismatidae*	Silverfish	Paper, flour-glue, rayon	On paper: superficial corrosion of irregular outline
Ord. *Isoptera*	Termites	Wood, paper, leather, fabric	In books: funnel-shaped holes, extreme, irregular erosion which goes from the edge towards the inside. In some cases the book is completely destroyed. In wood: the galleries run parallel to the fibres of the wood
Ord. *Coleoptera* fam. *Anobidae*	Woodworm	Wood, paper	In books: galleries of circular section with winding path which branch out from the edge and the back towards the inside. In wood: winding and irregular galleries of circular section
Fam. *Lyctidae*	Woodworm	Wood, paper	In books: galleries of oval section In wood: galleries of oval section which always run parallel to the wood fibres
Ord. *Blattodea* fam. *Blattidae*	Black beetles	Parchment, leather, paper, fabric	Surface damage
Ord. *Corrodentia*	Book-lice	Flour-glue	Superficial damage of irregular outline

principal groups of insects described. The type of damage is a valuable diagnostic characteristic which is sometimes sufficient for the identification of the destructive agent.

Damage caused by rodents and by man

Among the numerous zoological guests in libraries and archives it is necessary to note a small mammal, the mouse, which devours with incredible speed papers, skins and parchment, etc., causing characteristic damage sometimes of considerable proportions. Other damage results from its urine, rich in uric acid, which is absorbed by the paper and leaves it stained.

Man is another of the fearful enemies of the book—he who should be its most jealous custodian. In fact, the reader frequently causes damage of various types, such as tears, mutilations, stains, etc., which besides disfiguring the paper sometimes provide the basis for a future, and sometimes most profound, alteration. Some micro-organisms, for example, find in traces of saliva, grease, etc., the ideal material for rapid and vigorous development. In addition, readers use pieces of paper or strips of material as bookmarks, or else leave flowers or leaves to dry between the pages. All these objects can be carriers of infection, since they may contain insect eggs or spores of micro-organisms whose development sometimes constitutes the nucleus of serious and penetrating infestation and infection.

Micro-organisms: characteristics of schizomyceti and paper fungi

The problem of microbial changes is particularly serious in countries with warm climates and in northern countries where the climate is cold but unusually damp.

One could list dozens of cases in which rich and precious collections kept in unfavourable surroundings have been almost destroyed through the deleterious effect of bacteria or fungi.

Since the mid-nineteenth century the serious damage caused in libraries by micro-organisms has attracted the attention of numerous scholars, but detailed and systematic research into the species which could directly affect the book are collected in the still fundamental work of Sée, *Les maladies du papier piqué* (1919). The subject was subsequently treated and extended by numerous workers, amongst whom one must record Sanborn, Sartory, Mayer and Baumli, Fahraeus, Kowalik, Niuksha and Fiyinpporra, Siu, Verona, Bonaventura, Camposano, Levi della Vida, Florenzano and Sibilia. Their systematic researches have allowed a fairly clear distinction to be made between the micro-organisms habitually found in bibliographical material and those only found there occasionally.

Habitual: Belonging to this group are a limited number of schizomyceti and about 100 species of fungi which have their homes in books and destroy more or less profoundly paper, parchment and leather.

Occasional: This group includes some micro-organisms which are also dangerous to man; these normally live on other materials (plants, fabrics, etc.) and only occasionally on books. The greater part of them find a medium for their development in traces of organic substances (saliva, mucus, grease, etc.) occasionally present in minimal amounts on paper, parchment or leather.

The spores of the fungi and the schizomyceti of the habitual type are sometimes already present in the raw materials (rags, wood, old paper, etc.) used for the manufacture of paper, on which they remain latent for months or even years; then when they find themselves in particularly favourable surroundings they develop, producing more or less serious damage.

However, the infection of library material is more frequently attributable either to microbial spores in the air or dust in libraries or to contact with objects which carry infection.

Paper schizomyceti

The number of schizomycetes habitually found in paper is very low and is mainly limited to some forms of *Eubacteri* belonging to the genus *Cellvibrio* and *Cellfalcicula*, and to *Myxobacteria* belonging to the genus *Cytophaga*, which show a marked cellulose-dissolving activity.

Interesting investigations accomplished by numerous scholars have revealed that these micro-organisms are frequently found in paper of different chemical composition and of different ages, on which they cause yellow or orange stains.

Moreover, microscopic and technological examination of paper damaged by these schizomycetes shows that the fibres suffer profound processes of degradation, but the action of cellulose-dissolving micro-organisms is frequently accompanied by that of others which develop at the expense of the glue components. Their action is shown for the most part by the formation of stains of varying colour and intensity, and the area in which the microbial attack occurs becomes highly absorbent and hygroscopic.

In addition, it seems advisable to point out the numerous bacterial species, some dangerous to man, which frequently develop on traces of organic materials (saliva, grease) occasionally present on paper. They generally cause colour changes.

Finally I wish to draw attention to the discovery on archival material, through the work of some Polish scholars, of thirteen species of *Actinomycetes*.

Fungi

The number of fungoid species designated 'paper-attacking' is about one hundred. According to Levi della Vida, the notably greater number of fungi than schizomycetes is explained by their more modest way of life and their greater resistance to unfavourable surroundings.

Habitual guests on bibliographical and archival material are some Ascomiceti (*Chaetomium, Myxotrichum*, etc.) and numerous Deuteromiceti (*Trichoderma, Aspergillus, Penicillium, Stachybotrys, Stemphilium*, etc.), which vegetate on paper in various forms.

Among these micro-organisms some show a marked cellulose-dissolving activity. Niuksha has determined the percentage of cellulose degraded in cultures by the following species of paper mycelia:

Species	Cellulose degraded (%)
Penicillium luteum	25·0
Penicillium tardum	7·3
Penicillium diversum	14·5
Penicillium funicolosum	56·3
Penicillium pinophilum	52·6
Penicillium rubrum	9·0
Paecilomyces varioti	3·75
Chaetomium sp.	12·5
Chaetomium indicum	44·5
Aspergillus versicolor	2·3
Aspergillus flavus	15·3
Trichoderma lignorum	37·5
Trichoderma koningi	48·0
Sporotrichum bombycimum	13·4
Sporotrichum polysporum	18·3
Haplographium fuligineum	28·0

Chromatic action is frequently linked with the cellulose degradation, which is shown by the appearance on the paper of stains of various colours and intensity which are caused either by (1) coloured fungoid mycelia which infiltrate between the fibres of the paper, or (2) by coloured pigment secreted by the mycelia.

In the second case the stain has a characteristic appearance; that is, it is formed of a central dark nucleus and a lighter peripheral zone whose colour intensity decreases from the inside towards the outside. The colour of the pigments secreted by the fungi is very varied—yellow, rose, greenish-yellow, black, etc.—and varies also in the presence of some metals and according to the age of the culture and the pH of the substrate. The optimum pH for their production is, according to Wessel, between 4·8 and 5·6.

Such pigments have various chemical compositions, but are mainly composed of carotenoids and anthroquinones. Recent work carried out on some paper fungi has shown that the appearance of colour in the hypha has the following successive phases: first it is concentrated in granules, then it diffuses in the plasma and finally it passes across the cellular membrane into the surroundings. The chemical relations existing between the fibres of the paper and the fungoid mycelia have not yet been completely established.

The different colorations assumed by the paper are not, however, connected only with the invading species, but depend also on various other factors, among which the most common are:

(a) Type of paper and the chemical processes it has under-gone during manufacture.

(b) The conditions under which the infection occurred (atmospheric humidity, moisture in the paper, temperature, etc.).

(c) The length of action of the fungoid species (long or short period of latent infection).

(d) The co-existence of several fungoid species.

(e) The possible presence of traces of iron, copper or other metals in the paper.

(f) The acidity of the paper.

It is, therefore, impossible on the basis of coloration to establish the nature of the pathogenic agent. Whenever any alteration to paper material appears and it is required to identify the micro-organism responsible, an analysis must be performed.

A particularly interesting type of chromatic alteration is made up of small brown, rusty stains and commonly known as 'foxing'. In such stains, Iiams and Beckwith observed the presence of traces of inorganic and organic iron in greater percentage than in the areas of the pages not attacked and attributed these alterations to the activity of microbial reagents. According to these authors, the organic acids secreted by the fungi in the course of their metabolic processes react with the traces of iron present in the papers, forming salts which decompose with extreme facility to form oxides and hydroxides of iron, which have this characteristic coloration.

Recent research by Ambler and Finney has shown that micro-organisms alone are indirectly responsible for foxing. They develop at the expense of the glue materials, forming hygroscopic areas on the paper in which the water-soluble products of the decomposition of the cellulose accumulate. These assume a brown-red colour in damp surroundings. Opinions differ, however, on the nature of foxing, and the subject still presents many obscure points which merit a more profound examination.

In some cases fungi can exercise a mechanical action on paper, since their hypha may filtrate between fibres of the paper without actually entering them, or else the fruit bodies of the fungi are covered with bristles which infiltrate between one leaf and another, in both cases welding the various pages together.

Finally, it is necessary to give some indication of those fungi which develop on paper materials and which can cause disease symptoms in man, indicated by the medical term mycosis. This interesting problem deserves to be studied in more detail in order to discover the importance and the limits of the risk of contagion resulting from the handling of books on which fungoid forms pathogenic to man might be present.

Development of microbial forms

Numerous scholars have come to the conclusion that there exists a strict correlation between types of paper and their susceptibility to microbial attack. The previous chemical treatment exercises a particular influence, and Levi della Vida, Nobecourt and Barnoud actually observed that while papers of machine-produced paste are particularly susceptible to fungoid attack, those of chemical paste and those of rags (especially if made from new rags) are very resistant.

Investigations carried out by many workers have shown that a paper with an α-cellulose content of 95 per cent, a copper number less than 1, and a pH between 5·5 and 6·0 is only with difficulty damaged by micro-organisms. Sized papers are much more resistant than those not sized, probably because they are less hygroscopic. All the same, while some types of glue, such as colophony and resin, inhibit microbial attack, gelatine and starch glues can provide the optimum substrate for the growth of numerous species of bacteria and fungi.

Calendering is very useful because it makes paper materials less hygroscopic, smoother, and therefore cleaner.

Niuksha has observed that certain species of fungi, such as *Aspergillus terreus*, develop on paper which has been bleached with chlorine. It was noticed, in fact, that this fungus was capable of assimilating free chlorine and synthesizing its products.

Paper resistant to biological attack has been developed by including, during manufacture, either fungicides, insecticides or antimetabolites, or by applying to it a film of resistant material.

Measures against alteration by biological agents

Air-conditioning

Research into biological alteration of paper material in archives and libraries has permitted the identification of the entomological and microbial species responsible for the changes, and it has been ascertained that their vigorous development and rapid reproduction result from incorrect methods of pre-servation.

The places where books are collected are often below ground, resulting in the majority of cases in damp surroundings, unhealthy, poorly lit and ill-ventilated—all factors which favour the development and reproduction of insects and micro-organisms.

Weiss and Carruthers have written: 'Although few libraries are in a position to make "a climate" best suited for the pre-servation of books and although they have no control over the manufacture of books, yet light, temperature and moisture may in many instances be controlled within certain limits so that conditions unfavorable for insects and other book-deteriorating agents may be produced.'

A book, because of the heterogeneity of materials from which it is made, not only offers to micro-organisms a larger number of nutritive materials, but also a moister environment, for the fungus does not absorb water from the air but rather from the substrate. In effect, with a relative humidity of 80 per cent, for example, paper absorbs 9–14 per cent of water and leather 18–28 per cent. Block has shown that the water content of the material, in order that the development of fungi occur, must be at least 10 per cent. Naturally, the more hygroscopic the material, the lower the relative humidity needs to be in order to permit microbial growth. For example, leather, which is very hygroscopic, is attacked by fungi at humidities even lower than 70 per cent, while cotton does not suffer alterations at 92 per cent relative humidity.

Observations made in various countries of the world have established that a relative humidity varying between 40 and 65 per cent and a temperature restricted to between 16° and 18°C represent ideal conditions for the preservation of bibliographical and archival material. In fact, at a relative humidity of 65 per cent, the humidity of the various parts of the book varies between 6 and 9·5 per cent. Particular attention must also be paid to the ventilation because it is known that air impedes the deposition of dust, which is one of the major carriers of micro-organisms, and by causing friction, disturbs the development of pathogenic agents.

Moreover, appropriate lighting contributes considerably to obstructing the rise of focal centres of infection.

The control of temperature, humidity, illumination and ventilation limits the growth and reproduction not only of microbial species, but also of entomological species.

The attainment of the conditions described above can be brought about by air-conditioning plants which permit really constant temperatures and humidity in different climates. If for reasons of a technical or economic nature air-conditioning is not possible, dehumidifiers could be used, such as calcium chloride, silica gel, etc.

Temperature and humidity control obtained by various devices can, in many cases, prevent serious infection or infestation of even very susceptible material.

*Periodical dusting**

A periodical cleaning of books and documents, according to the following fundamental criteria, can also contribute considerably to the preservation of books and documents.

1. Remove all books from the shelves and take them outside onto terraces or into courtyards, or, lacking areas in the open air, onto window sills, using for transport (preferably) metallic receptacles which do not let insects, larvae, etc., fall off in the process. In no case should dusting be done on the spot.

2. Bang and brush the books one by one, noting all insect marks, moulds, or signs of alterations, and isolate those which appear in need of care or contain insects or show erosion. Provide immediate preventive work, disinfection and disinfestation, and eventually restoration.

3. Dust and clean the ceiling, walls, furnishings of every kind, keeping away the books, and, when insects are found, arrange for disinfestation.

4. Wash floors thoroughly.

5. Do not replace books on the shelves without making sure that there are no cracks or holes in the walls in which mice or insects could nest, or marks which show the infiltration of water or other dangerous substances. Also, ascertain that wooden bookcases do not contain nests of insects such as anobids, lictids, etc., which could damage the books. If these are found, adopt the necessary remedies.

---

* Standard for the dusting of libraries, distributed as a circular by the Istituto di Patologia del Libro, December 10, 1951.

Criteria for rational control

The preventive measures (control of temperature and humidity, cleanliness) described above are, however, rarely adopted and thus we frequently find ourselves confronted with a precious collection of books or documents severely damaged which must be promptly disinfected or disinfested.

I cannot deal in detail here with the insecticides and fungicides which can be used in these cases because it is a subject so vast that it requires separate treatment and cannot be summarized in a few pages. I shall limit myself to explaining the fundamental criteria to carry out rationally such operations and note briefly those insecticides and fungicides most commonly used. In order to obtain the best results it is necessary that the processes of disinfection and disinfestation should be carried out with great care, so that the biological agents are completely destroyed, and so as not to damage in the least the books and documents. Such operations require the cooperation of specialist biologists, chemists, technologists and toxicologists.

The biologist has the task of identifying the species responsible for the damage and the choice of methods of attack. The chemist and technologist must see that the chosen method does not cause damage. Finally, the toxicologist must estimate the toxicity to man of the compounds employed and advise on those devices necessary for safeguarding those who handle the materials and those who will occupy the places which are disinfested or disinfected.

In various countries attempts have been made in the destruction of insects and paper micro-organisms to use physical methods such as ultra-violet light, ultrasonics and high-frequency currents. However, their use is still in the experimental stage. Generally one uses chemical methods.

The characteristics of the compounds which can be used for disinfestation or disinfection of libraries and archives can be summarized as follows:

(a) Strong and rapid insecticidal and fungicidal action,
(b) Low toxicity to man,
(c) Harmlessness to the material.

In connection with point (a), it is necessary to emphasize the possibility of using substances which are both insecticidal and fungicidal.

An on-the-spot investigation by experts will enable one to establish whether the damage is slight and confined to a few books or whether the infestation or infection is of such proportions as to require urgent measures.

When one has to deal with a slight invasion of cockroaches, silverfish or lice use can be made of powder insecticides (DDT, etc.) applied repeatedly, especially in spring and summer, on the bookshelves behind the books and anywhere insects can make their way.

As a preventive rather than curative measure it is advisable to place in the library storehouse containers of p-dichloro-benzene, which has a mild insecticidal and fungicidal action.

A new and effective method is now being offered by the silica aerogels. Studies carried out by Tarshis, Gay and Wheterly, Wagner and Ebeling, and by Pence have shown the great efficiency of these compounds against cockroaches and termites. Their mode of action is not chemical but mechanical, since by coming into contact with the body of the insect they remove its fatty layer, quickly causing a rapid loss of water which is followed in a few hours by death. Silica aerogels are active against all insects with soft skins.

Contact insecticides are almost completely ineffective against woodworms, which leave their galleries only when they have reached the adult stage, and in some cases after having laid their eggs, by which time they are inoffensive. More effective against such insects and against micro-organisms are gaseous insecticides and fungicides. Their use, however, requires specialized technicians.

If the number of books damaged is limited, it is best to remove them from the bookshelves and proceed with the disinfection or disinfestation in suitable cells with convenient gaseous substances. Moreover, before replacing the treated material, one would be well advised to inspect thoroughly wooden bookshelving to find out whether it shows signs of damage by xylophagous insects, which could present potential damage for paper material. When such damage is found one must treat the bookshelving with liquid insecticides, which must then be left to evaporate completely before replacing the books.

Nevertheless, a partial disinfestation does not ensure the total destruction of the infecting species, since other books in the library can also present incipient alteration, not yet detectable by direct examination, which will show itself after a certain time. Therefore, when possible, it is advisable to carry out disinfestation or disinfection of all the volumes in the area in which the attack was found. Or, if all the books and the furniture show considerable alterations caused by insects or micro-organisms, it may be better to carry out fumigation in the place itself, if it would be technically complicated to move thousands of volumes.

While the disinfestation and disinfection of libraries and archives in large cities can be carried out easily, for libraries in small centres or isolated places where specialists and cells are not available, the solution of the problem is not easy because of lack of technical organization and cost. According to Feytaud, in such cases one can make use of mobile autoclaves, when the above-mentioned operations can be carried out everywhere with notable ease and rapidity.

Conclusion

I hope that this short report will give an overall picture of the principal biological enemies of paper materials.

However, some problems regarding the biological changes of books and documents and the methods of their control still await solution. Moreover, the many products synthesized by industry (adhesives, plastic materials, synthetic fibres, etc.) which find an application in the field of restoration continually confront biologists with new questions, which can be answered only by accurate experimental trials. From this the necessity arises for closer collaboration between laboratory technicians and scientists, a collaboration which in Italy is fully realized at the Istituto di Patologia del Libro, in which for many years, first under the direction of its founder, then under the guidance of Dr Grillo, and at present of Professor Muzzioli, a group of biologists, technologists and chemists study the multiple aspects of the problems of restoration and changes in bibliographical and archival material.

Bibliography

AMBLER, H. R. and FINNEY, C. F., Brown stain formed on wet cellulose, *Nature*, 179 (1957) 1141.

ARCAMONE, G., Relazione sull'attività della Commissione Inter-Ministeriale per la Lotta Antitermitica, *Boll. Ist. Pat. Libro*, 15 (1956) 63–69.

ARNOLD, J., Para and naphthalene as closet fumigants, *Soap N.Y.*, 29 (8) (1953).

BACK, E. A., *Bookworms*, Bureau of Entomology and Plant Science, U.S. Department of Agriculture, Washington, 1940.

BAYLEY, C. H., Microbiological process discussion: Some auxiliary effects of textile fungicides, *Appl. Micr.*, 4, No. 2 (1956).

BECKWITH, T. D., SWANSON, W. H. and IIAMS, T., Deterioration of paper: the cause and effect of foxing, *Publ. Univ. Calif. biol. Sci.*, 1 (13) (1940) 299–356.

BENVEDUTI, P., Diagnosi precoce delle infezioni microbiche della carta, *Boll. Ist. Pat. Libro*, 1 (1939) 153–54.

BLADES, W., *Les livres et leur ennemis*, Claudin, Paris, 1883.

BLOCK, S. S., Chemicals for fungus control, *Chem. Week Rep.*, 26 (1952).

BLOCK, S. S., Opportunity for manufacturers in mildew prevention, *Florida Engng Ind. Exp. Sta.*, VIII, No. 7 (1953).

BLOCK, S. S., Humidity requirements for mold growth, *Engng Progr. Univ. Florida*, VII, No. 10 (1953).

BONAVENTURA, G., Di una caratteristica alterazione della pasta di cellulosa di canapa, *Boll. Ist. Pat. Libro*, 1 (1939) 120–22.

BONAVENTURA, G., Sulla fisiologia di alcuni miceti carticoli, *Boll. Ist. Pat. Libro*, 3 (1941) 13–30.

BONAVENTURA, G. and CAMPOSANO, A., Secondo contributo alla conoscenza della microflora carticola, *Boll. Ist. Pat. Libro*, 5 (1943) 97–105.

BONAVENTURA, G. and PAGANINI, M. L., Primo contributo alla conoscenza della microflora del materiale bibliografico. Microorganismi isolati da materiali cartacei Yemeniti, *Boll. Ist. Pat. Libro*, 2 (1940) 1–16.

BRACEY, P. and BARLOW, F., Urea-formaldehyde resin as a vehicle for semi-permanent insecticidal and fungicidal coatings on bookbindings and bookcases, *J. Document.*, 9, No. 3 (1953) 157–68.

BRACKEN, A., *The Chemistry of Micro-organisms*, Pitman and Sons, London, 1955.

CAMPOSANO, A., Su alcuni caratteri morfologici e fisiologici di *Pullularia pullulans* (De Bary et Loew) Bekhout, *Boll. Ist. Pat. Libro*, 7 (1948) 46–75.

CAMPOSANO, A., Sul contenuto microbico dell'aria in ambienti destinati alla conservazione e al restauro del materiale bibliografico, *Boll. Ist. Pat. Libro*, 9 (1950) 35–47.

CZERWINSKA, E. and KOWALIK, R., Penicillia destroying archival papers, *Acta Microb. Polon.*, 5, No. 1–2 (1956) 299–302.

CZERWINSKA, E., SADURSKA, I. and KOZLOWSKA, D., Actinomycetes damaging old manuscripts and documents, *Acta Microb. Polon.*, 2 (1953) 160–63.

DEL VECCHIO, V. and CAMPOSANO, A., Primi risultati di ricerche sul potere antibiotico di alcuni miceti carticoli, *Boll. Ist. Pat. Libro*, 6 (1947) 15–23.

EBELING, W. and PENCE, R. J., UCLA entomologists evaluate research data in drywood subterranean termite control, *Pest Control*, 24 (1956).

EBELING, W. and WAGNER, R., Rapid desiccation of drywood termites with inert sorptive dusts and other substances, *J. econ. Ent.*, 52, No. 2 (1959) 190–207.

FAHRAEUS, G., Studies in the cellulose decomposition by cytophaga, *Symb. bot. upsaliens.*, 9 (1947) 2.

FEYTAUD, J., Les insectes ravageurs d'archives: comment les combattre? *Arch., Bibl., Collect., Document.*, 6 (1952).

FLORENZANO, G., Studi sul genere *Chaetomium* I, *Boll. Ist. Pat. Libro*, 7 (1948) 76–96.

FLORENZANO, G., Studi sul genere *Chaetomium* II, *Boll. Ist. Pat. Libro*, 8 (1949) 60–74.

GALLO, A., *Patologia e terapia del libro*, Ed. Raggio, Rome, 1951.

GALLO, A., La lotta antitermitica in Italia, *Boll. Ist. Pat. Libro*, 11 (1952) 3–34.

GALLO, F., Fatti e misfatti del pesciolino d'argento, *Boll. Ist. Pat. Libro*, 13 (1954) 78–92.

GALLO, F., Gli agenti biologici nemici delle biblioteche e degli archivi, *Boll. Ist. Pat. Libro*, 16 (1957) 141–199.

GALLO, P., Considerazioni sui rapporti tra i funghi ospiti della carta e le micosi umane, *Boll. Ist. Pat. Libro*, 12 (1953) 77–89.

GALLO, P., Elementi di igiene della biblioteca (ad uso dei Bibliotecari): Parte I, *Boll. Ist. Pat. Libro*, 16 (1957) 75–85.

GASCOIGNE, J. A. and GASCOIGNE, M. M., *Biological Degradation of Cellulose*, Butterworths, London, 1960.

HAGEN, H. A., Insect pests in libraries, *Libr. J.*, 4 (1879) 251–274.

HOULBERT, C. V., *Les insectes ennemis des livres*, Picard, Paris, 1903.

IIAMS, T. M. and BECKWITH, T. D., Notes on the causes and prevention of foxing in books, *Libr. Quart.*, 5, No. 4 (1935) 407–18.

ILLUMINATI, G., Introduzione allo studio della fauna carticola, *Boll. Ist. Pat. Libro*, 4 (1942) 25–33.

ILLUMINATI, G., Metodo di determinazione degli insetti carticoli dalle erosioni predette, *Boll. Ist. Pat. Libro*, 4 (1942) 77–79.

Istituto di Patologia del Libro, Circolare ai Sigg. Direttori delle Biblioteche Pubbliche Governative e ai Sigg. Soprintendenti Bibliografici. Oggetto: spolveratura, disinfezione e disinfestazione delle biblioteche, *Boll. Ist. Pat. Libro*, 3 (1941) 97–106.

KOWALIK, R., *Microorganisms that destroy the archival papers*, Prace Placowek Naukowo Badawczy Ministerstwa Przemyslu Chimiczenego Zeszyt 2/52, Warsaw.

KOWALIK, R., *Microorganisms destroying paper, leather and wax seals pathogenic for man*, Muzeum Mickiewicza, Warsaw, 1960, p. 175.

KOWALIK, R., and CZERWINSKA, E., The preservation of organic coatings in tropical conditions, *Acta Microb. Polon.*, 9 (1960) 59–60.

KOWALIK, R. and SADURSKA, I., Microorganisms destroying paper, leather and wax seals in the air of archives, *Acta Microb. Polon.*, 5, No. 1–2 (1956) 277–84.

KRAEMER KOELLER, G., *Compendio de la Conservación de Maderas*, Imp. Cervantina, Santander, 1958.

LANGWELL, W. H., *The Conservation of Books and Documents*, Pitman Publishers, London, 1957.

LEPESME, P., *La protection chimique des bibliothèques et des musées contre les parasites et les moisissures*, Cours-Conférences, Centre Perfectionnement Technique, No. 1024, 1943.

LEPIGRE, A. L., *Technique de la désinsectisation*, P. Lechevalier, Paris, 1947.

LEPIGRE, A. L., *Insectes du logis et du magasin*, Alger, Insectarium Jardin d'Essai, 1951.

LEVI DELLA VIDA, M., I microorganismi nemici del libro, *Accad. Bibl. Italia*, 10, No. 4 (1936) 234–50.

MALLIS, A., Preliminary experiments on the silverfish *Ctenolepisma urbani* Slabaugh (*Ctenolepisma longicaudata*), *J. econ. Ent.*, 34 (1941) 787.

McKENNY, H. A. W., Insect infestation of churches, *J. Soc. Archit.*, August, 1954.

MINOGUE, A. E., The repair and preservation of records, *Bull. nat. Arch.*, 5 (1943) 93–148.

NABUCO, J., *Em defesa do livro*, Antunes e Cia., Livreiros, Rio de Janeiro, 1959.

Naczelna Dyrekcja Archiwow Panstowowych, *Konserwacja Materialow Archiwalnych*, Warsaw, 1953.

NIUKSHA, I. P., Microflora of books and paper, *Bot. Zh.*, 41, 6 (1956) 797–809.

NIUKSHA, I. P., Microscopic study of paper stained by the fungus *Gymnoascus setosus*, *Microbiology, Moscow*, 29, 1 (1960) 133–36.

NIUKSHA, I. P. and FIYINPPORA, N. A., Krasnye Pigmentn Gribov na Bumage, Gosudarstvennaya Ordeno Trudogovo-Krasmogo Znameni, Publichnaia Biblioteka um M. E. Salmykova-Shtebruna-Opyt Raboty XIII, Leningrad, 1956, pp. 54–92.

NOBECOURT, P. and BARNOUD, F., Preservation des pates et des papiers contre les moisissures, *Ass. Tech. Ind. Papetière Bull.*, (1955) 35.

PENCE, R. J., Control of fabric-feeding insects, *Calif. Agric.*, (1960).

PETROVA-ZAVGORODNYAYA, A. P. and ERASTOV, D. P., Determination of mould contamination of paper by luminescence, *Bull. Acad. Sci. U.R.S.S.*, Ser. Biol., 3 (1959) 403–411.

PEROTIN, Y., Le problème des termites et autres agents destructeurs aux archives de la Réunion, *Arch. Dépt. Réunion*, (1953).

PLENDERLEITH, H. J., *The Conservation of Antiquities and Works of Art*, Oxford University Press, London, 1956.

PLENDERLEITH, H. J. and WERNER, A., Technical notes on the conservation of documents, *J. Soc. Archit.*, 1 (1958) 7.

QUATREFAGES, Souvenirs d'un naturaliste, *Rev. Deux Mondes*, Paris, 1853.

REDDISH, G. F., *Antiseptics, Disinfectants, Fungicides and Sterilization*, H. Kimpton, London, 1957.

SACCÀ, G., Reperti entomologici, *Boll. Ist. Pat. Libro*, 1 (1939) 123–25.

SACCÀ, G., Contributi alla conoscenza dei Coleotteri della fauna carticola. Osservazioni sulla biologia dello *Scleroderma domesticum*, *Boll. Ist. Pat. Libro*, 2 (1940) 157–66.

SACCÀ, G., Contributo alla conoscenza dei Coleotteri della fauna carticola, *Boll. Ist. Pat. Libro*, 2 (1940) 7–12.

SAMBORN, J. R., Development and control of microorganisms in pulp and paper systems, *J. Bact.*, 25 (1933).

SANTUCCI, L., Il contributo della chimica alla lotta antitermitica, *Boll. Ist. Pat. Libro*, 13 (1954) 15–74.

SARTORY, A. and SARTORY, R., Reproduction experimentale des maladies cryptogamiques du papier, *C.R. Acad. Sci., Paris*, 199 (1934).

SCHMIEDERKNECHT, M., Feuchtigkeit als Standardfaktor für mikroskopische Pilze, *Z. Pilzk.*, 25 (1959) 69–77.

SÉE, P., *Les maladies du papier piqué*, O. Doin et Fils, Paris, 1919.

SIBILIA, C., Le malattie crittogamiche dei libri, *Accad. Bibl. Italia*, 9 (1935) 274–80.

SIU, G. H. R., *Microbial Decomposition of Cellulose*, Reinhold, New York, 1951.

TARSHIS, I. B., UCLA tests with desiccant dusts for roach control, *Pest Control*, 27 (1959) 6.

VERONA, O., Sopra le cause microbiche di danneggiamento dei libri, *Accad. Bibl. Italia*, 11 (1937).

VERONA, O., Studio sulle cause microbiche che danneggiano la carta e i libri, Ente Naz. Cell. e Carte, Roma, 1939.

VERONA, O., Normale presenza di germi cellulosolitici sulle carta di antica e recente fabbricazione, *Boll. Ist. Pat. Libro*, 1 (1939) 15–24.

VERONA, O., Sopra alcuni ceppi di *Stachybotrys* rinvenuti in materiale cartaceo, *Boll. Ist. Pat. Libro*, 1 (1939) 202–10.

VERONA, O., Sulla durata della vitalità di alcune specie di funghi, *Nuovo G. bot. ital.*, 53 (1946) 323.

VERONA, O. and PAGANINI, M. L., Presenza di *Bacterium pyocianeum* Fl. in materiale proveniente dallo Yemen, *Boll. Ist. Pat. Libro*, 1 (1939) 223–27.

VEZZANI, R., Difesa degli edifici e del legno dalle termiti, *Boll. Ist. Pat. Libro*, 11 (1952) 23–74.

WEISS, H. B. and CARRUTHERS, R. H., *Insect Enemies of Books*, The Public Library, New York, 1945.

WESSEL, C. J. and BEJUKI, W. M., Industrial fungicides, *Industr. Engng Chem.*, 51 (1959) 52A–63A.

ZANGHERI, S., Su alcuni anobidi dannosi ai libri, *Boll. Ist. Pat. Libro*, 10 (1951) 29–33.

Antonio Tonolo and Clelia Giacobini

MICROBIOLOGICAL CHANGES ON FRESCOES

Introduction

The restoration of frescoes does not always turn out to be as permanent as expected, especially if they remain in their original atmospheric conditions. Apart from physico-chemical changes brought about by an unsuitable atmosphere, serious damage may also be caused by biological organisms[1-5]. The microbiological laboratory of the Istituto Centrale del Restauro therefore some years ago initiated a study of fresco alterations of microbiological origin, with the purpose of establishing the causes, studying the nature and gravity of these alterations, and classifying the various types of micro-organism by means of microbiological techniques for the isolation of pure cultures.

Changes caused by micro-organisms

Biological changes on frescoes can be sub-divided into two groups:

(1) Changes caused by the activity of autotrophic micro-organisms (algae and lichens);
(2) Changes caused by the activity of heterotrophic micro-organisms (bacteria, Streptomyces, fungi).

Autotrophic micro-organisms

Algae encountered by us on paintings exposed to light and in conditions of high humidity (above 95 per cent) can be systematically attributed to the large group of *Chlorophyceae*, which under a microscope appear as single unicellular micro-organisms or as filaments joined in groups of varying sizes. The macroscopic changes on the painting appear as stains of different tones, green or blackish, restricted in size and extended over all the picture surface (see *Plate IIa*). The immediate consequence of the presence of these micro-organisms on the fresco is an alteration in the appearance of the picture. In more serious cases prolonged action will weaken the paint layer.

Lichens are found exclusively on frescoes exposed to the open air, on which, according to their particular morphology, they can cause the most varied alterations. If they are of the crustose type, they mask the picture surface, and besides disfiguring it render it unrecognizable. Sometimes the fruiting organs, represented by point-like apothecia, seriously attack the surface and, having pierced it, nest in the ground to form a minute and diffuse sieve. Since such organisms are usually microscopic this type of alteration, which can be erroneously ascribed to physical causes, is seen to be biological only by direct microscopic examination.

Heterotrophic micro-organisms

Bacteria: Attack by the growth and direct action of bacteria is frequent and always very serious, generally manifested by changes in the picture surface, which in a very short time loses its original colour.

Because of the ubiquity of bacteria, the alteration resulting from a particular type can only be ascertained by an on-the-spot identification of the colonies of bacteria present, as was noted in the following examples: a fresco by Signorelli (Chiesa del Duomo, Orvieto) (*Figure 1*); a wall fresco in Ostia Antica (Casa di Giove e Ganimede: room 3); frescoes by Poussin (Chiesa di S. Martino ai Monti, Rome); a fresco by Domenichino (Chiesa di S. Luigi dei Francesi). In all these cases, on the already greatly altered picture surface, are found enormous bacterial colonies of the coccus form. Such bacteria, isolated in pure cultures, belong to a single species, *Sarcina lutea*, and are indications of a specific degradation of a microbiological nature. The macroscopic effect of the attack can be described either as a powdering of the paint and relative separation of the

Figure 1. Powdering of colours on a Signorelli fresco (Orvieto) caused by bacterial alteration.

picture surface or as the appearance of a calcereous and granular deposit superimposed on the whole painting. On the Signorelli fresco and the wall at Ostia Antica a rosy colour is characteristic of this alteration.

Streptomyces: Changes in frescoes through the development of Streptomyces were encountered for the first time on the wall-paintings in the vault of the Chiesa di S. Clemente, Rome, where the attack is the result of metabolic processes of a few characteristic species of Streptomyces. The progressive development of the Streptomyces on the painted walls occurred with the growth of mycelia of a whitish appearance, which have now covered the whole surface with a compact and copious efflorescence-like coating which alters the appearance considerably (see *Plate IId*). The microscopic changes above all occur in the paint, which, under the action of the metabolic products, flakes off, powders and becomes indistinct. In samples seen under the microscope the Streptomyces, formed of slender filaments, appear as numerous tangled heaps, mixed with fragments of pigments and ground.

Fungi: Changes resulting from fungi, also widespread and serious, can be separated into (a) changes to the picture surface and (b) changes in the picture structure.

Changes in the paint are due to the growth of fungoid forms, vegetative or reproductive. In these cases the fungoid development, besides reflecting on the decorative effects, damage the

Figure 2. Macroscopical alterations in the form of white dots on a detail showing St Paul's head (Church of S. Giovanni Battista, Parma).

vivacity of the original colours, made faint or changed in some way by the appearance of blemishes, black spots and a covering of mycelia which obscure the paint. The structural changes to the painting, caused by the growth in depth of the mycelia, affect the whole paint layer.

Raising and curling of paint films, crater-like tears in the paint and a decreased cohesion of the paint layers, which

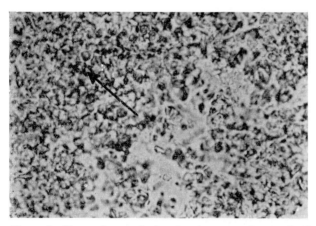

Figure 3a. Photomicrograph showing the stromatic growth of fungi.

Figure 3b. Section of painting of *Figure 2* under the microscope. Fungus attack has caused some swelling of the pictorial structure.

engender in the whole painting an exceptional friability that cannot be brought about only by alterations of a physico-chemical nature[3], can be the extreme consequence of fungoid attack in the depth of the structure. Microscopically the fungus is seen as vegetative and reproductive organs typical of these organisms and at the same time peculiar to the various fungus species.

Microbiological techniques for the isolation in pure culture have provided ways of observing that the changes always result from the metabolic action of some selected fungus species. Those most commonly isolated from nutritive sites are *Penicillium*, *Aspergillus* and *Cephalosporium* and some species belonging to the family of *Dematiaceae*. In some very interesting cases the fungus can organize itself into fruiting bodies represented by perithecia, pycnidia and stroma. A classic example of this type of alteration has been noted on a fresco by Correggio (Chiesa di S. Giovanni Battista, Parma, fresco on the vault of the cupola, detail of the heads of St Peter and St Paul), altered by a 'diffuse efflorescence'[6] in the form of black spots projecting out from the pictorial structure (*Figure 2*). The microphotograph of the section of a fragment of the picture shows how the course of the biological phenomena on the structure has caused small swellings in the paint film which will eventually lead to a circular tear in the paint, as can be seen in other adjacent places where this cleavage has occurred (*Figure 3*).

Finally, uniform fungoid mycelia can also grow and develop between the paint layers and the ground, as was seen in the examination of a section of a paint fragment taken from frescoes in the castle at Karlstejn (Bohemia, Czechoslovakia) for the study of the paint layers and the medium.

Conclusion

The microbiology of frescoes is of particular interest to all restorers, above all from the point of preservation and the control of the microflora of mural paintings. Such problems present enormous difficulties especially in the case of heterotrophic microflora, and we are of the opinion, therefore, that a work of art must be the object of preventive measures rather than curative intervention of uncertain solution when the microbiological alterations have already caused damage of extreme gravity.

Micro-organisms growing on a painted wall can be combated with physical and chemical methods of control, but at the present state of research the use of chemical substances is not advised, because they are not durable, nor very efficient, and not, on the whole, innocuous to the paint structure.

The various fungicides which find wide applications in other fields, even in restoration, are not of pre-eminent importance in the conservation of frescoes, because their effect is frequently temporary, uncertain and of doubtful truly curative value. More to be relied upon are physical methods of control which interfere exclusively with the atmospheric surroundings in which the microbial development occurs, thus assuring a greater effectiveness. No organic material used during restoration is immune from microbial attack and it is noted that the micro-organisms develop on the picture only if in the surroundings there is a sufficiently high relative humidity (above 75 per cent)[7] and a temperature which can vary from −5°C to 40°C. The preservation of frescoes against microbial attack must, therefore, be concerned mainly with the conditioning of the surroundings in which the work of art is to be preserved.

If the attainment of these measures is difficult in practice, then it should be sufficient to generate partial conditioning around the fresco with a toxic gas (e.g. ethylene oxide), and by successively refilling the case with inert gas one eliminates completely the growth of bacteria, streptomyces and fungi, which are aerobic, while assuring the perfect preservation of the fresco from microbial attack.

Glossary of technical terms

apothecium. An open, cup-shaped fructification or a club-shaped derivative.

autotrophic. Able to build up food materials from inorganic material.

coccus. A minute spherical bacterium.

crustose. Forming a more or less interrupted crust.

heterotrophic. Unable to make food from simple beginnings and therefore dependent upon dead or living organisms of another species, and ultimately on the green plant.

perithecium. A globose or flask-shaped structure with a sterile wall enclosing asci and paraphyses, the characteristic fruit body of the *Pyrenomycetes*.

pycnidium. A roundish fructification formed by many species of fungus.

stroma. A dense mass of interwoven hyphae, fleshy to horny in texture, cushion-like, columnar, club-shaped or branched, in which many fungi develop their fructifications.

References

[1] SECCO SUARDO, G., Freschi corrosi della crittogama: Il restauratore dei dipinti, *Manuale Hoepli*, 1927, p. 236–237.

[2] GETTENS, R., PEASE, M. and STOUT, G. L., The problem of mold growth in paintings, *Tech. Stud. fine Arts*, 9, No. 3 (1941) 127–143.

[3] AUGUSTI, S., Azione dei microorganismi e dei parassiti sulle pareti affrescate, *Boll. Soc. Nat. Napoli*, 55 (1944–46) 68–73.

[4] OHTSUKI TORAO, On the destructive damage of the temple Yakushi-ji caused by a mould, *Sci. Pap. Jap. Antiques Art Crafts*, No. 1 (1951) 18–21.

[5] EMOTO YOSHIKADRU, On the prevention of fungus injuries at the Toshogy Shrine, Nikko, *Sci. Pap. Jap. Antiques Art Crafts*, No. 16 (1959) 1–10.

[6] BRANDI, C., unpublished communication, 1960.

[7] TONOLO, A. and GIACOBINI, C., Importanza dell'umidità relativa per lo sviluppo di microorganismi nei dipinti su tela, *Boll. Ist. Cent. Restauro*, No. 36 (1958) 191–196.

F. Flieder

ÉTUDE DE LA RÉSISTANCE BIOLOGIQUE DES PROCÉDÉS DE RENFORCEMENT DES DOCUMENTS GRAPHIQUES

Qu'il s'agisse de documents précieux datant de plusieurs siècles et endommagés par l'humidité ou les insectes, de documents actuels dont le papier est prématurément affaibli par de multiples manipulations, ou enfin de papier journal dont la fragilité est bien connue, le problème de la restauration des papiers se pose fréquemment dans les bibliothèques et archives.

A l'heure actuelle les méthodes de renforcement des documents sont nombreuses. Les unes, que l'on peut appeler traditionnelles, utilisent comme moyen de renforcement soit un papier type Japon extrêmement résistant, soit de la résille de soie, et comme adhésif une colle à la dextrine[1]. Les autres méthodes plus récentes, dont la plus connue est désignée sous le nom de «Lamination»[2], emploient également comme renforcement le papier type Japon, ou la résille de soie, mais comme adhésif une matière plastique transparente, le plus souvent de l'acétate de cellulose. Le principe de cette méthode consiste à placer le document, après l'avoir neutralisé et désinfecté[3], entre deux feuilles de papier Japon (ou deux morceaux de résille de soie) et deux feuilles d'acétate de cellulose, et de faire adhérer le tout en liquéfiant l'acétate de cellulose, soit à chaud (150–175°C) au moyen d'une presse chauffante, soit à froid avec une solution d'acétone[4].

Pour se faire une opinion sur la valeur de ces différentes méthodes il convient de les étudier au point de vue physique, chimique et biologique. Ce rapport n'étudie que le point de vue biologique. Rappelons simplement qu'au point de vue physique les renforcements doivent présenter une résistance suffisante aux phénomènes mécaniques (abrasion, tractions, éraflures), et de plus être flexibles, légers, sans couleurs, transparents, permanents et en dernier lieu réversibles. Au point de vue chimique, le plus important est de conserver une neutralité relative (qui se mesure par le pH) tant pour le papier que pour les matériaux de renforcement et les adhésifs.

Les agents biologiques de détérioration des documents sont d'une part les insectes, d'autre part les champignons. Les attaques d'insectes, pour fréquentes qu'elles puissent être, gardent cependant un caractère accidentel. Au contraire nombreuses sont les bibliothèques qui, placées dans des conditions climatiques défavorables, ne peuvent procurer aux documents une ambiance convenable. Dans le cas des locaux humides le développement des moisissures est pratiquement inévitable.

C'est pour ces raisons qu'il nous a paru nécessaire d'étudier en premier lieu la valeur des méthodes de restauration au point de vue de la résistance aux microorganismes.

Résistance aux microorganismes

Pour réaliser cette étude nous avons appliqué à un certain nombre de méthodes de renforcement les tests classiques de résistance des matériaux aux microorganismes: nous nous proposons de faire ici un bref compte-rendu des expériences réalisées ainsi que des résultats obtenus. Les essais ont été effectués d'une part sur les matières premières—colle à la dextrine, résille de soie, papier Japon, acétate de cellulose—d'autre part sur les documents renforcés suivant les différentes méthodes indiquées plus haut. Nous avons soumis ces échantillons à différents essais: une spécification des Télécommunications de l'Air (CCTU 96.04), deux normes de l'Afnor(NFX 41.503 et NFX 41.504).

La spécification des Télécommunications de l'Air est un essai très sévère valable pour n'importe quel matériel. Les échantillons à essayer sont placés sur le mycélium d'un champignon en plein développement afin d'observer si la croissance de cette espèce de champignon est ou non arrêtée par la présence de l'échantillon. On réalise l'expérience en ensemençant le champignon dans les boites dites de Roux, sur un milieu nutritif composé de gélose et de maltéa Moser à 2 pour cent. Lorsque le mycélium a recouvert toute la surface du milieu, les échantillons à examiner y sont placés et les boites sont entreposées pendant un mois dans une étuve sèche maintenue à 25°C. L'expérience doit être réalisée avec 10 champignons différents[*]. Le coefficient de résistance du matériel à essayer est fonction de la croissance des champignons sur ce matériel. Dans le cas où l'échantillon est légèrement recouvert par des filaments mycéliens un examen microscopique permet d'évaluer l'importance de l'attaque.

Les normes de l'Afnor qui ont trait l'une à la protection des papiers, l'autre à celle des plastiques contre les microorganismes, sont moins sévères. Procédant d'un même principe ces deux normes diffèrent par le choix des champignons à utiliser[†]. Dans les deux cas on dispose les échantillons à analyser dans des boites de Roux sur un milieu non nutritif, et on les ensemence par une suspension de spores de onze champignons différents; au bout de quinze jours on observe l'état de fructification de ces champignons. L'essai est cette fois réalisé en étuve humide (95 pour cent d'humidité relative) maintenue à 25°C. Ces derniers essais, tout en étant moins sévères, se rapprochent plus de la réalité. Au cours de l'épreuve Afnor le champignon a beaucoup plus de difficulté à se développer que dans la spécification des Télécommunications de l'Air, car, au lieu de puiser le carbone nécessaire à sa croissance dans le milieu même, il le prélèvera sur l'échantillon; le même phénomène se produit

---

[*] Liste des champignons utilisés dans la norme CCTU 96.04: *Thielaviopsis paradoxa, Sepedonium chartarum, Aspergillus tamarii, Sterigmatocystis nigra, Lentinus tigrinus, Coriolus versicolor, Neurospora sitophila, Acrostalagmus koningi, Penicillium camerunense, Gyrophana lacrymans, Aspergillus nidulans.*

[†] Liste des champignons utilisés dans la norme Afnor NFX 41. 503: *Chaetomium globosum, Myrothecium verrucaria, Stachybotrys atra, Memnoniella echinata, Aspergillus flavus, Penicillium luteum, Acrostalagmus koningi, Paecilomyces varioti, Aspergillus amstelodami, Sterigmatocystis nigra.*

Liste des champignons utilisés dans la norme Afnor NFX 41. 504: La liste des champignons est identique à l'autre norme, mais le *Neurospora sitophila* est ajouté.

65

dans les bibliothèques lorsque les spores en suspension dans l'atmosphère se déposent sur le document et fructifient grâce aux aliments qu'ils trouvent dans le papier.

Les premiers essais ont été effectués suivant la spécification des Télécommunications de l'Air sur différents échantillons: papier de soie, résille de soie, acétate de cellulose, Mylar*, papier laminé avec de l'acétate de cellulose et de la résille de soie, papier collé avec de la colle à la dextrine. Seuls, l'acétate de cellulose et le Mylar ont parfaitement résisté à l'attaque des onze champignons tandis que les autres échantillons étaient complètement envahis. Le microscope révèle la décomposition totale du papier de soie et du papier collé avec la colle à la dextrine. La résille de soie n'apparait que partiellement décomposée.

Des échantillons identiques ont été soumis aux deux normes de l'Afnor qui donnent des résultats à peu près concordants avec ce qui précède:

(a) Le morceau de papier Japon, le morceau de papier collé avec une colle à la dextrine ainsi que le papier laminé avec du papier Japon et de l'acétate de cellulose furent tous les trois envahis par les champignons qui les ont complètement désagrégés (*Figure 1*);

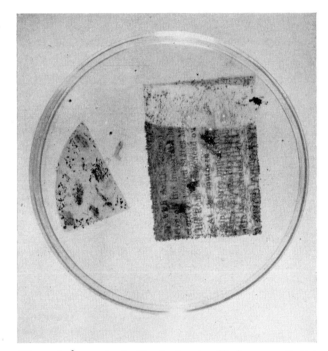

Figure 1. À gauche le témoin (papier filtre) recouvert par quelques champignons ensemencés tels que le *Stachybotrys atra* (Corda) et le *Chaetomium globosum*. À droite le document (renforcé par du papier de soie collé avec une colle à l'amidon sans fongicide) est complètement recouvert par le *C. globosum*.

(b) Par contre la résille de soie a très bien résisté et le papier laminé avec de la résille de soie et de l'acétate de cellulose n'a été que partiellement envahi (*Figure 2*);

(c) En ce qui concerne le Mylar et l'acétate de cellulose employé seul les essais furent tous excellents.

_____

* Le Mylar est une résine de polyester se présentant en feuille transparente extrêmement fine. Cette résine est utilisée à Delft (Pays-Bas) à la «Technische Hogeschool» pour la restauration des textiles.

Les résultats apparaissent donc mauvais; seuls le Mylar, l'acétate de cellulose, le papier laminé avec de la résille de soie et l'acétate de cellulose paraissent présenter une résistance aux microorganismes sans toutefois posséder des propriétés fongicides.

En ce qui concerne l'acétate de cellulose, nous avons remarqué qu'isolément il résistait dans tous les cas alors qu'il ne résistait

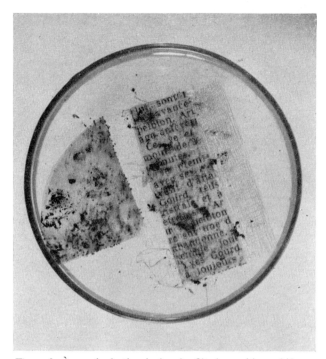

Figure 2. À gauche le témoin (papier filtre) envahi aux 3/4 par le *Chaetomium globosum*. À droite le document (renforcé avec de la résine de soie collé avec une colle à l'amidon sans fongicide) est légèrement attaqué par l'*Aspergillus tamarii*.

plus une fois laminé à 175°C, avec le document et le renforcement. On pourrait supposer que cette forte température, en liquéfiant l'acétate de cellulose, lui a fait perdre ses propriétés fongicides; nous avons réalisé des expériences d'une part en chauffant l'acétate à des températures inférieures à 175°C, d'autre part en le faisant adhérer à froid par dissolution, et dans les deux cas les résultats sont aussi mauvais.

Amélioration de la résistance fongique

Nous voyons donc que les méthodes actuelles de renforcement des documents sont toutes aussi peu efficaces contre les attaques des microorganismes. Afin d'apporter une amélioration à ces méthodes, des travaux dont voici quelques détails, sont en cours.

Colles destinées aux procédés traditionnels

Si l'on désire utiliser les méthodes classiques de renforcement il parait indispensable d'employer des matériaux peu putrescibles et en particulier une colle pouvant résister à l'attaque des moisissures. A l'heure actuelle la colle utilisée est à base de dextrine, produit extrêmement vulnérable; quelques gouttes de formol, comme on le sait très volatil, ne suffisent pas à la désinfecter, et il est illusoire d'en attendre des effets fongicides persistants.

Nous avons mis au point, au laboratoire, des colles*, les unes à base de dextrine, les autres à base d'alcool polyvinylique (que nous estimons bien préférable aux premières, car elles sont souples, incolorés et très adhésives), dans lesquelles nous avons incorporé de puissants fongicides et insecticides non volatils: un mélange d'acétate de mercure à 0,1 pour cent, de para-chlorometacrésol à 0,1 pour cent et d'hexachlorocyclohexane à

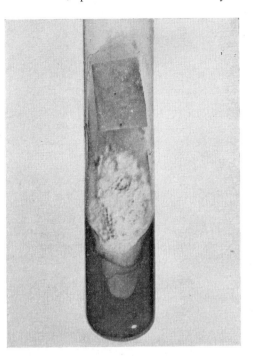

Figure 3. Morceau de papier filtre recouvert par une colle poly-vinylique additionnée de fongicide disposé sur un milieu nutritif recouvert par le mycélium du *Penicillium camerunense* (Heim) en plein développement. L'échantillon n'est pas attaqué; il est même entouré d'une zone d'inhibition.

0,1 pour cent. Toutes ces colles ont été neutralisées afin d'éviter une corrosion du papier. Les essais de renforcement effectués avec ces colles, soumis aux essais décrits plus haut, ont fait preuve d'une parfaite résistance aux microorganismes (*Figure 3*).

Imprégnation fongicide avant lamination

Dans le cas où l'on préfère utiliser des méthodes plus modernes telles que la lamination, il est également indispensable d'apporter quelques améliorations. Indépendamment du choix de la matière plastique, qui doit être résistante aux microorganismes et le demeurer après traitement, il convient de traiter le document lui-même, non seulement pour le désinfecter mais pour lui conférer une résistance persistante aux microorganismes.

Ce traitement a été réalisé d'une façon expérimentale en immergeant les documents, désacidifiés par la méthode Barrow[5], dans une solution fongicide de sels d'ammonium quaternaire, le bromure de lauryl-diméthyl-carbétoxyméthyl d'ammonium en solution dans l'eau. Nous avons soumis, toujours aux même essais de résistance fongique, les échantillons imprégnés de ce produit à la concentration de 0,5, 2 et 5 pour cent. La dose de

---

* Une de ces colles a fait l'objet d'un brevet pris par le CNRS sous no. 747-632 à Parisen septembre 1957.

0,5 pour cent s'est révélée inefficace, celle de 2 pour cent manifeste un pouvoir inhibiteur certain; quant à la dose de 5 pour cent elle arrête pratiquement l'attaque. Cette imprégnation semble donc constituer un moyen certain de préservation qui pourrait être employé avec une concentration variant de 2 à 5 pour cent suivant les conditions atmosphériques du lieu de conservation: la concentration de 2 pour cent suffirait pour les pays tempérés, alors que la concentration de 5 pour cent serait souhaitable seulement en milieu tropical (*Figures 4* et *5*).

En ce qui concerne les conséquences de cette imprégnation sur les propriétés physico-chimiques du papier, nous avons effectué une série d'essais sur un papier imprégné avant lamination. Ces essais ont été effectués avant et après vieillissement artificiel (48 heures en étuve sèche à 105°C), ainsi que sur du papier traité après vieillissement. Nous avons comparé les résultats avec ceux obtenus à partir du même papier, dans les mêmes conditions, mais sans imprégnation.

Ces essais tous normalisés par l'Association française de Normalisation furent les suivants*: *essais optiques*—degré de blancheur et d'opacité; *essais physiques*—résistance à la traction, à la déchirure, à l'éclatement et au pliage; *essais chimiques*—degré d'acidité, d'hydrolyse et de polymérisation.

Figure 4. Echantillons laminés à l'acétate de cellulose sur le mycélium de l'*Acrostalagmus koningi* (Duché et Heim) en pleine évolution. *En haut:* à droite, témoin non traité au Caequartyl BE; à gauche, échantillon traité par une solution à 5 pour cent de Caequartyl BE. *En bas:* à droite, échantillon traité par une solution à 2 pour cent de Caequartyl BE; à gauche, échantillon traité par une solution à 0,5 pour cent de Caequartyl BE.

---

* *Mesure du degré de blancheur des pâtes et du papier*, NFQ 03-008.
 Mesure de l'opacité de contraste, NFQ 03-006.
 Détermination de la résistance à la rupture par traction et de l'allongement à la traction, NFQ 03-004.
 Détermination de l'indice de déchirement, NFQ 03-011.
 Détermination de la resistance à l'éclatement, PNQ 03-014.
 Détermination de la résistance au pliage, NFQ 03-001.
 Détermination de l'indice de cuivre, NFT 12-004.
 Détermination du degré de polymérisation moyen viscosimétrique, NFT 12-005.
 Détermination du pH du papier, NFQ 03-005.

Figure 5. Echantillons laminés à l'acétate de cellulose sur le mycelium du *Myrothecium verrucaria* en pleine évolution. En haut: à droite, témoin non traité au Caequartyl BE; à gauche, échantillon traité par une solution de 0,5 pour cent de Caequartyl BE. En bas: à droite, échantillon traité par une solution à 2 pour cent de Caequartyl BE; à gauche, échantillon traité par une solution à 5 pour cent de Caequartyl BE.

Les essais physiques sont moins importants que les essais chimiques. En effet si le papier a perdu un peu de sa force physique, il la retrouvera une fois laminé. Par contre si les tests chimiques montrent un début d'hydrolyse, la lamination ne pourra sans doute pas l'arrêter et le papier risquera en vieillissant de poursuivre sa dégradation. Le papier utilisé à cet effet est un vélin d'Arches, composé en plus grande partie de pur chiffon. Le traitement par les sels d'ammonium quaternaire ayant le pouvoir de désencoller le papier, afin d'avoir des résultats plus comparatifs, nous avons désencollé également le papier témoin à l'eau. Malheureusement le simple désencollage à l'eau est infiniment inférieur au désencollage réalisé avec un sel d'ammonium quaternaire qui est un produit mouillant. C'est ce qui doit expliquer en partie la chute des constantes physiques du papier traité (voir le *Tableau 1*).

L'indice de cuivre par lequel on peut doser le degré d'hydrolyse* de la cellulose ne subit pas d'augmentation pour les papiers traités. Quant au degré de polymérisation† il ne semble pas avoir augmenté pour le papier traité et pour le papier vieilli et traité, alors que pour le papier traité et vieilli il s'est considérablement élevé. Les degrés de blancheur et d'opacité ne se sont pas considérablement modifiés.

On peut donc conclure que l'imprégnation par un sel d'ammonium quaternaire confère au papier une bonne résistance fongique, mais diminue légèrement sa résistance physico-chimique; cette diminution est plus sensible pour la concentration de 5 pour cent que pour celle de 2 pour cent. Toutefois cette expérience étant réalisée sur un seul type de papier, il nous faudra refaire l'expérience sur d'autres papiers de composition très diverses avant de tirer des conclusions définitives.

---

* Plus l'indice de cuivre est fort plus l'hydrolyse de la cellulose est élevé.

† Plus la viscosité est basse plus la dépolymérisation est élevée.

Tableau 1

Résistance physico-chimique d'un papier imprégné de solution de sels d'ammonium quaternaire

	Papier témoin	Papier imprégné		Papier témoin vieilli 48 h à 105°C	Papier imprégné et vieilli 48 h à 105°C		Papier témoin vieilli 48 h à 105°C et imprégné	
		2%	5%		2%	5%	2%	5%
Résistance au pliage (exprimée en nombre de doubles plis):								
sens machine sous 1 kg	136,1	54,8	29,5	40,3	23,4	20,6	22,6	14,6
sens travers sous 615 g	251,6	81,4	36,4	67,8	45,8	27,2	36,2	25,7
Résistance à la traction (en grammes):								
sens machine	4.286	3.261	3.143	3.761	3.356	3.114	3.340	2.999
sens travers	2.819	2.190	1.976	2.428	2.095	2.118	2.166	1.976
Résistance à la déchirure (en grammes):								
sens machine	118,5	116	114	99		81,5	86,5	90
sens travers	102,5	103	88	76	71,5	67		76
Indice d'éclatement	24,2	17,9	16,3	20	16,4	15,9	18,6	14,5
Degré de blancheur en %	81	79	80,4	70,7	69	65,9	71,8	71,9
Degré d'opacité en %	93,7	94,4	94,6	96,5	96,3	95,2	96,1	96,6
pH	5,3	5,3	5,4	5,6	5,12	5,15	5,2	5,3
Indice de cuivre	0,43	0,40	0,37	1	0,87	0,92	0,76	0,87
DPv	947	920	920	710	440	500	680	680

Bibliographie

[1] TOLLENAAR, D., L'acétate de cellulose et la lamination des documents, *Archivum*, 2 (1952) 51.

[2] BARROW, W. J., *Manuscripts and Documents. Their Deterioration and Restoration*, University of Virginia Press, Charlottesville, Va., 1955.

[3] DURYE, P., La restauration des documents aux Archives Nationales, *Cahiers franç.*, No. 3 (1956) 32–33.

[4] KATHPALIA, P., Hand lamination with cellulose acetate, *Amer. Archiv.*, 21, 4 (1958) 271–275.

[5] WILSON, W. K. and FORSHEE, B. W., *Preservation of documents by lamination*, National Bureau of Standards Monograph 5, October 30, 1959, pp. 14, 15.

F. Flieder

LUTTE CONTRE LES MOISISSURES DES MATÉRIAUX CONSTITUTIFS DES DOCUMENTS GRAPHIQUES

Les nombreuses taches colorées que l'on trouve sur les vieux papiers proviennent la plupart du temps des pigments secrétés par les moisissures. Cette flore est très importante et a fait l'objet de nombreux travaux.

En 1919, Pierre See[1] fit une étude systématique sur cette catégorie de champignons. Il en isola lui-même une vingtaine d'espèces différentes sur des papiers de composition diversess. Depuis, de nombreux auteurs reprirent la question en augmentant constamment la liste de ces champignons[2,3].

Les chercheurs russes[4] ont isolé 66 espèces, dont six nouvelles pour la science. Tout récemment, Mlle Gallo dans son important mémoire signale 200 espèces[5]. La classification de ces champignons peut se faire de la manière suivante:

1. Les *Ascomycètes*, dont les plus fréquents sont les *Chaetomium*.

2. Les formes imparfaites (*Fungi imperfecti*) plus spécialement réprésentés par des *Penicillium*, *Aspergillus* (champignons du papier et du cuir) et des *Fusarium*.

3. Les *Basidiomycètes*, très rarement rencontrés sur les matériaux constitutifs des documents graphiques à l'exception du *Gyrophana lacrymans*, plus communément appelé mérule, champignon spécifique du bois[6,7], que l'on a isolé souvent sur papier et cuir (*Figure 1*). Il est utile à ce sujet d'ouvrir ici une grande parenthèse: la mérule est un champignon spécialement résistant et très nuisible pour les matériaux sur lesquels elle se développe; elle peut se présenter sous des aspects très différents, fonction des conditions d'aération, de lumière et de localisation. Ces principaux aspects sont les suivants:

coussinets ouatés,
fins filaments noirâtres (forme pauvre), ou toile,
palmettes divergentes,
cordonnets blancs, ou rhizomorphes, longs et assez épais,
plaques orangées qui sont des réceptacles fertiles.

Le développement de tous ces champignons dépend d'une part des conditions climatiques, d'autre part de la nature du milieu où ils se trouvent. L'humidité, la chaleur et le manque d'aération sont des éléments favorables à la germination des spores et au développement des moisissures; par ailleurs, pour que le mycélium de ces champignons prolifère, et que son action destructive commence, il doit puiser dans son milieu des composés organiques indispensables à sa croissance; les constituants des documents graphiques—papier, parchemin, cuir, colle—possèdent tous ces éléments carbonés.

Afin que les spores des champignons, toujours présentes dans l'atmosphère, ne puissent fructifier, les magasins d'archives doivent être clairs, aérés, avec une température comprise entre 18° et 20°C et une hygrométrie au voisinage de 55 à 60 pour cent. Par ailleurs, du fait que les spores se trouvent toujours agglomérées à la poussière, on aura intérêt à nettoyer les dépôts (avec un aspirateur et surtout pas à l'aide d'un plumeau) le plus souvent possible.

Malheureusement, ces conditions étant difficiles à respecter, de nombreux dommages se produisent. C'est pour cette raison que la lutte contre les microorganismes doit être le souci primordial de toute personne s'occupant de la protection des biens culturels.

Figure 1. Reliure attaquée par le *Gyrophana lacrymans* ou plus communément appelé mérule. On aperçoit en haut et à gauche une énorme palmette blanche jaunâtre de ce champignon en pleine évolution.

Cette lutte se présente sous deux aspects différents—la lutte curative et la lutte préventive:

(a) La lutte curative est destinée, soit aux documents portant des filaments mycéliens qui se développent à leur détriment et les transforment parfois même en poussière, soit aux magasins dont l'atmosphère est supposée polluée.

(b) La lutte préventive est destinée aux documents où les spores risquent de fructifier.

C'est l'ensemble de ces traitements utilisés à l'heure actuelle en France que nous allons passer en revue.

Les méthodes curatives de désinfection

Les documents

Lorsque les ramifications du mycélium sont extrêmement serrées et que celui-ci se présente sous forme d'un épais duvet, on effectue des prélèvements afin d'observer sa vitalité et de l'identifier. Ces prélèvements sont déposés à l'aide d'une anse à ensemencer dans un tube à essais contenant un milieu de culture. Les tubes sont placés un mois au maximum dans une étuve bactériologique afin de faire germer les spores et d'identifier le ou les champignons ayant fructifiés. Avant tout traitement, on doit avoir soin d'enlever ce mycélium en brossant vigoureusement le document. Cette opération, qui a pour but de faciliter la pénétration de produit fongicide, doit obligatoirement s'effectuer en plein air, de manière à éviter tout risque de contamination.

Deux méthodes de désinfection nous ont donné satisfaction:

1. L'une s'effectue en étuve—elle ne nécessite pas un appareillage coûteux, mais n'est utilisable que pour un nombre limité de documents;

2. L'autre méthode, qui demande un vide poussé de 10 à 60 mm de mercure, nécessite un autoclave d'un type particulier. Cette méthode a l'avantage d'être très rapide et de pouvoir désinfecter un nombre considérable de documents.

La désinfection en étuve: Ce procédé est utilisé à la Bibliothèque Nationale depuis près de six ans. Nous avons désinfecté de la sorte un nombre considérable de livres, de parchemins et même de nombreux pastels appartenant au château de Versailles. Le produit utilisé est le formaldéhyde sous forme de vapeurs. L'opération s'effectue dans une étuve dont les dimensions sont suffisamment importantes pour y introduire un chariot à trois étages de dimensions $1,20 \times 0,40 \times 1,10$ m. Les documents sont disposés sur le chariot, debouts entr'ouverts et sans aucune compression de manière à ce que les vapeurs de produit pénètrent entre les feuillets. L'étuve étant hermétiquement fermée et maintenue à la température de 30°C, on vaporise alors à l'intérieur du formaldéhyde a raison de 250 g/m^3. Parallèlement, une même quantité d'eau est vaporisée, afin d'humidifier l'atmosphère et d'éviter toute craquelure du cuir ou du parchemin. Les documents sont maintenus dans l'étuve pendant 24 à 48 heures suivant l'importance des dégâts. Les prélèvements de contrôle sont effectués quelques jours après la fin du traitement, afin de s'assurer de l'efficacité de celui-ci.

La désinfection en autoclave sous vide: Cette méthode est utilisée depuis des années pour combattre les insectes. Les gaz utilisés sont en général le bromure de méthyle et quelquefois l'oxyde d'éthylène.

C'est tout dernièrement[8] que nous avons essayé de mettre au point une méthode de lutte contre les champignons à l'aide d'oxyde d'éthylène. Nous nous sommes rendu compte qu'une dose de 50 pour cent de gaz mélangé à l'air et agissant pendant 24 heures avait un pouvoir fongique certain. Des fonds des Archives Nationales ont été traités de la sorte en 1960 avec d'excellents résultats. On a également traité avec succès des livres où la mérule avait causé de très gros dommages. Actuellement, nous poursuivons cette étude afin de trouver la dose active minimum et les temps d'exposition les plus courts.

Après tous traitements, des prélèvements de contrôle sont effectués.

Désinfection des dépôts

Si les conditions climatiques sont mauvaises ou si le magasin a contenu des documents très moisis, son atmosphère peut être un foyer important de contamination. Il est donc indispensable de contrôler son degré de pollution avant le stockage des documents. Ce contrôle s'effectue aisément de la manière suivante: sur plusieurs points du dépôt, on ouvre pendant quelques minutes (10 à 15) des boîtes de Pétri contenant un milieu de culture solidifié. Les spores en suspension se déposent sur le milieu de culture. Il suffit alors de mettre ces boîtes en incubation une semaine dans une étuve à 25°C pour que les spores, en germant, donnent naissance à des colonies mycéliennes. On détermine de cette manière la nature de la pollution et son importance. Cette opération doit être réalisée portes et fenêtres fermées, afin d'éviter tout courant d'air et tout risque de contamination extérieure. Si la pollution est importante, on procèdera à une désinfection du local. Cette désinfection se réalisera par deux procédés:

1. La pulvérisation de produits fongicides à l'aide d'un compresseur à air comprimé et d'un pistolet muni d'une très fine grille (afin de briser les gouttelettes et d'obtenir une pulvérisation très dispersée);

2. La nébulisation des produits fongicides à l'aide d'un appareil à brouillard du type «swing-fog». Cette dernière méthode est de beaucoup la plus intéressante, car la dispersion du produit étant infiniment supérieure, la concentration en produit actif peut être moindre et son efficacité plus grande. En effet, Moreau[9] a montré «qu'un mm^3 de produit actif pulvérisé en gouttelettes de 50 microns de diamètre produit 92.000 gouttelettes lourdes retombant vite, alors qu'un mm^3 de ce même produit dispersé par un générateur à brouillard en gouttelettes de 2 microns de diamètre, produit 500.000.000 gouttelttes légères restant plusieurs heures en suspension dans l'air».

Nous utilisons les deux produits suivants:

(a) Un sel d'ammonium quaternaire, le bromure de lauryldiméthylcarbétoxyméthyl d'ammonium à 5 pour cent en solution alcoolique (afin de ne pas réhumidifier l'atmosphère par une pulvérisation de solution aqueuse), à raison de 5 cm^3 par m^3 à désinfecter. Pour limiter les risques d'incendie, on utilise de l'alcool dénaturé à 70°C. Ce produit étant irritant pour les muqueuses, le port d'un masque est indispensable pendant toute l'opération. Utilisé en pulvérisation, il a fait ses preuves depuis près de sept ans dans différentes bibliothèques et archives.

(b) Un composé organique du bore, le décahydrate de diborolactate de triéthanolammonium que l'on a utilisé jusqu'à présent en nébulisation et jamais en pulvérisation. Il a été mis au point par Moreau[10], qui a démontré que son pouvoir fongique était presque similaire à celui de sel d'ammonium quaternaire, tout en étant moins irritant pour l'opérateur. Il est utilisé en solution aqueuse à 80 pour cent de produit actif, à raison de 5 cm^3 par m^3 d'atmosphère. Récemment on l'a utilisé avec succès dans un très vaste dépôt des Archives Nationales. Après traitement, un contrôle doit être effectué afin d'en vérifier l'efficacité.

Avant de clore ce chapitre, il est indispensable de signaler que si ces traitements se sont toujours révélés efficaces dans le cas des locaux pollués par des champignons papyricoles ou par des champignons banaux du cuir, ils seraient tout à fait insuffisants pour des bâtiments envahis par la mérule. Dans ce cas, il est indispensable en plus de la désinfection, d'une part de brûler tous les matériaux en bois très gravement atteints, d'autre part de traiter par des imprégnations de produits antifongiques du type pentachlorophénol de soude, tous ceux qui apparemment ne présentent pas de gros dommages.

Les méthodes préventives de désinfection

Ces méthodes doivent avoir un effet aussi permanent que possible. Le formaldéhyde et l'oxyde d'éthylène, utilisés comme traitement curatif, ont, nous le savons, le pouvoir de tuer tout champignon en plein développement, mais, étant très volatils, ils ne peuvent conférer aux documents une protection contre des invasions ultérieures.

À cet effet, nous avons mis au point plusieurs traitements qui, tout en étant moins puissants au point de vue du pouvoir fongique, ont un effet beaucoup plus durable.

Traitement par pulvérisation de produits fongicides

Lorsque, pour des raisons accidentelles (inondation, défaillance de la climatisation, risques importants de contamination), on craint une fructification rapide des spores se trouvant sur les documents, mais qu'aucun filament mycélien ne peut être décelé à l'oeil nu, on aura toujours intérêt à prendre des mesures capables d'arrêter rapidement une éventuelle germination. Pour cela, on procèdera à une désinfection sur place, ne nécessitant aucune manipulation de documents. Cette désinfection sera réalisée par des pulvérisations de produits fongicides; le produit utilisé est le bromure de lauryl-diméthylcarbétoxyméthyl d'ammonium en solution aqueuse à la concentration de 2 pour cent suivant les cas. La pulvérisation, qui doit être extrêmement fine, a été réalisée sous une pression de 2,5 kg, à une distance de 1,5 m des documents et pendant 10 secondes.

Cette méthode a fait ses preuves depuis 1954. A cette époque, on avait effectué des essais sur de nombreux échantillons (cuir avec titres dorés, parchemin, papier de différentes époques). Ces échantillons conservés au laboratoire ne montrent actuellement aucune altération. Ce procédé a été appliqué depuis cette époque en France dans plusieurs bibliothèques.

Traitement par incorporation de produits fongicides

Nous avons pensé qu'il serait souhaitable que les matériaux graphiques possèdent en eux-mêmes une résistance fongique afin qu'ils puissent mieux se défendre contre les microorganismes et diminuer de la sorte leur vulnérabilité.

Tous les éléments entrant dans la composition des documents graphiques sont des éléments putrescibles, en particulier la colle. C'est pour cette raison que nous avons mis au point une colle insecticide et fongicide* qui peut être utilisée pour tous les travaux de restauration des documents, et qui leur confère une résistance fongique indiscutable.

---

* La colle et la cire insecticide et fongicide font l'objet de brevets pris par le CNRS sous les no. 747-632 et 747-630 à Paris le 19 septembre 1957.

Par ailleurs, sachant que la flore du cuir est aussi importante que la flore du papier, nous avons réalisé une nouvelle cire insecticide et fongicide, afin de protéger tous les documents possèdant une reliure en cuir ou en parchemin. En dehors de ses particularités biologiques, cette cire a l'avantage d'être neutre et de limiter de la sorte toutes les dégradations causées par des agents chimiques[11]. Ce produit est utilisé depuis 1957 à l'atelier de restauration de la Bibliothèque Nationale, aux Archives Nationales et dans de nombreuses autres bibliothèques françaises et étrangères (Amérique, Angleterre, Belgique, Suisse).

Il est à noter ici que si cette cire améliore beaucoup la conservation de la reliure et lui confère une résistance fongique et insecticide dans de nombreuses circonstances, il est illusoire d'en attendre un effet curatif: son application sur une reliure fortement endommagée par des mycélia ne serait, en aucun cas, suffisante pour stopper la propagation de ceux-ci et areantir les champignons en plein essor.

Après avoir passé en revue toutes les possibilités courantes de désinfection des matériaux constitutifs des documents graphiques, nous pensons qu'à l'heure actuelle nous sommes puissamment armés pour la lutte contre les microorganismes et spécialement contre les champignons. Aucun des produits employés ne causent de dégâts apparents sur les documents traités, même après plusieurs années de traitement. Nous estimons cependant que leur innocuité doit être contrôlée de façon plus scientifique: cette étude est en cours et nous ne pouvons donner encore les résultats.

Bibliographie

[1] SEE, P., *Les maladies du papier piqué*, Paris, 1919, 168 pp.

[2] SACCAS, A., Un nouveau champignon *Ascomyeète gymnoascé*, l'*Eidamelia papyricola* nov. sp., *Bull. Soc. mycol. Fr.*, 16, 3 (1950).

[3] ZAMBETTAKIS, C., Un nouveau champignon papyricole, *Bull. Soc. bot. Fr.*, 102 (1955) 219–225.

[4] Bibliothèque Lénine (Moscou), Département de l'hygiène et Restauration des livres. Recueil d'articles concernant la conservation des livres, fasc. III, Moscou, 1958.

[5] GALLO, F., Gli agenti biologici nemici della biblioteche e degli archivi, *Boll. Ist. Pat. Libro*, 16 (1957) 141.

[6] HEIM, R., Les champignons destructeurs des bois dans les habitations, *Inst. tech. Bât. Trav. publ.*, série H, no. 1 (1942).

[7] JACQUIOT, C., Les ennemis du bois dans la construction et l'ameublement, *Cahiers Cent. tech. Bois*, série 1, no. 3 (1958).

[8] FLIEDER, F. et BOISSONNAT, J., Étude des propriétés fongicides de l'oxyde d'éthylène, *Bull. Path. Document Prot. Archives Nationales*, (1961) 61–67.

[9] MOREAU, C., Pollution fongique de l'atmosphère et altération des denrées alimentaires, *Rev. Embouteill.*, 12, fasc. 52, Juin p. 43–44.

[10] MOREAU, C., Pourriture des fruits et conditions d'entreposages, *Fruits*, 12, no. 4–5 (1957).

[11] FLIEDER, F., Cire spéciale pour reliure, *Bull. Bibl. Fr.*, no. 1 (1957).

W. Boustead

THE CONSERVATION OF WORKS OF ART IN TROPICAL AND SUB-TROPICAL ZONES

The art conservator working in a tropical climate is often confronted with problems not usually encountered in more temperate zones. These problems are in most cases caused by environmental factors, which vary considerably in a large continent.

Although Australia is situated well below the equator, almost half its total area lies within the tropics. It can, in some respects, be compared with India, situated a similar distance north of the equator. Like India, it has a long and rambling coastline where climatic conditions vary from the mild and bracing to the hot and humid. Inland are vast deserts, which, except for similar high temperatures, are in direct contrast to the humid northern coastal areas, where lie vast areas of tropical jungle subjected every year to four months of monsoonal conditions which create havoc with materials of organic origin through the depredations of fungi and insect pests.

situated on the coastal areas. The dry climate with its exceptionally low relative humidity causes desiccation of oils, varnish and the glue adhesive of lined canvasses. Paint films become hard, brittle and cracked. They age considerably in a short time. Flies deposit their excreta upon the paint films, creating small nodules which are often impossible to remove. The slightest jar will create the familiar circular pattern of impact crackle of the brittle paint films. Canvasses, particularly those with fibres containing a high lignin content, rapidly lose their strength through the photochemical effects of the brilliant and at times almost blinding light. Termites and borers tunnel into panels and wooden objects of art until they are reduced to shells (*Figures 1* and *2*). Watercolours, drawings and documents become browned and yellowed through oxidation and show little resistance to tear.

It may well be asked, 'Surely, as there cannot possibly be any

Figure 1. Pencil drawing attacked by common furniture beetle (*Anobium punctuatum*). Note tunnellings between drawing and pulpboard support. The paper is also oxidized and stained from mould attacks.

The deserts, on the other hand, are hot and arid regions where the temperature by day can reach 130°F (55°C), dropping to 50°F (10°C) at night. Here mould growth is practically unknown, except for the rare occasions when the monsoons sweep over and bring relief to the parched earth. In these regions works of art react in a different manner from those

art museums in these out-of-the-way places, why should they concern the art conservator?'

Unfortunately they do, and for several reasons. Principally because it is only of recent years that responsible people have realized the rapid decline of our cultural and historic relics.

The New South Wales art collection is housed in a building which is, to say the least, totally unsuited to its purpose. It is dark, damp and rambling. Pools of water well up through the floors of the storage areas during the wet season and mould grows with an astonishing profusion. Vigorous sea breezes deposit their salts throughout the building. Ships moored in Sydney Harbour below, and neighbouring factories, provide a high concentration of atmospheric pollution. During the months of high humidity the walls drip with condensed moisture.

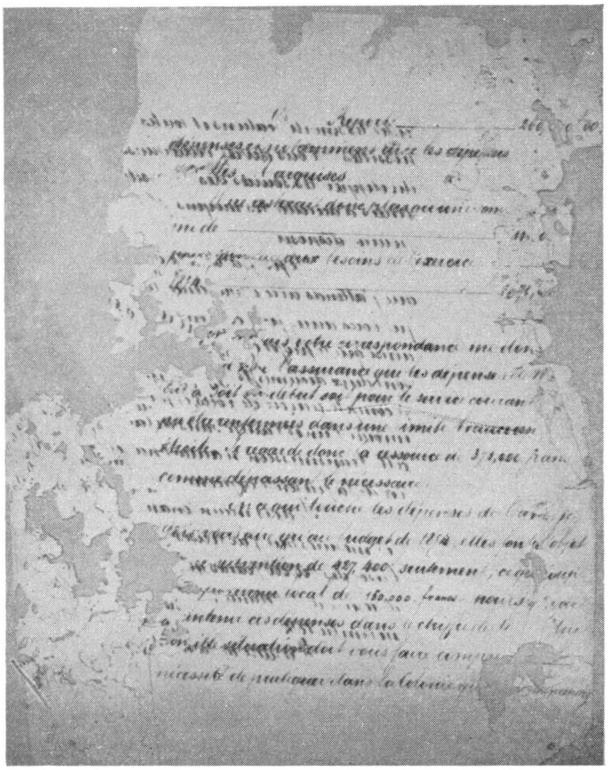

Figure 2. Early 19th century document showing damage caused by insect pests and the penetration of the iron-gall ink from opposite side of page.

These hazards and the deplorable condition of the collection forced the trustees of a poorly endowed collection to investigate their problems in a scientific manner by the formation of a conservation department.

Although our chief concern is the preservation of our own collection our methods and findings have received some recognition throughout the Commonwealth. We are often required to deal with problems not immediately connected with our own collection. These problems are not always institutional ones. We are not only approached by interstate and provincial art museums but also by long-established religious missions situated in desert regions and tropical areas. They are concerned with the decline of their religious paintings, their libraries of rare books and the relics of their Orders.

Situated in the western plains, the desert regions and the tropical north are many large homesteads. These are the residences of people of great wealth who control many thousands of acres of pastoral country. Some of them can only be described as baronial mansions and many of them house works of varying value bequeathed by ancestors or collected during tours abroad.

Like all art museums we are continually on the look-out for works of high artistic merit and historical worth; this obliges us to be continually assailed by submissions of all forms of artistic endeavour. These works must be thoroughly examined and reported on before a decision to purchase is made by our trustees. We are continually confronted with works which display the visible signs of long struggles with their environment.

One should also realize that, with the exception of the Melbourne Art Gallery with its fabulous Felton Bequest of £65,000 a year for the purchase of accredited masterpieces, most of the Australian art museums are unable to compete in the world's market for the acquisition of genuinely old paintings. They have to be content to build up collections which are essentially nationalistic or historical in character, supplemented occasionally by the bequest of a genuinely old painting.

By Old World standards our art collections must appear very insignificant indeed. We are a young nation isolated by distance from the age-old cultural influences of England and Europe, but very much in the immediate neighbourhood of people who are of much more ancient culture.

It is inevitable, however one regards the political issue, that the arts of Asia will eventually play as important a role in our cultural outlook as did the tastes and conditioning of our English forebears. Geographically we are closer to Asia than to Europe. Our climatic conditions are similar, and in consequence our conservation problems are similar.

Owing to our small budget and our limited purchasing power we have little chance of acquiring any of the established masterpieces of the Western world. We must perforce acquire the efforts of modern painters and, when they are available, the cultural works of Asia. Already we have a fine collection of Australian aborigine paintings and carvings to supplement our national works. The sculptural works of the South Seas are also receiving recognition. Many of these works come to us in a deplorable condition. We accept them because of their rarity and their cultural value.

The following paragraphs may assist in giving a brief outline of our findings and our methods.

Influence of tropical conditions on artists' materials

Supports

The customary support of easel paintings and drawings consists mainly of cellulose and partly of ligneous fibres. These fibres react to tropical conditions in accordance with their physical make-up.

Cotton duck, which is composed of pure cellulose, generally has poor resistance to tropical hazards. Its main virtue appears to be its resistance to the photochemical effects of light. Compared to bast fibres its reaction to high relative humidity and sudden climatic changes can only be described as violent. It provides a willing and highly nutritive host for mould growth. Its expansion and contraction, aided by the conventional glue sizing, are in continual warfare with the superimposed paint film. If the paint film happens to be glue distemper or pure egg tempera the results are usually disastrous.

To line a cotton canvas on to a flax canvas using a glue-paste adhesive is inevitably fatal, particularly if the paint film has reached maturity. Compression crackle develops, with 'saucering' of the paint film, then cleavage and finally widely developed flaking and eventually loss.

We recently had to deal with some oils by Indonesian artists. All were painted on cotton rice bags. No size had been applied, so there was little contraction, but there was practically no bond between canvas and paint film. Vacuum impregnation with wax-resin mixture and mounting on to tempered Masonite panels saved them from extinction.

Dust, dirt, grease, size and most finishing substances tend to encourage mould growth.

Bast fibres

Canvasses consisting of jute, sisal or ramie fibres highly incrusted with lignin are much more resistant to mould growth. They appear to absorb less atmospheric moisture and are much less affected by climatic fluctuations. However, if not properly sized they are more easily rotted by linseed-oil paint films. Their resistance to oxidation caused by the photochemical effects of light is considerably less than that of cotton fibres.

Pure flax canvasses appear to be the most stable of the woven painting supports. They are reasonably resistant to atmospheric fluctuations, do not oxidize as readily as jute and ramie fibres, and, although more resistant to fungi attacks than cotton fibres, are often prone to infection. This may be attributable to residual spores left after the rotting process.

Humidity cabinet tests have revealed beyond all doubt that both waterproof plywood panels and Masonite Tempered Preswood are far superior to fabric supports. Not only is their resistance to mould growth much greater, but they absorb far less moisture. This enables them to exhibit much more stability in a fluctuating climate. It is important to realize that the plywood tested is of a type specially made for lining or backing purposes. It is bonded with a synthetic resin, and each panel is soaked in pentachlorophenol for twenty-four hours. The five layers of plywood are carefully selected from kiln-dried stock.

Mould growth on paint films

Given the right conditions, mould growth will flourish vigorously on oil, tempera and casein paints. It is rarely found in good-quality watercolour paints but is sometimes encountered in heavy body colour and thick layers of gouache. Its propagation usually stems from the surface of the paint film where the migrating spores have settled and found the nourishment essential for their growth (*Figure 3*). Occasionally infection will have originated in the canvas and the glue size, the filamentous mycelia thrusting their way through cracks in the paint film and spreading over the paint surface.

Surface infection can originate during the actual execution of the work, the tacky surface of the paint film providing an excellent host for airborne spores. Infected brushes, resinous mediums and the type of oil binder all provide sources of infection. The embedded micro-organisms may lie dormant for years until favourable conditions stimulate them to growth.

Paint films with heavy impasto which are not varnished are highly susceptible to mould growth. Dust and dirt collected in the interstices of the brushwork absorb moisture and attract mould spores.

The practice of rubbing raw linseed over a paint film to freshen it up is to be soundly condemned. The tacky layer of unpigmented oil will inevitably attract mould spores and provide the nourishment necessary for their growth.

Resistance of paint binders to mould growth

Tests carried out in a humidity chamber at relative humidities of 68 to 98 per cent gave the following results:

Least resistant:
1. casein,
2. pure egg tempera,
3. tempera oil emulsion,
4. raw linseed oil.

Most resistant:
1. refined linseed oil,
2. heat-bodied alkali-refined linseed oil,
3. alkyd resins,
4. polyvinyl acetate,
5. polybutyl methacrylate.

Generally speaking the richer the paint film in medium the higher the incidence of infection. Increased pigmentation reduces infection, particularly when calcium carbonate is used as an extender. Calcium carbonate is not directly toxic but imparts a high degree of alkalinity to the paint film, an adverse condition for mould growth.

When a linseed-oil film is attacked by mould growth it becomes spongy, less elastic, more soluble in alkalis and more easily swollen by water.

Shellac and copal resin are highly resistant, while dammar, mastic and colophony are much more easily infected.

Pigments

Most of the common pigments are inert to mould growth, i.e. they neither encourage nor inhibit fungal activity.

Zinc oxide is usually classed as an inhibitor, but we have succeeded in growing mould on a zinc oxide paint film which had stand oil for a binder and a 0·2 per cent solution of pentachlorophenol as a fungicide. The test was carried out at a relative humidity of 90 per cent and a temperature of 80°F.

Titanium and white lead are also inert, but it is certain that the extender pigments, although biologically inert, assist in providing a high degree of resistance to these paints.

The extender with the greatest effect is calcium carbonate. Silica and magnesium silicate assist to a lesser degree. Red or brown paints containing iron oxide are usually severely attacked. Alizarin and carbon blacks are more susceptible to mould infections than are other pigments.

Figure 3. Mould growth on oil painting. Mycelium is deeply embedded in paint film.

Figure 4a. Watercolour portrait waterstained, oxidized and attacked by mould growth—before treatment.

Figure 4b. Watercolour portrait illustrated in *Figure 4a* after treatment with sodium hypochlorite, followed by antichlor, careful washing and finally resizing with size containing calcium carbonate and Shirlan fungicide.

Micro-organisms responsible for the mould growth are usually of the *Fungi imperfecti* genera, *Aspergillus*, *Penicillium* and *Cladosporium*.

Methods of investigation

A simple humidity chamber is used to promote mould growth by using supersaturated aqueous solutions of various salts. Salts such as calcium chloride, sodium chloride, potassium bromide and sodium sulphate in solution give varying degrees of humidity. Species are identified in the usual manner by staining with lactophenol cotton blue and investigating the spore structure under a microscope.

The investigation of mould growth which has deeply embedded itself, or has its origin in the paint film, can only be carried out under vertical illumination. Objectives such as the Ultrapak and the Epilum are essential in tracing the source of infection and assessing the rate of growth.

Methods of control

In the absence of complete air-conditioning mould infection can be controlled only by constant vigilance, regular inspection and the use of fungicides. Those works which display greatest susceptibility to mould growth must be regularly inspected under a binocular microscope. The entire surface of the paint film must be carefully investigated for signs of mycelium or fruiting spores. Both the paint film and the rear of the canvas must be thoroughly cleaned with a small high-powered vacuum cleaner.

Surface infection is treated by applying fungicidal solutions to the mould colonies with a small brush. This is usually effective in the early stages of growth, but once the mycelium has become deeply embedded it is relatively useless. The paint film must then be softened with solvents before the fungicide is applied. Staining caused by the secretions of the micro-organisms and deep-rooted mycelium can only be removed by using high-speed rotary dental burrs whilst working under the binocular microscope. This is very drastic treatment which takes a great deal of skill and patience.

In spite of all these precautions and varied treatments we have paintings which relapse regularly. Whenever conditions are favourable the insidious growth reappears with undiminished vigour. All we can do is to repeat the treatment.

Prints, drawings and watercolours

There are four main factors which produce deterioration in these works:

1. Fading of pigments or inks caused by exposure to light.
2. Discoloration of the paper support by exposure to light.
3. Discoloration and disintegration caused by mould growth.
4. Faulty or fugitive pigments.

Of these, by far the greatest damage to our collection has been caused by mould growth. A large proportion of our watercolours has been executed on low-grade papers which oxidize and become yellow on exposure to strong illumination. High temperatures, high relative humidity and atmospheric pollution are other factors which hasten deterioration.

Methods of treatment: Mould-infested and foxed black-and-white prints are treated with the usual bleaching processes. Chloramine T, the hypochlorites, potassium permanganate and citric acid are commonly used, their application depending upon the work and the type of paper (*Figures 4a* and *b*). Chloramine T is effective in mild cases, but if the paper is heavily foxed or waterstained one of the hypochlorites must be used, followed by antichlors, thorough washing and resizing. In some cases we find it advisable to use potassium permanganate and citric acid in separate solutions. This method is only applied to certain varieties of paper and although condemned by some research

Figure 5. Watercolour badly infected by mould growth. White patches show where the mould has destroyed size and eaten into the paper fibres.

workers is often put to good use by paper chemists to neutralize chemical instability caused by unsaturated substances in the paper. These papers usually contain mechanical wood pulp and are heavily sized with resin alum size.

The treated prints are thoroughly washed until all chemical residues are removed. They are then sized with a solution of laboratory gelatine, containing 1 per cent Shirlan and 4 per cent calcium carbonate. The calcium carbonate provides an effective alkaline barrier to mould growth and atmospheric pollution.

Fumigation in the usual thymol cabinet follows and the print is mounted on specially prepared mount board which has been treated with Shirlan.

Prints are hinged to their support by means of strips of pure linen paper. The adhesive used is a dextrin paste containing fungicide. Drawings and mounts are then placed in a de-humidifying cabinet for several hours. This reduces the amount of residual moisture absorbed from the external atmosphere. The mounted prints can then be placed in polythene envelopes without fear of sealing in moisture. The restored prints are stored in large metal storage cabinets with trays measuring 48 × 36 × 5 in. Each drawer contains 1 lb. of 100 per cent indicating silica gel to maintain a relative humidity of 55 per cent.

Paper hygrometers are placed in the drawers to give some indication by colour changes of the rise and fall in humidity. Saturated silica gel is replaced with dehydrated crystals and then placed in an oven at 100°C to be reactivated for further use.

The formula for paper hygrometers is as follows:

cobalt chloride	32 g
sodium chloride	16 g
calcium chloride	5 g
acacia	8 g
water	100 cm³

Blotting paper is soaked in this solution, hung up to dry and then cut into strips.

The following colour changes are noted at the various relative humidities (in per cent):

20:	cobalt blue
30:	powder blue
45:	light blue
52:	lilac or lavender
65:	orchid pink
95:	faded hydrangea pink

The restoration of documents and watercolours badly damaged by waterstains, mould growth and oxidation is a much more difficult proposition (see *Figures 1, 5* and *6*). However, by the skilful use of the following methods many watercolours condemned to oblivion as beyond restoration can be safely restored to something very close to their original condition.

Chloramine T is useless in such cases, and we find that only the right solution of calcium hypochlorite or sodium hypo-

Figure 6. A 19th century document showing oxidation, mould growth and waterstains on paper of poor quality.

chlorite will effect an improvement. The solution strength will, of course, be determined by the artist's technique, the type of paper and its age, the general condition of the work and the experience of the restorer.

The usual procedure is to place the watercolour face upward on a sheet of thick glass over which has been poured the solution of hypochlorite. Care should be taken to ensure that the solution does not seep in over the edges or through badly foxed areas. Otherwise stained and bleached patches will appear, ruining the work. A few minutes' treatment will usually dispose of most of the foxing, but if the surface is waterstained or browned by oxidation, or the mould patches are unusually large, the solution must be carefully applied to the painted surface. This is a most delicate operation and only long experience can tell how far one can go.

We carried out numerous experiments on watercolours of no value to perfect this technique before applying it to our own collection. Since then we have successfully restored dozens of watercolours without any bleaching of colour or loss of original values.

Antichlors such as sodium thiosulphate and sodium sulphite are used to neutralize chlorine and the restored drawing is then carefully washed before resizing. Potassium iodide starch papers are used to detect any residual chlorine which may be present in the paper fibres.

Tearing and bursting tests before and after treatment have shown that provided the process is properly carried out the paper fibres show very little loss of strength. Actually, in many cases the strength of the paper is considerably increased by the removal of decayed and unsuitable sizing and the application of specially prepared sizes containing fungicides and buffering solutions.

Conclusion

Although many of the methods described in this paper may be termed empirical it is obvious that this much abused term must also be applied to many other conservation techniques in common use today. These techniques usually work very well in practice and will continue to be used until better methods are devised.

We welcome the news that at least two European laboratories intend to carry out extended research programmes related to the preservation of paper and we eagerly await their findings. However, we are not so sanguine as to expect the development of new techniques that will entirely eliminate the need for skill and experience in their application.

In the meantime we intend to carry on our own modest researches with the help of an air-conditioned chamber of 2000 cu. ft. equipped with a specially modified package unit capable of operating within a range of 50 to 95 per cent relative humidity and temperatures from 50° to 90°F (10° to 32°C). This will enable us to observe *in situ* the behaviour of various works in their response to the fluctuation of temperature and relative humidity. It will also permit us to carry out the testing of materials in a stable environment of 70°F (21°C) and 50 per cent relative humidity. This will be particularly valuable where the testing of paper is concerned.

An Elemendorf tearing tester, a bursting strength tester and an Australian-made pH meter and electrodes of original design will enable us to test bleaching methods, fungicides and buffer solutions to control acidity.

We also hope to investigate the action of chelating agents on the metallic impurities in paper. We have prepared a design for a small fumigation chamber for use in tropical and sub-tropical zones, and by using different techniques fumigation of books, drawings and documents can be carried out as well as the disinfestation of wooden objects by the use of the vacuum process. This will provide small institutions in the tropics with greater means of control than is now possible.

Experimental data

Relative humidity, 75 per cent; temperature, 73°F (23°C). Bursting strength of the untreated paper = 14 lb./in.^{2}

Solutions used

Process No. 1
- (a) 0·26 per cent solution of potassium permanganate (first bath)
- (b) 1 per cent solution of sodium sulphite
- (c) 1 per cent solution of oxalic acid—50:50 of (b) and (c) second bath

Time: 5 min in first bath and 2 min in second bath.

Process No. 2
- (a) 1 per cent potassium permanganate (first bath)
- (b) 1 per cent citric acid (second bath)

Time: 5 min in first bath and another 5–10 min in second bath.

Process No. 3
- (a) 5 per cent Chloramine-T

Time: 5 min

Process No. 4
- (a) calcium hypochlorite (3 per cent available chlorine content)

Time: 2 min

1. Provision for the size dissolved by washing when under treatment—2½ per cent gelatine solution.

2. Provision for the fungicides against growth of micro-organisms—1 per cent Shirlan water solution.

3. Provision for acidity in paper—4 per cent calcium carbonate solution.

Bursting strengths (lb./in.^{2}) of treated paper

	Process 1	Process 2	Process 3	Process 4
Bursting strength after chemical treatment	13	13.5	13.5	13
Bursting strength after sizing and other provisions	18	17·5	18·5	18

Bursting strengths (lb./in.^{2}) of treated paper*

Antichlors	Hypo (1 per cent)	Sodium sulphite (7 per cent)	Hydrogen peroxide (100 vols)
Bursting strength of treated paper, not washed, before sizing	10	10	7
Bursting strength, after sizing	14	14	10

* Relative humidity, 75 per cent; temperature, 73°F (23°C). Bursting strength before treatment = 10 lb./in.^{2} Bleached with calcium hypochlorite (3 per cent available chlorine). Time of treatment, 2 min.

Elizabeth H. Jones

THE EFFECT OF AGING AND RE-FORMING ON THE EASE OF SOLUBILITY OF CERTAIN RESINS

Coating materials and their removal

Coating materials

Many different substances and mixtures of substances have been used for protective coatings on paintings in oil and tempera. It is often difficult to identify precisely the materials used in earlier times, either by analysis or by reference to documents. However, most coating materials fall within four general classes:

1. The water-dispersible substances, including egg-white, gums and glues.
2. The spirit resins, dispersible in organic solvents like turpentine or alcohol. Mastic, dammar and sandarac fall in this classification.
3. The thermosetting resins (amber and copal), dispersible only with heat, usually in oil.
4. The drying oils like linseed and poppy.

Curiously enough, over the centuries egg-white is the coating material most commonly mentioned in craftsmen's handbooks. Among others, Cennini[1] recommended its use as a temporary protection for a freshly painted picture. Poussin[2], in three letters from Rome, mentioned that he had applied only egg-white as a coating. The American edition of Tingry[3], published in 1831, states: 'A new painting often has no other covering than white of egg.'

Although old recipes usually call for the inclusion of several ingredients in the preparation of a varnish, coatings based on the drying oils and on amber and copal resins were probably the most common from the 13th to the 17th century. The use of copal and amber continued into the present century. Mastic and sandarac are mentioned with increasing frequency from the 17th century on. Trade from the Far East in dammar developed much later. Forni[4], writing in 1886, mentioned that it had been available for a short time, as a substitute for mastic. He considered it superior 'because it does not become yellow'. The first of the synthetic resins to be regularly applied as a protective coating to paintings was polyvinyl acetate, which came into use about 1929.

Removal of coating materials

All natural resin varnishes share a most troublesome characteristic: they deteriorate more or less rapidly with age. When their physical degradation becomes apparent by crazing, powdering or shrinkage or when their optical properties are seriously altered by darkening, opacity or the accumulation of fixed stains and grime, they must be removed and replaced.

Through the centuries, restorers have struggled to find safe ways to remove these coatings. Judging by the old handbooks, most of the paintings we now treasure have been through water and some have actually been through fire[5]. From the 17th century well into the 19th we find frequent references to the use of wood or pearl ashes (potash) mixed with water, applied with a sponge or a brush and then rinsed off with water[6]. Reading

these old accounts with horror, we wonder that any paintings have managed to survive to our day. Such drastic treatments certainly explain the many unpleasant surprises disclosed by modern tools of examination. In justice to the old craftsmen, however, we should note their frequent warnings of the dangers involved and their insistence upon the importance of knowledge, experience and a delicate hand.

Some coatings may be removed without solvent by friction. One 17th century source suggests the use of smalt, 'which is as some call it Powder-blew', and water, used as an alternative to wood ashes[7]. Before modern organic chemicals became available, a great variety of liquids was used to clean paintings. Some of these, like water or soap and water, were useful only in removing grime and the water-soluble substances on the surface of an oil or spirit varnish. Others, like butter and the various oils, were probably used to remove the more stubborn stains and to restore the gloss, if only temporarily. Our modern laboratories are rarely filled with the sweet scents of the essential oils, lavender, rosemary, lemon and balsam, but at least we are spared the pungency of garlic and other less pleasant natural products.

'Spirits of wine', mentioned regularly in the 18th century[8], is still commonly used today in its concentrated form, ethanol. As in former times, it is often mixed with turpentine in varying proportions as required. But the modern conservator has at his command not just one but a series of alcohols with a wide range of properties and a similar choice within other classes of solvents. The discussion of modern solvents, however, is not the purpose of this paper.

Any intelligent practitioner, of whatever period, has adjusted his methods of removing varnish to suit each individual painting and to the special requirements of local areas within it. And with a unanimity rather unusual in our field, the old accounts and modern practice agree upon the importance of minimizing friction in the removal of coatings with solvents. Stolow's study[9] of the swelling of drying-oil paint explained the reason for this precaution.

The American edition of Tingry (1831) contains a description of what might be considered the earliest systematic use of the preswelling of resins to aid removal. For certain cases it was suggested that the painting be placed in a horizontal position, flooded with rectified spirits of wine and kept moistened in this manner for some time without employing friction. Cold water was then applied to remove the spirit and the portion of resin which had been dissolved or softened[10]. For the removal of copals the book suggested that a rag dipped in 'pure sulphuric aether' be spread over the surface of the painting and covered with a glass or metal plate[11]. In 1864 von Pettenkofer[12] patented his process for restoring the optical properties of aged varnish by exposing the surface of the painting to alcohol vapour in a chamber. This was not intended to aid in the removal of the film at a later time, but Forni[13], in evaluating the method, stated that its greatest benefit was that the varnish could be removed with great facility. Although an initial exposure of 30 minutes was suggested, Secco-Suardo[14] noted that he had never been able to achieve the desired optical results in less than two hours. One of the limitations of the use of a vapour chamber is that the reaction cannot be constantly observed as it proceeds. A modern version of these techniques will be discussed later in this paper.

Effect of aging and re-forming

The effect of aging and re-forming on twenty different picture varnishes was reported in 1957 at the Intermuseum Conservation Association's seminar at Oberlin[15]. These coatings were part of a series of 31 coatings painted out on four sets of test panels in 1938. They included six specimens of mastic, three of dammar, five of copal and, of the synthetic resins, Vinylite A (polyvinyl acetate), Vinylite VYHH (polyvinyl chloroacetate), Alvar (polyvinyl acetal), poly-(*n*-butyl-methacrylate) and poly-(*n*-propylmethacrylate). Three synthetic coatings of little interest as picture varnishes and six unidentified proprietary coatings were not discussed in the report. Three sets of these panels were exposed under glass on the roof of the Fogg Museum in the summer of 1939 for periods of time ranging from one week to three months. The fourth control set was exposed to strong daylight in the laboratory.

The effect of aging

Testing methods: The untreated coatings have now been tested three times—in 1940, 1948 and 1961—for their relative ease of solubility in five organic solvents: naphtha, toluene, methanol, ethylene dichloride and acetone. Since naphtha had so slight an effect on most coatings after very little aging, results are not given in this report.

Two methods of testing were used. In the first method, the ease of solubility was judged by the number of rollings—20, 40 or 60—of standard-sized swabs dipped in the various solvents required to remove a fairly consistent amount of film. The second method was devised to study the time interval required for a given solvent to affect the coating without the help of mechanical agitation. The solvent was applied with a syringe. The reaction was observed through a binocular microscope and timed with a stopwatch. Usually the moment when the varnish first began to soften could be detected by its appearance and by probing gently with a needle. This time, as well as the interval necessary to swell or dissolve the coating enough to remove it with a swab, was recorded. Observations on the state of the coating at the time of removal (as a thin or thick sol, a soft and swollen or tough-dry gel) were noted. The tests were:

1. 1940: by the first method. These tests, which required a larger area than the subsequent ones, were run on a set of panels which had been exposed for the same period as the set used later.
2. 1948: by the second method on another set of panels.
3. 1961: by the second method, using areas of the second set of panels that had previously been untouched by solvent.

Summary of results: The record of the decline over 21 years of the ease of solubility of these 20 untreated coatings has considerable practical interest. Quite regular patterns can be found in the behaviour of the various classes of coatings in the four solvents reported. Although the 1940 tests cannot be compared directly with the later tests because a different testing method was used, such evidence is too important not to be included. It should be remembered that no mechanical agitation was involved during the swelling periods of all the later tests (see *Figure 1*, columns I, for results).

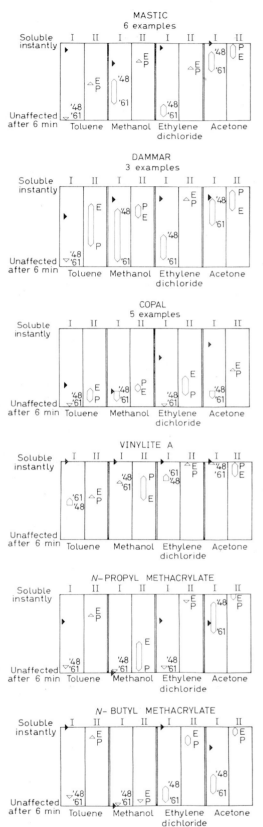

Figure 1. Effect of aging and re-forming.
I—untreated, II—re-formed, ▶—original solubility in 1940, E—re-formed with ethanol solution, P—re-formed with propanol solution.

Mastic exhibited the most regular and marked loss of ease of solubility between 1940 and 1948 in ethylene dichloride and particularly in toluene, in which every example was graded insoluble. The decline for all solvents continued for 13 years. By 1961 only acetone was consistently effective for complete removal of the coatings as thin sols in less than a minute.

The three dammars were impossible to remove in toluene and difficult to remove in ethylene dichloride by 1948. The effectiveness of methanol and acetone was about equal to that with mastic. By 1961 methanol had become quite ineffective. The usual comment on the dammars in 1961, except for acetone, was, 'Removable after three (more commonly, six) minutes as a thick sol or gel, leaving a residue.'

The five copals were fairly easily dissolved in ethylene dichloride and in acetone in 1940. By 1948 the general comment on their behaviour was, 'Actually dissolves in none of the solvents tested. Becomes a more or less removable gel after six minutes' exposure.' By 1961 most of the solvents required six minutes to form tough dry gels, necessitating considerable mechanical action to dislodge even a fraction of the coatings. The conviction of most modern conservators that the thermosetting copals are unsuitable as coatings for paintings is confirmed by these tests on 23-year-old samples. Their discoloured and crazed appearance reflects their physical deterioration. Their high resistance to solvents, the necessity for extensive mechanical action to achieve even partial removal and their low response to the re-forming technique (to be discussed later) all signal grave danger ahead for the paint films that they were intended to protect.

In dramatic contrast to the lack of response of the aged copals, Vinylite A (polyvinyl acetate) maintained its ease of solubility in test after test throughout the years. In 1961 the slowest reaction recorded, that of the unre-formed resin to toluene, required only 30 seconds' exposure for removal as a sol. The resin could be removed in less than ten seconds as a thin sol with all the other solvents. Tests on other Vinylite A coatings brushed out in 1928 confirm this continuing ease of solubility in toluene*.

However, Vinylite VYHH (the copolymer polyvinyl chloroacetate) maintained its original resistance to solvent action as compared to Vinylite A. In 1961 only ethylene dichloride permitted its removal as a thick sol in two minutes. It was swollen but not removable after six minutes with toluene and methanol and left lumps of swollen gel after six minutes with acetone.

The two specimens of Alvar (polyvinyl acetal) over the years retained much of their original ease of solubility in all solvents except toluene. However, their pronounced change of hue on aging makes them unsuitable for use on paintings.

The methacrylates' resistance to solvent action on aging, as reported by Thomson[16] and Feller[17], has caused many of us concern. Feller has noted that exposure to strong light, as well as to heat, is an important factor in producing the cross-linking of methacrylates. He is now testing the effectiveness of the addition of substances which act as combined ultra-violet absorbers and antioxidant inhibitors. At this time we can report that the ease of solubility of the Fogg's historic specimens of poly-(n-propylmethacrylate) and poly-(n-butylmethacrylate) has continued to decline since 1948 to the point of considerable

resistance to the action of all four solvents. Tests were run on two of the Fogg's test panels, one of n-propyl and one of n-butyl polymethacrylate. Bands of these panels had been exposed to strong sunlight on the roof in the summer of 1939 for periods ranging from three months to one week. Another section of each panel was shielded from light. This set of panels has subsequently been kept in the dark. The bands still exhibit, after 21 years, a marked difference in ease of solubility. The unexposed strips were removable as sols with a swab dipped in ethylene dichloride after one minute. On the strips exposed to light for three months only a small fraction could be removed as a soft swollen gel after six minutes in ethylene dichloride. However, coatings of poly-(n-butylmethacrylate) applied between 1945 and 1948 to paintings which were then exposed to normal lighting in the Fogg galleries or in Harvard lecture halls and common rooms have proven to be so swollen and disturbed by naphtha (it must be noted that the coating could not be removed with naphtha) that the coatings have had to be removed completely with toluene. Different coatings were then applied.

The effect of re-forming

The Intermuseum Conservation Association's publication[18] contains an extended report on the effectiveness of the re-forming technique in increasing the ease of solubility of most of these 20 coatings and of our search for a better understanding of the phenomenon through our investigations by infra-red spectrophotometry and by tests made with radioactive ethanol. Since that time two further series of tests of the effects of re-forming have been made, substituting (1) n-propanol and (2) methyl ethyl ketone for the ethanol of the original re-forming mixture. The second testing method was used (see *Figure 1*, columns II, for results obtained with ethanol and propanol).

To summarize that report: A distinct improvement in the ease of solubility of many varnish coatings may be achieved if the surface, free of grime, is sprayed briefly with a mixture of certain solvents. The length of exposure necessary is limited— usually two to four seconds for a given area. It has been established that on the average only 2 per cent of the amount of ethanol re-forming solvent applied remains in the coating after 48 hours. The underlying paint layer does not appear to be affected by the small amount of solvent applied. Only a fraction of this will penetrate to the paint level. The improvement in ease of solubility of the coating may be maintained for a considerable period of time. In the case of one painting the effect was noticed three months later.

After re-forming, the ease of solubility of the aged coatings of mastic, dammar, poly-(n-propylmethacrylate), poly-(n-butylmethacrylate) and of two vinyl polymers (Vinylite VYHH and Alvar) improved markedly in the solvents later used in testing. This was particularly noticeable in the non-polar solvents toluene and ethylene dichloride. The change was less apparent with Vinylite A, which had retained so much of its original ease of solubility. Examples of copal and of mastic and dammar coatings known to contain oil were less affected.

In 1961 the substitution of n-propanol and of methyl ethyl ketone for the ethanol of the re-forming mixture used in 1949 produced results quite parallel with those obtained with the first solution. Differences were too slight and variable to be conclusive. Methyl ethyl ketone, of which the solubility parameter (9·3) falls within the range of that of linseed oil (9·3–9·5)[19], did not improve the effectiveness of re-forming on the copals or on mastic and dammar that contained oil.

Other specimens of varnish have been less extensively tested after a preliminary spray with a variety of solvents and solvent

---

* Mr Helmut Ruhemann recalls that Mr George L. Stout showed a specimen of Vinylite A to members of a committee on conservation at the conference in Rome in 1930 and reported that it showed great promise for use as a surface coating for paintings. His recommendation, based on two years' observations of the new resin, was indeed a sound prophecy of its future behaviour.

mixtures. Attempts at removal of these coatings indicated that a single solvent like toluene, acetone or ethanol used alone was either totally ineffective or much less effective in improving the ease of solubility of these coatings. Among various mixtures of solvents the combination of ethanol, diacetone alcohol and cellosolve has generally proved to be the safest and most effective.

Investigations into the nature of aging and re-forming

The degradation of varnish films through aging, so familiar to us all because it is reflected by changes in their visual properties, and to chemists through analysis, may be recorded in graph form by an infra-red spectrophotometer. In studies of the spectra of mastic and dammar recorded by this instrument,

the pattern strengthened in the test run immediately following the re-forming spray, but this improvement had partially disappeared 24 hours after re-forming, when the last spectrum of this resin was taken.

These changes caused by aging in the spectra of dammar result from the degradation of the original materials by oxidation with an increase in the degree of hydrogen bonding. Similar effects undoubtedly take place in the other resins, both natural and synthetic.

Very possibly such effects are more pronounced in the top surface of varnish coatings, which receive the maximum exposure to light and air. In the re-forming technique the greatest concentration of solvent molecules from the quick spray is found in the outer layer of the coating. As we have

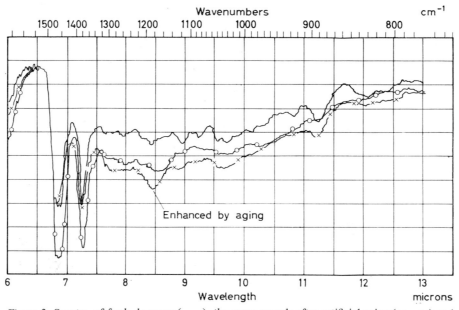

Figure 2. Spectra of fresh dammar (——), the same sample after artificial aging ($\times$—$\times$) and 1934 dammar in Nujol mull ($\bigcirc$—$\bigcirc$).

Feller[20] has reported the loss of detail after aging in the region from 800 to 1200 cm^{-1} (8·4 to 12·5 microns), which occurs in both resins. This change is confirmed in spectra of fresh dammar cast in toluene with that of the same sample artificially aged by exposure to 13 hours of ultra-violet light, which shows just such a loss of detail (see *Figure 2*). The spectra of two samples of a dammar which had been painted out on glass in 1934 were also taken. One, ground in a Nujol mull, showed even greater loss of detail in this region than did the artificially aged specimen. The other, redispersed in the ethanol re-forming solution for deposit on a salt crystal, showed a slight return of detail at these wavelengths. This also occurred to a lesser degree when the artificially aged sample was briefly sprayed with the re-forming solvent. As Feller reported in the same article, the characteristic absorption band of dammar at 8·90 microns disappeared on aging. We also found that an absorption band at 8·48 microns was enhanced by artificial aging of the fresh sample and appeared in both the 1934 samples. The band was less pronounced in the Nujol mull. These studies with infra-red suggest that dammar, a complex substance when fresh, on aging forms even more complicated materials*.

A similar loss of detail on aging is evident within about the same broad region when the 1950 spectra of fresh and artificially aged poly-(*n*-butylmethacrylate) are compared. Again

established by using ^{14}C ethanol, the original concentration at the surface falls with great rapidity (90 per cent of the amount applied had departed in five minutes)[21], effectively reducing the number of solvent molecules available for dispersion through the rest of the coating. The top layer of the coating is most affected by the spray. Extensive practical application of the technique has produced evidence in support of this theory. We regularly find coatings which, after re-forming, can be removed up to a certain stage with a particular solvent which did not remove the coating before. When the solvent again becomes ineffective in removing the residue of the coating, the spray must be repeated with the re-forming solvent. Once again the solvent used in cleaning will remove more of the coating. Such a reaction is not predictable, however.

In the re-forming technique, we believe, the small highly polar molecule of ethanol acts as a spearhead in initiating the

---

* Since 1950 the improvement in instrumentation allows finer results. Greater knowledge and experience permit better interpretation of the subtle changes found in the organic materials used in the fine arts. In 1950 we could find no published spectra of dammar for reference. Since an extensive body of comparative material is of the greatest importance in this field of research, I present these results, hoping that they may be of some use in the interpretation of such spectra.

solvation of the cross-linking bonds between the resin macro-molecules. Diacetone alcohol and cellosolve acetate help to swell the coating enough so that after the original solvents evaporate another solvent, previously fairly ineffective, can solvate these bonds more readily and swell or dissolve the coating enough for removal. The high percentage of coatings which are affected by re-forming can be removed more quickly, with a resulting reduction of the time of exposure of the paint film to the swelling action of the solvent. Furthermore, a smaller amount of solvent can be used. The varnish comes off in a less viscous form, reducing the amount of mechanical action necessary to lift the coating. For these reasons we believe that the technique is another useful tool in the hands of a skilled conservator.

References

[1] CENNINI, C., *Il Libro dell'Arte*, translated by THOMPSON, D. V. Jr., *The Craftsman's Handbook*, Yale University Press, New Haven, 1933, pp. 99–100.

[2] JOUANNY, C. (editor), Correspondence de Nicolas Poussin, *Arch. Art franç.*, 5 (1911) letter No. 135 (February 1646), p. 331; letter No. 159 (March 1648), p. 380; letter No. 194 (June 1655), p. 436.

[3] TINGRY, P. F., *The Painter's and Colourman's Complete Guide*, first American, from the third London, edition, Carey and Hart, Philadelphia, 1831, p. 141.

[4] FORNI, U., *Manuale del Pittore Restauratore*, Le Monnier, Florence, 1866, p. 91.

[5] SECCO-SUARDO, Count G., *Il Restauratore dei Dipinti*, third edition, Hoepli, Milan, 1918, pp. 369–70. (Secco-Suardo attributes this method to Professor G. Guizzardi of Bologna.)

[6] *The Excellency of the Pen and Pencil*, edited and printed by Thomas Ratcliff and Thomas Daniel, London, 1668, p.106; SMITH, J.C.M., *The Art of Painting in Oyl*, Samuel Crouch, London, 1705, p. 73; TINGRY, P. F., reference 3, p. 142.

[7] *The Excellency of the Pen and Pencil* (reference 6), p. 106.

[8] *The Handmaid to Arts, Sciences, Agriculture*, second edition, Norse, London, 1764, p. 238; DE PILES, M., *Eléments de peinture pratique*, revised by JOMBERT, C. A., Paris, 1766, p. 172.

[9] STOLOW, N., Solvent action: Some fundamental researches into the picture cleaning problem, *On Picture Varnishes and Their Solvents*, Intermuseum Conservation Association, Oberlin, 1959, p. 86.

[10] TINGRY, P. F., reference 3, p. 142.

[11] TINGRY, P. F., reference 3, p. 143.

[12] PETTENKOFER, M. VON, *Über Ölfarbe*, Vieweg, Braunschweig, 1870.

[13] FORNI, U., reference 4, pp. 431–32.

[14] SECCO-SUARDO, Count G., reference 5, pp. 418-19.

[15] JONES, E. H., Investigations on the removal of aged varnish coatings, *On Picture Varnishes and Their Solvents*, Intermuseum Conservation Association, Oberlin, 1959, pp. 164–198.

[16] THOMSON, G., Tests for cross-linking of linear polymers, *Nature*, 178 (1956) 807; Some picture varnishes, *Stud. Conservation*, 3 (1957) 64–79.

[17] FELLER, R. L., Properties of mature varnish, *On Picture Varnishes and Their Solvents*, Intermuseum Conservation Association, Oberlin, 1959, pp. 150–163.

[18] JONES, E. H., see reference 15.

[19] STOLOW, N., reference 9, p. 76.

[20] FELLER, R. L., Dammar and mastic infrared analysis, *Science*, 120 (1954) 1069–1070.

[21] JONES, E. H., reference 15, p. 191.

Nathan Stolow

APPLICATION OF SCIENCE TO CLEANING METHODS: SOLVENT ACTION STUDIES ON PIGMENTED AND UNPIGMENTED LINSEED OIL FILMS

Introduction

The function of a varnish coating is to offer physical protection to the underlying material. On paintings it also serves to improve, in an optical sense, the appearance of the colour pigments by 'colour saturation'. Usually the varnish coating is applied by brushing or spraying to a thickness in the range 1 to 50 microns, depending on the surface contours of the painting, the degree of absorption of the paint medium and the particular desires of the restorer. Since varnish coatings are very impermanent, in both the physical and chemical sense, it becomes necessary to remove them wholly or partially from the painted surface of the picture or other work of art at intervals ranging from a decade to a generation or more, depending on environmental conditions, state of historical research or the caprices of the art market. That cleaning is the least desirable of the restorer's activities can hardly be disputed. It has always been felt, in a pragmatic sense, that the application of solvents or other chemical reagents to remove varnish films was fraught with some danger. One needs only to refer to the literature to obtain some insight into earlier views on cleaning. Thus Déon[1] and Faraday[2] both refer to the possible danger to paint films by the use of alcohol, especially where the paint incorporates resinous material. Laurie[3], almost a century later, in 1937, showed that solvent vapours, as well as solvents in the liquid state, can soften paint. He had referred, of course, to the Pettenkofer process for the regeneration of varnish films. In this period there was a growing awareness of the danger in applying so-called active solvents to paintings. Thus xylene was used with the traditional alcohol to 'dilute' the activity of the alcohol, and turpentine (preferably medium-boiling petroleum distillates, boiling in the range 150–250°C) was applied as a restrainer when it was felt that the cleaning action was going too far or too rapidly. This technique of cleaning was doubtless a considerable step forward from earlier methods, which all too often caused over-cleaning and irreparable damage.

The cleaner of the present day can be said to use a wide variety of methods and techniques, stimulated no doubt by the rapid progress in the chemical industry. He can choose from among hundreds of solvents available to him. The possibilities of mixtures of solvents appear endless. Somewhere surely among this chemical wealth lies the answer to the problems of picture cleaning. The ideal liquid is, of course, not to be found; not so long as pictures represent such a wide variation in material construction, types of paint, varnish and age. It is necessary to re-approach the question of picture cleaning from the standpoint of the colloid chemistry of the paint. If this is properly understood in some typical systems, then it should be possible to select solvents, solvent systems, and thereby effective procedures for safe cleaning. It is perhaps time to re-examine the 'swab' method of cleaning and the present-day tests used for assessing safety in cleaning, in the light of improved know-ledge in the field of solvent action on polymeric films.

The report which follows is an attempt to present facts pertaining to the action of solvents on a very important type of paint film, that of linseed oil or linseed stand oil. In so doing it is hoped that some new light will be shed on the kinetics, mechanics and physics of cleaning, paying particular attention to the variables of greatest significance in the system: paint–varnish–solvent. The material presented is based partly on researches carried out at the Courtauld Institute of Art[4] and more recent studies in the laboratory of the National Gallery of Canada[5].

Leaching and swelling action of solvents

When a dried film of paint (based on linseed or linseed stand oil) is exposed to solvent for the first time, a marked action takes place. The solvent penetrates quite rapidly, the film swells, becomes appreciably softer, and soluble material leaves the film. When the solvent is allowed to evaporate, the film shrinks in volume resulting in a denser and more compact film.

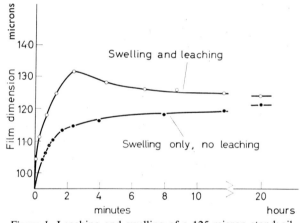

Figure 1. Leaching and swelling of a 125-micron stand oil film aged seven years with acetone solvent at 22°C.

If the film is exposed again to the same solvent the action is repeated, and further leaching of soluble components may take place. The nature or degree of this action depends on film thickness, age, film type, temperature, solvent and the thickness and type of protective coating. In any case it is to be expected that once solvent has been allowed to come into contact with a paint film an irreversible change takes place—that of leaching.

Figure 1 shows this process graphically. The film in this instance is vacuum-bodied stand oil, containing 0·5 per cent lead as naphthenate, cast on a glass plate, and aged for seven years at 20–30°C. The film thickness is 125 microns. The solvent action is measured in a special swelling measurement apparatus[6] which gauges film thickness or dimension very accurately (to within a fraction of a micron) and permits the study of the swelling or leaching (shrinkage) action at intervals of time. It is observed that after 2 minutes of contact with acetone, the dimension measured on the film has increased from 10·5 to 13·2 microns. The absorption of acetone by the film is extremely rapid as seen by the steep rise in the curve. The

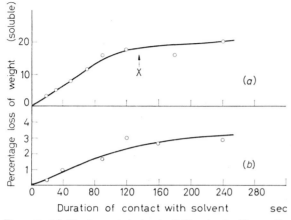

Figure 2. (*a*) Unpigmented stand oil film (as in *Figure 1*): loss in weight as a function of time. (*b*) Loss in weight versus time for white lead pigmented stand oil film aged for seven years at 20–30°C (thickness, 200 microns; unleached density, 3·48 g/cm³; solvent, acetone at 22°C).

action reaches a maximum swelling and starts to fall until an equilibrium level of swelling is reached, which takes several hours. When the film is allowed to evaporate completely and then once more brought into contact with acetone, under the same experimental conditions, the solvent action is represented by a new curve. The lower curve does not pass through a

that the 'virgin' film loses soluble material to an appreciable extent, within seconds of contact. At X, the film has achieved its maximum degree of swelling, and the leaching process continues, but at a reduced rate. The same behaviour is observed in a pigmented film, graphically represented in *Figure 2b*. This film is open-pot stand oil with white lead (19 per cent oil, 81 per cent white lead in the dried unleached film, by weight), aged for seven years at 20–30°C, of film thickness 200 microns, density 3·48 g/cm³. Within seconds of contact with acetone, soluble material is extracted from the film matrix. The maximum amount of material leachable is 4 per cent in this case. Pigmented films lose less weight simply because the oil content represents a smaller proportion by weight of the total weight compared with unpigmented films. Nevertheless the process is identical in both types of film. As a result of this leaching action the film of paint or oil becomes denser and shrinks in volume. For pigmented films the shrinkage may amount to 12 per cent by volume, and the density may increase from 3·48 to 4·00 g/cm³ (films of white lead as above). This action is, of course, irreversible.

It is interesting to follow through the loss in weight of a film at different points in its history. This is shown in *Figure 3*. After seven years' aging, or even after 25 years, the films still exhibit leaching action. Moreover, the amount of extractable material increases. The effect of adding cellosolve is to increase even further the degree of leaching. Acetone is observed to leach more than methanol, while toluene has about the same solubility action as methanol.

It has been suggested[4] that dried films of linseed oil, or drying oils in general, retain within the film matrix quantities of low polymeric triglycerides, monomers and decomposition products as a result of aging. As the film ages, there appears to be some film breakdown and the solubility therefore increases. The passage of the soluble components from the film is facilitated by

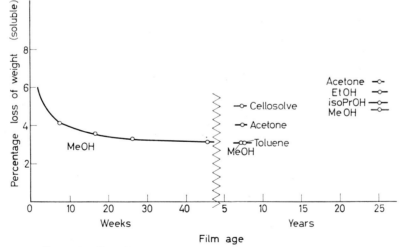

Figure 3. Effect of film age on solubility of pigmented white lead stand oil films at 22°C. Films were aged at 20–30°C.

maximum; it indicates that the leaching of soluble components from the film has stopped. The film, however, continues to imbibe solvent until an equilibrium degree of swelling is reached. If this reswollen film is then evaporated again, and brought into contact with acetone, the lower swelling curve will be repeated. The leaching action is studied separately in *Figure 2a*. The same type of film has been exposed to acetone for different intervals of time and measurements made of the loss in weight after vacuum-pumping off the solvent. It is seen

swelling action. The laws governing such processes are common to the study of kinetics and diffusion behaviour in polymeric systems. As a consequence of the films' losing their 'plasticizer', they become denser and embrittled.

Swelling as a function of the solvent

When a leached or unleached film remains in contact with solvent for a sufficiently long period of time an equilibrium

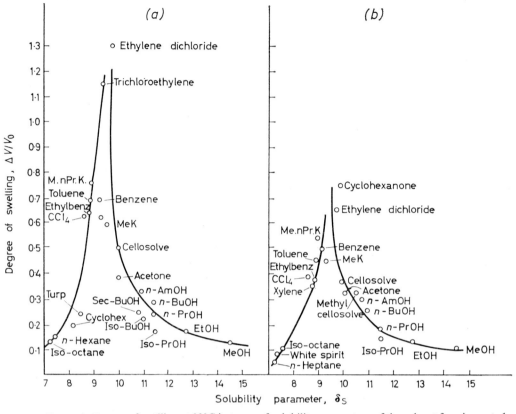

Figure 4. Degree of swelling at 22°C in terms of solubility parameters of the solvent for pigmented white lead stand oil films aged at 20–30°C: (*a*) 27 weeks old; (*b*) 7 years old.

degree of swelling action is obtained. Actually, the swelling of such films reaches a maximum at the outer edges of the film and then, by diffusion processes, the interior of the film is slowly swollen up to the boundary condition level. The equilibrium degree of swelling measured for the total volume of film serves as a useful measure of solvent action. This quantity is expressed as the change in volume of the film as a result of swelling action, divided by the volume of the film prior to the solvent being added

$$\Delta V / V_0$$

where V_0 is the unswollen volume and ΔV is the equilibrium volume change.

Much has been written about solvent action on polymers. A successful approach towards the understanding of solvent action on linseed oil films is by applying the solubility parameter concept[7]. This parameter is a thermodynamic function, which can be assessed for each solvent. The solubility parameters, δ_S, for a number of solvents have been recorded[8] in the literature. This concept has been applied to the present problem, as shown in *Figures 4a* and *b*. The equilibrium degree of swelling and solubility parameter have been plotted for white lead stand oil paint films 27 weeks and 7 years old. It is observed that a characteristic curve is obtained which reaches a maximum in the region $\delta_S = 9.3–9.5$. This is referred to as the solubility parameter of the polymer; in this case linseed oil polymer. Solvents with low degrees of swelling action apparently have parameters well removed from the region 9.3–9.5 units. Thus the lower alcohols, and the paraffinic hydrocarbons (iso-octane, *n*-hexane, etc.) have low swelling action. In contrast to this, solvents such as acetone, cellosolve, tri-

chloroethylene and cyclohexanone have great swelling power. The effect of aging the films is to reduce the shape of the curve to a lower level, as shown in the right of the diagram (see also

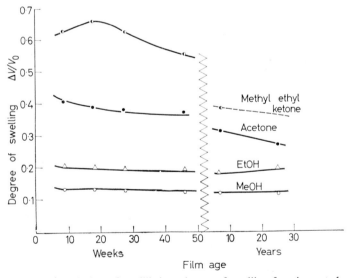

Figure 5. Variation of equilibrium degree of swelling for pigmented white lead stand oil films at 22°C (unleached density, 3.48 g/cm³) as a function of film age.

Figure 5). The solubility parameter behaviour is, however, unchanged after 7 years' aging. It should be possible to predict the action of untested solvents by locating the solvent position

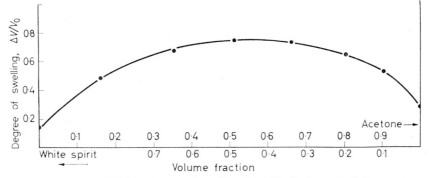

Figure 6. Equilibrium degree of swelling for white lead stand oil films at 22°C (46-week aging at 20–30°C) as a function of the volume fractions of acetone and white spirit.

on the curve from the solubility parameter tables[8]. Obviously, for cleaning of linseed oil pictures it is advisable to choose solvents which have low swelling action. There is, however,

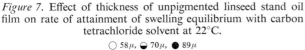

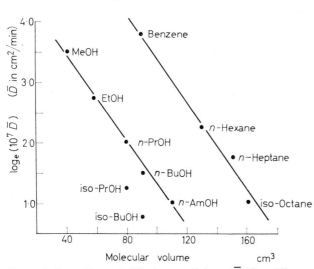

Figure 7. Effect of thickness of unpigmented linseed stand oil film on rate of attainment of swelling equilibrium with carbon tetrachloride solvent at 22°C.

○ 58μ, ◑ 70μ, ● 89μ

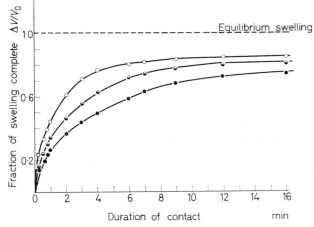

Figure 8. Logarithm of diffusion coefficient ($\overline{D}$) for different solvents against molecular volume of solvent in the white lead stand oil and solvent system at 22°C.

another factor to take into consideration, which will be dealt with in the next section of this report.

The effect of solvent mixtures can be predicted by using these curves and the solubility parameter concept. The parameters are additive according to the molecular fractions of the individual solvents in the mixture. In some systems a maximum swelling point is reached as shown in *Figure 6*.

Diffusion of solvents

It has been found that the swelling solvent advances through the films according to Fick's law of diffusion[9] for a 'semi-infinite solid'. The mathematical application of this law has enabled calculation of diffusion coefficients to be made for different solvents, and to interpret effects of film thickness and temperature on speed of penetration of solvent into and from the linseed oil film matrix. *Figure 7* shows the effect of film thickness on rate of attainment of swelling equilibrium, the solvent being carbon tetrachloride. Doubling the film thickness more than quadruples the time to attain the same proportion of absorbed carbon tetrachloride. In a more practical sense, thin films of paint reach swelling equilibrium much more quickly than do thicker films. *Figure 8* relates the diffusion coefficient to the molecular volume (shape factor of the molecule) of the solvent at 22°C for white lead–linseed stand oil pigmented films. It is seen that the alcohols form a series, as do the hydrocarbons. The latter apparently diffuse more quickly into the oil films than do the alcohols, considering equal molecular volumes.

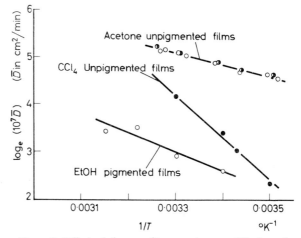

Figure 9. Effect of change of temperature on diffusion of solvents into linseed oil films.

The branched alcohols suffer from steric hindrance and therefore diffuse more slowly into the linseed oil films than the straight-chain alcohols. From this it is seen that methyl alcohol and benzene are very fast diffusers. Among the alcohols it is seen that iso-propyl alcohol is quite slow, and it also has an appreciably low degree of swelling for the films (see *Figures 4a* and *b*). The effect of temperature (*Figure 9*) is as expected; increasing the temperature of the solvent markedly affects the rate of diffusion and hence speed of attainment of swelling equilibrium. The degree of swelling at equilibrium, however, is not affected to any appreciable extent by temperature.

Conclusions

Linseed-oil films appear to be sensitive to solvent action, as far as these studies have been carried through to 25-year-old films. The swelling behaviour follows a consistent pattern, and is predictable within certain limits. An important feature of this study is that linseed-oil films appear to be somewhat more soluble in solvents as they grow older, although their capacity to swell may diminish. This indicates that the film experiences breakdown of polymer chains, probably enhanced by oxidation and exposure to light. Leaching of soluble components is an irreversible process and as such is inevitable in picture cleaning so long as solvents are used. If solvents are to be used for removing old varnish films, chemicals must be found that have a low swelling action on linseed oil films, low degrees of diffusion and at the same time are efficient for the swelling or softening of the varnish coating. It has been the experience of many restorers and conservators that leaching of soluble components occurs because of solvent action, even if no swelling is detectable. It would be worthwhile to see whether or not it is possible to replasticize leached films with compounds closely related to the extracted material. Empirical attempts have been made in the past to 'feed' so-called blanched or leached paint surfaces with linseed oil or stand oil. At best this coats the paint, but does not replasticize the paint film by

penetration. Some further research along these lines would be extremely useful. It is first necessary to define by analysis the materials which form the soluble compounds of linseed oil films. This presumably can be done by infra-red spectroscopy and gas chromatography, two instruments of great importance in the analytical protective coatings field. It may be that some fairly simple low molecular weight triglyceride, e.g. triolein or tristearin, could serve the purpose. At the moment this is mere conjecture.

Acknowledgements

The author wishes to thank Miss Elizabeth Jones, of the Fogg Art Museum, Cambridge (Mass.), USA, for the samples of pigmented film which were prepared in 1936, and were so wisely kept for such an occasion. Acknowledgements are also made to the Director of the National Gallery of Canada, Dr C. F. Comfort, for his encouragement and support during these researches.

References

[1] Déon, H., *De la Conservation et de la Restauration des Tableaux*, Paris, 1851.

[2] Faraday, M., *Minutes of Evidence of the Parliamentary Select Committee on the National Gallery*, House of Commons, London, 1853.

[3] Laurie, A. P., *Trans. Faraday Soc.*, 31 (1937) 293.

[4] Stolow, N., *Some investigations of the action of solvents on drying oil films*, Ph.D. thesis, University of London, London, 1955.

[5] Stolow, N., unpublished researches on solvent action in the Conservation and Scientific Research Division of the National Gallery of Canada, Ottawa, 1960–61.

[6] Stolow, N., *J. sci. Instrum.*, 31 (1954) 416.

[7] Stolow, N., *J. Oil Col. Chem. Ass.*, 40 (1957) Part I, 337; Part II, 448.

[8] Burrell, H., *Interchem. Rev.*, 14 (1955) 3, 31.

[9] Drechsel, P., Hoard, J. L. and Long, F. A., *J. Polym. Sci.*, 10 (1954) 241.

Rutherford J. Gettens

MINERAL ALTERATION PRODUCTS ON ANCIENT METAL OBJECTS

The surfaces of nearly all ancient metal objects, except gold, whether buried in the soil, immersed in fresh or salt water or exposed to air, rain and sun, have undergone some transformation because of chemical reaction with the surrounding environment. The surface alteration may be quite thin and superficial and hardly measurable or it may be so complete that none of the original metal remains. The metal eventually reverts to products similar to the minerals (ores) from which it was originally derived. It is convenient to call these corrosion end-products 'mineral alteration products', although some mineralogists insist that the intervention of man can play no part in the formation of a true mineral, and they refuse to accept for mineral classification any product formed on an artifact. Austin F. Rogers, Professor of Mineralogy at Leland Stanford University early in this century, did not hesitate to name as 'minerals' the corrosion products he observed on ancient Chinese coins[1]. Clark, an authority on geology, makes several allusions to 'minerals' on artifacts[2] and the present revisers of the classic 'Dana's System of Mineralogy'[3] cite a number of occurrences of minerals on specific man-made objects. There are no differences, either physical or chemical, between compounds created by purely natural processes and those formed on an artifact where the hand of man assisted in bringing the reactants together.

The mineral alteration products on copper and its alloys often add interest and even beauty to an object and increase its value in the eyes of collectors. The term 'patina' is applied to thin corrosion films which give evidence of age and long use. Green and red patina on ancient bronze is so much admired that it is sometimes applied artificially to increase the allure of objects that do not have it naturally. Old lead with thin crusts of cerussite and litharge is more interesting than raw lead. Most alteration products on metals, however, are ugly and disfiguring. Rust on iron has little appeal; likewise tarnish on silver is not admired. Even copper and bronze can be made ugly by certain types of corrosion crusts. When thick they can obscure fine details of decoration and modelling, and can entirely conceal inlays. They often act as cementing agents for clay and earthy crusts.

For these many reasons, and with the hope that they can be returned to a semblance of their original condition, there is often an urge to clean metal objects immediately after excavation from soil or sea or even after they have been stored or displayed in museums. Herein lie certain dangers and opportunity for oversight. I am not so much concerned here with harm to the object or with acts of malpractice as I am with the possible loss of historical and scientific evidence which may be contained in or concealed by ugly corrosion crusts. In these mineral crusts may be evidence of metal composition, of age and even of place of origin. They may serve as natural protective coatings for less stable compounds beneath. For these many reasons corrosion crusts should be carefully examined and identified by an expert before they are scraped or dissolved away by a technician and thrown into a waste jar or sink. There is one other good reason for taking a careful look at corrosion crusts: they may contain rare minerals unknown or little known to science, which add greatly to their interest and importance. Later in this paper I shall mention one mineral, chalconatronite, which was first discovered on archaeological material. I shall also cite other occurrences of rare minerals on metal artifacts.

Below, I shall describe briefly the mineral alteration products, some common, some less common, that are observed on metal antiquities.

Copper

Of all the metals used in antiquity, copper forms the most colourful and the most interesting group of mineral alteration products.

Oxides

Probably the most widely occurring alteration mineral of ancient copper and its alloys is *cuprite*, Cu_2O, the red lower oxide of that element. Usually most of it is concealed beneath overlying green basic salts of copper, and it seems to be an intermediate compound in the conversion of metal to basic salt. Cuprite underlayer is often revealed when the outer green oxidation crusts are removed by mechanical cleaning. In cast bronzes, cuprite sometimes forms along grain boundaries or in seams that penetrate deeply into the metal core. In some cases the cuprite is fine-grained and orange-yellow in colour, but more often it occurs in coarsely crystalline masses in which perfect crystals of cubic form abound. A fractured or scaled surface of cuprite on bronze occasionally has a sugary appearance caused by the light reflectance of numerous small crystal faces.

The black cupric oxides, *tenorite* and *melaconite*, CuO, are seldom reported; if present they seem to have been consistently overlooked. Sometimes there are black-looking products among thin inner corrosion layers, but these have never been sufficiently isolated to permit their certain identification, even by x-ray diffraction methods.

Carbonates

The two basic carbonates of copper, malachite and azurite, are perhaps the most familiar natural alteration products of copper artifacts.

Malachite, $Cu_2(OH)_2CO_3$: This usually forms smooth dark green compact layers on the surface of a bronze, but is often seen in scattered rounded masses described as mammillary, or botryoidal, because of their resemblance to clusters of green grapes. Sometimes malachite is observed on bronzes in delicate fibrous aggregates, sheaf-like in form. Patches of malachite can make an ordinary object of copper or bronze look interesting and precious.

Azurite, $Cu_3(OH)_2(CO_3)_2$: Although azurite is similar in composition to malachite, its colour is bright to dark blue. Like malachite, it sometimes occurs on objects as a compact continuous dark blue layer, but more frequently as fine crystal aggregates scattered among patches of malachite. As in nature, azurite on artifacts is less abundant than malachite. It is most often seen on the interior surfaces of hollow vessels where perhaps less humid conditions prevailed. Occasionally a bronze will appear to be completely transformed to crystalline azurite.

It is presumed that malachite and azurite are formed by contact with soil water or condensed water charged with carbon dioxide or carbonic acid. Cuprite is sometimes observed in an intermediate zone between the carbonate layer and the metal core, but it is not yet certain that cuprite formation is essential to the reaction.

Chalconatronite: A few years ago Gettens and Frondel[4] discovered on the hollow interior of an Egyptian bronze figurine of the deity Sekhmet, in the Fogg Museum of Art, a bluish-green chalky crust which did not have the properties of any of the copper minerals commonly found on ancient buried bronzes. After study, it was determined to be a hydrous double carbonate of copper and sodium having the composition $Na_2Cu(CO_3)_2 \cdot 3H_2O$, a new mineral species not previously described. It was given the name 'chalconatronite'[4]. This mineral was also observed on an Egyptian bronze group, 'Cat and Kittens', in the Gulbenkian Collection and on a Coptic censer in the Freer Gallery of Art. Chalconatronite seems to be a product of Egypt, where, in certain districts, alkali carbonates occur abundantly in the soil.

Chlorides

On ancient copper and bronze objects found after long contact with the saline soils of desert regions the green corrosion crusts are usually a mixture of the chlorides of copper.

Atacamite: Chief among these is atacamite, $Cu_2(OH)_3Cl$, which gets its name from the desert of Atacama in northern Chile, where it occurs widely among the secondary ores of copper. Since sodium chloride is highly reactive toward copper and its alloys, ancient artifacts of these metals are often converted to fissured and nearly formless masses of atacamite. The colour of the mineral ranges from emerald to blackish green. On the surface of many bronze objects from Egypt and Mesopotamia atacamite occurs as an all-over sugary-looking coating of dark green glistening crystals. Often the dark green crystalline atacamite is altered to a paler green powdery product which gives the x-ray diffraction pattern of *paratacamite*[5], identical in chemical composition but differing in crystal form (hexagonal) from atacamite (orthorhombic). One mineral seems to occur about as frequently as the other.

Nantokite: Cross-section studies on bronzes massively coated with atacamite sometimes reveal an inner layer of pale grey waxy-looking substance which has been shown to be cuprous chloride. It conforms to the unstable mineral called nantokite, named from its first-noted occurrence at Nantoko in Chile. This mineral, when exposed to moist air, rapidly oxidizes to red cuprous oxide (cuprite) and bright green basic cupric chloride (atacamite). This rapid alteration of nantokite can also take place on bronzes in museums, where it goes by the name 'bronze disease'. Since nantokite does not occur on the surfaces of bronze it is difficult to photograph except in specially prepared thin sections.

Botallacite, $Cu_2(OH)_3Cl \cdot H_2O$: This is another basic copper chloride mineral and was found originally at the Botallack mine, St Just, Cornwall, England. It was first described by A. H. Church in 1865, and the type specimen was placed in the British Museum. For nearly a century no other occurrence of this mineral was reported until a specimen of greenish-blue alteration product taken from the interior of an Egyptian bronze figurine of the deity Bastet in the Fogg Museum of Art was identified by Professor Frondel, of Harvard, as botallacite[6]. A second occurrence on an artifact was observed by R. J. Gettens on an Egyptian bronze censer in the Walters Art Gallery, Baltimore. Botallacite probably occurs on ancient bronzes more commonly than hitherto suspected. There are other basic copper chlorides mentioned by Frondel which may be found some day on a bronze.

Sulphates

The bright green basic sulphate of copper corresponding to the mineral *brochantite*, $CuSO_4 \cdot 3Cu(OH)_3$, is seldom reported on artifacts although it might be expected on bronze exposed to sulphur-bearing waters or atmospheres. Gettens[7] found evidence of basic copper sulphate in the green corrosion crusts of a bronze statue of Nathan Hale in Hartford, Connecticut. The refractive index indicates the green was more like *antlerite*, $Cu_3(SO_4)(OH)_4$ than brochantite. The source of sulphur seems to be the industrial atmosphere in which the statue had been exposed. More recently Gettens examined the thin green corrosion crusts on a number of bronze statues in the Garden Court of the Ringling Museum in Sarasota, Florida, and again found that the alteration product gave an x-ray diffraction pattern corresponding to brochantite. The sulphur at Sarasota originates in the hydrogen sulphide-bearing waters used in the irrigation system in the garden. Likewise a sample of green removed from a weather-exposed bronze lamp-post in front of the Freer Gallery of Art gives a brochantite pattern. There is good evidence that the green on copper roofs and statuary bronze in large cities is mostly basic copper sulphate, formed from sulphur compounds produced by the burning of fuels.

Sulphides

Sulphides are not often reported as occurring on copper artifacts, although they are to be expected where objects have been in contact with sulphur-bearing waters. Both Rogers[8] and Clark[9] mention the investigations of A. Daubrée and others, who examined Roman coins and metals recovered years ago from French thermal springs and report occurrences of *chalcocite*, Cu_2S, *chalcopyrite*, $CuFeS_2$, *bornite*, Cu_5FeS_4 and *tetrahedrite*, $(Cu,Fe)_{12}Sb_4S_{13}$. If the black deposits in copper and bronze could be given more attention perhaps the list of occurrences of sulphides and oxides would be extended.

Nitrates

Recently the writer had the privilege of taking samples of green crystalline corrosion products from bronze vessels found by University of Pennsylvania archaeologists in a tomb in the mound at Gordion in Anatolia. Preliminary studies showed that the crystals were basic nitrates of copper; the crystals gave x-ray diffraction patterns identical with patterns of synthetic basic copper nitrates, which have not yet been reported to occur naturally. There may be new minerals among these copper corrosion products from Gordion. It is feared, however, that most of the copper alteration products on Gordion bronzes have been lost through hasty and premature cleaning.

The natural blue-green silicate of copper, *chrysocolla*, has probably been observed but no occurrence has been reported.

Native or *redeposited copper* sometimes occurs sparsely among the inner layers of heavily chloride-encrusted bronzes. It is probably formed by the reduction of cuprous chloride (nantokite) by the more electropositive high-tin phases of bronze alloy. Redeposited copper can occur in isolated pockets or patches, or as a continuous inner layer. It is sometimes found as little scales underneath green corrosion crusts.

In spite of the considerable amount of research already done, there is still much to be learned about corrosion products and processes of copper and its alloys. Investigators in industry have been much concerned with corroding agents and corrosion prevention, but they have given little attention to corrosion products.

Lead

After copper, lead, among ancient metals, forms the widest variety of alteration products.

Carbonates

The commonest alteration product on lead is *cerussite*, or normal lead carbonate, $PbCO_3$. This is the dense adherent warm-grey deposit usually seen on old lead seals, lead sarcophagi and all sorts of buried lead objects. Fortunately, cerussite seems to form a protective layer on lead and prevents its progressive and complete disintegration. In 1959, during the restoration of the east front of the U.S. Capitol in Washington, sheet lead pads were found under the old marble columns when they were removed for replacement. The lead pads and columns were set in place in 1825. When uncovered, the lead was observed to be thinly encrusted with a white deposit, which was shown by x-ray diffraction methods to be *hydrocerussite*, $Pb_3(CO_3)_2(OH)_2$, corresponding to the artificial white lead commonly used as a paint pigment. When exposed to open air it will probably further alter to cerussite as it often does in nature.

Oxides

Next to the carbonates, the oxides of lead seem to be the most common. Caley[10] identified *massicot*, or yellow lead monoxide, on lead objects from the Agora in Athens. He also found thin dark brown patches of lead dioxide or *plattnerite* in a thin layer next to the lead metal. On the lead pads from the U.S. Capitol mentioned above, patches of a hard salmon-pink encrustation gave the x-ray diffraction pattern of *litharge*, another form of lead monoxide. The third oxide of lead, *minium*, occurs in nature but it apparently has not been reported on a lead artifact.

Sulphide

No occurrence of lead sulphide corresponding to galena has been reported.

Chlorides

Although the straight chloride of lead, *cotunnite*, $PbCl_2$, has not been reported, more complex chlorides have. In the Freer study collection there is a stem or column of an old Persian lamp which is made of highly leaded bronze. Most of the surface is covered with nondescript corrosion crusts of copper, but samples taken from scattered crystalline whitish patches give the x-ray diffraction pattern of the rare mineral *phosgenite*, $PbCl_2 \cdot PbCO_3$. Phosgenite was also observed many years ago on ancient metallic objects immersed in seawater near Mahdia, Tunis, and on leaden pipe in hot springs at Bourbonne-les-Bains, France[11]. Also on this subject, scattered small clusters were observed of deep blue, highly refracting crystals which x-ray diffraction analysis showed to be an even more rare mineral *cumengite*, $Pb_4Cu_4Cl_8(OH)_8$. It is named after the French mining engineer Edouard Cumenge (1829–1892) and only a single occurrence, from Baja, California, Mexico, is reported in Dana. This is one more example of a rare mineral appearing on an artifact.

The occurrence of *anglesite*, $PbSO_4$, and other lead and copper–lead minerals may have been observed but they do not seem to have been reported. Here is a possible opportunity which should not be overlooked by the archaeological chemist or the rare mineral collector.

Tin

Tin is a metal of prime importance in archaeology, not as a separate craft material but as a necessary adjunct to the making of bronze. Unfortunately, few objects of pure tin survive from antiquity even from centres of early bronze making, like Egypt, Mesopotamia and China. If much pure tin was made in antiquity it has perished, perhaps for two reasons. First it has been transformed by direct intercrystalline oxidation to mixed stannous and stannic oxides. Plenderleith and Organ[12] describe tin oxidation in some detail and Caley[13] and Mantell[14] both describe the important role of halides, especially sodium chloride, in stimulating corrosion attack on tin. This is perhaps another reason why so little tin has survived.

Tin oxide, however, is an important alteration product on the surfaces of ancient high-tin bronzes. It is a major constituent of the smooth grey-green corrosion layer on Chinese bronze ceremonial vessels sometimes called 'water patina'. It also occurs on high-tin Etruscan and other European bronzes. This alteration product, which may penetrate into the bronze for a distance of 1 to 2 mm, is a hydrous form of stannic oxide. The pale greenish colour is a sort of stain caused by a small impurity of copper. It appears that under certain conditions of soil contact the copper is dissolved away from the surface of bronze and is replaced, molecule by molecule, without volume change, by hydrous stannic oxide. The phenomenon is something like pseudomorphic substitution in mineralogy. The hydrous tin oxide encasing corroded high-tin bronzes is sometimes compact and translucent like ceramic glaze. In other occurrences the tin oxide is powdery and friable. The x-ray diffraction pattern of the hydrous tin oxide alteration product is similar to cassiterite, but the lines are broader and more diffuse, which suggests that it is cryptocrystalline and more finely divided than natural cassiterite.

The other reason why so little metallic tin has survived may be the phenomenon called 'tin pest', which is the transformation of tetragonal metallic white tin to cubic powdery grey tin by allotropic modification at an equilibrium temperature of about $13 \cdot 2°C$. This behaviour of tin is well described by Plenderleith and Organ[15], but since it hardly comes within the scope of mineral alteration it will not be considered here.

There is still much to be done before a complete understanding of the solution of copper and its replacement by tin oxide on bronze surfaces is gained.

Silver

Sulphides

Like tin, silver forms few alteration products. Black silver tarnish formed by the action of hydrogen sulphide is familiar to everyone. We have never known of the occurrence on artifacts of thick crusts of silver sulphide corresponding to the mineral *argentite*, Ag_2S, but they do, no doubt, occur on silver artifacts long exposed to sulphur-bearing waters. Perhaps black argentite and even the lesser silver mineral *stromeyerite*, $CuAg_2S$, are among those many interesting corrosion products that go down the drain unadmired for colour and unappreciated for rarity.

Chlorides

Cerargyrite: Silver objects retrieved from desert soils are often encrusted with a grey-brown or dull lavender crust of cerargyrite or silver chloride, $AgCl$. Silver coins recovered from salt water and saline soils are commonly altered to cerargyrite. Since cerargyrite, or 'horn silver', is dense and protective the silver metal beneath is little altered. Many of the silver ewers and bowls recovered from Ur of the Chaldees, now in the University of Pennsylvania Museum, were originally heavily encrusted with cerargyrite. After the crusts were removed by electrolysis and formic acid, much of the original appearance of these precious antiquities was restored[16].

We still do not find listed in Dana a compound mineral of copper and silver chlorides, although there is one of silver iodide called *miersite*, in which copper substitutes for silver. A new mineral of copper and silver chlorides may be found for the first time on some silver artifact. For this reason let us stay the hand of those who want to put ugly excavated silver objects through the cleaning bath before they can be properly examined.

Iron

Iron rust is so common and held in such disfavour that it is quickly removed if the object which bears it is of any interest.

Goethite and limonite: In the process known as rusting, iron is converted to its hydrous oxides, either goethite, $FeO(OH)$, named after the German poet, or limonite, $FeO(OH) \cdot nH_2O$. Goethite, which is the more crystalline mineral of the two, occurs on objects as fibrous aggregates, while limonite is amorphous or cryptocrystalline, with absorbed or capillary water.

Magnetite, $FeFe_2O_4$: The black oxide of iron, magnetite probably occurs on archaeological iron more commonly than realized, especially in the interior of deeply corroded large iron objects where reducing conditions are likely to prevail. There is much technical literature on the rusting of iron, but little that is available or useful to the archaeologist except that excellent short summary given by Plenderleith in Chapter 13 of his well-known work[17].

Other minerals like *siderite*, $FeCO_3$, *vivianite*, $Fe_3(PO_4)_2 \cdot 8H_2O$, and *pyrite*, FeS_2, must commonly occur, but they are seldom mentioned in archaeological reports. Some interesting observations on the role of tannates and phosphates in the preservation of buried iron objects have been made in England, where both vivianite and oxidized vivianite were identified in a Roman knife[18].

There is little doubt that even the familiar and well studied field of iron corrosion could be further examined with benefit to archaeology.

Zinc

Although the Romans and later the Chinese produced brass, or copper–zinc alloy, and although zinc metal probably came into use in China and India in the Middle Ages, it was not recognized in Europe as a distinct element until the 18th century. After that zinc gradually came into commercial production in the West. Because of their scarcity, and because of the chemical activity of zinc, few objects of that metal have survived from antiquity; hence little attention has been given to its alteration products. A greyish crust on a 19th century Italian pot of zinc, now in the U.S. National Museum, was

shown to be *hydrozincite*, $Zn_5(OH)_6(CO_3)_2$. *Smithsonite* and perhaps some rare copper–zinc minerals may appear some day.

Discussion

This list of mineral alteration products contains not only rare and little-known items, but also a number that are common and familiar. Even the modes of formation of some of the more common ones are not as well understood as they should be. The occurrence of the rarer minerals is perhaps only of academic interest for the present, but there is no knowing when the information will become useful. For this reason the author proposes to start to assemble material for a monograph on mineral alteration products of ancient metals. The minerals will be treated individually as in any compendium on mineralogy, covering composition, properties and occurrences. It may take several years to assemble this material and to organize it. I should like the help of all those assembled here in Rome to collect specimens, to report occurrences and to make suggestions. This monograph could be useful to archaeologists, to scientists and to curators and collectors in the field of archaeology.

References

[1] ROGERS, A. F., Minerals observed on buried Chinese coins of the seventh century, *Amer. Geol.*, 31 (1903) 43–46.

[2] CLARK, F. W., The data of geochemistry, fifth edition, *Bull. U.S. geol. Surv.*, 770 (1924).

[3] PALACHE, C., BERMAN, H. and FRONDEL, C., *Dana's System of Mineralogy*, Vol. I (1944), Vol. II (1951), Wiley & Sons, New York.

[4] GETTENS, R. J. and FRONDEL, C., Chalconatronite: an alteration product of some ancient Egyptian bronzes, *Stud. Conservation*, 2 (1955) 64–75.

[5] FRONDEL, C., On paratacamite and some related copper chlorides, *Miner. Mag.*, 29 (1950) 34–45.

[6] FRONDEL, C., reference 5, p. 42.

[7] GETTENS, R. J., Composition of the patina on a modern bronze statue, *Tech. Stud. fine Arts*, 2 (1933) 31–33.

[8] ROGERS, A. F., reference 1.

[9] CLARK, F. W., reference 2.

[10] CALEY, E. R., Coatings and incrustation on lead objects from the Agora and the method used for their removal, *Stud. Conservation*, 2 (1955) 49–54.

[11] PALACHE, C., BERMAN, H. and FRONDEL, C., *Dana's System of Mineralogy*, Vol. II (1951), p. 258, Wiley and Sons, New York.

[12] PLENDERLEITH, H. J. and ORGAN, R. M., The decay and conservation of museum objects of tin, *Stud. Conservation*, 1 (1953) 63–72.

[13] CALEY, E. R., The corroded bronze of Corinth, *Proc. Amer. phil. Soc.*, 84 (1941) 689–761.

[14] MANTELL, C. L., *Tin: Its mining, production, technology and applications*, second edition, Reinhold, New York, 1949, pp. 452–455.

[15] PLENDERLEITH, H. J. and ORGAN, R. M., reference 12.

[16] GRAHAM, A. K., Scientific notes on the finds from Ur, *Mus. J. (Philad.)*, 20 (1929) 246–257.

[17] PLENDERLEITH, H. J., *The Conservation of Antiquities and Works of Art*, Oxford University Press, London, 1956.

[18] FARRER, T. W., BIEK, L. and WORMWELL, F., The role of tannates and phosphates in the preservation of ancient buried iron objects, *J. appl. Chem.*, 3 (1953) 80–84.

Albert France-Lanord

LE PROBLÈME DE LA CONSERVATION DES ANTIQUITÉS MÉTALLIQUES EN FRANCE

Il est pratiquement actuellement impossible de faire une estimation précise de l'abondance du mobilier métallique ancien conservé dans les musées français, mais il n'est pas téméraire d'affirmer que l'ensemble des collections archéologiques protohistoriques, gallo-romaines et franques réprésente une masse d'objets métalliques pesant de 150 à 200 tonnes au minimum, ou encore certainement plus d'un million d'objets de toute nature. Ces chiffres n'ont d'autre prétention que de fixer des ordres de grandeur, mais ils montrent que la France est dans ce domaine un des pays les plus riches du monde, ce qui s'explique aisément du fait de la grande densité de la population dans cette partie privilégiée de l'Europe occidentale au cours des époques anciennes.

Ces objets de métaux précieux, de bronze ou de fer, sont dispersés dans les collections et dans les réserves de près de 900 musées, et si les pièces les plus spectaculaires sont bien connues, il n'en est actuellement pas de même de la plus grande partie du reste. Comme il se poursuit actuellement en France un remarquable effort de réorganisation des musées, accompagné d'un regain d'intérêt du public pour tout ce qui touche au domaine de l'archéologie, il m'a paru intéressant et opportun d'essayer de poser le problème de la conservation de ces antiquités tout en essayant d'en tirer quelques conclusions pour l'avenir.

Conserver un objet signifie essentiellement pour les gens de musées, prendre un certain nombre de mesures pour que cet objet qui nous a été transmis par des générations passées, et qui est un document dont nous ne pouvons pas toujours estimer l'intérêt, puisse d'une part échapper à toutes les destructions possibles qui le menacent, et servir d'autre part à tout moment à répondre à la curiosité des spécialistes ou du public. Il faut en bref en assurer la survie et le faire servir. Ceci représente au départ deux séries de problèmes totalement différents qu'il n'est cependant pas possible de considérer isolément. Je les appelerai la conservation matérielle et la conservation intellectuelle.

Les collections archéologiques françaises se sont constituées en grande partie au cours du XIXème siècle, soit à la suite de fouilles, soit grâce à l'activité de collectionneurs. Les fouilles ont été tantôt organisées par des missions officielles, ou des sociétés savantes, soit pratiquées par des amateurs plus ou moins qualifiés. Les collections ont été composées de manière essentiellement variable. La masse des objets ainsi recueillis est venue enrichir peu à peu les musées et ceci d'une façon très variable. Les musées nationaux conservent une part importante de ce patrimoine, à Paris ou à Saint Germain en Laye, mais la masse des musées de province conserve des collections très dispersées dont l'intérêt artistique ou scientifique est tout aussi grand. Tous ces musées sont maintenant controlés par l'administration de la Direction des Musées de France. Ils sont pourvus de conservateurs compétents et extrêmement dévoués. Ils reçoivent de la part des autorités locales dont ils dépendent des crédits qui ne sont pas toujours suffisants, auxquels s'ajoutent des subventions de l'État. Il y a dans ce domaine une amélioration très nette par rapport au passé.

Mais les locaux ne sont pas toujours suffisants, le personnel auxiliaire est pratiquement inexistant, et les collections archéologiques ne constituent en général qu'une part accessoire des collections dont les conservateurs ont la charge. En outre leur formation archéologique de base est actuellement insuffisante.

Les grands musées possèdent habituellement des inventaires complets et bien tenus, mais la plupart des autres sont moins favorisés dans ce domaine. De plus ces inventaires ne sont pas suffisants.

La conservation des collections a souvent été confiée dans le passé à des personnes dévouées et désintéressées qui n'ont pas toujours su tenir à jour les catalogues. L'identification des pièces provenant de collections privées est souvent difficile. Il existe heureusement d'innombrables collections de publications de sociétés savantes auxquelles il est possible de se référer, mais ceci réprésente un travail de dépouillement considérable. On peut considérer que ce dépouillement est en cours dans beaucoup de musées de province, et que l'inventaire des collections et des réserves est en progrès constant.

Le premier souci des conservateurs a été évidemment d'améliorer les conditions de présentation des collections dans des locaux presque toujours trop petits étant donné la richesse et la diversité des collections. La faveur croissante auprès du public de tout ce qui a trait à l'histoire ancienne et à l'archéologie, constitue un élément récent et favorable à la sauvegarde d'ensembles qui avaient été longtemps abandonnés, et il est réconfortant de constater la réorganisation des sections archéologiques de nombreux musées français. Mais il y a aussi beaucoup de collections en caisses faute de place ou de crédits.

Ceci montre qu'il y a en France un très important problème posé par la conservation des collections archéologiques, et en particulier par les antiquités métalliques, et la réalité de ce problème est constatée par l'ensemble des conservateurs. Que les conservateurs soient actifs et conscients de la réalité de ce problème, c'est là un fait nouveau particulièrement important, parce qu'il pose l'urgence des solutions à apporter pour les aider et leur permettre de mener à bien la tâche qu'ils entreprennent. Il faut aussi faire en sorte que le travail qu'ils entreprennent actuellement soit utilisable au delà du musée dont ils ont la charge.

Les collections d'antiquités peuvent être divisées en deux catégories, selon qu'il s'agisse d'antiquités nationales ou d'antiquités provenant de pays étrangers: Orient, Grèce ou Italie. La première catégorie, la plus importante, souffre de la défaveur dans laquelle les antiquités nationales ont été tenues depuis deux ou trois générations. La seconde a bénéficié de la compétence et du travail de nombreuses organisations, écoles ou instituts. Des savants et des spécialistes hautement qualifiés ont découvert ces objets, les ont étudiés, inventoriés et publiés. On possède de la sorte des ensembles qui peuvent à chaque moment être comparés aux ensembles similaires qui existent dans les pays étrangers. Ici, le travail scientifique est fait selon des normes internationales et le seul problème qui se pose est celui de la conservation matérielle, c'est à dire des moyens d'échapper à toutes les destructions possibles.

Pour la quasi totalité des antiquités nationales, il faut résoudre également ce problème, mais aussi celui de la conservation intellectuelle: classement, inventaire, en même temps que de leur diffusion.

Je commencerai donc par exposer ce dernier aspect du problème général, car c'est aussi par là qu'il convient de commencer dans le cadre même du musée.

Ce qui a été fait pour les peintures et les sculptures peut aussi se concevoir pour les objets métalliques. Il faut commencer par établir l'inventaire des collections et des réserves, cet inventaire se traduisant en pratique par des fiches d'un modèle unique pour les musées français et peut-être internationaux. Ces fiches donneront en plus des caractéristiques d'identité de chaque objet, ses caractéristiques physiques indispensables—mesures, poids, couleur, matière—ainsi que la description aussi précise et normalisée que possible de l'état de conservation—corrosion, patine, destructions, déformations, restaurations. Une illustration est absolument indispensable, photographie et dessin. Ici on se heurte à une première difficulté, car rares, pour ne pas dire exceptionnels, sont les musées qui disposent d'un service photographique.

Les musées ne possèdent ni personnel, ni matériel, ni crédit pour ce genre d'activité. La bonne volonté ne suffit pas et si quelques conservateurs parviennent le cas échéant à fournir avec des moyens de fortune des clichés acceptables grâce à des bonnes volontés ou à leur ingéniosité, cela n'a rien de commun avec les milliers de clichés normalisés que chaque musée devrait être en mesure de donner. Il faut donc commencer par doter chaque musée de son propre service photographique ou organiser des services ambulants ce qui serait plus économique, seuls quelques grands centres pouvant créer leur propre organisation. Chaque fiche serait établie en trois exemplaires, l'un restant au musée, le second allant au fichier central et le troisième servant à la préparation des opérations de conservation matérielle.

Il va de soi que la rédaction de ces fiches peut poser aux conservateurs des questions de définition ou d'identification difficiles à résoudre. Là aussi la collaboration d'un spécialiste ambulant, inspecteur qualifié sera nécessaire.

Ces opérations préliminaires ne sont pas par elles-mêmes très compliquées; la difficulté réside dans le grand nombre d'objets à mettre en fiche, ce qui représente finalement une dépense considérable que l'on peut estimer à plusieurs millions de Nouveaux Francs.

Les moyens de classement actuels rendent possible la création d'un fichier central qui présenterait un intérêt scientifique considérable. Un tel fichier n'est pas du domaine des utopies, et il semble possible d'en entreprendre la réalisation en partant d'un programme raisonnablement établi. Le personnel compétent est également assez facile à trouver du fait de l'intérêt de beaucoup de jeunes gens pour les questions archéologiques. Ceci pourrait constituer la véritable mise en valeur du patrimoine archéologique national. Étant donné que la création de ce patrimoine n'a en fait pas coûté grand chose à la collectivité, il n'est pas déraisonnable de mettre à la charge de cette collectivité les moyens d'en retirer tout l'intérêt scientifique souhaitable.

Sans ce travail préliminaire, les collections risquent de demeurer encore longtemps stériles. Il est aussi urgent de l'entreprendre car des sondages montrent qu'un peu partout on perd maintenant la trace d'objets autrefois publiés.

La conservation matérielle pose d'autres problèmes. Est-il possible de se faire une idée de l'état dans lequel se trouvent actuellement nos collections d'antiquités métalliques? Mon expérience personnelle m'a mis en présence des séries et des réserves d'un assez bon nombre de musées, tant à Paris qu'en province. D'une façon générale, les objets exposés sont en assez bon état: on présente justement ce qui est le plus correct, et bien des objets, surtout ceux qui ont un caractère artistique, ont été autrefois nettoyés. Mais souvent les objets travaillent dans les vitrines même, et ils se détériorent plus ou moins rapidement. Mais dans les réserves qui sont considérables, les collections sont encore le plus souvent à l'état brut et ont souffert du fait de mauvaises conditions de stockage. C'est précisément dans les réserves qu'il est possible de faire de véritables découvertes. Il est plus intéressant dans l'immédiat de fouiller dans les réserves de musées que sur le terrain: les chances de succès sont bien plus certaines.

Il faut également considérer les objets par catgéories: les pièces d'orfèvrerie, les objets de bronze, puis de fer. Les premières sont plus nombreuses dans les vitrines que dans les réserves: bijoux de toutes époques, trésors d'église. Mais aussi ces trésors restent enfouis dans des coffres du fait du manque de moyens de sécurité et de gardiennage. Si ces objets sont en grande majorité dans un état stable, la plupart d'entre eux devrait être consolidée ou partiellement restaurée, et tous auraient besoin de nettoyages.

Les objets de bronze de provenance orientale sont souvent en assez mauvais état, il en est de même des collections égyptiennes des musées de province ou des réserves. Le nettoyage systématique serait à faire et il serait prudent d'améliorer les conditions de dépôt par un aménagement rationnel des réserves. Il en est de même des bronzes grecs, étrusques ou romains.

Le plus gros travail reste la masse considérable des bronzes découverts sur le sol métropolitain. Si d'une façon générale ils sont assez stables, on peut affirmer que la quasi totalité d'entre eux devrait être nettoyée. Ce travail amènerait aussi d'agréables surprises, et les musées qui ont fait traiter systématiquement des séries d'objets au cours de ces dernières années ne l'ont pas regretté.

L'industrie du fer s'étant considérablement développée en Gaule, il est normal que nous possédions de grandes quantités d'objets façonnés dans ce métal. C'est justement cette abondance qui est un peu à la base de la défaveur dans laquelle ces pièces ont été longtemps tenues. On reconnait cependant maintenant que les objets les plus usuels sont souvent les plus utiles pour la connaissance des civilisations passées. Beaucoup d'objets de fer conservés dans les musées sont actuellement complètement perdus du fait de la corrosion, mais il est possible dans bien des cas d'en faire encore un bon dessin. Les autres sont plus ou moins malades et demandent des traitements appropriés pour retrouver une forme et un intérêt. Le travail en vaut la peine, une bonne preuve en est les quelques 1200 pièces d'orfèvrerie de fer damasquinées d'argent, révélées au cours de ces dernières années.

En face de ces besoins, quels sont les moyens dont on dispose actuellement en France?

Le Musée des Antiquités Nationales a été l'un des premiers au monde à posséder un laboratoire de traitement des objets. De ce fait, un grand nombre de pièces conservées dans ce musée ont été jadis traitées. Ce laboratoire était en outre spécialisé pour la confection de moulages et de reproductions galvanoplastiques. Actuellement, il ne fonctionne plus en tant que centre de conservation ou de restauration, mais il dispose de moyens modernes pour l'analyse des métaux non ferreux. Il y a à Paris quelques restaurateurs privés agréés par les musées nationaux et qui font de très belles restaurations, en particulier en matière d'orfèvrerie. En dehors de cela, il n'existe pour tout le pays qu'un seul laboratoire réellement spécialisé en matière de restauration et de conservation d'antiquités métalliques. C'est celui du Centre de Recherches de l'Histoire de la Sidérurgie (C.R.H.S.) à Nancy. Créé dans cette ville il y a un peu plus de dix ans par Edouard Salin, Membre de l'Institut, et par moi-même, il était rattaché au Musée Historique Lorrain. Actuellement ce laboratoire dont j'assure la direction scientifique est équipé d'une façon moderne et travaille avec un seul technicien et une assistante. Cela ne l'a pas empêché de traiter en dix ans quelque trois mille pièces pour une centaine de musées français, et de réussir quelques restaurations considérables. Mais notre organisation actuelle ne nous permet ni de nous développer, ni de former des spécialistes. Notre premier but a été de créer des méthodes de travail et de les adapter aux besoins des musées français, tout en sauvant le plus possible de ce qui était en péril dans certaines collections. Bien que nous disposions de l'appui, de la confiance et de l'amitié des pouvoirs centraux, Direction des Musées, Centre National de la Recherche Scientifique, notre organisation reste encore semi-privée, et les musées sont obligés de nous payer les travaux que nous exécutons pour eux. Souvent ils trouvent que les dépenses sont hors de proportion avec l'intérêt des pièces qu'ils nous ont confiées.

Nous sommes en rapport constant avec de nombreux spécialistes étrangers, et cette collaboration est des plus fructueuses. Nous avons aussi constaté que la conservation de la plupart des objets pour délicate qu'elle soit, ne présente pas d'autres difficultés que la discipline des techniciens, leur honnêteté professionnelle jointe à leur adresse.

La France possède donc une cellule active capable de mener à bien tout travail de restauration d'objets métalliques. En comparaison avec les pays voisins c'est bien peu, d'autres pays ne possèdent aussi qu'un seul laboratoire, mais considérablement plus étoffé que le nôtre. Notre organisation est donc nettement insuffisante, et les musées ne disposent que de crédits faibles qui leur permettent tout juste de faire traiter quelques objets qui leur paraissent intéressants, et ceci grâce à la Direction et à l'Inspection des Musées.

Il serait nécessaire, une fois l'inventaire systématique commencé, de définir l'ordre d'urgence des travaux de nettoyage de restauration à effectuer. Ceci peut être dégrossi grâce à l'examen des fiches photographiques qui portent les caractéristiques physiques et les observations des inspecteurs. Il suffirait pour cela qu'ils soient un peu familiarisés avec le travail des laboratoires. Il faudrait alors développer les laboratoires existants et créer quelques centres supplémentaires. Les nettoyages courants doivent pouvoir être effectués dans des centres régionaux, tandis que quelques laboratoires se spécialiseraient dans les travaux plus délicats nécessitant l'intervention de spécialistes qualifiés. Le passage dans ces laboratoires permet en outre l'étude technique des objets, comme cela se fait actuellement à Nancy.

L'expérience a montré aussi qu'il est bon de prévoir un organe unique de direction et de contrôle chargé de veiller à la bonne application des traitements, et capable de définir les travaux à effectuer dans les cas les plus difficiles.

Il n'est pas aisé de donner une estimation des dépenses à engager dans ce domaine, et c'est pourtant par là qu'il faut commencer. Mon expérience me permet de dire que les pièces très lourdes en très mauvais état reviennent à environ 25 NF le kilo alors que les petites pièces courantes reviennent à 250 NF le kilo, pour une moyenne de 9 objets au kilo. Ceci revient à estimer la mise en état de l'ensemble de notre patrimoine

archéologique national à quelque chose de l'ordre de 5 millions de Nouveaux Francs.

Ceci joint à l'établissement du fichier représente évidemment une dépense considérable, mais qui n'est pas impensable si ce travail est étalé sur quelques dizaines d'années.

Une dizaine de centres occupant chacun cinq personnes doit pouvoir traiter de 20 à 30.000 objets par an, compte tenu que beaucoup d'entre eux doivent seulement être nettoyés. Cela donne une dépense de 30 NF environ par objet, ce qui revient à l'ordre de grandeur précédemment donné.

Il est évident que 10 centres ne peuvent être établis en même temps étant donné les investissements à prévoir, mais ceci revient à dire que les budgets nécessaires restent dans l'ordre des choses admissibles. La plupart des collections n'ont reçu aucun soin depuis leur découverte qui date en moyenne de 75 ans; on peut admettre qu'il faille de 30 à 50 ans pour traiter l'essentiel des collections françaises, en commençant bien entendu par les cas les plus pressants et les plus intéressants. Le seul laboratoire du C.R.H.S. dans sa structure actuelle devrait travailler près de 3.000 ans pour atteindre ce résultat, et encore coûterait-il plus cher, car un seul opérateur même actif ne peut valablement absorber tous les frais généraux et investissements, même si, comme c'est le cas, la direction est bénévole.

Ces quelques données numériques, pour approximatives qu'elles soient, permettent de fixer les idées.

En admettant que le fichier puisse être réalisé en 20 ans, cela représente une dépense annuelle de 600.000 NF à quoi il faut ajouter 1.000.000 NF pour les laboratoires de traitement. Même en admettant que la moitié des objets actuellement conservés dans les collections et dans les réserves ne présente aucun intérêt et qu'il vaut mieux les abandonner à leur sort dans l'état où elles se trouvent, cela ferait encore 1.000.000 NF par an qu'il faudrait envisager pour que notre patrimoine archéologique (rien que les métaux) soit mis en valeur et conservé. Faute de réaliser quelque chose de ce genre, tous les objets métalliques découverts presque journellement par les fouilles nouvelles, iront s'accumuler dans les réserves de musées. L'énorme importance des dépenses à engager montre simplement l'étendue des richesses archéologiques françaises.

La conservation matérielle des objets ne se limite pas à la seule intervention des laboratoires de traitement. Les destructions qui menacent les collections sont de multiples natures. On s'est préoccupé de la protection du patrimoine en cas de guerre, on protège de mieux en mieux les musées contre le vol et l'incendie. Mais les métaux sont instables et ils ont tendance à retourner à leur état de départ: des oxydes. Le laboratoire nettoie, rend l'objet intelligible ou solide, mais son action ne dispense pas des soins habituels, surtout dans nos climats de forte humidité. Les conservateurs de musée doivent donc être instruits et avertis de tout ce qui peut arriver de néfaste à leurs collections métalliques. Ils pourront ainsi empêcher que des détériorations importantes ne se produisent.

Le problème de la conservation des antiquités métalliques n'est probablement pas très différent en France de ce qu'il peut être dans d'autres pays. Mais d'une part notre organisation muséographique s'est pour le moment préoccupée d'autres mises en valeur et a résolu bien d'autres difficultés, et d'autre part nos richesses sont considérables. Il est bien évident que la mise en état et l'étude de ces collections présenteraient un intérêt considérable pour une connaissance plus parfaite des civilisations qui ont occupé notre sol durant près de deux millénaires.

Si l'on compare les résultats obtenus dans le domaine artistique et scientifique par le seul petit laboratoire du C.R.H.S., force est de constater que le bilan est nettement positif et que les dépenses ont été nettement compensées par l'enrichissement de notre patrimoine.

Il n'est pas douteux qu'il puisse en être de même avec une organisation plus importante, à condition qu'elle soit rationnellement organisée pour utiliser au mieux les compétences de tous.

La cellule de Nancy a été à l'origine une entreprise un peu hardie, elle a pris ensuite un caractère expérimental qu'elle conserve encore actuellement. Pour le moment, nous disposons en France de tout ce qu'il faut pour organiser la sauvegarde complète et la mise en valeur de nos richesses archéologiques. Les organismes qui se développent à l'étranger ne peuvent que faciliter ce qui est à créer dans notre pays, mais la connaissance que j'ai pu acquérir depuis un certain nombre d'années, de l'état de nos collections métalliques, m'autorise à dire que, sous tous les rapports, le moment est venu de réaliser une organisation à l'échelon national.

Albert France-Lanord

LA RESTAURATION ET LA CONSERVATION DE GRANDS OBJETS DE BRONZE

Il est exceptionnel qu'un laboratoire de restauration reçoive de très grands objets. Les circonstances ont fait que le laboratoire du Centre de Recherches de l'Histoire de la Sidérurgie à Nancy ait été chargé au cours de ces années dernières de la restauration de trois monuments particulièrement importants: le célèbre cratère de Vix, la statue monumentale dite de Pacatien et le socle de bronze de Senlis. Chacun de ces objets pesait plus de 200 kilos, et je me propose ici de rappeler les principaux problèmes que présentaient ces restaurations et la manière dont le travail a été effectué.

Le vase de Vix

Le vase de Vix est bien connu; découvert en 1952, il avait fait l'objet d'une restauration provisoire pour en permettre la présentation. Par la suite on s'est aperçu qu'il fallait envisager quelque chose de plus définitif, et à la suite d'une conférence tenue au Musée du Louvre, les principes de la restauration définitive ont été discutés et adoptés. Le vase, qui mesure en tout 1,65 m de haut et pèse 208 kilos, se compose d'une cuve chaudronnée d'une seule pièce de 1,45 m de haut, de 1,27 m de diamètre maximum pour 1,00 m d'ouverture, fixée sur un pied massif de 20 kilos. Le bord de la cuve est orné d'une moulure rapportée, d'une frise de petits personnages rivés et de deux anses de 45 et 46 kilos. Lors de l'effondrement de la tombe, la cuve qui est très mince, en moyenne 1 mm d'épaisseur, avait été écrasée et fortement déformée. La restauration a consisté à lui rendre sa forme primitive et à lui donner une solidité suffisante pour supporter le poids des ornements. Le premier travail était donc une simple opération de chaudronnerie rendue délicate par l'état de durcissement et d'écrouissage du métal, heureusement très sain qu'il n'était évidemment pas possible de chauffer. La cuve était fractionnée en trois parties: le fond, la panse et le haut; elle présentait en outre de nombreux plis et de grosses déformations.

Nous avons tout d'abord commencé par construire un gabarit de la forme intérieure, en bois, rectifié au fur et à mesure que nous pouvions définir la forme exacte par suite du travail de redressement du métal, nous avons ainsi constaté que la forme donnée lors de la restauration provisoire n'était pas tout à fait exacte. Lorsque nous avons été sûrs que la forme soit parfaite, les déchirures ont été réparées par soudure à l'intérieur de bandes de laiton mises en forme et soudées à la soudure d'étain en utilisant de la résine comme décapant. Le métal était au préalable décapé par meulage pour permettre une bonne adhérence de la soudure. Au cours de ce travail effectué en chauffant le métal au minimum la patine extérieure du vase n'a subi aucune altération ni aucun changement de couleur. Quand toute la cuve a été réparée, il a été possible d'en achever le planage définitif de façon à faire disparaître presque toutes les déformations.

Telle qu'elle était alors, la cuve aurait pu supporter seule le poids des anses et des ornements, mais il était nécessaire de s'assurer une garantie et de prévoir un système de suspension pour manipuler le vase dans le musée. Nous avons construit un système de support intérieur amovible entièrement en laiton, composé d'une couronne inférieure chaudronnée qui épouse exactement la forme du fond et prend appui à l'endroit de sa jonction avec le pied de bronze, de façon que tous les efforts soient transmis à ce pied solide, comme c'était le cas à l'origine (*Figure 1*). Cette couronne supporte quatre montants tubu-

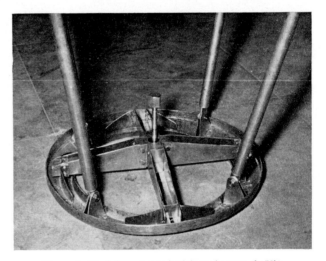

Figure 1. Pied du support intérieur du vase de Vix.

laires qui reçoivent eux mêmes la couronne supérieure. Elle est démontable afin de pouvoir être introduite par l'ouverture du vase, et elle vient soutenir le haut de la cuve à la hauteur du point d'appui des anses. De cette façon, tout le poids des anses est supporté par cette armature intérieure. La couronne supérieure reçoit aussi le système de suspension du vase pendant les manipulations.

Les anses qui avaient été déformées ont été redressées à froid. Les magnifiques personnages de la frise avaient plus ou moins souffert au cours de l'effondrement; certaines extrémités des pattes des chevaux avaient été brisées, elles ont été ressoudées au moyen de soudure à l'argent, sans altération de la patine. L'ensemble des travaux de restauration a représenté environ 700 heures de travail. La consolidation est excellente: la patine naturelle a été entièrement préservée et il n'a pas été nécessaire de combler de manques appréciables. L'aspect définitif a été donné par une simple couche de cire d'abeilles pure.

Ce travail est terminé depuis plusieurs années et le vase de Vix n'a plus présenté la moindre déformation malgré les vibrations auxquelles il est soumis lors du passage de nombreux visiteurs qui font sensiblement trembler le plancher de bois sur lequel il est posé (*Figure 2*).

Figure 2. Le vase de Vix après restauration (Musée de Châtillan-sur-Seine).

La statue dite de «Pacatien»

La statue dite de «Pacatien» est conservée au Musée de Vienne (Isère). Elle avait été trouvée en 1874 dans une cachette de récupérateur, oubliée depuis des siècles. Cette statue était brisée en environ 220 morceaux pesant en tout un peu plus de 200 kilos (*Figure 3*). Le métal bien que présentant une belle patine superficielle, était profondément corrodé. Des tentatives de remontage avaient été jadis tentées par soudure à l'étain, mais sans succès l'état du métal ne permettant pas la prise de la soudure. Une autre tentative avait été aussi hasardée au moyen de pattes de fer fixées par des vis. Nous avons alors utilisé les plastiques stratifiés que nous étions en train d'essayer pour des restaurations plus modestes. Après un tri préalable et nettoyage des fragments, les morceaux qui pouvaient se rejoindre étaient fixés ensemble par des bandes de tissus de verre imprégnées de résine polyester. Une prise rapide était obtenue par chauffage à la lampe infra-rouge. Peu à peu, nous avons pu remonter toute la statue, malgré de nombreux manques qui ont été comblés avec du polyester stratifié armé et teinté. Pour faciliter le transport et le remontage dans le musée, nous avons fragmenté la statue en cinq éléments. Il fallait aussi que cette lourde statue puisse reposer sur ses deux pieds dont un manquait. Nous avons fait une plaque de base en acier de 10 mm d'épaisseur sur laquelle nous avons fixé deux tubes d'acier convenablement coudés qui passent par les pieds, dont un est refait en polyester.

Enfin, les divers morceaux de la statue ont été fixés par des boulons amovibles sur cette sorte de squelette intérieur. Ce délicat travail a nécessité la mise en oeuvre de 50 kilos de résine polyester, de 15 m² de tissus de verre. Toutes ces opérations ont demandé près de 900 heures de travail. Après remontage total, les bavures de résine qui s'étaient produites à l'extérieur ont été grattées et le bronze repoli avec le papier abrasif employé

humide que les carossiers en automobile utilisent. Ce papier a l'avantage de ne pas altérer la patine quand elle est solide comme c'était le cas (*Figure 4*).

La statue complètement terminée mesure 2,10 m de haut; elle doit dater de la fin du Ier siècle, mais la tête rapportée et qui se trouvait être intacte doit dater du IIIème siècle. Comme le métal était sain et ne présentait aucune trace de corrosion active nous avons simplement passé une couche de cire d'abeilles pure. Le durcissement total de la résine a demandé plusieurs semaines. Nous avions pris en temps voulu toutes dispositions utiles pour éviter les retraits et déformations qui sont importantes lorsque l'on opère sur de grandes surfaces de stratifié.

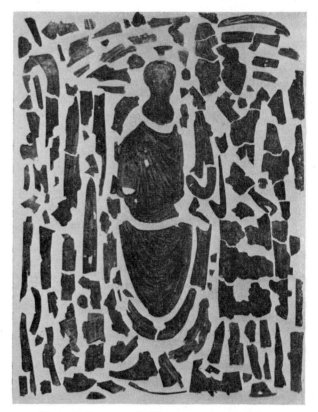

Figure 3. La statue de Vienne avant restauration.

Le socle de bronze de Senlis

Il y a quelques années, des fouilles pratiquées à Senlis à quelques dizaines de kilomètres au nord de Paris, ont mis au jour les restes d'un important monument de bronze qui vient d'être reconstitué par le laboratoire du C.R.H.S.

Dans une couche de remblais ayant servi à combler un fossé au IIIème siècle, on a recueilli environ 800 morceaux de métal de forme très irrégulière, et pesant au total plus de 250 kilos, mélangés à d'épais morceaux de bois calciné et à une gangue compacte d'oxydes métalliques. Après un tri rapide il s'est avéré que tous ces fragments appartenaient au socle de bronze d'une statue de l'empereur Claude dont une face portait une magnifique inscription.

L'état du métal était déplorable, il s'agissait d'un bronze riche en étain et en plomb qui avait en outre été très fortement chauffé. La structure micrographique du métal montrait que celui-ci n'avait plus aucune solidité et qu'il réagissait à toute élévation du taux d'humidité.

La remise en état de ce socle a demandé un travail considérable. Les fragments ont tout d'abord été triés, nettoyés et débarassés de leur épaisse gangue d'oxydes et de charbon de bois. Il a fallu ensuite reconstituer les éléments du socle en recherchant les morceaux qui pouvaient provenir de la même pièce, car nous ne savions pas au départ comment ce socle était fait. Nous n'étions pas comme pour le vase de Vix guidés par une forme géométrique simple, ni comme pour la statue de Pacatien où nous n'avions qu'à suivre les dispositions classiques du drapé de la toge d'un personnage debout.

Il a fallu redresser de nombreuses déformations du métal surchauffé, ce qui n'a pas été possible sans provoquer des cassures supplémentaires.

Ce travail a demandé environ 1200 heures d'un labeur souvent pénible au milieu des poussières d'oxydes de cuivre et des vapeurs de résines plastiques. Comme pour la statue précédente nous avons fait l'assemblage au moyen d'un doublage intérieur de toile de verre épaisse noyée dans de la résine polyester. Il a fallu employer 110 kilos de résine et 30 m² de tissus de verre.

Figure 4. La statue monumentale dite de Pacatien
(Musée de Vienne).

Le socle est haut de 1,44 m et se compose de quatre faces rectangulaires unies dont l'une porte l'inscription. La base en est un carré de 1,10 m de côté. Les faces sont entourées d'une moulure plate de 10 cm environ de large, elles mesurent 65 sur 85 cm de surface vue. La base est ornée d'une moulure de 16 cm de haut. La partie supérieure comporte une moulure presque semblable, mais moins haute, qui forme corniche et supporte une plate bande horizontale sur laquelle repose une partie

verticale moulurée en haut et qui servait à entourer la base de la statue (voir la *Figure 5*). Il y a de la sorte neuf pièces par face, soit 36 en tout.

Tous ces éléments étaient très soigneusement exécutés en bronze coulé et bien poli. L'intérieur du socle devait être garni de maçonnerie, mais les diverses pièces de bronze étaient

Figure 5. Le socle de la statue impériale en bronze (Musée de Senlis).

soudées à l'étain. La statue de l'empereur, d'après les fragments qui ont été actuellement retrouvés devait être un peu moins grande que nature. Il était debout en toge, comme Pacatien de Vienne.

Les faces ont été soigneusement repolies et présentent une patine assez extraordinaire à grandes marbrures rouges, vertes et bleues, les caractères de l'inscription sont bien dégagés et la dédicace est profondément gravée dans le bronze en capitales d'un magnifique style (*Figure 5*).

Le métal qui n'avait présenté aucune trace d'altération dans l'atmosphère du laboratoire, s'est assez récemment recouvert en maintes places d'efflorescences vertes, pâles, caractéristiques de corrosion récidivante. Le taux d'humidité de la salle où le socle est conservé à Senlis est monté à 97 pour cent et s'est maintenu pendant trois jours à ce chiffre élevé, par suite de conditions atmosphériques un peu exceptionnelles. Par la suite tout est rentré dans l'ordre et après enlèvement de la poussière verte il ne s'est plus manifesté de traces de corrosion.

Conclusion

La restauration de ces gros ensembles présente toutes sortes de difficultés particulières, car il faut faire intervenir la masse de ces objets et par conséquent résoudre de vrais problèmes de construction. L'emploi systématique des polyesters stratifiés nous a rendu les plus grands services, et les pièces ont pu être remontées solidement sans que leur intégrité ait à souffrir. Au cours de ces travaux, nous avons pu constater qu'il fallait veiller à avoir une bonne ventilation des locaux dans lesquels on travaille afin d'éviter au maximum des vapeurs extrêmement désagréables; il convient aussi de travailler avec une température toujours assez constante et de prendre toutes les précautions nécessaires pour éviter des déformations et des retraits trop importants.

C. Panseri and M. Leoni

ADVANCED METHODS FOR THE METALLURGICAL EXAMINATION OF ARCHAEOLOGICAL METAL OBJECTS

Introduction

Conventional methods for the metallographical examination of metal objects normally require sectioning of the object, causing considerable damage to it. For this reason, the directors of public and private museums are extremely reluctant to release any object of interest and rarity for examination by students of ancient metallurgy, and this seriously hampers development in this field of study. Quite recently, however, new non-destructive techniques and equipment have become available for the metallographical examination of metal articles in the industry. These procedures can be advantageously applied to the study of wrought objects of historical or technological importance.

Micro-sampling technique

When sectioning of the object is out of the question, its chemical, mechanical and structural properties can be studied on tiny cylindrical samples (known as 'cores' in metallographic terminology), which can be extracted from the object either by

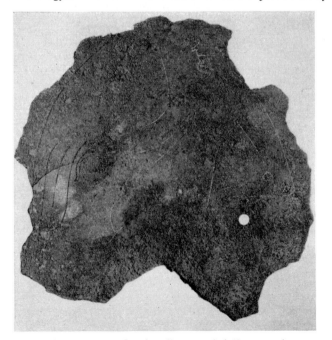

Figure 1. Fragment of a heavily corroded Etruscan bronze mirror from which a core has been extracted by the Ultraelectro machine for micrographical examination.

means of special miniature grinding tools or—more conveniently whenever the size of the object is no problem—by employing a special machine marketed by the Federici Company of Milan under the name of 'Ultraelectro' and specially designed for the industrial cutting of extremely hard materials—either

conductive or non-conductive (heat-treated steels, Stellite, hard stones, ceramics, glasses, etc.). This machine enables us to extract very thin cores through the combined action of high-frequency electrical discharge and elastic vibrations at acoustical and ultrasonic frequencies. Cylindrical samples of 2–3 mm diameter can be obtained by such a method, producing in the object a hole only slightly greater than the sample itself. The electrode employed is, in fact, a little copper tube having the desired diameter and very thin walls. This electrode does not cause any mechanical strain upon the piece, and it is then possible to obtain satisfactory samples even from objects deeply corroded and embrittled. For reasons of cooling and insulating, the processes must be accomplished in an oil bath, and the dimensions of this bath are the sole limits of the process. The holes left in the objects by the cores can easily be repaired by introducing little bosses of the same metal as the tested piece. Experimental tests have been run by the authors on several specimens in various conditions, such as bronze and iron arms and utensils from different historical periods: Etruscan, Roman, Gallic, Medieval and Modern.

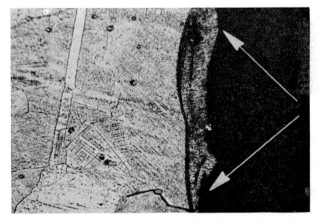

Figure 2. Microstructure of cut surface of core taken from Etruscan bronze mirror. Arrows indicate thin layer of material disturbed by the cutting operation ($NH_3 + H_2O_2$)($\times 500$).

Figure 1 shows a fragment of a heavily corroded Etruscan bronze mirror, from which a core was taken with the Ultra-electro machine without causing any further damage to the object by drilling. In this case it would have been impossible to take out the core with a normal cylindrical miller because the mechanical stress would have broken the object.

Micrographic examination of the various cores showed that the modification of the material in the cutting area caused by the heat of sparking is very limited in depth and, in any case, is easily detectable during the examination. The thin surface layer melted during the boring process is clearly evident in the micrograph of *Figure 2*.

Figure 3 (top) shows a detail of a Japanese sword from which three cores were extracted by means of the Ultraelectro machine. The holes left in the blade by the cores were subsequently plugged with similar material (*Figure 3*, bottom). The

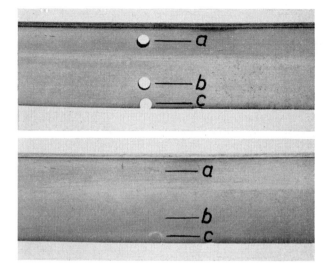

Figure 3. Blade of Japanese sword: (top) holes made by Ultraelectro machine after extracting metallographic specimens; (bottom) blade after plugging of the holes.

macrostructure of the middle section of one core is shown in *Figure 4*. The samples so obtained can be used not only for macro- and microstructural examinations but also for spectrographic, sclerometric and other studies.

Figure 4. Macrostructure of middle section of core cut from Japanese sword blade (× 20).

Spot etching and electrolytic polishing

Whenever no modification of the object to be studied can be allowed, metallographic examination of its surface can be performed by local electrolytic polishing and etching. After this process, the surface can be directly examined with a microscope, or—as will be explained below—the microscopic examination can be performed on replicas exactly reproducing the area to be studied.

The methods for local electrolytic polishing and etching of the objects are based on the same rules followed in laboratory

polishing and etching of samples; local polishing, in fact, is obtained by anodic solution of surface roughness with suitable electrolytic baths. Suitable adjustment of the electric characteristics of the circuit and the quality of the electrolyte causes etching of the surface and reveals its structure. Normal laboratory equipment may not always be adaptable for the

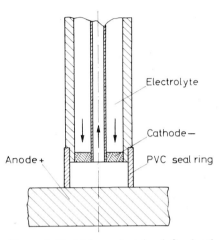

Figure 5. Portable contact head for local electrolytic polishing and etching of metal objects.

examination of objects having very varied shapes and dimensions; special equipment had to be designed for this purpose, with particular attention to the cathodic device where the electrolyte circulates. The apparatus employed in our laboratory embodied a cylindrical electrolytic cell equipped at one end with a plastic ring providing for perfect adherence of the cell to the area to be polished (*Figure 5*). The cathode is fixed

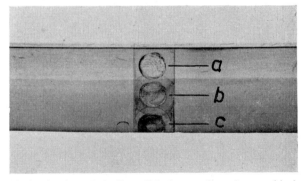

Figure 6. Electrolytically polished spots for micrographical examination of a Japanese sword blade.

in the interior of the cell and the electrolyte comes through a tube, forced by a pump plunged in the container of the electrolyte itself. The cathode is connected to an electric circuit which ranges from 0 to 100 volts d.c. For this research the Struers Society's apparatus 'Movipol' was found to be very suitable.

By this process, polishing is performed on a circular area 7 mm in diameter (*Figure 6*). A typical application is the nondestructive examination of a Japanese sword blade (*Figure 7*) which was carried out with a common metallographic microscope after local polishing.

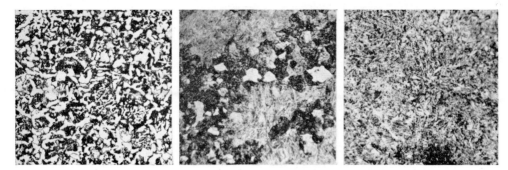

Figure 7. Microstructure of the three electropolished spots (*a*, *b* and *c*)
of the sword blade shown in *Figure 6* (× 153).

Replica technique

Quite often it is impossible to employ a photographic microscope in order to document the structure of a locally polished specimen. In this case, the 'replica' technique can be advantageously employed for the observation and reproduction of areas that have previously been electrolytically polished and etched to document their structures. Several tests have been run on various types of sample in order to establish the technique of replica copying, which is essentially as follows:

(a) The area to be examined—previously prepared by etching and polishing—is coated with a suitable resin solution in such quantity as to obtain a film about 0·2 mm thick. During this operation it is imperative to avoid any movement which could cause the formation of little bubbles, which would prevent perfect duplication of the structure.

(b) The resin is dried in air or—more quickly—with infra-red rays.

(c) The resin film is carefully detached with small pliers and then mounted on a microscope slide, avoiding any alteration.

Another method that can prove advantageous for examination of flat pieces involves preparing a thin resin film on a flat glass plate and transferring it, with slight pressure, on to the metallic surface to be studied, previously prepared by wetting with a suitable solvent (benzol, amyl acetate). This method is known as 'fax film'.

Excellent results have been obtained in a great number of experiments with replicas prepared with methacrylic resins, in particular a nitrocellulose resin made in France and commercially known as 'Replic'. *Figure 8* shows the microstructure of a

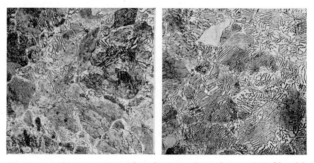

Figure 8. Microstructure of carbon steel as observed (left) with normal metallographic procedure and (right) with the replica technique (× 150).

carbon steel reproduced both with the normal metallographic method and with the replica technique. The replica method was particularly effective when employing phase-contrast microscopy.

Conclusions

New possibilities have been described for the study of archaeological metallic objects which, because of their high value, are not suitable for normal destructive methods of metallographic examination.

These new techniques include ultrasonic micro-sampling, local electrolytic polishing and the replica process.

R. M. Organ

THE EXAMINATION AND TREATMENT OF BRONZE ANTIQUITIES

Introduction

The result of a scientific examination of an antiquity is a knowledge of its actual condition at the time of the examination. From this can be inferred something of its past history from the time of its beginning as raw material and it can lead to an estimate of practicable methods for its conservation against the further ravages of time or for its restoration to its original appearance.

Examination of the object with the naked eye is an essential preliminary which, in the case of an experienced observer, may provide many of the required data. This experience results in an ability to relate outer appearances to inner constitution and may be acquired through studies of metal antiquities and of various layers of mineral corrosion products which have grown upon them. Records of such studies are of the greatest importance, and this paper details some of the methods which may be employed in making and recording such examinations, illustrates their application to deducing past history and shows how they can lead to a sound choice of conservational methods.

Observation at low magnification

Use of the naked eye is the natural method of observation. An experienced observer will have a favourite window at which to make his observations and will turn a particular feature of the object in all directions whilst examining it in order to build up a composite mental picture by the aid of which to make his final pronouncement on the meaning of what he sees. An effort to produce objective evidence in the form of a photograph may well fail if the difference between two forms of observation—the single-lensed view of a camera in a single quality of light and summation of the binocular views of an observer in several qualities of lighting—is not fully appreciated. Failure to appreciate this is one of the reasons for the failure of many photographs to illustrate their subject matter in the absence of lengthy captions.

So long as the powers of the naked eye are supplemented only with lenses mounted on the head of the observer or by one mounted so that the object can be moved in the hands beneath it, no difficulties of observation arise and it may even be possible in favourable conditions, by immobilizing the object and replacing the eye by a camera lens, to record what the eye has seen. But it has occurred that even so apparently simple a task has required several weeks of strenuous effort in adapting equipment before the casual observations of an observer could be captured on film. Some of the lessons resulting from such an effort are embodied below.

Apparatus

Apparatus which has been found useful in the recording of macroscopic details (i.e. at magnifications up to ×10) is as follows:

1. Support for the object:

(a) A substantial wall carrying a shelf whose height can be adjusted.

(b) Soft wood behind the shelf which will accept pins to support material for backgrounds.

(c) Rings of various diameters, made of cork or thick rubber tubing, or sheet metal edged with split rubber tubing, into which the convexities of the object can nestle at an angle at which the small area to be photographed is presented normal to the axis of the camera.

2. Lighting the object:

(a) Daylight. Whilst it is known that a certain kind of daylight is superior to other forms of lighting for the preservation in a photograph of the detail in relief, the writer has not yet succeeded in specifying it sufficiently precisely to enable it to be duplicated artificially.

(b) Artificial light. This is essential if photographs in true colour are to be made, because daylight is not constant in quality.

(i) Photo-flood illumination may be used because commercial colour emulsions are balanced for this. The lamps should be mounted in small reflectors so that they may be placed close to the small object. If they are supplied with current from a variable auto-transformer ('Variac') their life can be conserved, their colour temperature adjusted as they age and the object subjected to the minimum of heat radiation whilst setting up. Detail in polished metal surfaces may best be lit by surrounding the object with a tube of white paper which is brightly illuminated from outside. This type of light source may be compared with a shadowless illuminator—a ring of lamps arranged to encircle the lens. It is much less expensive and superior to this since the light source appears from the standpoint of the object to be almost infinite in extent.

(ii) For directed lighting a Pointolite lamp behind a condenser is useful but may not be mixed with other light sources when photographing in colour because its colour temperature is low.

(iii) An excellent but expensive light source comparable in colour with daylight is the xenon arc.

Lighting should normally be arranged in accordance with the convention that the principal light source is above and to the left. The reverse arrangement tends to make relief appear to be in intaglio.

3. The camera:

If the detail to be recorded is in one plane, almost any camera will serve provided that it has a screen upon which to focus and arrange the image and that it has the required magnification. A Leica camera can be used with a revolving carrier. A metallurgical inverted microscope with a suitable objective can also be used if its stage will support the sometimes considerable weight and bulk of the object.

On the other hand, if the detail to be recorded is in the round or in several parallel planes in depth, then the only satisfactory method of obtaining sufficient depth of field is to use a lens of 175 mm or even 300 mm focal length. In order to obtain the required magnification a bellows extension (distance from lens to emulsion) of 1 metre or more will then be necessary.

4. The camera stand:

When using a long bellows it is convenient to be able to fix the extension to provide the required magnification and then to focus by moving the whole camera along its own axis towards the object whilst observing the focusing screen. Final adjustment of focus is conveniently made at the back of the camera rather than at the lens. A counterpoised or rack-and-pinion vertical movement of the camera is highly desirable and a rising and cross movement at the back is essential when placing the image in the frame. Rigidity is also essential since exposures of many seconds' duration may be required.

Typical results

Figure 1, at a magnification of ×10, shows a joint between two sections of a figure made in copper alloy which had been soldered together with a copper–silver–zinc alloy and which included a section of probably modern copper sheet as a packing piece. At best this is evidence of a modern repair.

Figure 2. Method of supporting object on stage of metallurgical microscope in order to photograph minute cross-section made on underside.

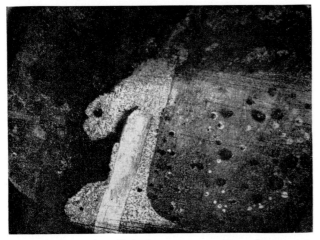

Figure 1. Outer edge of joint between two sections of figure cast in copper alloy. Joint contains hard solder and strip of modern copper (magnification, ×10).

Figure 2 shows how the above photograph was taken on a projection microscope.

Figure 3, at a magnification of ×10, shows a detail on the Wandsworth shield boss, which is dated to the 2nd century B.C. The decoration had been lightly traced on thin sheet bronze, then deepened with a punch held at an angle and rocked along the line, alternate blows on the punch sometimes being omitted.

Figure 4 presents evidence deduced from the 'shadows' above certain letters on a Roman folle of the 3rd century that the bronze blank was tinned before the coin was struck from it (magnification, ×14).

Figure 5, magnification ×4, shows one of three gold beaded-wire decorations which alone remains in a blue glass bead. The shape of the unoccupied impressions indicates how the hot plastic glass was forced around the preformed wire. The top of the glass was 2 mm above its base and both planes are in acceptably sharp focus.

Figure 6, actual size, represents a fracture in a Chinese bronze adze. No metal remains here. It has all been converted to copper minerals and tin minerals and much of the copper mineral has been leached out of the outer layer.

Preparation of cross-sections

The illustrations above result from observations of surface topography. When patina is present more penetrating

observation is necessary, sometimes at high magnification, and best made on a cross-section of the object if such a section were permissible. Since this is seldom the case other expedients have to be adopted.

One expedient is to detach a fragment of patina in such a manner that it separates cleanly from the metal. If this does prove possible it is already an indication that there is a plane of

Figure 3. Detail of decoration on boss of Wandsworth Shield (magnification, ×10).

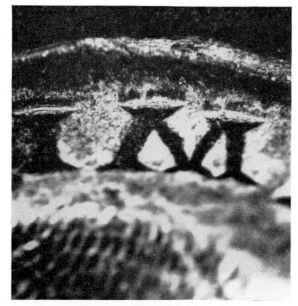

Figure 4. Detail of tinned bronze Roman coin. Thickness of tin reduced by stretching of metal when struck (magnification, ×14).

Figure 5. Hemispherical bead of blue glass containing one decorative gold wire. Acceptably sharp focus, in planes 2 mm apart (magnification, ×4).

cleavage along the metal surface which may be the seat of a soft mineral. The fragment of patina thus obtained may be mounted with its cross-section in one face of a cube of cold-setting polyester resin or in a disc of methacrylate. The cross-section can then be ground and polished to form a plane surface.

As another expedient a taper section may be made through both mineral sheathing and metal by grinding and polishing a plane through a small convenient convex surface of the object. This procedure can often yield considerable information on the

Figure 6. Fracture across completely mineralized Chinese bronze adze (actual size).

structure of a patina, both above and inside its parent metal, without defacing the object. It is therefore applicable to valuable bronzes. On the other hand, such convexities are not present on all antiquities and when present may not be completely representative of the remainder of the object.

For all types of section, grinding and polishing follows the sequence: silicon carbide abrasive papers, 280 then 400, lubricated with water and supported on plate glass; 30-micron diamantine (γ-Al_2O_3) in a wax lap, applied dry by hand or revolved mechanically; diamond pastes of successive sizes 6, 1 and $\frac{1}{4}$ micron, supported in the thinnest nylon fabric upon a flat lap; finally, heavy magnesia made into a paste with freshly boiled distilled water and supported upon the thin pile of a metallurgical cloth. Each operation is carried out in the same polishing plane but in a direction at right angles to the previous one. The last operation may be neglected if only mineral is to be examined but is necessary for high-quality photographs of inclusions in unetched metal.

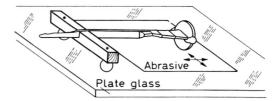

Figure 7. Jig for grinding section on disc pommel.

The problem to be solved in making a taper section is to maintain each successive operation parallel to the previous one. One solution to the problem relies on making the convexity to be sectioned into one of three points of support for the object. The other two points are arranged to be as distant as practicable from the first and take the form of two balls mounted upon a jig into which the object is fixed securely but harmlessly. Whilst the convexity is rubbed upon a sheet of abrasive these two balls are allowed to ride upon the plate glass which supports it (*Figure 7*). In the case of heavy objects it may be necessary to fix the object whilst moving the abrasive: when the convexity is being polished by a rotating lap the balls must ride upon a glass plate which has been arranged level with the lap (*Figure 8*).

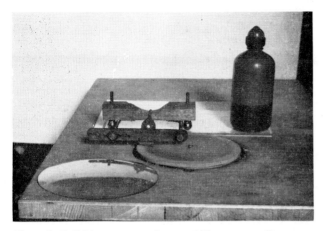

Figure 8. Polishing cross-section on 14th century gilt copper bookclasp, held in jig, by means of rotating lap charged with diamond paste.

The design of such jigs calls for a little ingenuity and a knowledge of the strength of materials and is best exemplified by diagrams of actual cases (*Figures 9* and *10*).

Observation of polished sections is quite straightforward since all their detail is in one plane. Nevertheless, methods of illumination must be selected to suit the work. Thus, detail in

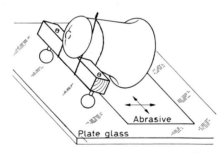

Figure 9. Application of jig to polishing a section on the thin lip of silver a cup.

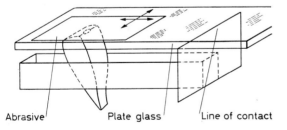

Figure 10. Jig for making taper section on edge of heavy bronze anvil.

metal which has been polished to a mirror-like surface is best observed in vertical illumination, whilst the characteristic colours of minerals are more saturated in hue if viewed by light scattered from their surface (i.e. 'dark field' illumination). By far the best differentiation of minerals is obtained when they are viewed by vertical illumination between crossed polars. The

majority of the examples which follow has been recorded by the latter method.

Results of examination

Typical sections through metal and mineralization: Plate Id is a photograph, at a magnification of ×6, of part of a copper chisel excavated at Jericho by Miss Kenyon. Resulting from an accident, a thick mineral sheath has become detached from the remains of the tool, which may be seen protruding from its box of mineral. Two features are noteworthy: a dark line which represents the original surface of the metal, and a green effloresing 'bronze disease' induced at the present surface of the metal by exposure to moist air.

A cross-section of this chisel clearly shows the minerals present in the sheath. The dark line separates an outer region

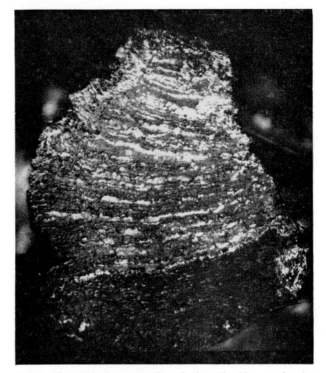

Figure 11. Polished cross-section of mineralized bronze droplet from Roman-British funeral pyre, viewed through crossed polars (magnification, ×5).

of stratified crystals of cuprous oxide from a core of polygonal crystals of the same mineral. It is of interest that the pioneers of cathodic reduction used to electrolyse the antiquity for a period and then remove the reduced surface mechanically in order to recover this original surface. This method, in its simple form, has been superseded because it leaves the object in an unstable condition. For example, had it been applied to this chisel, the area which could have been stimulated into active 'bronze disease' might still have remained beneath the mineralized original surface which had been exposed.

Figure 11 shows a cross-section (magnification ×5) through metal and mineral on a drop of bronze which had fallen through a funeral pyre in Roman-British times and become lodged in charcoal, which had protected one end of the drop from corrosive electrolytes. Of particular interest in this example is the presence of some 60 strata, like the growth rings of a tree, which each have the same arrangement of mineral layers. It is unusual for such strata to be present in a patina, and it is worth noting their absence on the side of the drop, much less corroded, which has been buried in charcoal.

As an experiment, this drop was exposed to a relative humidity of 95 per cent for some hours. It developed a line of pulverulent green powder ('bronze disease') only at the interface between metal and mineral (*Figure 12*). This agrees with

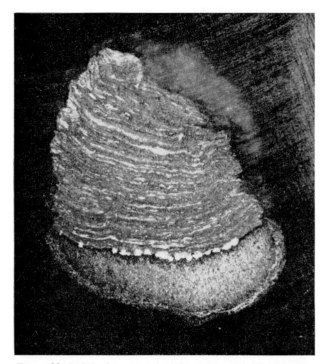

Figure 12. Polished cross-section of another mineralized bronze droplet, exposed to relative humidity of 95 per cent for some hours. Note location of 'bronze disease'.

observations over many years that such an interface is the normal site of the grey mineral which is the source of bronze disease.

Note on minerals present in corrosion layers on bronze

Identification of minerals is discussed in other papers at this conference. In order to describe them here it will be helpful to regard the various colours which they assume under crossed polars as an indication of their chemical nature, which can be verified by other methods:

Blue:	basic cupric carbonate, azurite
Green:	basic cupric carbonate, malachite
	basic cupric chloride, paratacamite or atacamite
White:	tin oxide
Red or orange:	cuprous oxide, cuprite
Grey, wax-like:	cuprous chloride, nantokite

The precise identification of the mineral species is of little importance in the present context. For purposes of conservation it is sufficient to know how the mineral can react with chemical reagents.

Typical sections through patina which has been flaked off a metal surface: Plate Ic shows a flake (magnification ×24) off a bronze from Nimrud. Three layers are visible: grey cuprous chloride next to the metal; red cuprous oxide; then green basic cupric carbonate plus possibly a little basic chloride.

Plate Ib is a flake from a Chinese bronze Li dating from the 10th or 9th century B.C. (magnification, ×90). An arrangement of layers similar to that in *Plate Ic* is visible here but the relative proportions are different, the cleavage layer being very thin and cuprous oxide accounting for the bulk of the patina. An etching technique applied to the mineral appeared to reveal that the oxide layer was made up of numerous small crystals.

Typical taper sections: All features are magnified much more greatly along the axis of the taper than across it.

Plate Ia (magnification, ×34), made on the tip of a foot of a Chinese Chueh dated 1000 B.C., shows the various layers and their 'roots' in the metal quite clearly. The distinction between the metal of the Jericho copper chisel (*Plate Id*, cross-section not shown) and that of the present example, which is to be deduced from the rather ragged entry of the mineral into the copper of the former compared with the regular 'pitting' of the latter, is that the copper chisel is made of metal of greater homogeneity than this bronze, which contains dendritic ('tree-like') crystal formations.

Results of study of bronze patina

The various minerals are present in strata: cuprous chloride adjacent to metal, basic cupric carbonate or massive basic cupric chloride on the outside, with cuprous oxide sandwiched between the two. Tin oxide may occur in pockets or be distributed throughout the cuprous oxide layer.

The pulverulent green mineral which is the mark of 'bronze disease' is basic cupric chloride (paratacamite) which is formed from cuprous chloride in the presence of moisture and atmospheric oxygen. The same mineral may occur massively in a slowly grown patina.

An indication of the position of the original metal surface is sometimes, but not always, preserved within the cuprous oxide layer.

Bronze disease may occasionally appear on completely mineralized bronze because pockets of cuprous chloride remain at the stratum in the patina from which the last vestiges of metal have corroded away.

Selection of methods of treatment

Treatment of bronze antiquities is undertaken for two principal reasons:

(a) To stabilize patina against change under the influence of an adverse environment.

(b) To restore surface features which are obscured under thick mineralization. This topic cannot be discussed in detail here, for lack of space.

It will be clear from the foregoing observations that complete stability in a patina can only be guaranteed if the cuprous chloride in it is either removed or is prevented from reaction with atmospheric moisture and oxygen, which may on occasion penetrate overlying patina in sufficient quantity to build up a reactive concentration on its surface. Hence one of the methods which has been employed to preserve a bronze antiquity has been to maintain it at a low relative humidity. Experiments show that a perceptible quantity of basic cupric chloride will form on cuprous chloride exposed to a relative humidity of 95 per cent in 2 hours; of 78 per cent in 4 hours; of 58 per cent in 24 hours; whilst at 35 per cent the chloride appears to be stable indefinitely.

A further important property of cuprous chloride is that it is almost insoluble in water. This statement may be underlined by mention of a laboratory method for its preparation in which the cuprous chloride is prepared in a solution of concentrated hydrochloric acid and is then precipitated out of solution by addition of water. Because of this insolubility, methods of treatment which rely on boiling a bronze in distilled water alone are unlikely to be effective.

Methods for removal of cuprous chloride

These methods are permissible when patina may be sacrificed.

In order to attack cuprous chloride easily, overlying mineral must be removed first. Numerous reagents suitable for this purpose exist, all having the necessary ability to dissolve copper salts without rapid attack on copper alloys when they have been exposed. Some of these reagents are unable to dissolve cuprous salts until the latter have been oxidized to the cupric form by access of atmospheric oxygen.

Comparison of stripping reagents

An experimental comparison of suitable reagents has been undertaken. Antiquities having the same variety and thickness of minerals were chosen so that each reagent could react under similar conditions. They were a small group of Roman silvered-bronze coins minted in the reign of the short-lived emperor Probus, A.D. 276–281, at a single *officina* and having similar obverse and reverse, selected from a hoard of 20,000 which was discovered in a single covered jar. Because of the method of selection this group contains coins which had been as nearly as possible of identical alloy, weight and surface area, which had been in circulation for a similar period and which had finally been exposed together in a restricted space to a similar corrosive environment. The reagents tested fall into three groups, as follows:

(1) Acids which dissolve both cupric and cuprous compounds: formic and citric acids;

(2) Alkaline sequestering agents which are customarily used to dissolve cupric compounds and would then be followed by dilute sulphuric acid in order to dissolve cuprous oxide: alkaline Rochelle salt and alkaline glycerol;

(3) Sequestering agents which dissolve cupric salts more readily than cuprous salts: Calgon (sodium hexametaphosphate) and Detarol (Detarol is an ethylene diamine triacetate, supplied by F. W. Berk and similar to Chel DM41 supplied by Geigy).

Results of a pilot experiment indicate that the initial rate of removal of mineral by the two acids is similar but that citric acid continues its action after formic acid has ceased. All the coins treated thus displayed, unbrushed, a coating of copper powder. This is a product of the reaction between cuprous compounds and acids which, in the absence of oxidants in solution, yields cupric salts and copper metal, e.g.

$$Cu_2O + H_2SO_4 = CuSO_4 + Cu + H_2O$$

It is usually possible to brush this powder away, but at the site of concentrations of cuprous chloride the metal may be formed in an adherent layer which can be removed only with difficulty.

Alkaline Rochelle salt* and alkaline glycerol† were found equally rapid in removing cupric salts and equally slow in dissolving cuprous compounds, the rate of removal of the latter being dependent on the rate of access of atmospheric oxygen. The choice between these reagents is a matter of economics; alkaline glycerol is more readily prepared and is cheaper. Coins treated by these reagents for the removal of cupric compounds had the pink appearance of freshly exposed cuprous oxide.

_____

* 50 g sodium hydroxide, 150 g sodium potassium tartrate, in 1 litre of water.

† 120 g sodium hydroxide, 40 ml glycerine, in 1 litre of water.

Detarol removed cupric compounds as rapidly as alkaline glycerol and continued to remove cuprous oxide with only slightly diminished rapidity. On the other hand, Calgon was excessively slow in its initial attack but maintained its activity against cuprous oxide. It required 500 min to remove the same quantity of mineral as was removed by alkaline glycerol in 30 min. At this stage the appearance of the coin was most unsatisfactory: dark in colour but enlivened with vivid green patches of reacting cuprous chloride.

Another possible sequesterant which was tested was benzotriazole dissolved in sodium hydroxide. Its use was discontinued when it was found to cause blackening accompanied by gain in weight. But suitable conditions for its use may yet be found.

This pilot experiment suggests that the most satisfactory reagent for the removal of cupric compounds only is alkaline glycerol and that Detarol will be most satisfactory for removal of all copper minerals. Whilst long experience with alkaline Rochelle salt suggests that no difficulties are likely to arise from the use of alkaline glycerol, which reacts in a similar manner, there is not the same certainty about Detarol, and these results should not be taken as recommendations.

Acknowledgement is made to D. E. Bisset for the careful carrying out of these experiments.

Cathodic reduction and 'intensive washing'

Following removal of superficial minerals, patches of cuprous chloride remain exposed or may have been removed already by the stripping reagent. Remembering the deep penetration of minerals into cast metal illustrated earlier in this paper, together with the location of cuprous chloride at the interface with metal, it is to be anticipated that removal of last traces of cuprous chloride will be difficult and that it will also be difficult to demonstrate that they have indeed been removed.

The first of these difficulties can be surmounted by cathodic reduction in alkaline solution, for the hydrogen liberated at the cathode by this well-known process can penetrate to the end of deep pits in the metal.

Demonstration of complete removal of cuprous chloride can be achieved by 'intensive washing'‡. In this process the cleaned object is soaked in almost boiling distilled water for 7 hours, followed by slow cooling to room temperature, in order to flush the closed capillaries in the metal. When cold, the electrical conductivity of the water is measured as an index to the concentration of salts in it. This process is repeated daily with fresh water until the electrical conductivity remains sensibly constant. During the following few days the water is not changed daily, merely being 'topped up' to constant volume, and the conductivity is found to rise to a constant level at which the concentration of salts in the water is in equilibrium with those in the interior of the object, with oxides on the metal, with the glass of the vessel and the gases in the atmosphere. At this stage a test for chloride is made under conditions conducive to the highest sensitivity. If chloride is not found, it is reasonable to believe that cuprous chloride is absent from the interior of the object and that it is therefore safe for all time against variations in relative humidity. But if chloride is found, then cathodic reduction and intensive washing must be repeated until the test is satisfied. The whole process may require seven or eight months to complete but this period can be reduced by a factor of five if ultra-sonic vibrations are applied occasionally in the early stages of washing, immediately before measurement of electrical conductivity.

_____

‡ *Museums Journal*, 55 (1955) 112–119.

Stabilizing a patina which must be preserved

Since in this case the cuprous chloride may not be removed it must either be converted into an innocuous compound or be protected from reaction with moisture or oxygen or both. Methods of putting these two principles into practice will be considered in order:

(a) *Wet method using sodium sesquicarbonate:* The reaction of cuprous chloride with water in the absence of oxygen may be written

$$Cu_2Cl_2 + H_2O \rightleftharpoons Cu_2O + 2HCl$$

In the presence of sodium sesquicarbonate, which in the crystalline form has the formula $Na_2CO_3.NaHCO_3.2H_2O$, the reaction moves toward the right-hand side because the hydrochloric acid is removed by the carbonate as fast as it is formed. Hence, by soaking a patinated object containing cuprous chloride in aqueous sodium sesquicarbonate the cuprous chloride is slowly replaced by cuprous oxide. The displaced chloride appears in solution as sodium chloride and is removed from the vicinity of the object whenever the solution is replaced. The reaction may be regarded as complete when chloride ions can no longer be found in the sesquicarbonate solution by means of the silver nitrate test. The process is completed by washing with distilled water sufficiently long to remove any sesquicarbonate solution which remains, followed by thorough drying and finishing with clear cellulose lacquer, maranyl nylon or paraffin wax, as other considerations dictate.

This process is long: it is seldom that tests show it to be complete in less than three months when the sesquicarbonate solution has been changed at intervals of one week. Often the duration of the process must be measured in years.

Occasionally, when pockets of cuprous chloride have been present near the surface of a patina, it has been possible to observe orange-coloured cuprous oxide actually forming. A test for possible change of volume, causing strains in the patina, was made upon a completely mineralized bandeau from Jericho. This object had been made from a curved strip of very thin metal. A record was made of its shape before treatment. After three years in changes of sodium sesquicarbonate solution, only very little change in curvature was observable.

Throughout the process there is no loss of the original blue or green patination. Indeed, an increase in blue patina may be observed. This will take on a very satisfactory green colour when finally treated with any of the media which have been suggested above.

Although this process may appear impracticably lengthy, there are occasions when it is the only method which it is permissible to adopt. The conservator may then comfort himself with the reflection that it is esthetically satisfying to be able to replace cuprous chloride by a mineral which is of natural occurrence in a patina.

(b) *Dry method using silver oxide:* Various methods have been employed from time to time to deal with spots of bronze disease in an otherwise acceptable patina. One typical technique follows dental practice by excavating the 'disease' and filling the cavity with molten paraffin wax. This method has seldom given long-lasting protection because this wax is slightly permeable to water vapour. The intention of the new method is to form a seal of silver chloride ('hornsilver') over an exposed surface of cuprous chloride. The method has been found satisfactory during four years' experience in two institutions.

Briefly, the technique is to excavate the bronze disease down to a fresh surface of wax-like cuprous chloride, using a needle or other suitable tool under a lens ($\times 5$ to $\times 10$). The interior of the cavity is then treated with finely powdered, dry, salt-free silver oxide of analytical reagent quality. The oxide may be rubbed in with a match-stick or applied in suspension in industrial methylated spirit (alcohol).

In order to mature the protection and as a test of efficacy of treatment, the bronze is next exposed to a relative humidity of 78 per cent, which is a condition frequently encountered in museums in the temperate zone on a summer day. If the treated areas show a green efflorescence of basic cupric chloride after 24 hours in this environment, the bronze should be thoroughly dried, a further quantity of silver oxide worked into the cavity and exposure repeated. More than two such treatments are seldom required.

A relative humidity of 78 per cent may be achieved in a closed space quite simply by including in it a tray containing a slurry of crystals of photographic 'hypo' ($Na_2S_2O_3.5H_2O$) in distilled water at $20°C$.

The brown colour of the silver oxide blends well with most patina. Despite the high cost of silver compounds, the method is economical since very little silver oxide is required. It is very rapid in execution.

An object which is too weak to sustain the physical forces applied or which is too thin to support the oxide cannot be treated by this method.

Full details have been published in the *Museums Journal*, 61 (1961) 54–56.

Adrienne R. Weill

APPLICATION À L'ÉTUDE DES PIÈCES DE COLLECTION EN MÉTAL DE QUELQUES MÉTHODES NON-DESTRUCTIVES UTILISÉES EN MÉTALLURGIE

Introduction

Les techniques non-destructives ont pris un essor considérable depuis quelques années tant pour le contrôle des fabrications que pour l'analyse des pièces métalliques.

Nous indiquerons brièvement celles de ces méthodes qui nous paraissent recommandables pour l'étude scientifique des métaux anciens, et plus spécialement de ceux qui ne sont pas corrodés ou très peu attaqués.

Nous examinerons successivement les méthodes strictement non-destructives qui ne laissent aucune marque sur l'objet observé ou analysé, et les techniques qui n'exigent ni sacrifice, ni prélèvement, mais qui laissent une marque sur la pièce.

Méthodes strictement non-destructives

Techniques d'observation

Les méthodes d'examen non-destructives sont en quelque sorte le prolongement de l'observation visuelle qu'il s'agisse de microscopie, de radiographie ou de gammagraphie.

La microscopie s'entend ici sans préparation de la surface. Elle est donc d'application restreinte; néanmoins, le cas des surfaces protégées mérite d'être retenu.

Ainsi à grossissement modéré ($\times 63$), nous avons obtenu une photographie donnant les détails de la ciselure de fins «paillons» supportant une tablette transparente en grenat ornant une plaque mérovingienne[1].

La radiographie a fait ses preuves depuis de nombreuses années dans la lecture du décor d'une pièce corrodée avant toute tentative de restauration[2]. Nous l'avons utilisée dans ce dessein[3], l'ayant précédemment mise à profit pour faire apparaître les transformations subies par des clous d'épaves romaines[4]; ceci à titre de simple rappel (voir les *Figures 7* et *8*).

La gammagraphie est appelée en maintes circonstances à remplacer la radiographie du fait que la source de rayonnement est extrêmement petite, de l'ordre d'une fraction de centimètre cube, et que, même avec l'enveloppe massive qui protège les opérateurs contre les radiations, elle n'occupe qu'un volume réduit à quelques décimètres cubes.

On peut donc désormais utiliser ces sources sur le champ de fouilles pour repérer dans un volume déterminé de gangue la nature et la situation des objets en métal, comme on les emploie sur le chantier pour le contrôle des soudures*.

Les premiers travaux de ce genre ont été effectués à l'aide de postes de radiographie médicale. Ainsi, dès 1950, le Musée historique de Stockholm (Suède) a transporté en son laboratoire un sarcophage de bois totalement ensablé et reconnu avant de

l'ouvrir, l'emplacement des bracelets de poignets et de chevilles et celui des armes, par rapport au corps enseveli. Un autre image radiographique a permis la reconstitution d'un plat métallique réduit par la corrosion à l'état de puzzle par suite de sa fragmentation[5].

Discussion: Pour clore cette section, insistons sur l'importance de la qualité des reproductions des observations et sur les soins qu'exigent soit les photographies sous différentes illuminations[6], soit les techniques radiographiques.

De notre expérience propre, il résulte qu'il y a toujours avantage à exposer très largement l'objet sous l'irradiation x ou γ, quitte à tirer, suivant l'objectif de la recherche, des épreuves plus ou moins poussées à partir du cliché d'origine[3].

Ajoutons que les méthodes stéréographiques s'appliquent maintenant non seulement en optique, mais dans le domaine des rayons invisibles: Loose[7] et Kozlowski[8] en ont donné des exemples très frappants.

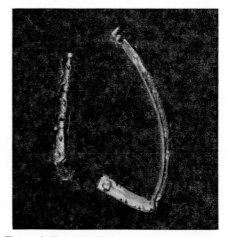

Figure 1. Exemple d'objets difficiles à photographier: cornières mérovingiennes en or ($\times 1$).
(Par courtoisie de *La Revue de Métallurgie*)

Mais la photographie n'est plus le seul moyen de reproduction des surfaces: on dispose aujourd'hui d'une gamme de vernis nitro-cellulosiques capables de prendre l'empreinte du décor le plus fin que la main sache tracer, et même de détails beaucoup plus ténus relevant de la structure intime de la matière[9].

Toutefois, la réplique opère une manière de nettoyage de la surface, ce qui peut être avantageux ou non†. Cette méthode est surtout intéressante pour prendre l'empreinte d'une pièce dont la forme ne se prête pas à la photographie (cylindres babyloniens, cornières coudées; par exemple—*Figures 1* et *2*),

---

* Il existe dans le commerce des appareils montés sur chariot qui peuvent être équipés par exemple avec 250 microcuries de cobalt-60 ou 27 curies d'iridium-192 enfermés dans une coque de 10 kg dont les dimensions ne dépassent pas 105×120 mm (voir *Nature (Paris)*, No. 3308 (1960) 537).

† Voir la section suivante: «Techniques physiques d'analyse».

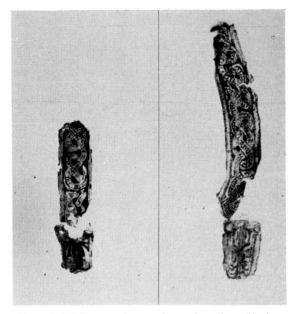

Figure 2. Répliques prises sur les surfaces (non développables) des mêmes cornières (×1).
(Par courtoisie de *La Revue de Métallurgie*)

ou dont la surface est en mauvais état. Dans le cas de souillures gagnant l'empreinte, il suffit de métalliser celle-ci sous vide pour obtenir une image impeccable: c'est ainsi que fut déchiffré un poinçon au revers d'une plaque mérovingienne[3] (*Figure 3*).

S'il convient d'appliquer cette technique avec discrimination, puisqu'elle n'est pas toujours strictement non-destructive, elle mérite attention vu sa simplicité.

La réplique est un document que l'on peut projeter directement et qui est moins onéreux qu'une photographie. De plus, elle peut se répéter plusieurs fois sur l'objet et s'envoie facilement par la poste (voir la *Figure 4*).

Figure 3. Réplique métallisée d'un poinçon tracé sur une surface brute de coulée au dos d'une plaque mérovingienne (×4,5).
(Par courtoisie de *La Revue de Métallurgie*)

Techniques physiques d'analyse

Les rayons x permettent d'une part l'analyse élémentaire non-destructive par fluorescence, d'autre part l'identification des phases ou composés par diffraction.

Les appareils nécessaires à l'exploitation de ces méthodes classiques sont dans le commerce, mais le dépouillement et l'interprétation des résultats exigent de sérieuses connaissances scientifiques.

Analyse par fluorescence: L'analyse se pratique sans modification des appareils courants sur des surfaces n'excédant pas 3 cm de diamètre et pour la recherche des éléments dits moyens.

L'analyse quantitative demeure approchée lorsque la pièce examinée porte un relief, comme celui d'une médaille. La précision augmente avec la planéité et même le poli de la surface.

Dame Arnegonde, noble Mérovingienne[10], nous a livré sa bague, trouvée récemment à Saint-Denis par M. Michel Fleury, Inspecteur des Fouilles de la Seine (*Figure 4*). L'or qui en

Figure 4. (*A gauche*) La bague de Dame Arnegonde (×2 environ).
(*A droite*) Réplique de la partie gravée montrant le détail de la ciselure (même échelle).

forme la base contient, d'après le compteur à scintillation, quelque 4 pour cent d'argent, 2 pour cent de cuivre et du cobalt (environ 1 pour cent), outre les impuretés de la mine: nickel et fer. On note également l'absence de manganèse. Il y a tout lieu de penser que le cobalt indique une contamination de l'or par le moule de fonderie.

La bague, après cet essai, retourne intacte en son écrin.

Une boucle en argent massif appartenant au même mobilier funéraire contenait une quantité notable de cuivre, et 1 à 2 pour cent de cadmium, sans doute une impureté de la mine.

Notons au passage que pour l'analyse quantitative du système or–argent–cuivre, les spectres de référence sont faciles à obtenir: il suffit de faire appel aux monnaies d'or ou d'argent dont les titres sont officiellement définis. En conséquence, une pièce fausse est ainsi très rapidement identifiée.

Analyse par diffraction de rayons x: L'analyse par fluorescence jouit d'un avantage certain par rapport à celle par diffraction du fait que l'état d'écrouissage de la surface ne joue pas. Au contraire, en diffraction, toute déformation réagit sur le diagramme au détriment de sa précision. Parfois, l'écrouissage superficiel peut même donner des indications sur le mode de fabrication des objets examinés[11,12].

En principe, l'analyse des phases ou composés par diffraction suppose connue la nature des éléments constitutifs. A défaut d'analyse élémentaire, on peut tenter l'interprétation d'un diagramme en s'appuyant sur une mesure physique, optique ou gravimétrique, ou sur une observation magnétique. Pour le système or–argent–cuivre, la mesure de la densité est tout indiquée[12,13].

Malheureusement, si l'antique méthode d'Archimède reste valable dans la plupart des cas, il semble que, dans les laboratoires modernes, bien peu de chercheurs soient disposés à l'appliquer avec les précautions minutieuses indispensables à la précision de la mesure.

En certains cas, spécialement pour les métaux lourds, on obtiendra des résultats valables, quoique approximatifs, en s'adressant à l'absorption des rayonnements pénétrants. Par exemple, on peut juger de la détérioration de la situation politique en Gaule au moment de la conquête romaine en constatant l'inflation qui se traduit par la diminution de la teneur en or des monnaies[12,14].

La prise de réplique ouvre de nouvelles perspectives à l'analyse par diffraction de rayons x puisqu'elle détache de la surface les produits faiblement adhérents en les conservant point par point en leur emplacement primitif sur leur nouveau support.

Appliquée pour la première fois à une plaque d'orfèvrerie mérovingienne, cette méthode a montré qu'en l'occurrence seuls les produits de décomposition de la décoration originale étaient ainsi détachés, tandis que le niellé primitif faisait corps avec le bijou[1,3].

La technique s'applique aujourd'hui couramment à l'étude des cassures[15].

Discussion: Toutes deux bien établies dans leurs principes, les méthodes d'analyse par diffraction ou fluorescence de rayons x sont strictement non-destructives.

Les seules précautions à envisager, en cas de fluorescence, concernent l'échauffement qui pourrait se produire sur des échantillons très minces en métaux à très bas point de fusion dans certains dispositifs commerciaux courants.

C'est précisément pour éviter cet échauffement que l'on utilise la fluorescence, c'est-à-dire le rayonnement secondaire de l'objet au lieu de placer celui-ci dans le tube à vide et d'analyser le rayonnement x primaire qu'il produirait sous excitation par électrons.

En cas d'examen non-destructif, on doit donc renoncer aux services du microanalyseur à sonde électronique[16] et ceci malgré l'intérêt qui s'attache aux problèmes ainsi étudiés, en particulier à celui de la diffusion, si important dans l'étude des métaux de l'antiquité. D'une part, comme le note Hall[17], la diffusion à partir du coeur de l'objet vers la surface fausse les analyses superficielles. Mais le même auteur note également qu'en contrepartie cette diffusion renseigne sur l'âge de l'objet dans la mesure où l'on sait exploiter le phénomène.

Un problème de ce type s'est présenté à nous lors de l'étude d'une plaque mérovingienne[3]; il est certainement parmi les plus fascinants de ceux que nous avons rencontrés. Il permet en effet d'obtenir, sur un objet daté, des données scientifiques dont le chercheur ne peut s'assurer la conquête étant donné la brièveté de toute existence humaine. Réciproquement, ce lent cheminement dans le réseau métallique imparfait pourrait, une fois mieux connu, servir au moins à classer certains objets, sinon à les dater.

Ces remarques confirment notre assertion première: les techniques de rayons x, comme celles qui font appel à des branches de la physique en actif développement et que nous citons pour mémoire n'ayant pas eu l'occasion de les pratiquer nous-mêmes (activation par neutron, datation par carbone-14, magnétisme résiduel, nettoyage par ultra-sons, etc.), ne sauraient être fructueuses qu'entre les mains de spécialistes capables de faire jouer les modalités expérimentales en faveur de l'objectif de la recherche.

9

Méthodes non strictement «non-destructives»

Sans exiger le prélèvement d'un échantillon, qui caractérise du point de vue du laboratoire les méthodes destructives, certains procédés font appel à une préparation de la surface, d'autres laissent une trace sur celle-ci.

Techniques d'observation

Parmi les premières, il convient de citer au premier chef la métallographie dite non-destructive qui s'applique aujourd'hui à toute pièce métallique après polissage local d'une plage dont l'étendue peut varier de quelques millimètres carrés à plusieurs décimètres carrés[18].

Au lieu de transporter le microscope en regard de la pièce ainsi préparée, on prend une réplique locale et on l'examine au microscope optique, soit par transmission, soit par réflexion (après métallisation), jusqu'aux plus forts grossissements dont il est capable. Si besoin est, rien n'empêche même, grâce à la double empreinte vernis-carbone, de prolonger l'examen au microscope électronique.

Tout reste à faire dans ce domaine encore inexploité en ce qui concerne les objets d'art. La plupart des études entreprises jusqu'ici ont porté sur des pièces volontairement sacrifiées, ou sur des débris. Et cependant, les résultats sont substantiels[19].

Remarquons, précisément à propos de l'ouvrage de Cyril S. Smith et des méthodes dont il retrace l'histoire, que la réplique locale permet de reprendre sur des bases tout à fait nouvelles l'étude des cassures. Les observations de cet ordre sont certainement parmi les plus anciennes que l'homme ait pu faire puisqu'elles sont fondées sur ses échecs. D'après Smith, elles pourraient remonter à l'âge du bronze. Aujourd'hui, leur interprétation est fondée sur des assises scientifiques grâce aux filiations que sait établir l'analyse morphologique[20], grâce aussi aux précisions apportées par l'examen au microscope électronique sur les conditions d'amorçage et de propagation des fissures[21].

Bien que nous n'ayons pas encore d'exemple à présenter de ce mode de recherche appliqué aux métaux anciens, je suis bien convaincue que cette anticipation est à court terme.

Techniques d'analyse

Suivant Hall[17], nous tenterons de voir si la jeune et séduisante méthode d'analyse par fluorescence x risque de porter ombrage à sa soeur aînée, la spectrographie optique. Pour cela, nous reprendrons en fluorescence x les débris d'épaves, plaques de plomb et clous de cuivre gréco-romains, que nous avions précédemment analysés par spectrographie[4] (*Figure 5*).

Des échantillons similaires de plaques de plomb ont fourni les analyses qualitatives reportées en tête du *Tableau 1*.

On note des résultats identiques pour le cuivre, le bismuth et le fer, additions non intentionnelles.

La fluorescence x ne renseigne pas sur les éléments légers, calcium et magnésium, dont les raies, comme celles de l'argent, n'appartiennent pas au domaine de longueurs d'onde exploré ici. Le nickel provient sans doute du cuivre voisin, par diffusion. Enfin, nous reprendrons le cas du chrome et celui du strontium après avoir étudié les clous de cuivre qui, enrobés de plomb, fixaient ces plaques sur le pont du navire (*Figures 6–8*).

L'analyse spectrographique quantitative a été faite sur un fragment de clou sacrifié, fragment indemne de toute corrosion[4]. Au contraire, l'analyse par fluorescence x a porté sur deux points d'une tête de clou très corrodée. L'un, à l'intérieur, était au contact de la plaque de plomb; l'autre, à l'extérieur, avait dû être primitivement protégé par du plomb, mais a été recueilli apparemment dénudé, sauf incrustations de petits coquillages.

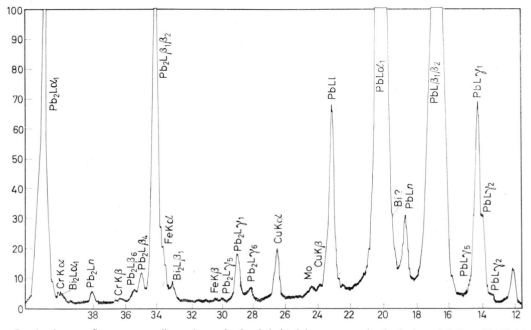

Figure 5a. Analyse par fluorescence x d'une plaque de plomb (cristal de quartz, anticathode de molybdène, 48 kV, 24 mA).

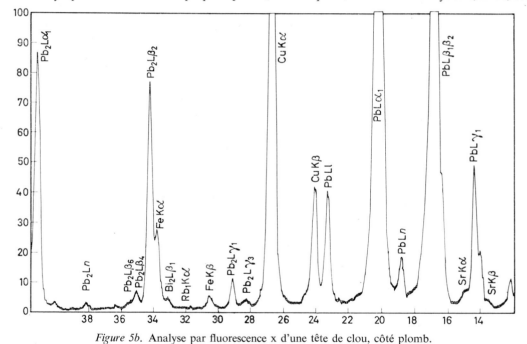

Figure 5b. Analyse par fluorescence x d'une tête de clou, côté plomb.

En suivant les analyses du *Tableau 1*, on voit comment le cuivre des clous s'est chargé en plomb et en ses impuretés. Ceci confirme en particulier que le chrome, absent de l'analyse spectrographique du cuivre, doit provenir du plomb.

On voit également que le clou corrodé ne garde trace ni du nickel—parfois égaré dans le plomb—ni du zinc, ni des traces d'étain et d'antimoine. En revanche, l'arsenic n'a pas complètement disparu.

Reste la question du strontium pour lequel deux origines sont possibles. La plus plausible est la mine: les Mines du Laurium en Grèce sont parmi les plus riches en strontium, et le Commandant Cousteau pense que ce navire a été construit à Délos[22]. Mais les régions les plus riches en strontium sont aussi celles

du clou en contact avec la mer. Or, on sait que cet élément est fixé par les animalcules de la faune sous-marine. Rien ne permet donc d'affirmer qu'il n'y a pas eu également apport de strontium d'origine organique.

Ainsi, cet exemple montre combien il peut être avantageux de disposer de deux analyses faites par des méthodes différentes. Réservant toutefois ce luxe de moyens à des cas particuliers, on pourra en général se contenter de l'une ou l'autre méthode.

Les examens en série, sur des pièces comparables, sont certainement plus rapidement exécutés en fluorescence; la spectrographie conserve ses avantages, au moins pour l'instant, en ce qui concerne la détection des éléments légers.

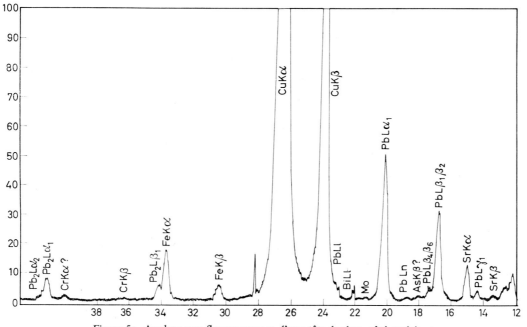

Figure 5c. Analyse par fluorescence x d'une tête de clou, côté extérieur.

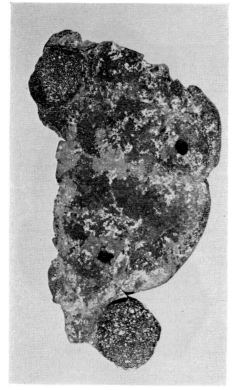

Figure 6. Plaque de plomb avec têtes de clous sur lesquelles sont incrustés des coquillages (×1).

(Par courtoisie de *La Revue de Métallurgie*)

Figure 7. Clou demeuré dans le bois (×1).

(Par courtoisie de *La Revue de Métallurgie*)

Tableau 1

Analyses de débris d'épaves gréco-romaines échouées en Méditerranée (Ilôt du Grand Congloue)

	Fluorescence x			Spectrographie dans l'ultra-violet		
	Base	Additions	Traces	Base	Additions	Traces
Plaque de plomb (voir *Figure 5a*)	Pb	Cu Bi† Fe	Cr Sr	Pb	Cu Bi Fe	Ag Ca Mg Ni
Tête de clou (intérieur) (voir *Figure 5b*)	Pb Cu	Fe Bi* Sr*	Cr	Cu	Zn:0,3 à 0,4% Fe + As:0,2% Ni:0,1%	Sn + Sb: 0,010%
Tête de clou (extérieur) (voir *Figure 5c*)	Cu	Pb Sr† Fe As	Cr			

Pour les analyses qualitatives, les éléments sont rangés par ordre décroissant du taux estimé. Le signe† indique un taux supérieur par rapport au signe*, d'une analyse à l'autre.

L'une ou l'autre méthode est indispensable pour déterminer les impuretés de la mine, ce qui permet de rechercher l'origine géographique du métal, parfois son histoire[23].

Figure 8. Radiographie du même clou non dégagé du bois montrant sa corrosion (×1).

(Par courtoisie de *La Revue de Métallurgie*)

Conclusion

L'étude des objets de collection, l'analyse de leur constitution, intéressent à la fois l'historien du point de vue de l'évolution des techniques[24], le conservateur du point de vue de la préservation des témoins du passé, l'expert pour découvrir les faux.

L'analyse prend aujourd'hui rang, comme l'observation, parmi les techniques non-destructives. Mais le choix judicieux de la méthode la plus appropriée à chaque cas d'espèce exige au départ une confrontation entre l'archéologue et l'homme de laboratoire, confrontation qui s'avérera d'autant plus féconde que chacun saura renseigner plus exactement son interlocuteur sur ce qu'il peut attendre de lui.

Or qu'il s'agisse d'archéologie ou de physique, un danger menace toutes les spécialités—celle de s'enfermer dans un langage hermétique au reste des humains. Ce ne serait donc pas un succès négligeable pour l'analyste, sur le plan culturel, que

de montrer le parti à tirer du classement, laborieusement établi, des raies d'émission x des éléments naturels, ne serait-ce que pour repérer la mine de plomb d'où fut tirée la garniture d'un navire gréco-romain.

Mais ceci n'est qu'un début: il faut dès maintenant penser au classement non moins laborieux des analyses qui doivent croître en nombre et en qualité avec l'application des méthodes non-destructives. De cette classification méthodique des résultats déjà acquis, dépend en fait la valeur de toute nouvelle analyse et son passage du laboratoire à l'histoire.

Bibliographie

1 WEILL, A. R., *Stud. Conservation*, 4, No. 4 (1959) 121.
2 SALIN, E., *Métaux et Civil.*, 1, No. 3 (1945) 50.
3 WEILL, A. R., *Rev. Métall.*, 57, No. 6 (1960) 459.
4 WEILL, A. R., *Rev. Métall.*, 51, No. 7 (1954) 459.
5 Communication privée de Mmes RYDBERG et PELLING (Stockholm, 1951).
6 HOURS, M., *Nature (Paris)*, No. 3290 (1959) 270.
7 LOOSE, L., *Stud. Conservation*, 5, No. 3 (1960) 85.
8 KOZLOWSKI, R., *Stud. Conservation*, 5, No. 3 (1960) 89.
9 WEILL, A. R., *Bull. Lab. Mus. Louvre*, No. 4 (1959) 21.
10 FLEURY, M. et FRANCE-LANORD, A., *Art de France*, première année, Ed. Hermann, Paris, 1961, pp. 5–18 (Les bijoux mérovingiens d'Arnegonde).
11 WEILL, A. R., *Metall. ital.*, 42, No. 12 (1951) 597.
12 WEILL, A. R. et AMBROSINO, G., *Bull. Lab. Mus. Louvre*, No. 1 (1956) 53.
13 WEILL, A. R., *Stud. Conservation*, 1, No. 1 (1952) 30.
14 AMBROSINO, G. et PINDRUS, P., *Rev. Métall.*, 50, No. 2 (1953) 136.
15 WEILL, A. R., *Rev. Métall.*, 58, No. 5 (1961) 323.
16 CASTAING, R. et DESCAMPS, J., *J. Phys. Radium*, 16 (1955) 304.
17 HALL, E. T., *Endeavour*, 18, No. 70 (1959) 83 (Édition Française).
18 JACQUET, P. A., Technique non-destructive pour les observations, en particulier de nature métallographique sur les surfaces métalliques, Ed. Office National d'Études et de Recherches Aéronautiques (Châtillon-sous-Bagneux), Seine, France, *Note Technique no. 54*, 1959.
19 SMITH, C. S., *A History of Metallography*, University of Chicago Press, Chicago, 1960.
20 DE LEIRIS, H., *Métaux, Corros., Industr.*, No. 316 (1951).
21 PLATEAU, J., HENRY, G. et CRUSSARD, C., *Rev. univ. Min.*, 9ème série, 12, No. 10 (1956) 543.
22 COUSTEAU, Y., *Nat. geogr. Mag.*, 55, No. 1 (1954) 1.
23 WEILL, A. R., *Rev. Métall.*, 54, No. 4 (1957) 270.
24 WEILL, A. R., De l'analyse des objets à l'histoire des techniques de métallurgie, *Act. VIIIe Congr. Int. Hist. Sci. (Florence, 1956)*, 3 (1958) 949.

Ouvrages à consulter

Analyse non-destructive

BALLARD, D. W., Orientation and scope of the present non-destructive testing field, *Non-destr. Test.*, 18 (1960) 177–179.

Fluorescence de rayons x

GIAVINO, A., Lo stato attuale della spettrometria con raggi x di fluorescenza, *Metall. ital.*, No. 6 (1960) 306–314.

PARRISH, W., Analyse spectrochimique aux rayons x, *Rev. Tech. Philips*, 17, No. 12 (1956) 385–405 (et nombreux articles du même auteur).

WERNER, O., Die Röntgen-Fluoreszenz-Spektralanalyse und ihre Bedeutung für die Metallkunde, *Arch. Eisenhüttenw.*, 26, No. 12 (1955) 721–737.

Diffraction des rayons x appliquée aux métaux

BARRETT, C., *Structure of Metals*, McGraw-Hill Book Company, New York, 1952, et sa traduction française par Dunod, Paris, 1957.

KLUG, H. P. et ALEXANDER, L. E., *X-ray Diffraction Procedures*, J. Wiley and Sons, New York (et nombreux ouvrages en toutes les langues).

Applications de la méthode des répliques

JACQUET, P. A., Non-destructive techniques for macro and micrographic surface examination of metallic specimens (electrolytic local polishing and replica technique), *Proc. Amer. Soc. Test. Mater.*, 57 (1957) 1290–1302.

JACQUET, P. A., Neuartige zerstörungsfreie elektrolytische Polierverfahren und Abdrucktechniken auf Metalloberflächen, *Metalloberfläche*, 14, No. 5 (1960) 132–6; 14, No. 6 (1960) 161–170.

JACQUET, P. A., Une nouvelle technique: La métallographie non destructive, *Atomes*, No. 171 (1960) 337–342.

JACQUET, P. A. et MENCARELLI, E., Application du tampon électrolytique à la micrographie électronique, *Rev. Métall.*, 56 (1959) 129–142.

JACQUET, P. A. et MENCARELLI, E., *Techniques non destructives pour la métallographie optique et électronique des cassures*, Association Technique Maritime et Aéronautique (Session 1959) (et nombreux articles du même auteur dans les revues de métallurgie françaises ou autres).

Leonetto Tintori

METHODS USED IN ITALY FOR DETACHING MURALS

The necessity for removing murals from their original sites in order to preserve them has led to the development in Italy of specialized techniques which I shall describe here. The different methods are of three types:

1. The wall behind the painting is cut away; this method is often used in archaeological work (*Figure 1*).

Figure 1. Fourteenth century Madonna and Child, and other 'cut away' frescoes, the work of an 18th century restorer, conserved today in the Refectory of Ognissanti, Florence.

Many of these frescoes, coming from various parts of the city, are now conserved in Ognissanti. They were removed during the destruction of the centre of Florence towards the end of the last century. Some are in good condition, but all are condemned to the same wear and tear as mural paintings *in situ*. Fortunately the best were cut away before the wall suffered decay which would have involved the painted intonaco. In spite of their weight, which makes them almost immovable, when well executed this method is the best for detaching frescoes. However, the pictures must have firm paint and be in a good state of preservation.

By courtesy of the Gabinetto Fotografico della Soprintendenza alle Gallerie, Firenze.

2. The painted plaster is detached together with a layer of mortar, thus keeping the wall intact. This is the *distacco* method (*Figure 2*).

3. Only the paint layer is removed (*strappo* method). This is the best method for cases where there is little adhesion between the paint layer and the plaster and when one wants to save the *sinopia* beneath the plaster.

Satisfactory restoration depends on making the right choice from among these methods according to the individual case. It would, for instance, be useless and even dangerous to choose the first or second method when the cause for a mural's decay

Figure 2. Masaccio—Crucifixion—S. Maria Novella, Florence. Restored 1850–1860.

Fresco removed by the distacco method, with all the intonaco, and put onto a wooden frame about 1860. Mechanically the process turned out well, the canvasses are properly adhering to the wood all over, and the metal strips support the weight entrusted to them very well. For a certain time the fresco caused much worry because of the flaking away of the paint, which threatened to destroy the whole work. The cause of this was glue left from the preliminary relining. This having now been accurately removed, the picture is well preserved, without signs of decay.

By courtesy of the Gabinetto Fotografico della Soprintendenza alle Gallerie, Firenze.

lies in the plaster, since the preservation of such a plaster would only lead to further trouble. Damage could also result from applying the third method to cases where the paint film is tenaciously fixed to the plaster, either because of the painting technique or through perfect lime-bonding in the course of time.

The first method

I shall not deal at length with the first method, in which the wall is cut away behind the painting. Although it has been used for centuries and has preserved many precious pictures, it is now rarely used. The chief objection to this method is, as we have said, that the main danger to the mural often originates in the wall beneath it. This is especially true on damp sites, where removal of the wall would be of no help. Even if dampness is not undue and the wall proves to be in good condition, the responsible restorer must keep in mind that during such an operation the wall will inevitably be demolished, involving substantial cost. Also, the excessive weight of the mural so detached will prove to be an awkward factor even if the picture is not very large.

The procedure for this method is briefly as follows. After it is ensured that the *intonaco** is firmly fixed to the wall and the paint to the intonaco (without, however, using a facing canvas), an incision is made in the intonaco and plaster is applied around the area which is to be isolated. The cut beneath the painting is made to the required depth (either the entire thickness of the plaster layers, or, if this is too much, a part of it). In the crack so obtained, pieces of iron or wood are inserted. These should be of a size and strength suitable for the dimensions of the area to be detached. When these supports have been inserted, care must be taken that the whole wall rests on them; wedges should be set in places which are insufficiently secure.

After this, the wall is demolished from behind, first one section and then another. Planks of wood or iron bars are inserted here too; these, in turn, are wedged and propped during the rest of the operation. Finally the wall will be freed from the top, thus completing the support of the block to be preserved.

The difficulty of transporting the block so obtained and the expense of such an operation means that this method remains the least used. Nevertheless, one should know the procedure because with this method there is an absolute respect for the original state of the mural. The state of the original permitting, the condition of the picture will remain unchanged.

The principal dangers in the other methods of transfer lie in the necessity of applying facing canvasses. This can, in fact, give rise to the most insidious complications. These are completely avoided when using the above method.

The distacco method

This method must be described more fully. The first essential is to ascertain the state of preservation of both paint and intonaco. If either suffers from any serious defects that would threaten their holding together during the transfer, then this method should not be considered. In such cases only the paint layer should be detached (strappo method). There are many murals in which a defective intonaco has been preserved after a distacco transfer. The deterioration will then continue and may even be aggravated by the transfer. Organic materials, such as those in many types of glue, introduced during the transfer can accelerate the decay because micro-organisms stimulate the processes of disintegration.

It is imperative, therefore, to make absolutely sure that both the paint and the intonaco are in good condition. Every particle of the surface must be firm and resistant to washing with hot water, which is a necessary part of the operation, as we shall see. It must be remembered that any tempera superimposed on the original painting, although resistant to washing with cold water, is often extremely susceptible to hot water. Therefore a protective fixative must be applied. Fixatives which

have a tendency to contract (casein, egg-white) are to be avoided. Shellac, of the so-called reversible type, can be used if care is taken after completion of the transfer to remove it all immediately. If any bits remain, these can produce a bleached effect which can only be made transparent again by the application of an oily substance.

Better than shellac are a number of acrylic resins which, in the present state of knowledge, are best suited to paint consolidation (especially Paraloid B-72—a product of Rohm and Haas—acrylate-methacrylate copolymer, known in the United States as Acryloid B-72). Paraloid B-72 is, however, rather difficult to use. If too much is applied to the paint surface then the glue of the facing canvas will not adhere properly, with possible grave consequences when the distacco is attempted. In any case, it should be kept in mind when taking the necessary precautions that both shellac and Paraloid B-72 have almost the same degree of penetration and both are equally resistant to hot water. Paraloid B-72 has the advantage of greater elasticity as well as the guarantee of reversibility even after a long time. It affects the tonality of the paint less than shellac and has little tendency to yellow. Whichever is chosen, it should be used in the smallest possible amount and must always be thoroughly removed at the end of the operation.

Having thus ensured the safety of the paint film we can proceed to the facing. This can be done with cotton canvasses placed on top of one another, or one canvas can be of cotton while the other is of hemp. When using the distacco method, the adhesive should be a fairly fluid glue that is rich in glucose or molasses. The addition of these materials makes the glue more flexible so that there is no risk of peeling off part of the paint as a result of contraction, which the use of glue alone would entail. Furthermore, such a mixture of glue is more soluble, making the final washing easier.

Some restorers prefer to use canvas divided into small pieces because of the fear that with large canvasses air bubbles will remain trapped between the material and the paint. This was a real danger when, not long ago, it was customary to soak the canvas—even the small pieces—in hot glue in order to stretch them by hand. But now that this habit has been abandoned even large pieces of canvas can be glued, thus eliminating many overlapping canvas edges. Facings with animal glue were used up to the end of the last century and still give good results today if the painting to be detached is in particularly dry surroundings. Otherwise cellulose or other resins are better adhesives.

When the facing has thoroughly dried, whether a glue or a resin has been decided upon, the intonaco is lifted off the lower layer of plaster, working from the bottom upwards using steel scalpels. Unfortunately, the distacco method almost always involves the loss of the sinopia which may have been drawn on the plaster layer beneath the intonaco. If not destroyed, the sinopia is, at the very least, severely damaged. By using the strappo method (described below), however, the sinopia can usually be saved.

When the mural has been detached from the wall, the rear surface is smoothed off, aiming as far as possible at an even thickness of the intonaco which is to be preserved. In the past it was customary to support the rear of the detached mural with canvasses or a metal mesh. There are still some who like to use such supports. Instead of this, I prefer to use a rigid sheet composed of three layers of sized Masonite, prepared in advance, with which the intonaco (first fixed on to a canvas) makes a perfect adhesion. The fixing of the intonaco on to its support, whether the latter be of canvas and Masonite or of canvas and metal mesh, can be done either with calcium

---

* For fresco painting the wall is roughly plastered. On this the drawing or *sinopia* is carried out, usually in dark red or black ochre. Then an area sufficient for one day's work is covered with a layer of finer plaster—the *intonaco*. The pigment, ground up with water, is applied to this while it is still wet, so that on drying the colour is firmly bound into the surface. Occasionally, tempera paint is used for the final details.

caseinate or modern synthetic resins. I prefer the resins, especially acrylic emulsions, for most cases. However, if such resins have already been used to face the mural in surroundings with excessive humidity, calcium caseinate must be used on the rear because the solvents necessary for the removal of the front facings would also dissolve the resin employed for fixing the mural to its support—with obviously disastrous results.

Whichever is used, the scraped-down back must first be consolidated with a coating of liquid gluten, which should be allowed to dry before fixing the canvas on it. This canvas should be strong, preferably of hemp. When this has also dried, the mural is laid on its final support of either Masonite or metal mesh. If the latter is used, the frame and the network must be of an unoxidizable material. Once it is immersed in casein or resin, any oxidation could be dangerous.

After this, the facing canvasses must be removed. When glue has been used as the adhesive the removing agent is hot water spread on with brushes and mopped up with sponges after it has dissolved the glue. Jets of steam can be used for the same purpose if the jets are not too strong. This method has the double advantage of eliminating all mechanical action on the paint surface and of removing the glue without getting the intonaco too wet. This also prevents the glue from percolating into the intonaco as would inevitably happen if brushes and sponges were used with the hot water. After the mural has dried out, as much of the fixative as possible must be removed.

It is, of course, very useful to know the two methods described above and to be able to apply them whenever conditions require. However, the best method for saving murals, even in an advanced state of decay, is the strappo method.

The strappo method

This method was already used at the beginning of this century on several murals, among them two famous ones by Paolo Uccello in the Chiostro Verde of Santa Maria Novella in Florence. The success of these operations, however, was not complete; part of the paint remained on the wall and more was lost during the washing. The marks of these losses are all too evident today. After this not very brilliant effort, the then authorities decided to leave the other murals in place and to fix the paintings already removed into a plaster bed. Fifty years later, in spite of repeated treatments on those left *in situ*, the only pictures of the entire cycle which are still visible are those which were removed with the strappo method, albeit with limited success. At the present time this method is being used on the remaining murals, although many of these are now only confused shadows. The history of this case confirms the necessity of removing all murals judged to be in a precarious condition. Indeed, today no one questions the need for isolating the paint layer and giving it a new support better adapted to the surrounding conditions of the site.

The most frequent causes for the decay of murals are to be found in a hardening of the surface. This can result either from impregnation with fixatives which have become irreversible or from changes which the carbonates have undergone as a result of weathering. Another cause is dampness, which, through capillary action or other means, can rise from the ground or other sources to penetrate the back of the picture. This is one of the most insidious enemies of murals.

The various damaging agents all produce different effects, so that one cannot prescribe general solutions. All cases must be examined separately. As we have said, hardening of the surface is caused by old fixatives which have become insoluble and cannot be removed. Their tendency to contract causes the paint to flake off. In such a case, each section must be studied carefully and its resistance defined so that the most suitable fixative will be chosen. Then the paint film can be consolidated, which is essential before proceeding. Under these conditions, the possible materials which can be used here are skim milk, casein and reversible shellac, which is the best of both the natural and synthetic resins. Again, the most suitable is Paraloid B-72. But n-butylmethacrylate and isobutylmethacrylate also give good results. However, there is less certainty about their permanent irreversibility. The different degrees of elasticity of these resins make one or another preferable according to the individual case.

Figure 3. Andrea del Castagno—Pippo Spano. Fresco removed from the Villa Pandolfini at Legnaia, Florence. Restored by Rizzoli in 1874.

This was relined onto canvas with calcium caseinate, and stretched on a wooden frame with wedges. As the caseinate is not very resistant to the action of hot water, the restorer was unable to remove completely the glue used during the strappo. Moreover, the canvas, undergoing alterations in humidity, has visibly slackened and crumpled. By courtesy of the Gabinetto Fotografico della Soprintendenza alle Gallerie, Firenze.

After every part of the picture is made firm and resistant to washing, the facing can be applied. For this the humidity of the picture's surroundings must be taken into account since it may determine the choice of glue to be used. If the site is very dry a strong bone glue is advisable. If, on the other hand, the site is damp, but not excessively so, then glue from bones and skin will be best. It is not advisable, however, to use skin glue alone or even parchment glue, because both are less easily wetted and therefore more difficult to remove.

A first coat of glue, hot and not very liquid, is spread with a brush over an area of paint which can be covered by one canvas or, at the most, two. This canvas must first be washed in order to remove the finish and to allow for any shrinkage. All selvedges must be cut away. As soon as the glue has been spread, the dry canvas can be stretched, but not over-stretched. Then another coat of thicker glue is brushed on, taking care that no air bubbles are trapped between the canvas and the mural. Following ancient usage, it is best to start fixing the

Figure 4. Prato: Detail of a Crucifixion from the Chapter Room of San Francesco, by Niccolo di Pietro Gerini. Restored by Tintori in 1956.

The most obvious repaints were removed and the loose colours consolidated. The mural was partly detached using glue for the facing, but where there was too much moisture nitrocellulose was used. As an adhesive for attachment to the new support, a mixture of calcium carbonate and a vinyl emulsion (Vinavil) plus a third part of calcium caseinate was used. The calcium carbonate had the function of resisting the solvent which was used to remove the nitrocellulose, which otherwise might have weakened the vinyl emulsion. The original character of the mural colours has been preserved. Because of the large size of this mural, it was detached using five pieces of tempered Masonite.
By courtesy of the Gabinetto Fotografico della Soprintendenza alle Gallerie, Firenze.

canvas from the bottom right, working in such a way that drops of glue are kept from drying on the surface. If this should occur, the contraction will tear off the paint before the facing has been applied. After the first canvas a second is put on. If the mural is small, the canvas can be of cotton; otherwise it is better to use hemp. For the second canvas a more fluid glue can be used. The glue for the first canvas has to be thick both to prevent the weave of the material from leaving an impression on the painting and because its greater contraction helps the strappo. The second canvas is only for purposes of reinforcement and therefore it is better to have it more flexible.

When the facings are thoroughly dry, the strappo can be started. In good, dry weather this would be after a maximum of two or three days, but in winter it may take longer. Therefore, the glue must not be allowed to become mouldy. If necessary, artificial drying must be used. The faced mural usually comes away easily when pulled from the edges. Sometimes certain areas of varying size offer considerable resistance. It is a good idea then to use long scalpels and proceed as in the distacco method. Any bits of intonaco or other plaster left on the back must be removed so that only the paint film is left.

At this point one must decide which adhesive to use for attaching the new canvas and then the support. Calcium caseinate, acrylic resin emulsions or acrylates in solution? None of the three is to be excluded *a priori*, since each has different properties making them suitable for different cases. Let us examine each one.

In Italy and elsewhere there are many murals which have been fixed down with calcium caseinate. Many such transfers in the 19th century have lasted well (*Figure 3*). However, it requires fairly dry surroundings with only moderate fluctuations of temperature. If the air is very dry, there is a tendency for the paint to 'cusp'; if damp, then efflorescence of calcium carbonate can occur.

An acrylic emulsion (*Figure 4*) has the advantage of greater resistance because it does not contract. It stays flexible longer and only deteriorates slowly under the influence of dampness. However, it is not as clear as casein and if not used in exactly the right proportions it can gradually influence the general tone of the painting—especially when this has been reduced to a very thin layer.

Figure 5. Florence, Chiostro dello Scalzo. *Andrea del Sarto:* The head of St John presented to Herodias—detail. Restored by Tintori in 1960.

In the strappo transfer all the paint came away easily with the facing canvas. The very thin and pliant paint layer was more inclined than in other cases to move with the glue. Therefore, use of one of the various systems normally employed would inevitably have involved damage to the paint surface. Laboratory experiments seeking ways to avoid this have been carried out for many years and have been most useful in this case, allowing a safe transfer with complete respect for the soft unevenness of the surfaces. The picture is now entrusted to a mixture of acrylic resin and calcium carbonate and is supported on a triple layer of sized Masonite.
By courtesy of the Gabinetto Fotografico della Soprintendenza alle Gallerie, Firenze.

The third possibility, that of a resin dissolved in benzene and acetone instead of water, is undoubtedly the best. Like the resin emulsion, it has good resistance, flexibility and adhesion to the paint. It does not alter the tone of the colours in any way and, in addition, follows faithfully the finest undulations of the paint so that one cannot tell from the surface of the mural thus transferred whether the intonaco has been left or not. The reason for this is that the solvents used do not affect the facing adhesive at all, whereas the water present in either the casein or the resin emulsion will soften the glue and the finished surface will show signs of this. Objections can be raised that there has been insufficient experience to show whether or not the acrylates will retain their intrinsic properties. But many experiments have been carried out on the artificial aging of these and similar materials and they do give the best results. Acrylic resin in solution was used with excellent results for the final fixing of the murals by Andrea del Sarto removed from the Chiostro dello Scalzo in Florence (*Figure 5*).

Once the adhesive has been chosen, a thin solution is painted on to the back of the mural. Then the relining canvas of cotton, impregnated with a mixture of the adhesive and calcium carbonate, is applied. If a thicker paste is required, powdered pumice can be added.

At this point the painting is enclosed between two canvasses. When the back is completely dry, the facing canvas and glue can be removed with hot water and steam as in the distacco method. All the glue must be removed; if even a small quantity is left, dangerous consequences could result.

In Tuscany today, the mural is then generally glued on to a sheet of sized Masonite. At Pisa, in the Camposanto Monumentale, just after the war, sheets of 'Eternit'* were used

_____
* 'Eternit' is a mixture of cement and asbestos compressed into sheets about 5–6 mm thick.

screwed down on to wooden frames. Now Masonite is preferable because it is more flexible, and by virtue of its composition it is not susceptible to fluctuations of temperature and humidity.

In Lombardy, the canvas used for relining is often bound to the wooden frame by means of bands of glued canvas which hold the mural against the frame.

In Rome, relining is done with very strong hemp canvas which is then stretched on to a metal frame.

I must, therefore, conclude that in the final stage of the work there is still doubt concerning the preference of one method over another. It is to be hoped that this aspect of the problem will be thoroughly studied by comparing and inspecting the results already obtained.

Bibliography

Acryloid: Acrylic Ester Resins for Coatings, Rohm and Haas Co., Philadelphia, 1958.

ALLYN, G., Outdoor exposure of acrylic emulsion paints, *Paint Varn. Prod.*, 47, Nos. 6–7 (1957).

FELLER, R., STOLOW, N. and JONES, E., *On Picture Varnishes and their Solvents*, Inter-Museum Conservation Association, Oberlin (Ohio), 1959.

SECCO-SUARDO, G., *Il Restauratore dei Dipinti*, Manuale Hoepli, second edition, Milan, 1894.

Paolo Mora

SOME OBSERVATIONS ON MURAL PAINTINGS

Before serious consideration is accorded to any project for the transfer of mural paintings, it is necessary to have clearly in mind the theoretical basis upon which the restoration of such paintings depends. It would, of course, be quite wrong to suppose that the restoration of mural paintings necessarily involves their detachment from the wall by any of the three recognized processes collectively known, in Italian, under the term *stacco*. Once the decision has been taken to restore a painting, the next stage is to initiate a series of preliminary tests. This is all very evident, and perhaps might be considered to be subsidiary to our main theme, but in a matter of such grave importance as restoring a fresco no excuse should be required for recapitulating matters which are fundamental to the development of a rational programme. These are:

1. Examination of the condition of the wall or structure which carries the painting, with the object of locating possible sources of humidity, i.e. capillarity, condensation or infiltration. Humidity, it will be remembered, is the chief cause of the deterioration of murals.

2. Examination of the stability of the wall after locating and removing the sources of humidity and taking measures to prevent its recurrence.

3. Careful investigations to determine the degree of cohesion in the layers of the intonaco and the adherence of the intonaco to the underlying brickwork.

4. Tests of the paint layer, with particular regard to discovering the technique of execution and its composition (detailed chemical analyses) and the state of its conservation.

5. Collection and study of all documents relative to the condition of the painting in times past and to previous restorations, with particular emphasis upon the materials employed in conservation.

After having evaluated objectively the results of these inquiries and having considered every possible means of solving the problems that are outstanding, one can consider the possible advantages of carrying out a stacco. If there seems to be no objection against this operation one must nevertheless be on guard against rushing into a decision, because although the detachment of a mural painting is an operation which is now well understood and no longer presents any serious danger, it remains in the class of surgical operation and is carried out at the expense of the material support of the painting, which constitutes an integral part of the work of art. Thus the good surgeon, when necessary, operates, dissects and removes, but if he finds it possible to gain results by other means he will do so.

If the decision has been taken with the necessary prudence that it is desirable to perform a stacco, the following problems have to be considered straightaway.

1. The removal of the layer containing the picture from the wall; the wall being the support or basis, which may be of variable composition, even rock.

2. The attachment of a new support to the back of the picture after it is removed.

3. The structure of the new support.

The technical problems involved in stacco may be considered to have been almost entirely resolved for normal cases. For special cases, as when the walls or surroundings are very wet, researches are still being carried out to discover improved types of adhesive and methods of application. The problem of the attachment of the painting to its new support, although not yet solved satisfactorily, may be claimed to be in the final stages of solution. If one uses calcium caseinate instead of the other more modern alternatives, which have also given excellent results, it is not only because of its accepted affinity to the materials of frescoes but above all because before adopting a new system it should be subjected to effective aging tests extending over at least some fifteen years. As to the requirements of structure and composition of the new support, definite conclusions have not yet been reached. For this reason the Institute continues to use as a support a textile freely stretched on a frame, so that when a better solution is eventually found among the methods that are at present under experiment, the possibility of adopting it for murals already detached without fundamentally affecting the system will remain open. One must, however, know the desirable properties of the supports for a transferred mural painting.

Since, as already suggested, mural paintings have been conceived and created for a particular site in which they will, if possible, remain after their restoration, it appears to be essential that the thickness of the new support will approximate as far as possible to the thickness of the original layer of mortar, in order to avoid disturbing changes of level and surface and alterations in the architectural scheme. It follows from this that it should be possible to vary the thickness of the support to suit the task in hand.

Secondly, a fundamental property of every type of restoration and not least for murals, and in this matter I cannot do better than quote Professor Brandi, is that 'no operation concerned with restoration is valid that blocks the way for future restorations'. The requirement is clearly that the new support of frescoes must be removable at any time with the greatest of ease and without causing any danger to the paint layer.

To this may be added the requirements that the new support must be unalterable in time and resistant to atmospheric agencies (at present we are dealing with indoor murals) and also to animal and vegetable pests.

Furthermore, it must (a) offer the minimum of resistance to possible movements and changes in volume of the paint layer resulting from variations in temperature and humidity; (b) isolate the paint layer from changes in the temperature and humidity of the walls and it must not itself promote the condensation of atmospheric humidity; (c) it must be light and manageable as heavy objects are exposed to greater risks of all kinds; (d) it should possess a high degree of flexibility so that it can be made to conform with the undulations of a wall that is not perfectly flat and be applicable to the case of frescoes on a ceiling or on irregular surfaces. To flexibility should be added the proportionately small but definitely important feature of elasticity so that the fresco will not incur damage from minor shocks.

From a consideration of the above-mentioned properties we have formulated our policy and have been working for several years towards obtaining an improved solution. Other restoration laboratories have also taken these matters into consideration in their search towards the same end.

We feel that the solution of our problems may be to use a foam-forming resin, which would be spread on the back of the detached fresco to form a semi-rigid stratum which, of course, could be reinforced as required: this system would be easily removable if further restoration is envisaged.

The application of this plastic backing to the wall is also being studied. One may add that we are prepared to dispense with the stretchers where we achieve a system of mechanical adhesion to the wall which is immediately and easily removable and which can be re-established in a moment.

For those who are interested, therefore, in studying the possible methods of supporting detached mural paintings we feel that we can give an assurance that a solution of the problem is in sight. There remain only some practical refinements which we hope to be able to introduce and make available shortly.

A. E. Werner

CONSOLIDATION OF FRAGILE OBJECTS

When objects have been buried in the ground or exposed to unsuitable environmental conditions, they may suffer changes which result in the loss of their original mechanical strength so that they become fragile. The consolidation of objects in such a fragile state is a constantly recurring problem in conservation and there are many aspects to it, because the fragility may exhibit itself in a variety of ways. In the present article attention will be concentrated on materials of an organic nature such as wood, leather and ivory, and on siliceous materials. It is difficult to lay down any general principles to be observed since the individual problems are so varied, and the method of consolidation must be adapted to meet the requirements of the specific cases. However, as will emerge from the cases which have been selected for detailed consideration, the consolidant used must be one which is itself durable and permanent and does not tend to exert undue stresses on the object. Many of the consolidants used in the past, such as natural resins and waxes, do not meet these needs and in the field of conservation the introduction of synthetic materials has undoubtedly led to improved methods of consolidation. In order to illustrate these advances in technique, a number of examples which seem to merit special consideration has been selected according to the nature of the material involved.

Water-logged wood

When wooden antiquities have been buried in wet soil for a long period, degradation of the cellulosic components of the cell walls occurs and, if this degradation has reached an advanced stage, the wood will become quite soft, almost like cheese, and will have a very low mechanical strength. Owing to the weakened state of the cell wall structure, it is clear that if the liquid water is allowed to escape by the normal process of evaporation the surface tension forces involved would cause the cell walls to collapse, with consequent serious warping and cracking of the wood. The problem of consolidation involves two factors: first the actual removal of the large excess of water without causing serious deterioration of the wood, and then the conferring of dimensional stability on the dried wood. Several techniques have been proposed which merit consideration. These are the following:

The alum process

This process depends upon the replacement of the excess water in the wood by an aqueous solution which can become a solid consolidant by change of temperature. Potash alum was chosen because it is freely soluble in hot water but only soluble to about 10 per cent at room temperature. Therefore if the wood is soaked in a hot concentrated solution of alum for a period of time sufficient to permit penetration of the water-logged wood, the mass will solidify as soon as the wooden object is removed from the hot solution and shrinkage will be prevented. This method has proved successful in certain cases which have been reported by Rosenberg[1] and Moss[2], where further details will be found, and it was also used for wooden objects found with the Viking ship of Oseberg[4].

The alcohol–ether–resin process

This process, which was developed by Christensen[3], is based on the biological technique of drying tissues in successive baths of ethyl alcohol and then following this by immersion in baths of diethyl ether to remove the alcohol. If a resin is dissolved in the final ether bath this will remain in the wood and the structure may be rigidly fixed. The success of this method depends upon the fact that diethyl ether has a very low surface tension which does not cause collapse of the weak cell walls when it evaporates. In order to reduce shrinkage further the ether can be allowed to evaporate rapidly by the sudden application of a vacuum. This method is admirable for small objects, but a serious drawback is the fact that ether is both expensive and rather dangerous to handle.

Freeze-drying process

This process is also based upon a biological technique whereby the water in the specimen is frozen and the ice allowed to sublime *in vacuo*. Rosenqvist[4] has described this method as a promising one, but Organ[5] has found the results of this technique to be disappointing. A modification of this technique of freeze-drying was advocated by Christensen[6] in which the water in the wood was first gradually replaced by trimethyl carbinol (tertiary butanol)—a hygroscopic substance with a melting point of $25 \cdot 5^{\circ}C$. The wood was then allowed to freeze and the solid trimethyl carbinol sublimed away *in vacuo*. This method has also been tried by Rosenqvist and Organ; the results on the whole are satisfactory but the process is rather tedious and time-consuming, and for large-scale work expensive equipment is necessary.

Electrolytic process

In 1949 Professor Cebertowicz of the Polytechnic School in Dansk, Poland, carried out experiments on a method for the stabilization of shifting ground. This consisted of the successive saturation of the ground with solutions of sodium silicate and calcium chloride and the simultaneous passage through the saturated ground of a direct current in order to produce electrokinetic effects—mainly electro-osmosis. This technique resulted in the successful petrification of the ground by the precipitation of calcium silicate in the pores of the soil. This electrokinetic method has been applied to consolidation of wood; successful results were claimed from Poland, but experiments carried out in other laboratories have not confirmed this claim.

All the above-mentioned methods must be regarded in general as either unreliable, limited in scope or requiring elaborate vacuum equipment. More recently, therefore, interesting techniques based on the use of new synthetic materials have been evolved which offer certain advantages. The principle of these methods is that the water is replaced by a solid material which fills all the voids in the wood and thus prevents any deformation and gives the wood reasonable mechanical strength. Various materials such as long-chain aliphatic alcohols, sulphonated fatty alcohols, methyl cellulose, and a range of plastics used as water emulsions have been tried, but of these the materials which appear to have proved most successful are the polyethylene-glycol waxes and a melamine-formaldehyde resin. The methods using these materials will therefore be discussed in greater detail.

Polyethylene glycol process

The polyethylene-glycol waxes are available in a polymeric series ranging in physical consistency from soft materials like vaseline to hard materials like ordinary paraffin wax. Although they have the physical characteristics of waxes, they have the unusual property of being soluble in water. Experiments showed that the wax of average molecular weight 4000, which is hard and non-hygroscopic, was most suitable for the treatment of water-logged wood. (The actual material used was Carbowax 4000 made by Union Carbide Corporation.) Some workers have adopted the practice of immersing the water-logged wood directly in a bath of the molten wax, but it has been found that this method is not always satisfactory since complete penetration of the wood by the wax and replacement of the water may not be achieved. Organ[5], therefore, devised a special procedure in which the wooden object is initially immersed in a 12 per cent solution of the Carbowax at room temperature, and the temperature slowly increased over a period of weeks, during which the water slowly diffuses out of the wood and is replaced by the wax; at the same time the supernatant solution is allowed to evaporate slowly, so that at the end of the treatment the wooden object is left lying immersed in the molten wax. It is then merely necessary to remove the object and wash off any excess of wax on the surface. This is a simple procedure and no elaborate equipment is required. The results achieved in the British Museum Research Laboratory during the last few years have been eminently successful and many different woods, including yew, have been consolidated in a satisfactory manner. LeFève[7] has recently described the consolidation of a Roman bucket using Carbowax 4000.

Arigal C process

This process is based upon the idea of impregnating the water-logged wood with a monomeric compound which is then induced to polymerize in situ in the wood. Arigal C is a melamine-formaldehyde condensation resin, which is freely soluble in water and can be converted into an insoluble mass at low temperature by the addition of an appropriate hardener. This material was introduced by Müller-Beck and Haas[8] for the consolidation of water-logged wood and has been successfully used for the treatment of many specimens of prehistoric wood from neolithic strata. The procedure has certain advantages for the treatment of small objects when sufficiently deep penetration of the hardener can be achieved within the prescribed period of 48 hours. A disadvantage is the fact that the object is left unnaturally light in weight. A similar process using a urea-formaldehyde resin has been tried out in Moscow for the consolidation of wooden implements found in Novgorod.

The consolidation of very large water-logged objects such as boats presents a special problem because of their size. Any of the methods already discussed would be extremely expensive owing to the cost of materials for impregnation and the construction of suitably sized tanks. Such objects, however, are usually so massive that they still retain a fair degree of mechanical strength, and a different method of treatment is therefore possible. As a first step the object can be allowed to dry out very slowly by being wrapped in moist sacking and kept in a cool place. This drying-out process proceeds without serious deformation except for the fact that the surface may become slightly flaked. For the final consolidation of the surface it was found that an epoxy resin was very suitable. A special formulation devised by the author which consists of Araldite CY 219 (50 parts), hardener HY 219 (25 parts), accelerator DY 219 (1 part) and dibutyl phthalate (10 parts) was found to be sufficiently mobile to penetrate the surface of the wood where it set in situ and consolidated the wood. By this method a large clinker-built dug-out canoe excavated at Kentmere in West-morland was successfully consolidated[9].

Worm-eaten wood

Wooden objects which have suffered the ravages of wood-eating insects may be reduced to a very fragile condition, and impregnation with consolidant is necessary. In practice it has been found that if impregnation is attempted with solutions of resins—either natural or synthetic—the results may not be entirely satisfactory. Evaporation of the solvent tends to reduce penetration and to leave the consolidant concentrated in the surface layers. For this reason non-solvent consolidants based on epoxy resins or the polyesters have proved to be most suitable[10]. Consolidation by immersion in wax has also been carried out on a large scale by Rosen[11] in Baltimore and by Coremans in Brussels.

Leather

Leather objects may be found in a fragile condition as the result of desiccation, which reduces them to a very brittle state, and it is then necessary to restore their flexibility. In the past this was done by impregnating the leather with an oil, such as Turkey red oil, essentially a sulphonated linseed oil. However, a simpler procedure which has proved very effective is based on the use of polyethylene-glycol waxes[12]. The particular grade used by the author is Carbowax 1500, which is a blend of equal parts of the solid grade 1540 and the liquid grade 300, and has the consistency of vaseline and melts to a liquid at about 40°C, whereas LeFève recommends the use of Carbowax 750, which is a methoxypolyethylene glycol. The leather object to be treated is immersed in the molten wax for a few days. When impregnation is completed, the leather is found to be quite flexible, and it is only necessary to wash the excess of wax on the surface and allow the leather to dry. The Carbowax 1500 is slightly hygroscopic and if exposed to humid air the treated leather may become moist, but this should not occur under normal museum conditions.

If leather is recovered in a water-logged condition and is excessively soft it can also be treated in a similar manner by direct immersion in the molten wax. The mobile wax readily penetrates the leather and replaces the water so that the leather object is recovered in a satisfactory state.

Ivory and bone

Antiquities made of ivory and bone may often be in a dry powdery condition and, as a result, extremely fragile. Since they are extremely porous in this state they can safely be consolidated by the application of coats of dilute solutions of transparent synthetic resins, notably polyvinyl acetate or the polymethacrylates; if necessary the treatment can be carried out under vacuum to ensure deeper penetration of the consolidant. Todd[13] has described the use of this method to consolidate ivory spatulas of the Shang dynasty. Similar methods can also be used for strengthening bone.

Water-logged bone and ivory provide an easier problem than water-logged wood and they can be consolidated by direct vacuum impregnation with dilute emulsions of polyvinyl acetate or polymethacrylates. Details of this technique have been described by Purves and Martin[14] in the case of bone specimens from a mesolithic site. Haas[15] has also described the use of a solution of an acrylic resin in toluene for the consolidation of horns and bones of the neolithic period.

In the examples which have been discussed so far the fragile state of an object has been due to the loss of its bulk mechanical strength. Attention must, however, be devoted to those objects which may be regarded as being in a delicate state owing to the friable nature of the surface layers.

Wall-paintings

If wall-paintings are exposed to adverse atmospheric conditions, the paint layers may become detached from the ground and require consolidation. In such cases it has been found by the author that re-attachment of the flaking paint can be achieved by the application of a dilute alcoholic solution of a special modified soluble nylon (manufactured under the trade name Maranyl nylon polymer C109/P by Imperial Chemical Industries Ltd). This new synthetic material is supplied as a white powder which is soluble in methyl and ethyl alcohol or in industrial methylated spirits; the solution tends to gel at room temperature but it can be reliquefied by warming to about 40°C. In practice it is merely necessary to brush a warm 5 per cent solution of the soluble nylon over the areas of flaking paint and to apply gentle pressure. Since the alcoholic solution has a low surface tension, it readily penetrates any minute cracks in the paint layer and flows underneath protruding flakes of detached paint, drawing them back into position, so that a secure bond is formed between the reattached paint and the ground layer. Soluble nylon has two advantages which make it particularly useful in this work. Firstly the adhesive film is rather flexible and does not tend to exert undue contractile forces, and, secondly, the film is very matt so that an esthetically unpleasant sheen is not apparent on the treated areas of a painting. The same technique has also been successfully used to consolidate friable paint on illuminated manuscripts[16] and powdery friable patina on metallic antiquities can be similarly treated.

Siliceous materials

Limestone and unglazed earthenware objects, e.g. carved reliefs or *ostraka*, which are porous, tend to absorb soluble salts when they have been buried in a salty environment. When these salts crystallize out on the surface of porous objects they weaken the surface layers to such an extent that there is a danger that they may flake off. For this reason it is necessary to consolidate the fragile surface layers before the washing process is carried out to remove the salts. This can be achieved by applying a thin film of soluble nylon, because this material has the important property of being readily permeable to water[17].

The porous nature of unglazed earthenware renders its consolidation by impregnation a relatively simple matter. On the other hand, the strengthening of the surface of stone objects —with the exception of porous limestone, mentioned above—is a more difficult problem. Unless deep penetration of the stone is achieved by the consolidative agent, the treatment may actually aggravate the condition, since there is grave risk that any thinly consolidated surface layer may tend to flake off in the course of time, with disastrous results. A detailed discussion of the methods suggested for the consolidation of stone objects will be found in Plenderleith's book[18]. In this particular field of consolidation there is one outstanding problem for which a thoroughly satisfactory solution has not yet been found; namely, the question of the strengthening of objects made of shale—a dark bituminous material. At present the only safe way of preserving such objects is to keep them permanently wet so as to prevent the opening up of a series of cracks along the bedding planes which will occur as the shale dries. In cases where it is desirable to dry a shale object, the most effective procedure is to immerse the object in a series of alcohol baths and then to carry out impregnation under vacuum with a consolidant such as an alcoholic solution of shellac. (Objects of shale differ greatly in their appearance and behaviour after excavation, and the process of drying and consolidation is one which requires careful consideration.)

Conclusion

This discussion of the problems associated with the consolidation of fragile objects may perhaps be concluded by summarizing the desiderata which an ideal method of consolidation should fulfil. These are:

1. The treatment should result in the least possible extent of deformation of the object.

2. The procedure should be simple to carry out and involve the minimum expenditure of labour and equipment.

3. The consolidant should show the minimum of shrinkage so that there is no risk of damage to the object resulting from contractile forces.

4. The consolidant should be permanently stable to aging and not react with the material of the object itself.

5. The surface appearance of the object should not be substantially altered.

The introduction of the newer synthetic resins has made it possible to achieve these desiderata in a limited number of cases. It is to be hoped that progress will continue to be made so that ideal methods of consolidation will cover an ever widening field.

References

[1] ROSENBERG, G. H., *Mus. J.*, 33 (1933) 432.

[2] MOSS, A. A., *Mus. J.*, 52 (1952) 175.

[3] CHRISTENSEN, B. B., *Aarboeger for Nordisk Oldkyndighed og Historie*, National Museum, Copenhagen, 1952.

[4] ROSENQVIST, ANNA M., *Stud. Conservation*, 4 (1959) 62.

[5] ORGAN, R. M., *Stud. Conservation*, 4 (1959) 96.

[6] CHRISTENSEN, B. B., *Aarboeger for Nordisk Oldkyndighed og Historie*, National Museum, Copenhagen, 1956.

[7] LEFÈVE, R., *Bull. Inst. R. Patrimoine art.*, 4 (1961) 97.

[8] MÜLLER-BECK, H. and HAAS, A., *Stud. Conservation*, 5 (1960) 150.

[9] see *Technical Notes 218* of Ciba (A.R.L.) Ltd, Duxford, Cambridge.

[10] PLENDERLEITH, H. J., *The Conservation of Antiquities and Works of Art*, Oxford University Press, 1956, p. 136.

[11] ROSEN, D., *J. Walters Art Gallery*, (1950–51) p. 45.

[12] WERNER, A. E., *Mus. J.*, 57 (1957) 3; LEFÈVE, R., *Bull. Inst. R. Patrimoine art.*, 3 (1960) 98.

[13] TODD, W., *Tech. Stud. fine Arts*, 9 (1940) 160.

[14] PURVES, P. E. and MARTIN, R. S. J., *Mus. J.*, 49 (1950) 293.

[15] HAAS, A., *Der Präparator*, 5 (1959) 58.

[16] GOWERS, H. J., *Mus. J.*, 58 (1959) 278.

[17] WERNER, A. E., *Chron. Egypt.*, 33 (1958) 273.

[18] PLENDERLEITH, H. J., reference 10, pp. 297–306.

R. M. Organ

THE CONSOLIDATION OF FRAGILE METALLIC OBJECTS

Introduction

A better title for this paper would be: 'The consolidation of once-metallic objects', because fragility is not one of the characteristics of a metal. The conversion of ductile metal into brittle mineral is a result of corrosion processes which have sometimes occurred more readily because the metal has been alloyed. Such metals may fall ready victims to corrosive attack and, in course of time, become archaeological finds which owe preservation of their shape to a sheath of mineral. The end-product of this process is complete mineralization, but at the other extreme is a condition in which the metal, thinly mineralized on its surface, is crystalline and cracked and suffering from losses.

This paper presents concisely a selection of methods of strengthening which have been found useful in the British Museum Laboratory and workshops in dealing with the three conditions listed above. The selection includes applications of both traditional and newer materials to solve problems of common occurrence and does not neglect methods of application which, if properly chosen, can often render useful an apparently unsuitable consolidant. The fragile metals are arranged in sequence, from completely mineralized to clean but weakened by cracks. Types of consolidation suitable for various needs, from local patching to complete encapsulation, are discussed. Finally some of the more important properties of the various materials employed for consolidation are compared.

It is hoped that the paper will suggest to the reader means of solving other problems which cannot be discussed for lack of space.

Completely mineralized metal

Wax impregnation of cracked iron oxide

The objects were sections of iron straps of Iron-Age origin whose principal interest lay in their size and shape. Having been stored in the well heated museum for some years since excavation, they were completely dry and had developed cracks which made them difficult to lift without loss. They appeared to be chemically stable.

Consolidation with Cosmolloid 80H, a microcrystalline wax, promised well provided that the weight of the fragments could be supported independently of the wax. To this end a close-fitting bed of plaster of Paris was formed as follows. A layer of plaster about 1 cm thick was cast in a suitable surround. At the moment during setting when thickening commenced, a sheet of latex rubber about 0·375 mm thick* was placed upon its surface and the fragile rust was gently pressed into the yielding plaster until submerged to half its thickness (*Figure 1*). Wrinkles in the latex rubber surrounding the object were smoothed out and the object was removed just before the final setting took place (the temperature rises appreciably at this

---

* Or 0·1 mm thick if particularly fine detail is present which needs local support.

stage). This procedure avoids the trapping of plaster in undercuts on the surface of the object. The plaster support was now trimmed to final shape, dried in a ventilated oven at 120°C for several hours, the object replaced in its well-fitting cavity without the rubber, and the whole assembly impregnated with Cosmolloid by immersion in the molten wax at 120°C until bubbles ceased to rise. After this the assembly was lifted out on to supports above the molten wax and allowed to drain whilst still in the hot oven.

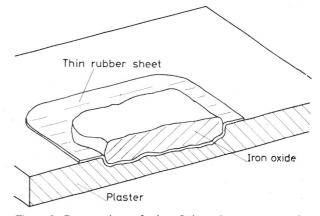

Figure 1. Construction of close-fitting plaster support for fragments of iron oxide.

Of a considerable number of objects treated thus, some of which exhibited brown droplets indicative of the presence of ferric chloride, only one has shown evidence of chemical instability during four years of exposure in a damp provincial museum. One repetition of the treatment appears to have cured this. Such stability would not have been anticipated had paraffin wax been employed, since it has greater permeability to water vapour. Stability can be assured, at the cost of greatly prolonged treatment, by soaking out soluble salts from the unwaxed oxide in changes of hot distilled water whilst it lies in its waxed plaster support. The melting point of Cosmolloid (85°C) is sufficiently high to permit this. This method costs little in material or time, but requires skill in handling plaster.

Completely oxidized iron fittings on remains of a wooden beam

Found in 1960 at a Roman arsenal, a D-ring attached to a bolt embedded in wood protected by a D-shaped iron plate may be the remains of an attachment to a heavy wooden construction for hauling purposes. Associated with this were fragments of flat iron plates, whose treatment is described here, to which decayed wood adhered, powdery and friable and invaded by iron oxide. In order that the wood could be handled it was consolidated by spraying with a 5 per cent solution of Maranyl nylon in industrial methylated spirits. This treatment added strength with scarcely any change in appearance—a very important property in this case because colour, direction

stirrups. When the Tensol had set the trough was removed, the cast inverted, strips of wax applied to its sides and a further few millimetres' thickness of Tensol applied to the edges of the fragments which had been resting on the wax base. Finally the edges and ends of the encapsulation were shaped and the whole surface polished (*Figure 7*). This encapsulation was successfully

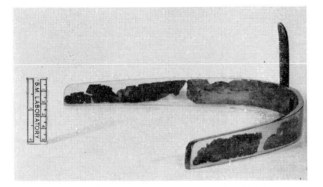

Figure 7. Bandeau encapsulated in Tensol No. 7 (methacrylate).

accomplished despite the fact that Tensol shrinks by 14 per cent on hardening. Success was due to the provision of a free surface at which change of volume could occur freely.

Mineral plus metal

Consolidation of mineralized lead by cathodic reduction

A group of leaden bullae, of various dates around the 14th century, which had been in the collection for many years were found to be corroded to lead carbonate to such a depth that

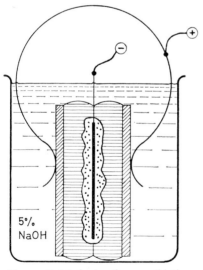

Figure 8. Method of consolidating loose lead carbonate by slow cathodic reduction. Thick corrosion layers on lead bulla still possessing metallic core are held in place by foam pads tightly compressed between spring-loaded anodes.

removal of the mineral would mean loss of the inscription, without which the bullae are worthless. Fortunately the lead carbonate, although powdery, was fairly compact. The bullae

were therefore cathodically reduced at a low current density of 100 mA/dm^2 in 5 per cent aqueous sodium hydroxide with a platinized titanium anode (iron or lead would have served equally well) for three days without interruption (*Figure 8*). Only at the end of this period were small bubbles of hydrogen gas observed at the bullae. This very slow reduction resulted in the formation of a compact mass of lead in place of the mineral.

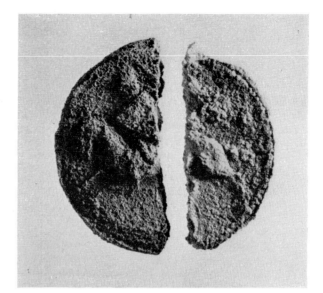

Figure 9. Lead bulla corroded and broken into two halves: (left) electrolytically consolidated; (right) untreated.

Following reduction, the lead was bathed in changes of N/500 sulphuric acid until the pH of the acid remained unchanged in the presence of the lead for 30 minutes and then similarly in distilled water until the pH of the water remained unchanged for the same period. After thorough drying, the surface of the lead was brightened gently with a glass-bristle brush and the lead impregnated with hot paraffin wax (congealing point 49°C) (*Figure 9*). This particular after-treatment is at present under review since a few pieces of the many hundreds treated in this manner have been found to be unstable. In spite of this, the general method of slow reduction may be regarded as sound.

Silver hanging bowl from St Ninian's Isle

The treatment of this unique bowl, which dates from about A.D. 800, has already been described fully in *Studies in Conservation*, 2 (1959) 41–50. The problem encountered was that the silver–copper alloy of the bowl was paper-thin and sandwiched between layers of mineral. It became necessary to remove this mineral support in order to restore the original appearance to the bowl. After removing the mineral from the inside this was replaced by a temporary liner of polystyrene, which was applied in the form of successive layers of solution. This support served for seven days, by which time normal loss of residual solvent from the resin layer had caused so much shrinkage that the liner detached itself harmlessly from the smooth interior of the bowl. By this stage of the work, the outside had been cleaned and a new permanent liner was provided in the form of a thin film of transparent epoxy resin which reinforced the whole inner surface, supported the many fragments in their proper positions and itself replaced lacunae. An epoxy resin was selected because of its very low shrinkage on hardening and its excellent adhesion to metal, both essential properties in this case because the liner was to be on the inside, and failure in these respects would have led to detachment. A risk of its reacting with residual copper minerals in the silver alloy had to be accepted in this case; this precludes the application of an epoxy-resin system to many bronze objects.

Clean but cracked and fragile metal with lacunae

Fragmentary leaden bullae

After cleaning and stabilization by a variety of methods, many bullae may require consolidation of the fragments remaining, especially at the cord, where the thin membrane of metal has frequently corroded away. If the cord remains, the method of consolidation should be selected so as to expose it to view and to permit future students to examine both its make-up and material. For the latter reason the consolidant must be removable. The consolidant not only offers protection against crushing and the careless fingernail but also fills spaces in which vapours capable of initiating corrosion may linger despite generally good ventilation in the storage space.

Materials which have been adopted include: Cosmolloid 80H tinted to match the colour of the lead by an admixture of lampblack and titanium white; Tensol No. 7, either clear in order to exhibit tapes embedded in it or slightly tinted with a little grey cellulose enamel; complete encapsulation in a clear methacrylate applied as a powder and compacted under pressure in a mould whilst heated to 160°C; and variants of these. All these materials may be removed with a suitable solvent.

The Birdlip bronze bowl

This Roman-British bowl, some 10 cm in diameter and 0·5 mm thick, had already been completely stripped of mineral when received, but so much metal had been lost through mineralization that the bowl, although now chemically stable, was physically frail and unable to support its own weight (*Figure 10*). The strengthening material chosen was 'Technovit', a

Figure 10. Birdlip bronze bowl before consolidation.

cold-setting methacrylate. Formulation 4004a clear consists of a powder and liquid which, when well stirred together, set in about 20 minutes at room temperature. Immediate shrinkage is negligible but there is some evidence that slow shrinkage occurs subsequently. It has the great merit that whilst setting it passes through a pasty stage, rather like a stiff putty, during which it can be worked into shape.

The surface of the bronze was first cleaned of polyvinyl acetate lacquer, which had been applied earlier. The spring-hard metal was then manipulated with the fingers until matching edges which had become separated were brought together. It

happened that one such joint, once made, restored the general shape of the bowl. The joint was held together temporarily with a small clamp. Gaps in the immediate neighbourhood of this joint were then bridged with Technovit and the clamp removed. A number of bridges made at key points served to allow the bowl to fall into its natural shape. Thereafter the missing areas and part of the rim were re-created in Technovit. The method employed was to warm and shape a sheet of dental wax against the outside of a sound area of bowl, then to slide it round to the missing area, making any slight adjustments to the contour which became necessary, and finally to fix it to the metal by

Figure 11. Birdlip bronze bowl after consolidation with Technovit (methacrylate).

application of a hot spatula. It was unnecessary to paint the wax with a parting agent because clarity of the Technovit was not required. Technovit was then mixed and de-gassed *in vacuo* and the liquid brushed on to the inner surface of the wax and the edges of the metal. Three layers were applied in all, care being taken that the edges of the metal were well overlapped as a precaution against poor adhesion. When the Technovit had hardened the wax was removed and excessive thickness tooled off. Careful work of this kind was required under the rim.

Thus strength was restored to the bowl area by area, in contrast to the work on the St Ninian's bowl, to which the whole support was applied at one time. Colour was applied using flake metallic aluminium and gold, stippled into a film of shellac, with the intention of enabling a casual glance to observe a complete bowl whilst leaving the student in no doubt as to the losses which had been sustained (*Figure 11*). A similar technique was applied to the repair of the Scunthorpe bowl and the Nijmegen mirror.

Heavy silver disc brooch from Canterbury

This 7th century convex silver brooch, some 15 cm in diameter, was embellished with gold roundels and niello inlay. Two large segments were missing which had originally contained roundels and panels of filigree work.

After lengthy and difficult cleaning had restored the original appearance of the silver, a considerable gain in strength was achieved by inserting shaped pieces of sheet Perspex, 1·5 mm thick, in the lacunae. The shaped Perspex was bent by hand whilst hot to match the convexity of the disc and was glued in place with general-purpose Araldite. The edge of the Perspex was filed and polished in order to carry the eye around the contour of the disc, and the panels and roundels were then mounted in position.

The silver Emesa helmet

The restoration of this Syrian treasure has been fully described in *The Conservation of Antiquities and Works of Art*, by H. J. Plenderleith, pp. 226–229. Features of interest concerning the consolidation were the annealing and the use of silver gauze as reinforcement because it can be made to conform to difficult contours. Gauze was also used in the work on St Ninian's bowl.

The sword of Kanta

This sword belongs to the regalia of the Emir of Argunga, Sokoto Province, N. Nigeria, and is used in very energetic ceremonies on State occasions. As a result of much service the decorated silver scabbard had suffered much wear of its raised portions and many dents and tears elsewhere (*Figure 12*). It

Figure 12. Part of scabbard of sword of Kanta before restoration, showing worn raised decoration.

was necessary to restore the scabbard in such a way that it would give a further long period of hard service.

Space does not permit a full description of the restoration. Of special interest is the use of a tin–silver alloy named 'Plumbsol' to restore a wearing surface to the raised decoration. The

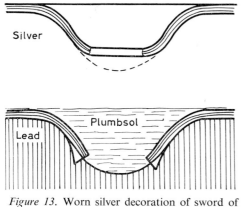

Figure 13. Worn silver decoration of sword of Kanta reshaped into greased lead mould.

method was permissible because lead solders had already been used in extensive repairs, and as a result the silver could no longer be exposed to high temperatures without loss. Plumbsol contains about 5 per cent silver and has a melting range of

221–225°C. It can therefore be applied with a normal soldering iron. Very fluid when molten, it wets silver readily using a non-corrosive activated-resin flux. It solidifies with a very smooth surface which matched the colour of this particular silver throughout normal polishing operations. In order to restore the damaged relief, metal repoussé punches were made up to match the inside contours of the indentations. The relief was then laid face down on a sheet of lead which had been smeared with high-melting grease. The punches were used to bend back the damaged metal and to continue the contour of the missing portions as depressions into the lead. Then Plumbsol* was used to 'tin' the back of the relief and to run into the depressions in the lead (*Figure 13*). Elasticity of the silver was a contributory factor in the success of the result (*Figure 14*).

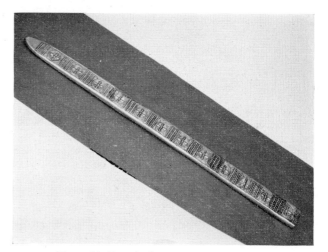

Figure 14. Sword of Kanta after restoration.

Gallium–copper alloy

Mention of this material is included because it has some potential uses. The alloy contains 34 per cent by weight of gallium plus 66 per cent copper. In order to prepare it, freshly deoxidized copper powder (200-mesh or finer) is ground into gallium which has been melted at a temperature just above 30°C. The resulting soft mass may be worked into a mould or cavity and after 4 hours at 25°C it will have become quite hard and will then withstand heating to about 900°C. Like a dental alloy it expands on hardening and will adhere to clean warmed copper alloys. It will readily accept impressions from the 1/100 in. divisions on a steel rule and finer details could be reproduced if finer copper powder were available. In colour it is naturally grey, but it can be electroplated with other metals without preparation. The cost of the alloy is high: at present about 10s. per gram.

Discussion

When faced with a new problem in conservation, the factors to be considered in reaching a satisfactory solution become more numerous as the capabilities of the restorer increase. A few of the obvious factors are the following: whether or not the object can be made chemically stable; eventual environment of the object, e.g. hot exhibition case or possibly damp storage; acceptable final appearance and mode of display; intended life of the consolidation—to be measured in decades or

---

* Available from Messrs Johnson Matthey, London, E.C.1.

centuries; time available for the work; allowable cost. Other factors may exist which are not overtly recognized; for example, the restorer may prefer a series of difficult operations using traditional materials skilfully rather than an untried simple method using newer techniques.

There is insufficient space available here in which to develop the thesis that there is only one wholly acceptable solution to a particular problem within the confines imposed by such relevant considerations. It is certain, however, that the more clearly the various limitations are recognized, the more important it becomes to have a comprehensive knowledge of the properties of the consolidants which might be employed. For this reason, a list is appended of the more important properties of the materials used in the foregoing examples.

Acknowledgements

Colleagues responsible for particular examples discussed above are as follows: P. Shorer*, Miss M. Wood*, P. Smith, D. E. Bisset, Miss V. H. Foulkes, L. H. Bell, L. Langton.

Properties of materials for consolidation

Plaster of Paris

Unless restrained by addition of certain chemicals, this sets rapidly by reaction with water, with liberation of heat, to a rather soft white solid of density about 2·3; expands on setting; grease or silicone fluid as parting layer; thoroughly damp environment when setting; slightly soluble in water; poor adhesion to smooth, better to rough, surfaces; once set, does not flow at room temperatures; very cheap (relative cost† in U.K., by weight, 0·2); permeable to gases and liquids.

Paraffin wax

White translucent solid; less dense than water; available in various congealing points, 49–60°C; solidifies in tens of minutes with contraction of about 10 per cent; parts readily from all smooth, less readily from rough, surfaces; setting environment contains hydrocarbon vapours; insoluble in water and acetone but soluble in alcohol, aromatics, chloroform; subject to flow at room temperature; impermeable to water, permeable to water vapour; cheap (relative cost 4).

Cosmolloid 80H‡

As for paraffin wax, but melting point about 85°C, slightly more sticky and less permeable to water vapour. Flash point in presence of naked flame 283°C, in absence of naked flame 360°C.

Bondafiller¶

Polyester plus filler; hardens in 10–20 minutes at room temperature with linear contraction of 2–3 per cent; forms hard grey solid of density similar to plaster; interface with air does not harden; parts readily from plasticine, grease, silicones; destroyed by chlorinated solvents, resists weak alkali; some adhesion to smooth metal; setting environment contains organic vapours and peroxides; reacts with cuprous chloride; no flow at room temperature; good compressive strength but rather brittle; relative cost about 6; probably slightly permeable to water vapour.

Tensol*

Methacrylate plus benzoyl peroxide plus dibutyl phthalate; hardens in 10–20 minutes at room temperature with liberation of heat and initial expansion followed by volume contraction of 14 per cent to form glass-clear solid of density 1·18; parts readily from polyvinyl alcohol, silicones, smooth metal, less readily from wax; grease must be absent; dissolved by chlorinated solvents; setting environment contains methacrylate vapours and peroxides; stable at room temperature; permeable to water vapour; relative cost 17.

Technovit†

Detailed composition unknown; properties as for Tensol except that there is no change in volume on setting, a little more heat may be liberated, and it is less clear; relative cost in U.K., 100.

Mobile epoxy resin

10 g Araldite MY750‡ + 1 g HY951 + 1 g dibutyl phthalate; sets in 2 hours at 40°C to form a pale amber-coloured solid with contraction of less than 1 per cent, gains strength during subsequent 10 days; parts readily from polythene and silastomers but not from P.T.F.E. layers formed from dispersions; excellent adhesion to metals but least to copper; setting environment contains little organic vapour but amines are present in the liquid; reacts slowly with cuprous chloride; no flow at room temperature; strong; relative cost 12.

Maranyl Nylon†

C/109P 5 per cent solution in industrial methylated spirits gels at about 24°C; loses most of its solvent during days; film cracks under contractile stresses but is itself so weak that destructive forces are not exerted; film has no gloss; drying environment contains alcohol and a little water; permeable to liquid water; relative cost 80.

A-J-K dough

Polyvinyl acetal plus short jute fibres plus kaolin plus solvent; hardens during 5 hours—do not disturb joint because the adhesion is poor; immediate contraction considerable, subsequent contraction over 6 months; relative cost 2.

Gallium–copper alloy

Relative cost 4500.

---

* Members of IIC.
† Costs quoted relatively throughout this section.
‡ Messrs Astor Boisellier and Lawrence Ltd, London, W.C.2.
¶ Bondaglass Ltd, 53–55 South End, Croydon, Surrey.

* I.C.I. Ltd, P.O. Box 19, Templar House, 81–87 High Holborn, London, W.C. 1.
† Rubert and Co. Ltd, Acru Works, Cheadle, Cheshire.
‡ Ciba (A.R.L.) Ltd, Duxford, Cambridge, England.

Hanna Jedrzejewska

SOME NEW EXPERIMENTS IN THE CONSERVATION OF ANCIENT BRONZES

Various mechanisms and a multitude of agents may be active in the corrosion phenomena of metals, but in every case a certain amount of moisture is necessary to keep the reactions going. In dry conditions even the most aggressive agents cease their activity.

In consequence, one might expect that permanent isolation from any access of moisture would be a good method for protecting ancient bronzes against corrosion. Unfortunately, this rather interesting theoretical idea can find no practical application[1] owing to technical difficulties. The impermeable coatings so far tried do not give sufficient isolation, and the other alternative, of keeping the specimens in special dry cases, can have only a very limited application.

Some years ago the author decided to try a new method of impermeabilization, using an internal hydrophobic impregnation instead of the conventional surface coatings. The procedure was based on a thorough analysis of various corrosion mechanisms, of states of equilibria in corroded objects and of conservation problems in ancient bronzes. The results seem quite promising. The following is a short summary of the basic points of the work.

Disadvantage of stripping method

Corroded metallic objects may be in various degrees of stability, but even when in apparently stable condition they are always in danger of some corrosion process being started afresh. These reactions may occur in the metal itself, or, more often, in the corrosion products. The oxidation of cuprous chloride is the best example of this.

As the corrosion products may be a source of secondary corrosive processes their removal seems the best way to ensure the stability of objects. This is a very popular method, used in the conservation of bronzes wherever possible, and is done by chemical or electrochemical means. The stripping to raw metal proves very effective in many cases, but certain points must also be remembered here:

1. Only specimens in sound metallic condition can be submitted to these treatments. Electrolysis especially may be very dangerous.
2. The stripping, especially by electrolysis, destroys completely any technological characteristic of the object's past history, which may be of greatest importance from the technological, as well as the esthetic, point of view.
3. In many cases the exposed raw surface no longer represents the authentic surface but is only some accidental boundary between the corroded metallic phase and the corrosion products.
4. The exposed metallic surface, for the sake of appearance, often requires some artificial patination, eventually followed with a thin coating of protective lacquer.
5. During cleaning new elements may be deposited on the object, and these may interfere with some future technical examination.
6. In the course of chemical or electrochemical cleaning soluble chlorides of other cations are formed from insoluble copper chlorides.
7. Zinc chloride, formed when zinc is used for reduction in acid solutions, can become a source of serious trouble if not properly neutralized, as it is highly hygroscopic and becomes acid in solution (hydrolysis).
8. The considerably porous surface and some internal parts of the cleaned metal will easily retain chemicals from solution, owing to adsorption effects. Washing will probably not be able to remove the last traces of them.
9. Prolonged soaking in aqueous media during cleaning and washing helps to spread the soluble substances all over the object. It also provides favourable conditions for new corrosion processes.
10. During drying there is a pronounced danger of chemical activities, with residual thin films of moisture, traces of salts and a good access of oxygen and carbon dioxide.
11. The cleaning is often not carried out to the end in order to avoid the possible disintegration of weakened metal. The remaining deposits unfortunately become a perfect shelter for soluble substances.

Notwithstanding all these complications, stripping methods are indispensable where problems of restoring the metallic character of objects, of exposing fine decorations, engravings, etc., from under the mineralized corrosion products are to be dealt with.

But there are also many cases where the preservation of the actual state, together with all mineralization products, is of greatest importance. It is also sometimes desirable to take off, for example, only the most disfiguring accretions and to preserve the patina underneath them. In all these cases the drastic methods used for stripping purposes are of no use.

Sometimes the stripping methods are applied to small spots only (bronze disease), where they seem to be a very effective cure. Where patina has to be preserved, mild chemicals are used to remove the disfiguring layers of cupric salts, with apparently no effect on the products in the patina. But even these mild chemicals change in some way the colour and composition of the patina (removal of cupric compounds encrusted in cuprous oxide, alteration of the red colour of cuprite). Besides this, soluble chlorides are also formed here, and are retained in the patina layer. Soaking in aqueous media with subsequent drying may be dangerous to the conditions of stable equilibrium.

The above considerations point to the need for some means of conservation that will preserve the actual state of objects without introducing any chemical changes or disturbing naturally established equilibria. Here we are back again to impregnation methods.

Impregnation

It is understood that no protective surface coating can prevent or arrest corrosion in an adequate manner. There may be cracks and pores in the film, or the adhesion may be poor, the coating not uniform, or too permeable to water vapour. Also, even if the film were perfectly all right, there is always the possibility of minute pockets underneath it with enough air and moisture present to keep corrosion processes active, eventually leading to disruptions of the protective coating. Then a more pronounced activity sets in. It is also clear that beeswax and paraffin wax have the best protective properties for this purpose.

for several hours, and have it as hot as possible before impregnation.

2. Immediately afterwards brush freely with impregnating liquid, taking special care of porous areas which must be well saturated.

3. Put under the infra-red lamp again for several hours to help soaking and evaporation of the solvent and to prevent any moisture condensation.

Figure 1. Bronze statuette of Isis (height, 23·5 cm): (*a*) before cleaning—the thickness and tendency to separation of the green layer can be seen on the left arm; (*b*) and (*c*) after cleaning—the unnatural thinness and deformation of the right arm, stripped to raw metal before coming to the laboratory, can be compared with the left arm, cleaned to the cuprite layer only.

The logical consequence of the difficulties described would be to apply protective materials not only on the external surface but also on the internal surfaces (cracks, cavities, porous areas). In this way the object would no longer be able to absorb moisture.

The first step would be to look for a material that can penetrate deeply enough. Such a material should fulfil the following conditions: (a) excellent hydrophobic properties; (b) good spreading properties; (c) good wetting properties; (d) high penetration power (low molecular weight, low viscosity); (e) good smearing properties; (f) chemical stability; (g) be inert to materials in the object; (h) be easy to apply and to remove; (i) not in any way change the appearance of the object.

Liquid paraffin (paraffin oil) seems to be the material best fulfilling the above conditions, especially when well thinned with white spirit (1:10, or even more). Chemically pure paraffin oil has to be used: impurities in the technical grades may cause some darkening of impregnated layers.

The basic points of the treatment are:

1. Dry the object thoroughly by infra-red radiation, at least

4. Repeat points (2) and (3) two or three times.

5. Wash off with white spirit any superficial excess of oil. The surface must have a matt appearance.

6. Brush the warmed object with a saturated solution of beeswax (alternatively, paraffin wax, microcrystalline wax or polythene wax) in white spirit. The coating must be rather thin. Wax paste is not appropriate. When cooled, finish with a soft brush.

The basic principle of the whole treatment is to have the surface as dry as possible before impregnation, and to keep away any possibility of moisture condensation during the treatment. It is also necessary to avoid any oversaturation of the object with oil. Its amount should be just sufficient to wet all the internal surfaces. The appearance of the object after impregnation is no more changed than after the popular wax-paste finish. The impregnating materials can easily be removed with a bath in white spirit. All technical evidence is safely preserved. The objects should be kept under observation.

To leave the natural equilibrium undisturbed it is better to avoid any contact of the object with water. If this is necessary, a thorough drying under infra-red lamps must be applied immediately afterwards. In some cases, washing with white spirit or soaking in alcohol may be useful to clean the objects or to dissolve certain copper salts (traces), but where possible it is much better to do all the necessary cleaning by dry mechanical methods.

Results

The method described above was devised for and first tried on ancient cannon barrels on outdoor exhibition[2]. Later it was

(b)

Figure 2. Bronze hanging bowl (I) (height, 12·5 cm to the rim). Bowl (a) and a fragment (b), partly cleaned to cuprite surface. The lowest part of the uncleaned strip on (a) was left on the bowl as evidence.

adapted to antique bronzes. Further systematic investigations will, of course, be needed to select the materials most suitable for deep impregnation and to determine the effective limits of

the treatment, but even now the method seems to be directly useful in dealing with objects in an unstable condition, as may best be illustrated by the following examples.

Statuette of Isis, in bronze (National Museum, Warsaw, No. 147824—*Figures 1* and *4a*).

A hard mass of green cupric carbonate (from 0·1 mm thick at the front up to 1·5 cm at the back) covered a compact and very hard layer of dark red cuprite (almost transparent on Horus, the child, but up to more than 5 mm thick at the back), with only traces of chlorides and no detectable amounts of cuprous chloride. The natural zone of separation was in the red layer just beneath the green layer, and corresponded rather closely to the original surface of the object.

The green layer was removed mechanically, and the products are preserved as evidence. No metal, but only the smooth and shiny surface of cuprite was exposed. Chemicals were not used for cleaning since they could change the composition and structure of the corrosion products. The object was impregnated in 1958. No further treatment was needed.

Hanging bowl (I), in bronze, from the Middle East (National Museum, Cracow, No. 1232—*Figures 2* and *4b*).

A disfiguring layer of green cupric carbonate (0·2–0·4 mm thick) was removed mechanically from a smooth and shiny layer of deep-red cuprite (almost transparent at places, up to 1 mm thick). No metal was exposed. An uncleaned patch of about 6 cm² was left on the surface as evidence. The removed products are stored. The interior of the bowl, with interesting incrustations and unidentified remains, was left untouched. There are traces of small amounts of cuprous chloride under the cuprite. The bowl was impregnated early in 1961. No changes are observed.

Bronze bird, origin unknown (National Museum, Warsaw, No. 126997—*Figure 3*).

The object is made of two bronze sheets (about 0·3–0·5 mm thick) pressed over a ceramic porous core. The open seam between both parts is joined with thin wire in a few places only. The feet are cast. A very fine, grainy and soft layer of deep reddish-brown cuprite (about 0·2–0·3 mm thick) was partly covered with green incrustations of cupric carbonate and with white salt deposits (chlorides, sulphates, sodium, magnesium, calcium) especially abundant near the front seam. The deposits were cleaned mechanically from the cuprite layer. A tendency to active corrosion was observed. The porous core and the surface were thoroughly impregnated early in 1960. The object is well stabilized.

Hanging bowl (II), bronze (National Museum, Cracow, No. 1231—*Figure 4c*).

A flat bowl, 38 cm in diameter, was covered with a mineralized, muddy yellowish-green layer of dirt and accretions. Underneath was a layer of bright green and blue mineralized cupric carbonates (up to 0·5 mm thick). The dirt was removed by careful abrading to reveal the colourful layer of carbonates. Here the cleaning did not follow the natural zone of separation, which was between the metal and the carbonates. The slight tendencies to corrosion were stopped by impregnation (early in 1961).

Etruscan mirror, bronze (National Museum, Warsaw, No. 199021—*Figure 4d*).

The mirror (about 18 cm in diameter) is badly damaged with craters, blisters and deposits. Cuprous chloride is abundant. As experiment, a small area (8 cm²) was cleaned mechanically to a smooth and shiny layer of red cuprite (partly covered with a black layer), very near the present surface, with layers of cuprous chloride, grainy cuprite and green carbonates underneath. Several impregnations were required to stop the active

Figure 3. Bronze bird (height, 9·5 cm): (*a*) before cleaning—green and white deposits; (*b*) detail before cleaning—green deposits and grainy surface of cuprite.

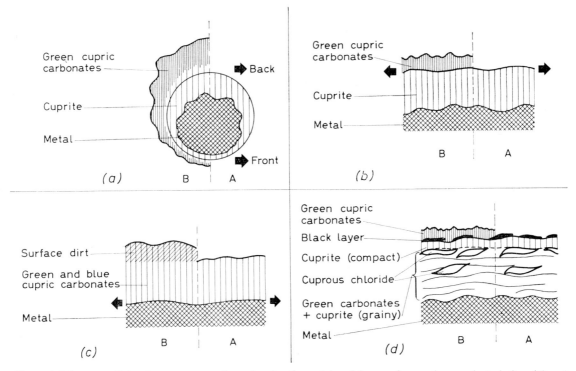

Figure 4. Diagrams of structures: cross-sections showing the metal and layers of corrosion products before (B) and after (A) cleaning. Natural zones of separation are indicated by arrows ◀▮ ▮▶. (*a*) Statuette of Isis: the present shape of the metallic core is very different from the original shape (preserved in the cuprite layer), which is a circle. (*b*) Hanging bowl (I): cleared to the separation zone (in the bird a very similar situation exists). (*c*) Hanging bowl (II): not cleaned to the separation zone. (*d*) Etruscan mirror: no distinct separation zone.

processes. After one year the stability is still being maintained and the shiny layer is well preserved.

Small bronze objects: About a hundred small bronze objects, mostly Egyptian statuettes, in various states of corrosion but mostly with green spots of bronze disease were cleaned mechanically, soaked in alcohol, dried and impregnated. As a result, the corrosive activities were stopped.

References

[1] PLENDERLEITH, H. J., *The Conservation of Antiquities and Works of Art*, Oxford University Press, London, 1957, p. 236.
[2] JEDRZEJEWSKA, H., Some general problems connected with the conservation of ancient gun barrels on outdoor exhibition, *Muzealnictwo Wojskowe* (*Warsaw*), 1 (1959) 127–137 (also *IIC Abstract* 2364).

Anna M. Rosenqvist

NEW METHODS FOR THE CONSOLIDATION OF FRAGILE OBJECTS

The actual consolidation of the fragile archaeological objects in a conservation institute is preceded by the important cleaning and stabilization treatment. Sometimes it will be necessary to start the consolidation process in the field. Very seldom are ideal conditions of stabilization realized. In fact, only gold and certain ceramic products and stones are stable in the temperatures and average humidities of a museum, and often unstable products of corrosion and vitrification have to be preserved. Burial in the earth for a long time may have conserved objects which in an ordinary atmosphere would have corroded and rotted away.

Special reducing conditions may yield products which react instantly with oxygen when exposed to air, e.g. sulphurized iron from a certain depth of the sea, which glows when dried in the air.

What we aim to do is, in fact, contrary to the chemical nature of matter: it is natural for organic matter to rot and for metals to be oxidized in air at normal temperatures.

The aim of consolidation, as the name implies, is primarily to give the object a physical strength which will enable it to be handled. Of equal importance is protection from the atmosphere, dirt and abrasion.

An important part of consolidation is also to restore the original form of an artifact from pieces. To obtain the effect of consolidation, a substance in the liquid phase is introduced into the object and then solidified in some way. The substance may be introduced by brushing, spraying, impregnation in vacuum, etc. In the past the methods used were largely of an empirical nature, and the materials, such as beeswax, natural resins and glues of animal and vegetable origin, were selected simply because, of those available, they were the only ones having the physical and chemical properties most appropriate to the work. However, in the last two or three decades, advances in high-polymer chemistry have led to the development of a wide range of new synthetic materials—materials which often possess a combination of physical and chemical properties not to be found in any of natural origin. The assessment of the potential value of these synthetic materials in the development of new, more reliable methods for the repair and restoration of antiquities is an important function of a museum laboratory.

In treating our artifacts with an impregnant, we have a system consisting of one discontinuous phase, e.g. dry wood or the powdery corrosion products of bronze, and one continuous phase: the impregnant. The property of this system which is of importance to us is its solidity. This is given by

$$S = f + c$$

where S is the solidity, f its internal friction and c its cohesion. S is also called sheer strength (g/cm^2) and is measured with a dynamometer.

The friction is a product of the difference between the external pressure (Σ) and the internal pressure (u) of the system and a constant k

$$f = (\Sigma - u)k$$

The solidity is then expressed by

$$S = (\Sigma - u)k + c \quad \text{(Coloumb–Hvoslef's equation, 1923)}$$

If we want to increase the solidity, this can be achieved either by increasing Σ or the cohesion c or by decreasing the internal pressure, u. The opposite effect is observed when opening a bag of vacuum-packed coffee.

To increase the external pressure is of no interest, as we want to keep our artifacts under atmospheric pressure conditions in their cases.

In the discontinuous phase there will always be areas of contact, otherwise the whole thing would be a powder. By impregnation with a substance that wets the solid phase, viz. adheres to it, the particles will be held together. If the impregnant contracts, either by solidifying or by the evaporation of a solvent, the internal pressure inside it will decrease. Its surface will be sucked in because the internal pressure is lower than the external, and the forces needed to remove the particles from one another will increase. For example, if the system consists of sand and water we can build a castle of sand, but when the water disappears by evaporation the areas of contact disappear and the castle falls apart. If, however, the impregnant contains a non-volatile substance which adheres to the discontinuous solid phase, this will give areas of contact after the evaporation of the solvent and a solidity depending upon the value of the internal pressure. If this value becomes very small or even negative, the solid substance itself may break. This is what we see when a very fragile material like old wood is impregnated with a thin solution of a resin. When this system dries, cracks develop and the object may be totally destroyed. Nearly all substances contract or solidify, so even when using melts or substances which solidify by chemical reaction there is always a danger of the strength of the material to be treated being too small to withhold the negative pressure in the pore liquid. The elastic modulus must be lower for the impregnant than for the discontinuous phase of the system.

After these considerations we can establish certain requirements for the properties of the substances to be used for the impregnation of fragile materials:

1. It must adhere to the solid.
2. It must penetrate as deeply as possible, especially when a vacuum is used.
3. It must set with preferably no loss in volume.
4. The cohesion must be strong.
5. The surface formed must be a transparent, colourless barrier against the atmosphere.
6. No harmful chemical reaction must take place between the impregnant or its solvents and the artifact.
7. It must be possible to remove the consolidant by resolving it again.

Our first requirement was that the consolidant should adhere to the object treated. It will be useful, I think, to define the concepts of adhesion and cohesion in a simple way. The forces between the molecules in a substance are called the cohesion forces: the forces acting between the molecules in two different substances are called the adhesion forces. If, for instance, the adhesion of a liquid to a surface is greater than the cohesion in the liquid, the liquid will wet the surface.

Adhesion forces will always act between two substances. These interfacial forces are of an enormous order of magnitude. Mica sheets can be made to adhere spontaneously when cleaved in vacuum; this automatically makes them smooth to within a few Ångströms. The shear strength of the joint is 14,000 lb./in.^{2}, i.e. 1 t/cm^2, which is as strong as the mica itself. The forces in this case are chemical. Usually the roughness of the surfaces in an atomic sense makes it convenient to obtain contact by the use of a liquid adhesive that will run into the irregularities. This liquid is usually solidified.

There are many factors that will influence the effective adhesive action. These may be broadly grouped as physical and chemical. In both instances the phenomena involved are closely related to the surface chemistry of the materials being bonded. Among these factors are:

1. Surface tension.
2. Porosity of the surfaces being bonded and their smoothness.
3. Physical properties of adhesive film.
4. Relative thickness of adhesive film and viscosity of the adhesive solution.
5. Methods of applying the adhesive.

The suitability of a liquid adhesive for a particular surface is related in part to the wettability of the liquid for that surface. The wettability is dependent upon various factors, including the viscosity of the liquid and its surface tension.

Materials such as wood, ceramics, paper and leather are porous in the sense that numerous capillaries are present which will conduct away the more highly mobile portions of the adhesive, disturbing the balance of molecular weight distribution in the polymers. Impregnation may be viewed as contributing to bonding in three dimensions, while surface bonding at a glue plane is a two-dimensional process. The impregnation may be described either as a diffusion of low molecular weight constituents into the cell wall, where this is possible—for instance, in wood and textile fibres—or as a mechanical penetration, usually through heat and pressure. The higher molecular weight of fully polymerized thermoplastics renders true penetration difficult. The thermosetting resins in an advanced stage of cure do not penetrate too effectively.

The modulus of elasticity of the impregnant is an important physical constant, which reflects the ability to absorb and distribute loads from one surface to another. This should preferably be comparable to that of the materials being bonded.

More recent investigations of plastic masses reveal a definite relationship between the physical properties and surface adhesive forces. This does not mean that the greater the tensile strength of a film the greater will be the adhesive strength.

In fact, there is a limited range in which the optimum adhesive properties can be obtained. This arises from the above-mentioned fact that the adhesive films must also serve as load-transmitting media, and must possess within themselves adequate cohesive strength if they are to function as acceptable adhesives. A proper balance must be maintained between good specific adhesion for the intended surface and good cohesive strength within the material. For thermoplastics this is accomplished by the selection of appropriate plasticizers, on the addition of which cohesive strength decreases and adhesive strength increases. For thermosetting polymers this may be accomplished to some extent by plasticizers, though more

usually by proper molecular weight distribution at the time of application. Lower molecular weight fractions will then move towards the surface and secure chemical bonding while the higher molecular weight fraction within the adhesive will establish the necessary strength and rigidity. The plasticizers should be non-volatile. Some polymers—for instance, poly-(n-butylmethacrylate)—are internally plasticized.

The physical properties of the adhesive film are related to the thickness of the adhesive film which is formed and the amount (percentage) of voids due to the evaporation of solvents. While the true adhesion of the adhesive film for the surface of the solid is independent of the thickness, the solvent employed may have some bearing owing to the particular polarization induced at the interface upon its evaporation.

The viscosity of the adhesive solution is related indirectly to the film thickness in that for a given solids content the more viscous solution tends to form the thickest film with the most voids. Hence the greater the probability of loss in cohesive strength of the adhesive film when employing highly viscous adhesives.

When no volatile matter is present, the apparent strength of an assembly will be independent of the glueline thickness.

The viscosity of a solution may be increased by the addition of non-volatile plasticizers.

After this short survey of the physical factors determining the properties of impregnants, we turn to the chemical factors. However, the path which leads to a complete understanding of the characteristics of adhesives from their molecules is very long and difficult. Improvements in the field of adhesives must be expected from direct trials by technologists rather than from theoretical predictions by pure scientists.

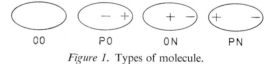

Figure 1. Types of molecule.

Therefore, as technologists we should have a concept of what chemical factors influence the adhesion and what kind of chemical substances have been used as means of consolidation.

The most important chemical factors influencing the adhesion are:

1. The polarity of the surface being bonded and the adhesive material.
2. The process of polymerization, formation of by-products and influence of molecular weight.
3. The nature of side-groupings on polymer chains.
4. The action of thin films of gases and vapours adsorbed on the surface being bonded and adsorption by adhesive films.
5. Evaporation or diffusion of volatiles from adhesive films.

We shall try by some very simple argument to describe qualitatively the effect of polarity.

By defining the polarity of a molecule as the distribution of the electric charges in space within the molecule, I hope not to have said anything incorrect about this very complex molecular characteristic. A molecule may be completely non-polar (class 00), it may contain active positive polarity only (class P0), active negative polarity only (class 0N), or have both positive and negative active surfaces (class PN) (*Figure 1*). This dimensional scale of molecular properties does not, however, account for the whole specificity of molecular interaction.

Examples of non-polar substances (class 00) are hydrocarbons, carbon tetrachloride and carbon disulphide.

Common substituted atoms like nitrogen and oxygen and halogen atoms (fluorine, chlorine, bromine and iodine) are all negatively charged. Hydrogen atoms may become positively charged if negative atoms are nearby and, as they have a very small radius, they then constitute very active positive centres. Alcohols, amines, amides and acids belong to class PN, having both positive and negative spots. Esters, ethers, ketones and pyridine derivatives belong to class 0N, as their positive charge is not concentrated enough to be active. Chlorine, bromine and iodine atoms do have a negative charge, but the polar character of the halides is slight, presumably because the radius of these atoms is large. What are generally called polar substances are compounds from class PN—alcohols, amines and the like. It is clear that, as molecules of these substances attract each other strongly with electrostatic forces and as they do not find any electrostatic counterpart in non-polar compounds of class 00, they will not mix with or adhere to these non-polar substances. But there are no repulsive forces acting between molecules of classes 00 and PN. On the contrary, other forces which act between all atoms, whether electrically charged or not, give an attraction between molecules of like as well as unlike class, which is nearly equal in each case. However, the extra mutual attraction between the polar molecules is so strong that they stick together very tightly and thus repel non-polar molecules.

The substances encountered in our work will nearly always be of a polar character. In wood we have a cellulosic structure with strong polar hydroxyl groups attached, and bone (carbonates, phosphates and proteins) is also polar. Textiles may belong to the proteins if they are of animal origin like wool and silk, or to the celluloses if they are of plant origin like flax and cotton.

Another polar group is the silicates, to which belong ceramics and glass. All the corrosion products of metals are polar, but not the metals themselves. However, if an electric charge approaches a metal surface, the metal is polarized in such a way that the electric field can be described as resulting from the approaching charge and another charge of opposite sign situated, with respect to the former charge, symmetrically at the other side of the metal surface. Hence if a molecule with an active positive spot approaches the metal, an active negative spot is induced in the metal, and strong attraction results. The inference is therefore that polar substances in particular will adhere to metal surfaces.

As the most important adhesives are reviewed, the presence of strong polar groups appears to be the rule rather than the exception. For thermosetting materials the following groups offer polar characteristics:

1. OH group in phenolic resin series.
2. CO and NH_2 groups among the amino resins.
3. Carboxyl groups of the polyester resins.

When the resin cures *in situ*, there is an opportunity for favourable polar adjustments to develop optimum qualities.

Among the thermoplastics the OH group of the polyvinyl series appears most useful in realizing outstanding adhesive properties. Useful polar groups appear among the cellulose derivatives, particularly cellulose nitrate, though there may be some question about the degree of rotation for polar adjustment of these high polymers, which exist as micelle units of long-chain molecules.

Somewhere between the more highly polymerized and the unpolymerized fractions lies a range of molecular weight or degree of polymerization best suited for adhesive purposes. The solubility characteristics of the polymers must be kept in mind since they vary from one degree of polymerization to

another, and it is sometimes the more favourable tolerance for solvent or plasticizer which explains an improved performance. Thermoplastics are polymerized before application and therefore require more judicious selection of their molecular weight ranges than the thermosetting polymers. These are polymerized *in situ* and expose a greater selection of polymers, the most favourable of which are adsorbed on the face of the material being bonded.

Not only good adhesion but also good cohesive strength must be exhibited within these ranges of degrees of polymerization. The ideal combination should be possible with an intermediate degree of polymerization for specific adhesion and components of higher molecular weight for best cohesive strength. It may also be reasoned and confirmed by practice that the longer the polymer, the less readily will it adjust itself in the presence of a solvent or plasticizer to a favourable position where the polar groupings can be adsorbed on the surface.

The nature of the side-groupings on the high-polymer chain is of the utmost significance in determining the merits of the polymer as an adhesive. Two factors appear to be directly related to the influence of the side-chains: polar characteristics and chemical compatibility. In the manufacture of high polymers, a cross-linking agent may be introduced which will raise the softening point of the polymer. By this the chemical compatibility may be affected and the adhesive properties rendered less effective. However, if at the time of application cross-linking agents are introduced which do not take effect until the polar groups have been properly adsorbed upon the surface, then the cross-linking may be of distinct benefit in creating improved cohesive strength. In our case we have to be very careful with cross-linked polymers as this may render them insoluble, and we shall always want to be able to remove from the artifact what has been added to it. In the thermosetting polymers the molecular weights are largely indeterminate. However, it is quite likely that side-groups influence adhesive properties as polymerization takes place *in situ*.

The evaporation and diffusion of volatile solvents from adhesive films are important in the development of good adhesive strength. Except for the temporary benefits of permitting molecular rotation and polar adjustments, volatile solvents do not contribute much to the final adhesive properties. The tenacity of high polymers for organic solvents is remarkably high, and even though from weight measurements we may decide that the solvents have been substantially evaporated, 'substantially' may still imply the retention of several per cent of the volatile solvents. High-temperature drying following room-temperature drying will prove most effective.

If, as mentioned earlier, the contraction in volume by the evaporation of the solvent is great, the internal pressure may become small and even negative, and this may lead to a breakdown of the solid phase.

Protection from dirt, gases and abrasion is the second aim of consolidation. The object is usually coated with a film which keeps the dirt from being embedded in it and protects it from suffering abrasion during handling, dusting, etc. If the film is too soft it may pick up dirt. Not only may there be an electrostatic attraction of charged particles of dust, but at higher temperatures polymers assume the state of a highly viscous liquid, which will then fasten dirt in such a way that it cannot be removed by dusting or washing.

The protection which a film will give to an artifact against damage done by radiation is of less importance to us than to the people dealing with paintings, but of equal importance in both cases is the barrier effect which the surface film has. The permeability of the film is the property which interests us.

Measurements of permeability refer to the rate of transmission through a film. It should be emphasized that organic coatings generally do not prevent transmission. They are seldom complete vapour barriers, but they reduce the amount transmitted in a given time. The rate of transmission may, of course, be so low that little change in conditions takes place in a brief period, but we are concerned with very long periods of protection. Investigations on the protection of metals by organic coatings have indicated that more than enough oxygen and water vapour are transmitted by these than is needed to account for the rate of oxidation of the metal; that is to say, more of these reactive substances are able to pass through the film at any given time than are actually consumed by the metal. It has been demonstrated that it is not so much the reduced permeability of a coating which retards the corrosion of metals as it is the increased electrical resistance given to the surface.

The effect of the water vapour in the atmosphere is not the only concern in protection. Gases such as oxygen and hydrogen sulphide also act upon both inorganic and organic materials. *Table 1* shows the permeability to water of a number of materials. The permeability to water is often considered to reflect the relative permeabilities of different coatings with respect to other gases, but this is not always the case (see G. Thomson, p. 178).

Table 1

Relative permeability to water

grams water/100 in.^{2}/day at 39·5°C, 100 per cent relative humidity. Film thickness, 0·001 in.

Film	Water (g)	Per cent water absorption (24 h at 25°C)
Saran (polyvinylidene chloride)	0·3–1·5	0·1
Paraffin wax	0·5–0·8	
Polyvinyl chloride–acetate	4–11	0·05–0·15 (0·1–0·6)
Dammar, mastic (one month old)	5–6	
Polystyrene, amorphous	25–35	0·00–0·06
Linseed oil (1–6 months old)	28–35	
Methyl methacrylate polymer	35	0·3–0·5
n-butyl methacrylate polymer	56	
Isoamyl methacrylate polymer	42	
Polyvinyl acetate	70–180	2
Polyvinyl butyral		18
Polyethylene		0·01

Materials showing a complete amorphous structure will probably be found to have a rather high moisture permeability. There can be no argument that coatings of wax have a low rate of transmission for water vapour.

The permeability of the methacrylate polymers is among the highest in the table, yet these exhibit lower permeability than many paints and varnishes.

We must always take precautions to be able to remove from an archaeological object the modern substances that have been used for its conservation. I need only mention the problems encountered when the method of ^{14}C age determinations was introduced in archaeology. Further physical and chemical deterioration may make it necessary to remove and renew the impregnant.

Oxidation is the most common chemical reaction considered to be responsible for the physical changes observed. Oxygen is not solely responsible for reactions classified as oxidations. Ozone, chlorine, sulphur dioxide and other gases in the atmosphere can also cause oxidation.

It is possible to choose chemical structures that are expected to be resistant to reaction with oxygen and other reactive agents. For example, the energy required to break the bonds in silicones and fluorocarbons is high and these substances may some day find application as permanent materials. Polystyrene and polyvinylidene chloride, in comparison, present special problems with regard to their stability to sunlight. Polyvinyl acetates and polymethacrylates, the thermoplastics that have attracted much attention in conservation, have been shown to be highly resistant to deterioration at normal temperatures. Many new compounds present new and special problems in adhesion and solubility. One cannot generally recommend or condemn the use of a synthetic resin, but must consider the merits of each one individually for a given application.

Linear polymers may deteriorate by several mechanisms: depolymerization, oxidative degradation and cross-linking. By depolymerization the chain may break up into the monomeric units. The atomic arrangement within the polymeric substance may break down, degraded by general chemical oxidation.

The third method of alteration is by cross-linking. If, in the course of aging, an atom or group of atoms on a linear polymeric chain becomes activated, it is possible that the activated group may link with a neighbouring chain. This gives us molecules of ever increasing molecular weight, leading eventually to a network of attached molecular chains that is insoluble, a characteristic of tridimensional or thermosetting polymers. In certain polymers or at certain stages of the process one type of reaction may be taking place. It has been observed that cross-linking reactions tend to predominate in polystyrene and polyethylene. On the other hand, a depolymerizing reaction is characteristic of methacrylate polymers at sufficiently elevated temperatures. Polyvinyl acetate is found to be highly resistant to cross-linking. It has been demonstrated that a certain type of structure in the methacrylate side-chain yields polymers that are particularly prone to cross-linking. For example, poly-isoamyl methacrylate in films becomes very difficult if not impossible to remove in toluene. It has been estimated that the resistance to removal of isoamyl or isobutyl methacrylate in toluene may be developed in 42 to 100 years in a gallery without sun louvers, 126 to 300 years with sun louvers, or 600 years with incandescent illumination at a certain level.

Finally I should like to give a classification of consolidants and adhesives, which was given by Dr Werner to the members of a British Council Course in 1960 on the conservation of antiquities, with my own comments added.

The classifying principle is the mode of setting.

1. Setting is due to change of temperature only: To this group belong the structural adhesives which solidify from a liquid by a physical change, like the waxes and resins.

2. Setting is due to change in temperature and loss of solvent: To this belong all types of animal glue.

3. Setting due to loss of solvent by evaporation: To this group belong the soluble natural and synthetic resins. According to the nature of the solvent, this group may be divided into:

3a. The solvent is an organic substance: This is a very large group, to which belong nitrocellulose, the equally important polyvinyl acetate and other polyvinyl derivatives, the polymethacrylates and modified nylon, and the I.C.I. product Calcton CA, soluble in ethyl alcohol. This last has been used with great success by Dr Werner in treating wall paintings. Like cellulose nitrate, it is readily permeable to water, thus permitting elution of the soluble salts; furthermore, it possesses a marked degree of flexibility so that it does not exert any undue contractile force on the frail surface layers. It gives a very matt surface layer and, having a relatively low surface tension, has found use in the consolidation by penetration of friable paints.

3b. The solvent is water: This group of aqueous adhesives may again be divided according to whether it is a pure solution or an emulsion:

3b(1). Pure aqueous solution: The classical starch and dextrin adhesives belong to this group; also solutions of inorganic salts—for instance, the saturated alum solution which was used for the consolidation of water-logged wood. The new agent for treating water-logged wood is also a water-soluble substance, polyglycol. The polyglycols have a wide range of viscosity, and one of them having the consistence of butter has been used directly on wet leather. It protects against mould growth. Polyvinyl alcohol is soluble in water, and has been used for the treatment of archaeological finds; mostly, however, it has been used in alcoholic solutions. My experience shows that the film becomes difficult to remove by alcohol and water after some time. Methyl cellulose is water-soluble, but is in my experience a very bad consolidant for wet material. In Holland they claim to use it with good results for the consolidation of wet wood (1960).

3b(2). Emulsions: This group has become very popular; emulsions of polyvinyl acetates and of acrylates are used for many purposes, both as glues and impregnants. Emulsifier and stabilizer must be added. Polyvinyl alcohol is a good stabilizer for polyvinyl acetate. Not too volatile plasticizers should be added to give flexibility if the polymer is not internally plasticized.

A film formed from the substances belonging to group 3b(1) is always soluble in water, whereas a film from 3b(2) will be insoluble.

4. Setting due to chemical reactions: In this case a hardener is added to a liquid which consequently sets. According to the kind of chemical reaction that takes place we have two possibilities:

4a. The setting is followed by a loss of volatile material: The volatile material is mostly water, the polymerization often being a condensation reaction. Examples are urea formaldehyde and the melamine formaldehydes.

4b. The setting takes place without loss of volatile material: With no loss of volatile material the contraction of volume will not give a value of the internal pressure, which may break down the structure, and the object impregnated will keep its form as constant as possible. There are very few substances that do not contract to some extent during solidification. Therefore all the groups we have dealt with earlier will show considerable shrinkage. To the very important and useful group which sets without loss of volatile material belong the epoxy resins and polyesters. These thermosetting plastics may be cold-setting, or may require various degrees of heat.

The above groups contain the fundamental new methods and substances that have come to the aid of the conservator, say, after the Second World War. On the other hand, our knowledge of both the materials we have to treat and the mechanism of the treatments at our disposal has increased enormously in the 30 years since the last conference in Rome. I believe that in this knowledge and in our use of it lies the most important new method in the field of conservation. Still we shall very often have to use empirical and trial-and-error methods, but the large amount of facts which is now at the disposal of the worker in conservation will in many cases enable him to know exactly what to do: a great benefit to archaeological objects and a source of reassurance to the conservator's conscience and nerves.

Robert H. Brill and Sheldon Moll

THE ELECTRON-BEAM PROBE MICROANALYSIS
OF ANCIENT GLASS

Introduction

Electron-beam probe microanalysis is a relatively new analytical method, the first probe having been built by Castaing in France in 1948[1]. Several detailed descriptions of the instrument[2] and review articles[3] on its applications have been published, so only a brief description is required here*.

As with so many of the complicated instruments of modern science, the operating principle of the probe is really rather simple. In effect it performs qualitative and quantitative analyses by x-ray fluorescence. *Figure 1* is a schematic drawing of the probe used for this study. It is located at the Advanced Metals Research Corporation laboratories in Somerville (Mass.), USA. A beam of electrons produced by a hot tungsten

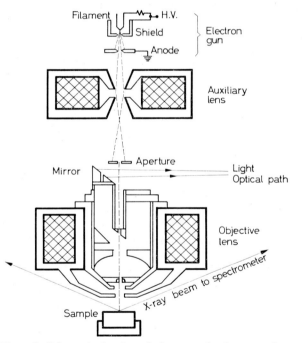

Figure 1. Schematic drawing of electron microbeam probe at Advanced Metals Research, Somerville (Mass.), USA.

filament and accelerated through a direct-current field is directed toward the surface of the sample to be analysed. When the electrons strike the sample the atoms at and near the surface of the sample are excited to higher energy states and emit or fluoresce x-rays. The x-ray spectrometer unit of the instrument collects these x-rays and performs two sorts of measurements. It separates the x-rays into their component wavelengths, much as a prism separates white light into its

component colours, and records which wavelengths of x-rays have been fluoresced by the sample. These wavelengths can be used to determine what chemical elements are present in the sample, since atoms of any given element can emit x-rays of only certain precisely defined wavelengths which are uniquely characteristic of that element. In addition, the instrument measures the intensity of each wavelength, which can be used to evaluate the amount of each element present in the sample. The signals are automatically recorded in graphical form, compared with responses from standards of known concentration and then converted into weight percentages of the elements detected.

The unique feature of the probe, however, is that the electron beam can be focused very sharply by electromagnetic lenses on a very tiny area of the surface of the sample, and can therefore be made to excite fluorescence within an extremely tiny volume of the sample. For example, the instrument used for this investigation can be focused on an area as small as one to two microns in diameter ($0.001 - 0.002$ mm). This means that the probe is capable of performing chemical analyses of objects which are too small to be seen by the unaided eye. In fact, some of the analyses in this study were made on objects which in their largest dimension are only 1/20th the diameter of a human hair. During the course of the analysis a sample may be viewed visually through an attached microscope, and manipulated so that many different areas of the sample may be studied.

Objective

Previously the probe has been used chiefly for the analysis of metallic systems. The work discussed here is an innovation in that it represents the first concerted attempt to use the probe for analysing glasses. The primary objective of this work was to explore the possible ways in which the probe might be used to study objects of ancient glass. The importance of the work, therefore, is not necessarily in the objects studied, but rather in the demonstration of the capabilities of the probe for studying such objects. It is hoped that this research will suggest uses of this technique for scientists studying other archaeological and art materials.

Types of problem studied

Table 1 lists the problems which were studied. In each case objects contained either tiny bits of glass which could not be analysed non-destructively by any other means, perhaps not even destructively, or tiny bits of occluded matter which were either intentionally or accidentally present in the glass. These experiments were preceded by and interspersed with calibration work on samples of glasses of known chemical composition.

Preparation of samples

With the exception of the 'Alexandrian' mosaic plaque all the samples investigated were cut from larger fragments or

---

* The reader is referred particularly to Castaing's work, and to that of Liebhafsky *et al.*[3], which contains a helpful bibliography.

objects. The samples were mounted in bakelite and polished on a metallographic polishing wheel. Diamond paste was used in several stages ranging from 14 micron to 1/4 micron grade.

The samples were coated by vacuum deposition with a film of aluminium to conduct away electrons which would otherwise build up a static charge on the sample and repel the oncoming beam. The method is non-destructive providing the sample to be analysed is small enough to be accommodated by the one-inch diameter sample chamber on the instrument. The action of the electron beam on many materials produces tiny brown spots, barely visible to the eye, which can be removed, along with the conducting coating, by gentle warming or very slight polishing.

Restrictions of probe analysis

The application of the electron probe to the analysis of glassy systems was, in general, quite successful. However, two difficulties should be discussed.

At the time these experiments were conducted the instrument was capable of analysing elements of atomic number greater than eleven, which, unfortunately, just excludes sodium, an element of interest in most glasses. Development of suitable detectors and monochromators to extend the analysis range to lighter elements is now under way. In the analyses presented here, sodium oxide levels were determined by taking the difference between 100 per cent and the sum of the percentages of all other oxides determined.

The second difficulty is a result of the complex composition of the glasses studied. The concentration of a particular element of interest is generally determined in the following way. The x-ray intensity available from the unknown is compared with the intensity from a pure-element standard. The resulting intensity ratio is corrected for matrix absorption and fluorescence effects and the concentration calculated. For systems composed of more than two or three elements a better method is to calibrate experimentally the intensity ratios with glasses of known composition. This procedure was employed for this work.

Table 1
Types of problem investigated

Quantitative analyses of ancient glasses
1. 'Alexandrian' mosaic plaque (1st century B.C.–1st century A.D.)—six different coloured glasses
2. Roman millefiori fragment (1st century B.C.–1st century A.D.)—four different coloured glasses
3. Egyptian XVIII Dynasty glasses from El Amarna (ca 1370–1350 B.C.)—three different coloured glasses
4. Fragments from Nishapur (9th–12th century A.D.)—two glasses
5. Fragments from medieval glass factory at Corinth (11th–12th century A.D.)—one glass
6. American Colonial glasses (17th century)—two glasses

Intentional inclusions in ancient glass	Accidental inclusions in ancient glass
1. Opacifying agents in three Roman glasses	1. Stones (nine samples) 2. Metallic inclusions in four glasses
Weathering crusts on ancient glasses	Concentration gradients
1. Two samples of crusts 2. An unusual plug formation	1. One experimental melt

Table 2
Estimated accuracies

Oxide	Concentration level (per cent)	Probable error (per cent)
SiO_2	65	± 2
CaO	30	3
CaO	5	1
K_2O	10	1
K_2O	4	0·4
MgO	15	3
MgO	4	0·3
Al_2O_3	4	1
Fe_2O_3	1	0·2
Sb_2O_5	5	0·5
PbO	20	1
PbO	1	0·2
CuO/Cu_2O	3	0·2
MnO	2	0·2
CoO	0·3	0·02
Na_2O	15	4

If, however, the compositions of the glasses to be analysed deviate to some extent from the standard compositions, or if other minor constituents are present, the calibrations will not be precise.

As a result of these considerations, there are limits to the accuracies of the determined compositions. *Table 2* lists the probable accuracies, at an estimated 90 per cent confidence level, for the experimental values reported in the tables which follow. The errors are expressed in absolute percentage units, not as relative errors. For example, a reported value of 20 per cent PbO implies a range of 19–21 per cent PbO, not 19·8–20·2 per cent.

Analyses of ancient glasses

Roman millefiori fragment

Plate IIc shows a single design motif removed from a fragment of a Roman millefiori bowl (*ca* first century B.C. or first century A.D.). The target-shaped design consists of three concentric rings of red, yellow and white opaque glasses mounted in a matrix of clear glass which contains amethyst-coloured streaks. Each of these four different coloured glasses was analysed with the probe and the results are shown in *Table 3*. The metallic elements were determined and converted to weight percentages of the oxides. All the compositions are about what one would expect for Roman glasses. Further results on interesting inclusions found in this sample are reported in later sections.

'Alexandrian' mosaic plaque

Plate IIb shows a mosaic glass object dating from the first century B.C. or the first century A.D. and possibly made in Alexandria. The design runs completely through the one-centimetre thickness of the piece, which was apparently formed by fusing together small pieces of glass of six different colours. The object is only two centimetres across the base and one cannot help but marvel at the remarkable detail that some ancient artist was able to build into this object. The six glasses were analysed using the probe and yielded the results in *Table 3*. Once again the results are those that would be expected for Roman glasses. The high concentration of lead in the red opaque appears at first glance to be unusual, since few analyses of ancient glasses (other than Far Eastern) show as much lead. The few instances of lead glasses that have been reported,

Table 3

Analyses of ancient glasses

Per cent oxide	'Alexandrian' mosaic plaque							Roman millefiori fragment			
	WO	DBT	DBO	LBO	RO	YO	X	WO	YO	RO	C
SiO_2	58	66	62	69	54	53	67	59	59	55	65
CaO	5·9	4·8	4·2	3·7	8·6	3·4	5·0	5·8	3·9	4·3	9·0
K_2O	0·3	0·5	0·3	0·4	0·6	1·3	0·4	2·4	1·8	1·8	2·7
MgO	4·9	0–0·5	0–0·5	0–0·5	2·3	0–0·5	0·5	0·8	0·8	0·8	0·8
Al_2O_3	2·2	2·2	1·8	2·5	2·2	1·8	2·0	3·2	4·5	4·0	~3
Fe_2O_3	0·4	1·5	2·1	0·9	1·8	1·9	0·4	0·4	2·2	2·9	1·4
Sb_2O_5	8·9*	1·3	8·1*	5·8*	0·8	2·2*	1·0	6·0*	2·8*	1·3	0·8
PbO	0·2	0·1	0·2	0·4	29·0	21·5	0·2	1·6	16 *	4·5	0·0
CuO	0·0	0·3*	0·8*	3·7*	—	0·1	—	0·06	0·28	—	0·02
Cu_2O	—	—	—	—	1·7*	—	—	—	—	1·1*	—
CoO	0·0	0·13*	0·05*	0·0	0·0	0·0	—	—	—	—	—
MnO	0–0·05	0–0·05	0–0·05	0–0·05	0·3	0–0·05	—	1·3	0·8	1·5	2·7*
Na_2O	19	23	21	13	0–5	14	23	19	23	23	15

WO—White opaque   LBO—Light blue opaque   C—Colourless transparent
DBT—Dark blue transparent   RO—Red opaque   X—Hypothetical parent glass
DBO—Dark blue opaque   YO—Yellow opaque   * Colouring or opacifying agent

however, have been opaque reds from Egyptian, Roman and Mesopotamian sources[4].

These analyses illustrate well the action of colouring agents. For example, the addition of copper to a molten glass, followed by heating in an oxidizing atmosphere, produces a transparent blue colour, which can be very much deepened by the addition of some cobalt oxide. The blue colour is attributed to individual cupric ions, which may be visualized as existing in solution in the glassy network. When a copper-containing glass is heated with a reducing agent a red opaque colour is produced owing to the appearance of tiny crystals of metallic copper or cuprous oxide. The use of a lead-containing glass facilitates the development of this red colour by increasing the solubility of copper in the glass[5]. The usefulness of lead glasses in this connection apparently was learned early in the history of glassmaking. The white opaque and yellow opaque colours are due respectively to combinations of calcium with antimony and lead with antimony. These opacifying agents were studied in detail and are discussed in a following section.

In order to check these results further, a series of glasses was synthesized according to the results of the analysis of this object. The synthetic glasses produced results nearly identical with their prototypes when analysed by the probe.

Clearly, one must use caution when speculating on the inter-relationships between the compositions of the six different glasses in this object because certainly the artist who made this object would have had at his disposal for starting materials dozens, or more likely hundreds, of fragments of different coloured glasses which would accumulate in any glass shop. In spite of this, having now in our hands analyses of a group of six different glasses which we know with certainty were available to one artist at one time and which very likely were made at the same glass shop, possibly at the same time or within a few months of one another, we cannot resist the temptation to seek correlations between the compositions. For example, we ask ourselves, 'Were all or any of the glasses made from one common ancestor, a clear glass to which colorants and opacifiers were added?'; or, 'Were the blue opaques made by mixing the dark blue transparent glass with the white opaque, by adding an opacifying agent (Sb_2O_5) to the transparent blue glass, or perhaps by adding copper to the white opaque?'

After careful examination of the data, no such simple relationship could be definitely established. The first three glasses listed, however—the white opaque, dark blue transparent and dark blue opaque—do have compositions which are consistent with a common parent glass having a composition close to that shown in *Table 3*. The variations in other elements could have been produced by the addition of CaO and some MgO as an opacifier for the white glass and a cobalt–copper colouring agent for the blue glasses. This blue colorant would be likely to be rich in iron, thus explaining the differences in iron content of the resulting glasses. This is not offered as a definite conclusion, but more as an example of the sort of information that might be gathered from studies of this sort when the anticipated calibration experiments enable further refinements.

A comparison of the millefiori fragment with that of the mosaic piece shows that the compositions are not very different (except in the case of the lead in the one red opaque), but the systematic variations between the K_2O, MnO and Al_2O_3 are illustrative of the expected variation to be found between different factories using different sources of raw materials but following similar 'recipes'. Variations of this magnitude, however, have taken on new significance.

In a recent publication[6], Sayre and Smith have shown that ancient glasses may be separated into five compositional categories on the basis of the concentrations of magnesium, manganese, potassium, antimony and lead. Although the precision of the values reported in *Table 3* is not as good at present as one would like to have for such comparisons, it is rather definitely indicated that the 'Alexandrian' mosaic plaque compositions are closer to the pre-Roman 'antimony-rich' category than the 'Roman' category. The Roman millefiori fragment, on the other hand, seems to be roughly a hybrid of the two categories, but the conclusion in this case is more tenuous.

Other ancient glasses

The analyses of the three Eighteenth Dynasty glasses from El Amarna seem to match well the 'second millennium B.C.' category described by Sayre. These results are reported in *Table 4*, along with analyses of samples from Nishapur and Corinth[7]. These analyses were conducted in order to aid in the interpretation of results of data included in the next section. In an incidental way they do point out that the source of alkali for the Corinthian and Nishapur glasses contained an appreciable amount of potash (K_2O) as well as soda (Na_2O). This can safely be taken as an indication that plant ash was the source of alkali. There is reason to believe that the still appreciable quantity of soda is evidence that the plants used came from a coastal or desert environment rather than an inland environment[8]. The high MgO content may be a result of the use of dolomite ($CaCO_3.MgCO_3$) as a source of lime in the Nishapur glasses.

Opacifying agents

A microscopic examination of the opaque white and opaque yellow regions of the Roman millefiori fragment reveals that the opacity and colour are due to myriads of tiny particles suspended in a colourless glassy matrix (see *Figure 2*). In the case

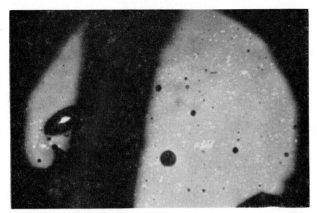

Figure 2. Photomicrograph of yellow opaque region of Roman millefiori sample. Light specks are particles of $Pb_2Sb_2O_7$ opacifier. The black band is a human hair placed across the sample to illustrate the magnification.

of the opaque white, the crystals are usually in the shape of rods about 15 microns long. The flakes in the opaque yellow are irregularly shaped and somewhat smaller. By focusing the electron beam on the largest of the individual flakes it was possible to obtain quantitative analyses. The white flakes were shown to be $Ca_2Sb_2O_7$ with coprecipitated potassium, magnesium, aluminium and lead oxides totalling 2–3 per cent. The analysis of the yellow flakes was consistent with a composition of $Pb_2Sb_2O_7$ containing perhaps as much as 4 per cent iron oxide as an impurity. These findings agree with those Turner and Rooksby[9] obtained by x-ray powder techniques.

The colouring agent in the red opaque glass is undoubtedly

Table 4
Analyses of some ancient glasses

Per cent oxide	EA-6 El Amarna green opaque	EA-7 El Amarna lt. blue opaque	EA-12 El Amarna red opaque	CNE-9 Corinth transparent	N-6 Nishapur blue transparent
SiO_2	65	66	64	66	57
CaO	4·0	6·8	5·3	10	10
K_2O	0·5	0·4	0·5	7·3	10
MgO	~4	~4	~4	1·6	6
Al_2O_3	1·7	2·4	3	1·2	2·9
Fe_2O_3	0·3	0·3	0·3	1·0	1·5
Sb_2O_5	0·1	0	0	—	—
TiO_2	0·1	0·1	0	0·9	0·07
CuO	1·3	1·0	—	—	—
Cu_2O	—	—	4·3	—	—
CoO	—	0·04	0·06	—	—
Cr_2O_3	0	0	0·1	0	0
Na_2O	23	18	18	12	12

suspended copper and/or cuprous oxide. The individual particles were too small for analysis but analyses of somewhat larger particles in a red opaque from El Amarna (*Table 4*) showed that the flakes were cuprous oxide.

Stones

Among the interesting inclusions found in the glasses studied were several types of tiny crystals which glass scientists refer to as stones (see *Figure 3*). In general, stones result from three different causes. They may be bits of incompletely fused raw materials, bits of refractory which have broken away from the walls of the melting crucibles, or they may result from devitrification. Devitrification is a process whereby the components of a glass crystallize from the glassy network. Devitrification in ancient glasses may be associated with glasses of unstable composition or glasses which have been subjected to elevated temperatures for extended periods.

In most cases the individual crystals analysed are of microscopic dimensions, although in a few cases clusters of the crystals are large enough to be visible to the unaided eye. *Table 5* contains the results of the probe analyses of these stones.

Five of the stones analysed proved to be silica. It is presumed that these are the residues of grains of sand which did not completely melt when the glasses were manufactured. Microscopic examination shows that they have rounded edges, which, along with their occurrence as single crystals rather than groups of microcrystals, indicates that they are not devitrification products.

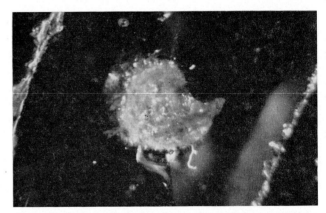

Figure 3. Stone in fragment of glass from Nishapur (sample 4-5). Diameter approximately 0·6 mm.

In the case of two of the stones, the most probable origin is devitrification, which might be attributed to annealing at excessively high temperatures, accidental heating through catastrophic events in the history of the objects, or perhaps to the combination of age and local instabilities in the glass resulting from poor mixing. The last possibility suggests that a method might be developed for dating ancient glass by examination of devitrification phenomena, but the prospects do not look very promising.

The devitrification stones identified were sodium disilicate, wollastonite and diopside. From the phase diagram[10] of the system Na_2O–CaO–SiO_2 one can predict the expected devitrification products for a glass of known composition. In the case of the stones attributed to devitrification, the analysed compositions of the stones agree with those predicted for the given glass matrices. The stone in sample 4-6, which was shown to be diopside ($CaO.MgO.2SiO_2$), is probably a devitrification product. The high MgO concentration (greater than 9 per cent)

Table 5

Analysis of stones

Sample	Composition	Probable origin
2–10 Irreg. stone (75 μ × 25 μ), dark blue, semi-opaque glass, El Amarna (*ca* 1370–1350 B.C.)	SiO_2	Incompletely fused raw material (sand)
3–1 Rounded rectang. stone (100 μ × 50 μ), violet glass, Thebes (*ca* 1400–1370 B.C.)	SiO_2 (trace Al_2O_3)	Same
Rounded stone (80 μ × 40 μ), yellow band Roman mille. fragment (1st cent. B.C.–1st cent. A.D.)	SiO_2 (trace Al_2O_3, MgO)	Same
3–4 Rounded triang. stone (*ca* 20 μ largest dimen.), lt. blue opaque glass, Thebes (*ca* 1400–1370 B.C.)	SiO_2	Same
2–6 Irreg. shaped stone (*ca* 20 μ across), green opaque glass, El Amarna (*ca* 1370–1350 B.C.)	SiO_2	Same
3–2 Many small crystals, uniform size (*ca* 6 μ), cubic and triang. cross-sections, blue opaque glass, Thebes (*ca* 1400–1370 B.C.)	Probably $Na_2O.2SiO_2$ (sodium disilicate)	Devit. product
4–1 Cluster small stones (largest *ca* 40 μ × 46 μ), clear blue glass, medieval glass factory, Corinth	$CaO.SiO_2$* (wollastonite)	Devit. product expected from glass of comp. as in *Table 3*
4–5 Cluster small stones, reg. shape (*ca* 50 μ), clear blue glass, Nishapur (9–12th cent. A.D.)	SiO_2, CaO, Na_2O, R_2O_3*†	Probably devit. product
4–6 Different cluster stones from same object as 4–5. Irreg. shaped (*ca* 50 μ)	$CaO.MgO.2SiO_2$* (diopside)	Devit. product. Adj. area rich in MgO

* Confirmed by x-ray analysis.
† X-ray analysis shows wollastonite and melilite-like phases.

Figure 4. Photomicrograph of same stone as shown in *Figure 3*. Largest crystals are about 50 microns in greatest dimension. Analysis was made by focusing electron beam on individual crystals.

in the immediate neighbourhood surrounding the stone and in the rest of the glass is consistent with the crystallization of diopside. This may also be taken as an indication that dolomite was the source of lime used for at least some of the compositions mixed in this particular factory. The findings of the direct chemical analysis of two of the stones by the probe were confirmed by x-ray diffraction experiments.

The remaining stone (*Figure 4*), which had the form of a cluster of tiny crystals, was found to be rich in SiO_2 and CaO, and contained some Na_2O and other oxides. Mr H. P. Rooksby[11], of The General Electric Company Limited, Hirst Research Centre, very kindly assisted the authors by interpreting the x-ray data for this stone. Mr Rooksby concluded that it consists of a mixture of wollastonite and a melilite-like phase, which is consistent with the analytical data.

Metallic inclusions

Within the red area of the millefiori fragments was found a metallic inclusion, perfectly circular in cross-section, having a diameter of 250 microns. The inclusion consists of three distinctly different phases. The analysis showed the compositions given in *Table 6*. Because this inclusion was found in the

Table 6

Analyses of metallic inclusions (percentages)

	Millefiori fragment			Metal flake Corinth CNE-y		Metal inclusion Corinth C4-8		Spherical inclusions— weathering crust PR-1	
	a	*b*	*c*					Fe	pr. > 95
Cu	99·0	60·0	~1·0	Fe as Fe_2O_3	92	Fe as Fe_2O_3	85		
Sb	0	39·0	0	K_2O	12	K_2O	21		
Pb	1·0	1·0	~100	Al	0·9	Al	0·7		
				Ca	0·1	Ca	0·9		
				Mn	0·3				

red band and because it consists chiefly of the copper-rich phase, (*a*) in the table, it is presumed that this is the undissolved remains of a piece of copper which was added to this glass as a colouring agent. Its circular cross-section suggests that it was once molten. The melting point of pure copper is 1083°C, although this might have been depressed somewhat by impurities in the metal. Nevertheless, the molten history of the copper inclusion confirms that temperatures in excess of 1000°C were available to the Roman glassmakers.

Two explanations are possible for the existence of the three separate phases. If the original colorant was a copper–lead bronze, the heat treatment might have caused a segregation of the lead phase (*c*), which exists as pockets of lead dispersed throughout the copper-rich phase. It is known that slow cooling of copper–lead alloys containing about 30 per cent lead will cause such a separation[12]. The absence of tin in the inclusion argues against this point of view for this particular sample, since tin was invariably a component of Roman bronzes, even those that contained lead[13], and no tin was detected in this inclusion.

If it is assumed rather that relatively pure copper metal was added as a colorant, the presence of the lead and antimony might be explained by reduction of Pb^{2+} and Sb^{3+} ions in the glassy matrix, perhaps near the surface of the molten globule, followed by diffusion into the globule.

The antimony–copper phase (*b*), which is distributed as streaks throughout the copper-rich phase, has a composition corresponding to the γ-phase found in the copper–antimony phase diagram[14]. This represents a solid solution of antimony in a hexagonally close-packed copper lattice. The γ-region on the phase diagram ranges from about 30 to 39 per cent antimony. This composition also corresponds exactly to the formula Cu_3Sb, although there is some doubt about whether or not such a compound actually exists.

The production of the metallic antimony and lead from the Sb^{3+} and Pb^{2+} ions in the glass seems best explained by reduction by the same agent needed to keep the copper in a reduced state. The metallic copper itself would not be expected to be a sufficiently strong reducing agent to bring about the reduction.

In order to study this effect further, a molten glass containing 10 per cent Sb_2O_5 and 20 per cent PbO was prepared (remainder: soda–lime–silica). Eight per cent by weight of metallic copper was added at about 1100°C. The melt was stirred for half an hour. After cooling and annealing, cross-sections of the glass were cut and polished and the exposed inclusions of undissolved copper were examined. Phases closely resembling those in the

millefiori piece were found. Spectrographic analyses confirmed that lead (7–10 per cent) and antimony (3–5 per cent) had been extracted from the glassy phase.

Sample CNE-y is a fragment of glass excavated at the site of a medieval glass factory at Corinth (11th–12th century A.D.). It is a greenish glass with occasional dark streaks running through it. One of these streaks originates from a thin flake of metal embedded in the glass. The flake evidently is a bit of metal that had broken away from some tool used in the manufacture of the glass. The probe analysis shows it contains principally iron and iron oxide, a surprisingly large amount of potassium and traces of manganese, aluminium and calcium. Since it would be difficult to account for the presence of elemental potassium in the system and since potassium would not be expected to alloy with iron anyway, it must be presumed that the potassium is present in some state in which it is chemically bound to oxygen and iron. If the iron flake had partially oxidized, which is clearly the case, the oxide might have reacted with potash in the glass melt to form a potassium ferrate. It might also be possible that some sodium ferrate could be present which would not have been detected by the probe.

A similar interpretation must also apply to another inclusion of metallic appearance in a flat fragment of yellow opaque glass also found at the Corinthian Agora. This inclusion (C4-8) has a similar composition, with an even greater concentration of potassium oxide.

Within the weathering crust of sample PR-1, but not within the glass itself, were found a number of microscopic spherical inclusions which show a metallic lustre when exposed by polishing. The probe analysis of these inclusions showed them to be essentially pure iron. No explanation of the origin of these inclusions is offered other than the possibility that they might also be traces of metal broken away from tools.

Weathering crusts

Analyses were also made of several badly corroded ancient glasses. On each sample there are weathering crusts consisting of decomposition products remaining after hundreds of years of attack by water. The analyses of the glasses and weathering crusts are given in *Table 7*.

Sample N-9 was cut from the base of a glass vessel found in Nishapur. The sample had been dated by the counting technique[15], which indicated that it had been buried in the 12th century A.D. The pale yellow glass bears a green weathering crust about 1·5 mm thick, which in turn is covered with a chalky yellowish crust about 0·3 mm thick. The glass and both

Table 7

Analyses of weathering crusts

Per cent oxide	N-9 glass	N-9 green layer	N-9 yellow crust	J-4 glass	J-4 intrusion (tip)	J-4 intrusion (base)	PR-1 glass	PR-1 weathering crust
SiO_2	66	87–92	87–92	~65	~85	85	65	67
CaO	5·2	1·6	2·9	~22	3·2	0·6	22*	0·4
K_2O	3·4	1·6	1·7	6	0·2	0	6·0*	~6
MgO	4·4	0·4	0·4	2·5	0	0	3·0*	18–23
Al_2O_3	1·5	4·5	4·5	2·3	4	4	2·7*	2·0
Fe_2O_3	0·5	0·3	1·0	0·9	2·1	1·4	1·2	1·1
Sb_2O_5	0·1	1·8	0·9	0·3	0·7	0	0·3	0·4
TiO_2	0	0	trace	trace	2·3	1·5	trace	trace
P_2O_5	0·2	0	0	1·0	0	0	0	0
MnO	1·1	0	0	0	0	0	0	0
Na_2O	18	⩽3	⩽2	0–1	—	—	1·1*	3–5*

* Combined probe and wet chemical analyses

weathering crusts were analysed by the probe. The Na_2O was apparently completely leached out by soil water, along with a good portion of the K_2O, CaO and MgO. The excesses of Fe_2O_3, Al_2O_3, CaO and Sb_2O_5 in the weathering crusts as compared with the undecomposed glass result from two effects which are superimposed on the overall leaching process. These are the absorption of ions from soil water and the redeposition of leached ions near the outer surface of the crust. Increases in Fe_2O_3 and Al_2O_3 have been noted by both Geilmann[16] and Turner[17].

Figure 5. Close-up photograph of cross-section of sample J-4, showing weathering plugs which have intruded into the glass. The upper and lower margins mark the outer surfaces of the glass, which is about 1·7 mm thick.

Sample J-4 was removed from a fragment of window glass excavated in 1935 at the site of the First Statehouse in Jamestown, Virginia. The counting technique[15] indicated that it had been buried in soil in about 1669. The weathering on this particular piece took the form of intrusions which worked into the glass from the outer surfaces. *Figure 5* shows a cross-section of this sample. The upper and lower edges of the photograph coincide with the surfaces of the glass, which is about 1·7 mm thick. Once again the analyses show that the K_2O, MgO, CaO, P_2O_5 and (within experimental error) the Na_2O were leached away almost completely. The Fe_2O_3 and Al_2O_3 contents appear to have been somewhat increased. The analysis at the tip of the intrusion, which should represent the more recently decomposed glass, seems higher in Sb_2O_5, TiO_2, Fe_2O_3 and CaO than the other surfaces.

The rather high concentration of TiO_2 at the tip of the plug, as compared to that in the glass as a whole, may be related to the cause of the peculiar decomposition, which very clearly has proceeded preferentially along an axis into the glass. The excesses of Sb_2O_5 and Fe_2O_3 at the tip are perhaps doubtful. Further experiments are being conducted to study these intrusions.

The study of another weathered sample, PR-1, salvaged from Port Royal, Jamaica, after 267 years' submersion in salt water, yielded extremely interesting results. The glass itself has a composition very close to that of J-4. The high CaO content is common in certain glasses of this period. The conditions of leaching were quite different from those of the prior samples, since the object was in salt water and buried in a deep layer of blue sediment which covers the bottom at the site of the submerged portion of the city of Port Royal. The most striking change seems to be the substitution of MgO for CaO in the glassy network on an almost equimolar basis. This perhaps proceeds by an ion-exchange mechanism. When analyses of the sediment become available it should be possible to say more about these results.

Concentration gradients

Another useful application of the probe in research on ancient glass is the investigation of cords and other striations which occur in glass. Work is under way on such studies. In addition, concentration gradients of various elements are believed to exist near the surface of glass. When a glass object is annealed, for example, it is heated for extended periods at elevated temperatures. Na_2O, K_2O, Sb_2O_5 and other volatile components may then be lost by sublimation, and the loss is most marked near the surface of the glass. In order to observe this effect, an experimental glass was examined in cross-section. The probe scanned the glass from the interior toward the surface and measured the concentrations of several elements along the scan path. Although the preliminary experiments did not detect any reproducible decrease in the concentration of any element as the surface was approached, it was found that the K_2O seemed to be highly segregated, whereas the CaO and MgO were uniformly distributed. Al_2O_3 was intermediate. This work is being pursued because of the important implications such effects have on the mechanism by which glasses are attacked by water.

Acknowledgements

The authors thank Miss Susan Schur for her valuable assistance in conducting some of the experimental work. We are also indebted to Mr H. P. Rooksby of The General Electric Company Limited, Hirst Research Centre, Wembley, England, for the interpretation of certain of the x-ray diffraction data used for confirming the analyses of the stones.

References

1 CASTAING, R. and GUINIER, A., *Proc. int. Conf. on Electron Microscopy, Delft, 1949*, 1950, pp. 60–63.
2 CASTAING, R., *Advanc. Electron. electron Phys.*, 13 (1960).
3 LIEBHAFSKY, H. A., WINSLOW, E. A. and PFEIFFER, H., *Analyt. Chem.*, 32 (1960) 240.
4 CALEY, E. R., *Analyses of Ancient Glasses* (Tables II, III, VI, XIX, XXVII, XXXIV, LXIX and CV), The Corning Museum of Glass, Corning, New York, 1962.
5 WEYL, W. A., *Coloured Glasses*, Dawson's, London, 1959, p. 424.
6 SAYRE, E. V. and SMITH, R. W., *Science*, 133 (1961) 1824–1826.
7 (DAVIDSON) WEINBERG, G. R., *Corinth*, Vol. 12, The American School of Classical Studies at Athens, Princeton, N.J., 1952.
8 TURNER, W. E. S., *J. Soc. Glass Tech.*, 40 (1956) 277T–300T.
9 TURNER, W. E. S. and ROOKSBY, H. P., *Glastech. Ber.*, 32K (1959) 17–28.
10 MOREY, G. W., *Properties of Glass*, Reinhold, New York, 1953, p. 48.
11 ROOKSBY, H. P., private communication.
12 *Metals Handbook*, Vol. 1, 8th edition, p. 849, American Society for Metals, 1961.
13 CALEY, E. R., private communication.
14 BERGHOFF, H. L., *Metals Handbook*, p. 1202, American Society for Metals, 1948.
15 BRILL, R. H. and HOOD, H. P., *Nature*, 189 (1961) 12–14.
16 GEILMANN, W., *Glastech. Ber.*, 29 (1956) 145–168.
17 TURNER, W. E. S., *J. Soc. Glass Tech.*, 38 (1954) 445T–456T.

Rolf Wihr

REPAIR AND REPRODUCTION OF ANCIENT GLASS

Ever since fragments of antique glass have been discovered, suitable materials for their restoration have been sought. In the beginning one was compelled to use materials such as gypsum; this, however, is an opaque material which only permitted repairs of a rather limited kind. Later materials such as wax, colophony and celluloid were tried, and finally plastic materials such as the methacrylates in sheet form (Plexiglas, Perspex)[1].

These materials possess certain obvious advantages: they are glass-clear, they do not yellow and they are resistant to age. They are, however, rigid, so that they had to be cut, sawn and bored. They can be softened by being slightly warmed and pressed over prepared forms. However, the process and the preparation of the necessary tools, etc., are rather expensive and in the case of complicated repairs demand a large amount of work on the part of the restorer.

The next step involved the use of a finely powdered pre-polymer methacrylate which was worked into a dough with the monomer and the mixture allowed to polymerize. This process overcame two difficulties; namely, the shrinkage and the heat of polymerization were considerably reduced. One material which proved particularly useful was produced by the firm of Kulzer and Company under the trade name of 'Paladon'[2]. However, the polymerization of Paladon required a temperature of about 100°C, and this raised serious difficulties regarding the restoration of antique glass. For this reason it was necessary to look for other similar systems in which the polymerization would take place at room temperature. As a result of research along these lines a material called Palavit was first developed, and later the material Technovit 4004A[3]. These materials contain special accelerators which are distributed in the powdered pre-polymer and the liquid monomer. When these are mixed, the polymerization reaction starts in about 10–15 minutes and proceeds at room temperature.

This material in most cases is sufficiently transparent, and it is only in the case of completely colourless water-clear glasses, such as Venetian glass, that the very slight yellowish tone may be regarded as a slight disadvantage.

The proportions in which the powder and liquid are mixed can be varied between $5:2\frac{1}{2}$ and $5:3$. Normally one will try to work with the smallest amount of liquid. At the same time, in a cube of 8 cm³ volume, the temperature will rise to 80–90°C; this means that the thickness to be cast should not exceed about 5 mm, which, however, is rarely necessary in the case of glass objects. If, however, the resin has to be cast in greater thickness, this should be done by pouring the material in a number of layers which will adhere completely to each other.

If it is necessary to colour the material to match a particular glass, this can easily be carried out by adding to the liquid so-called 'Zaponecht' pigments[4]. These can be obtained as powders that are dissolved in a nitrocellulose lacquer, which is then added drop by drop to the monomeric liquid. In this way, the coloured material does not lose its transparency. If one wishes to use opaque materials (for example, for the reproduction of ancient ivory) one can either add a suitable opacifier or

alternatively use Technovit 4012A, which is supplied as an opaque material.

We now come to the question of the moulding which is to be used in connection with the above-mentioned grades of Technovit. A suitable moulding material must have the following properties:

1. It must reproduce all the finest details on the surface of the original.
2. It must be elastic, and its chemical nature must be such that one can readily remove the mould from the original.
3. It must be applied and set at the lowest possible temperature, since ancient glass, much of which will already have been repaired by sticking together fragments, will not withstand elevated temperatures.
4. It must show the smallest possible degree of shrinkage.
5. It must withstand the heat of polymerization of the resin to be used for repairing without undergoing any deformation.
6. The complete mould must remain indefinitely stable.

There has recently come on the market a material which satisfies all these requirements. This is a so-called 'silicone rubber'[5]; by the addition of different quantities of hardener the setting time can be varied between 2 minutes and 24 hours. In practice one does not choose the shortest possible hardening time, so that one can apply the more or less viscous silicone material to the original without running the risk of making any mistakes. A layer 2 mm thick will suffice for glass objects of a height or diameter of 20 cm.

In order to give the relatively thin elastic silicone skin further support, one can enclose it in a gypsum cast.

The shrinkage in the beginning is almost nil, but after a few hours may amount to about 1 per cent; it does not, however, increase any further. In most cases this slight shrinkage is of no consequence. However, if necessary, one can swell the mould to its original dimensions by leaving it for a few hours in a closed container in which is placed a dish containing either benzene or the monomeric liquid. The vapours evolved swell the material without causing any damage. By leaving the silicone material for about 12 hours, it is possible to swell it and obtain any desired enlargement of the mould form[6].

In the moulding of objects which have large undercuts, the elasticity of the silicone mass is not sufficient, so that it cannot be used with success. In such cases it is necessary to use another material, such as a polysulphide rubber, which is produced on the market in various grades under the trade name 'Naftoflex'[7]. However, when this material is used it is necessary to employ a suitable isolating material to separate it from the original object[8].

In the case of small repairs it is sufficient to make a temporary mould of dental wax[9] upon which an isolating layer of a poly-vinyl alcohol (Trennlack F 86) has been brushed. In the case of undercut parts, it is necessary to form an elastic mass, and after this has hardened to set it into position in the area that is to be repaired, taking care that it sits correctly so that the liquid resin will not flow out.

(a) (b)

Figure 1. Deep blue Roman ribbed dish (*a*) before restoration and (*b*) after restoration.

(a) (b)

Figure 2. Clear yellowish Roman dish (Abraham and Isaac): (*a*) original; (*b*) copy.

With these synthetic resins, the restorer is now in a position to replace effectively the missing parts of antique glass objects.

In the restoration of a deep blue Roman ribbed dish of which many parts were missing, it was first necessary to model these in places, using the model to prepare the silicone rubber mould. This mould was then used for casting resin necessary to replace the missing parts (*Figure 1*). The completion of this work took only 72 hours, and the cost of the material was 15 DM. It was reckoned that a similar repair, if carried out in rigid plastics such as Perspex, would have required at least 300 hours' work although the cost of the materials would have been only 2 DM.

By using these quick-hardening transparent synthetic resins and the elastic mould materials, one is in a position not only to carry out repairs with great precision, but also to make reproductions of glass objects in which the finest engravings and any other marks on the original object are faithfully reproduced. Furthermore, the transparency and the colouring of the replica can be carried out in such a way that, judging by appearances alone, it is very difficult to distinguish between the copy and the original. However, differences in the weight of the synthetic material compared with the glass will, of course, enable one to distinguish between the two. The procedure in the preparation of such replicas is similar to that described above for carrying out the repairs. In this way I have made replicas of a whole series of Roman glass vessels and ivory carvings—most of which are in the possession of the Rheinisches

Figure 3. Diatrete from Niederemmel (original).

Figure 4. Bowl of the Niederemmel diatrete (copy).

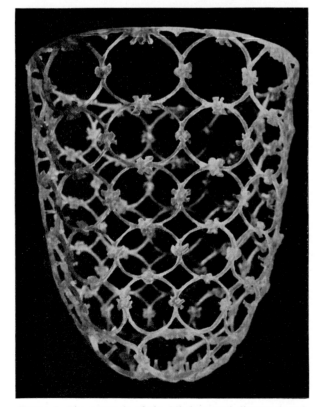

Figure 5. The network of the Niederemmel diatrete (copy).

Figure 6. The finished copy of the Niederemmel diatrete.

Landesmuseum. Concerning these, the following points are worthy of particular mention[10]:

1. *Figure 2a* shows a clear yellowish Roman dish with a design of Abraham and Isaac. Comparing its engravings with those of the copy, the reader will find them reproduced in detail (*Figure 2b*).

2. In another case, weathering of the glass had loosened small particles from its surface. These particles are still firmly bound to the body of the dish, but the recognition of certain details has become rather difficult because of the refraction of light.

and the replica was made using a plaster copy of the original. This necessitated a good deal of extra work, but the result was very satisfactory (*Figure 7*).

The use of these materials thus enables a more satisfactory repair of damaged glass objects, and also the production of replicas of glass, ivory and objects made in similar materials. These replicas can be of great help in the study of such objects since they sometimes reveal details which cannot be seen clearly in photographs. Recently, experiments have been carried out with other materials, including other methacrylate

Figure 7. Copy of the Portland vase (reconstructed).

In the replica this refraction does not occur, so that the engravings on the replica can be seen more clearly than on the original.

3. In the making of the replica of the extremely delicate diatrete glass from Niederemmel in the Moselle valley (*Figure 3*), it was necessary for technical and other reasons to attempt a slightly different technique. First of all a model of the bowl of the glass (without the network) was formed free-hand instead of by the potter's wheel (*Figure 4*). From this the silicone rubber mould was made, and from this mould a replica in Technovit 4004A was cast. The network was incomplete, and of the 12 repeat patterns only three remained intact. A reproduction of these three repeat units was carefully made, using silicone rubber as the moulding material. Four sets of these repeat units were then prepared in Technovit 4004A so that the complete network could be reproduced (*Figure 5*). This was subsequently attached to the bowl of the glass to complete the replica (*Figure 6*).

4. In order to show what can be achieved by the use of these synthetic materials, I should like to mention the fact that it was possible to make a reproduction of the famous Portland vase. For obvious reasons it was not possible to obtain the vase itself,

resins and materials such as polyesters and epoxy resins. But they are not yet finished and only a few of them are encouraging. It is, however, worth mentioning that epoxy resins are extremely satisfactory as adhesives for the repair of ancient glass objects.

References

[1] Supplier: Roehm and Haas, Darmstadt, West Germany.
[2] Supplier: Kulzer and Co., Bad Homburg v.d.H., West Germany.
[3] Supplier: Kulzer and Co., Bad Homburg v.d.H., West Germany.
[4] Supplier: Farbwerke Hoechst, Frankfurt a.M., and Siegle and Co., Stuttgart-Feuerbach, West Germany.
[5] Silicone rubber hardness T or 'Giessmasse 56, lappig', Wacker-Chemie, Munich, Prinzregentenstr. 22.
[6] WIHR, R., Die Quellung von natürlichen und synthetischen Kautschukformen, *Z. Museumstech.*, 5 (1959) 2, 53–55.
[7] Supplier: Kautschuk-Gesellschaft, Frankfurt a.M., West Germany.
[8] Polyvinyl alcohol in water, or Trennlack F 86, Wolff-Chemie, Hamburg-Eidelstedt, West Germany.
[9] Toughened Wax, Amalgamated Dental Distributors Ltd., London, W.1.
[10] HUSSONG, L. and WIHR, R., *Trier. Z.*, 23 (1954/55) 231–238; *Dtsch. Kunst u. Denkmalpfl.*, 2 (1957) 137–145; *Z. Museumstech.*, 6 (1960) 1–11.

Richard D. Buck

SOME APPLICATIONS OF MECHANICS TO THE TREATMENT OF PANEL PAINTINGS

The treatment of panel paintings has always been and still is one of the most serious and baffling problems in the whole field of conservation. There is no need to present the evidence because it is so familiar. The problem has not been neglected. Great skills have been employed in the treatment of panel paintings. Treatment of many different kinds has been used. Panel paintings are coddled in their care. We recognize that they are inherently vulnerable to damage and must be treated rather like invalids in delicate health, likely to contract a mortal illness with any change in climate. Some museums have a policy that panel paintings are no longer available for loan exhibitions. Such attitudes reflect a general state of alarm regarding the care of panel paintings. If the margin of safety is low, may our methods of treatment be at fault? We cannot continue indefinitely to take chances with such an important part of our artistic heritage.

I want to suggest in this paper that there is still opportunity for improving our handling of panel problems, not so much in craftsmanship as in our general understanding of the mechanical behaviour of a painted panel, a very special field of mechanics. It is a field which the physicist or mechanical engineer would comprehend, but one in which it is probable that neither has had much experience nor given much thought. We may specify this field with a name, adopting a phrase suggested by Mr Ian Rawlins some years ago when he declared that our problem is one of 'picture mechanics'.

In inquiring into our special field we may find help from the paint technologist, but we must remember that his objective is to produce a coating to decorate and to protect a structure of wood. We may find help from the wood technologist and from the cabinet-maker, bearing in mind that these specialists also treat wood to preserve its structure. Our purpose is to treat an object of wood and paint primarily to preserve the paint. From our point of view, a panel painting is almost unique among artifacts because it is the paint, not the wood painted, which commands our attention. Towards this end we take measures to stabilize the shrinking and swelling of a wood support, to prevent splitting and disjoins and to reinforce a panel weakened by rot or insects. We may even discard the wood altogether and transfer the paint to a new support.

A secondary objective of treatment is to correct the warp of a wood panel. We shall find, I believe, that certain procedures used to control warp mechanically contradict our primary objective. We stand to profit if we review the mechanical implications of treatment to make sure that there is no confusion of purpose.

Let us first study the common defects of paint and wood panels to determine some of their mechanical causes.

Characteristic defects of paint

Let us, for the sake of simplicity, recognize that the ground layer and the paint layers are structurally similar, probably endowed with similar mechanical behaviour, and use the word 'paint' to include both paint and ground.

The most common defect of paint is crackle. This is most certainly induced by mechanical stresses, but because we find crackle in paint on any support we may conclude that the stresses to blame are inherent in the mechanical behaviour of paint. Similarly, cupped or curled paint islands, in which crackle edges are raised, are not restricted to paint supported by wood. These defects, therefore, may be dismissed from this discussion.

Buckled paint—that is, paint islands which are elevated into a tiny tent—a defect commonly called a blister, is another matter. Buckling is only rarely found in paint on other supports; it is a characteristic defect of panel painting. So also is flat or blind cleavage. This is a separation, usually between paint layers and support, and sometimes of considerable area, in a plane parallel to the paint. Often blind cleavage is not visibly evident either by a crack or an elevation, but is detected by sounding. It is serious because under aggravation the condition may lead to a large loss of paint. Neither buckling nor flat cleavage can be explained in terms of the inherent behaviour of paint. An external agency must be responsible.

If we take a typical cross-section through a panel painting, we have a layered structure of wood surmounted by several layers of paint. This is almost a textbook model for a study of shear stresses. The wood is an active material moving in a horizontal plane as it swells or shrinks. The paint, in another

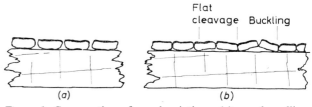

Figure 1. Cross-section of panel painting: (*a*) wood swelling; (*b*) wood shrinking.

parallel plane, is limited in its ability to accommodate movement. Thus we have forces in one plane opposed by forces in another plane of the same solid body. Except for the rigidity of the body, these forces would cause one layer to slip past the other in order to relieve the resulting stress. Physicists define the stress between two opposing forces acting in different parallel planes of a solid as a shearing stress. Much of the peculiar behaviour of panel paintings can be explained with reference to shear stress.

In a young film the paint may have enough elasticity and plasticity to yield to the movement of the wood without rupture. Shear stresses from the support will exist even if they are of low magnitudes, and they undoubtedly play some part in determining the pattern of the crackle system that develops as the paint itself ages and shrinks. In maturity the paint becomes more rigid, but it will have developed a craquelure and will have lost its continuity. If the supporting wood swells, the cracks between paint islands simply open up (*Figure 1a*). The paint can no longer oppose significantly the swelling forces in the wood, and shear stress in the paint will be small. However, when the wood shrinks below its normal dimensions, crackle apertures in the paint close to form a continuous train of paint islands adhering to the wood (*Figure 1b*). The paint, now a continuous structure, opposes further shrinking forces. At this point shear stresses rise rapidly with any increase of shrinking forces. Undoubtedly some of these stresses are absorbed by the elasticity and plasticity both of the paint layers above and the wood below. If the adhesive strength between paint layers and between paint and support is high, and if the cohesive strength within the layers is high, the paint may endure shear stresses of some magnitude without failure. This condition is one of potential danger, close to the threshold of rupture. If the threshold is exceeded, rupture may be expected in two ways. An adhesive bond may rupture, resulting in cleavage between two of the horizontal layers, usually between paint and support, to produce the condition we have defined as flat or blind cleavage. The compression may persist, causing an elevation of the detached paint which is commonly called a blister. The term buckling is preferred by some of us because it suggests that the rupture is caused by compressive stresses.

Buckling and flat cleavage are defects characteristic of paint on a wood support because wood is the only common support material that puts paint under large compressive forces.

If, like the expansion joints in a bridge, the crackle system acts to allow some tolerance of movement that would otherwise be destructive, it follows that the security of the paint layers requires that the crackle apertures be kept open. Any solid material which is permitted to fill the crackle apertures blocks this tolerance to some degree, and paint rupture from wood shrinkage may be expected sooner. Revarnishing, or varnishing a cleaned paint layer, must be carried out with this risk in mind. It is quite obvious that a thin plastic type of varnish is to be preferred to a thick brittle film which is capable of re-creating a continuous paint-varnish layer, intolerant to any movement.

Mechanical properties of wood

Before we are in a position to review the common defects of a wood support and to seek their mechanical causes, we should refer briefly to some of the mechanical properties of wood.

The basic material of all wood, regardless of species, is a surprisingly uniform combination of cellulose, hemicelluloses and lignin. These make up the solid substance of wood. Barkas[1], at whose feet we may sit with great profit, refers to this solid complex as gel material. Gel material is half again as heavy as water; weight for weight it is stronger than steel. On the other hand, it is a gel; it adsorbs and desorbs moisture along the interfaces of its internal elements. As a result, it shrinks and swells. It is variably elastic and plastic, depending on its moisture content. But gel material does not exist as an homogeneous solid. Wood may be thought of as a solid foam of gel material. If the voids are sparse and small, the wood will be hard and dense. There are tropical woods which even when dry will not float in water. Cutting a single plank from a log of rosewood may hopelessly dull an ordinary saw. A sequence of decreasing wood density and strength—such as oak, ash, chestnut, pine and spruce—follows a sequence of increasing void volume. Near the limit is balsa, in which the gel material exists only as a filmy structure of thin membranes. As cell walls become thinner, they may yield more easily under mechanical stress, or even collapse into the cell voids.

The cellular structure modifies the external dimensional stability of wood. Since it is the gel material and not the void

volume that swells, dense woods shrink and swell more than light woods. Moreover, the dense summer wood of a ring porous wood like oak swells more than the lighter spring wood. The variations of dimensional movement across each growth ring in a panel of oak may determine the orientation of crackle and other paint defects along the wood grain.

The terms elasticity and plasticity have been introduced[2]. These rheological terms need some explanation. An elastic body is one that spontaneously recovers its normal bulk or shape after any distortion by an external force. The purely elastic or recoverable component of any stress–strain behaviour is represented rheologically by a simple spring. The remarkable thing about a spring is not that it yields when a force is applied to it, but that it recovers its original shape and dimension after the load is removed, provided the force does not exceed the elastic limit of the spring material. The elasticity of wood is familiar to all of us. For instance, we may recall that the long-bow has had a profound influence on the course of history. It was the elastic recovery of wood that made the arrow such a deadly weapon. Having mentioned the bow, we may note further that a well maintained bow is unstressed when it is not in use. This precaution is taken because it has been observed that if the bow is stressed for a long period of time, it becomes permanently bent. It has not lost its elasticity, but it has been subject to plastic deformation.

Rheologists have used models to analyse such complex behaviour as that of the longbow[3]. What has been called the Maxwell body may help describe the behaviour, even though the analogy is not strictly accurate. The Maxwell body consists of a dashpot and a spring connected in series. A dashpot is a tube filled with a liquid in which a loosely fitted stopper can move as a piston. The dashpot illustrates viscous flow. The piston will move without accelerating at a rate proportional to the force applied to it. The piston stops and remains at rest when the force is removed and there is no recovery. Imagine that the dashpot of our Maxwell body is filled with a liquid of high viscosity, and that a relatively light spring is attached to the piston. If a small force pulls on the spring and is then released, the spring will stretch and return almost exactly to its original position. If a larger force is applied and held, the spring will extend, but now the piston may be detected moving slowly through its viscous medium. The distance moved by the dashpot piston depends not only on force but also on time. If the spring in our experiment were extended a certain distance and fastened, the piston will be pulled slowly through the dashpot until the spring has recovered from its distortion and the system comes to rest free of stress. The behaviour of the Maxwell body seems roughly parallel to that of wood under stress. It is thus that wood is both elastic and plastic.

It has been noted that the elastic and plastic properties of gel material vary with its moisture content. We know from common experience that wet wood is more plastic than dry wood. If wet wood is heated, plasticity is further increased. We may assume, then, that small changes in plasticity may result from small changes in the moisture content and temperature. These broad assumptions have been confirmed experimentally, but it is difficult to find quantitative data applying to our particular problem.

Elasticity of wood also varies with moisture content. Barkas gives approximate figures for the rigidity modulus—which is one of the elasticity coefficients—of gel material at equilibrium in various humidities[4]. These coefficients indicate that the force required to produce a certain elastic yield in extremely wet gel material must be increased as much as seven times to produce the same yield in extremely dry gel material.

Warping of wood

The main facts regarding the mechanism of swelling and shrinking are well known. There is a corollary of this phenomenon that may not be so well understood. It concerns the development of warp in wood. In order to analyse the forces at work in a piece of wood let us consider a block of wood in transverse cross-section.

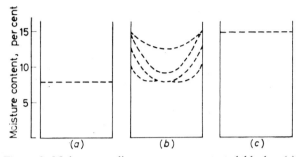

Figure 2. Moisture gradient curves, unprotected block: (*a*) equilibrium at 8 per cent moisture content; (*b*) swelling stages; (*c*) equilibrium at 15 per cent moisture content.

Assume that there is a uniform moisture content of about 8 per cent (*Figure 2a*). This would be normal for wood in equilibrium with an atmosphere about 42 per cent saturated. If the relative humidity were then raised to 80 per cent and held at that level for a prolonged period while moisture diffused completely through the block, the moisture content would rise to about 15 per cent and there would be swelling (*Figure 2c*). Let us represent the equilibrium moisture content throughout the block at the beginning and end of the experiment as two straight lines. These lines are referred to as moisture gradient curves. Between the start and finish, these curves will not be straight, but U-shaped (*Figure 2b*) because the exposed surfaces will absorb moisture first, and the core will be unaffected until moisture diffuses into the centre of the block. The U curve will become more and more shallow as the moisture content approaches the new equilibrium. During the experiment the wood will have swelled equally on each side without warping.

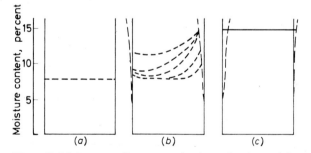

Figure 3. Moisture gradient curves (moisture barrier on left side); (*a*) equilibrium at 8 per cent moisture content; (*b*) swelling stages, showing temporary warp; (*c*) equilibrium at 15 per cent moisture content, showing permanent warp.

If we repeat the experiment with a similar block coated on one side with a moisture barrier material such as paint (*Figure 3a*), the moisture gradient will develop through a series of asymmetrical U-shaped curves, higher on the unprotected than on the protected side (*Figure 3b*). Eventually, when an equilibrium is established, the gradient will again be a straight line at the high level as before (*Figure 3c*). During the experiment,

however, the swelling forces on the unprotected side will be greater than on the other. The block will be subjected to complex shear stresses: major swelling on one side, restraint from the dry central mass, and minor swelling on the protected side. Being elastic, wood usually accommodates these stresses without rupture, but they do produce a temporary warp (*Figure 3b*). If wood were perfectly elastic, the warp would disappear when the gradient curve became flat at the new equilibrium moisture content; that is, there would be complete recovery. However, we have already recognized that wood is a plastic material. Its plasticity should be evident in the experiment. Under the shear stresses of swelling we have noted that the dry core of the block would restrain, to some degree, the swelling of the unprotected surface. Thus the core should have been under tension and the moist surface should have been under compression. If there was any plastic yield, it might be expected to be greater in the region of higher moisture content along the unprotected surface. The plastic yield might take place partly as deformation of cellular structure, and partly as slippage of crystallites in the gel material. Since there is no recovery from plastic yield, we might anticipate that when the final equilibrium was reached the wood would not only recover from its temporary concave warp at the painted side but would take on a slight permanent convex warp (*Figure 3c*). The shrinkage on the unprotected side illustrates a well-known phenomenon called compression shrinkage[5].

Presumably this sequence of events is not restricted to a theoretical experiment. We may infer that a panel painting unprotected at the back and passing through many swelling and shrinking cycles will accumulate these slight plastic deformations and develop a permanent warp, concave at the unprotected side. We know from our experience that panels do warp in this way. The mechanism described appears to be the explanation.

Let us consider briefly another variant of this experiment. Suppose our experimental block had moisture barriers on both sides, and that one was somewhat more effective than the other. Moisture barriers are not seals, but they retard the transfer of moisture to and from wood[6]. Under our experimental conditions we would expect to find our asymmetrical U-shaped gradient curve again, but because the surface transfer of moisture is retarded there is more time for the moisture to diffuse into the dry wood core. It follows that the moisture gradient curves would be shallow and that warping stresses would be slight.

We may make a final and very important deduction from our hypothetical experiments. A panel painting with an unprotected back will not shrink and swell in a simple lateral movement across the grain. In a moist atmosphere it will swell and at the same time warp, so that it is concave on the painted side. In a dry atmosphere it will shrink and warp, so that it is convex on the painted side. Actually, this is not in accordance with our usual observations. We are familiar with aged panels which already have developed a permanent convex warp at the painted side as a result of compression shrinkage. Therefore, what we observe in a moist atmosphere is general transverse swelling and some flattening of the permanent warp. In a dry atmosphere we find shrinkage and an aggravation of the convex warp. If we could speed up our observation by an elaborate time-lapse cinematic process, probably we should find that panels move with an awkward flapping motion.

Treatment of panel paintings

Let us now make a generalized application of these mechanical facts to the treatment of panel paintings. An examination

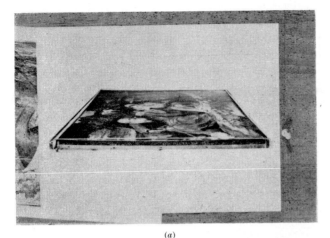

(a)

(c)

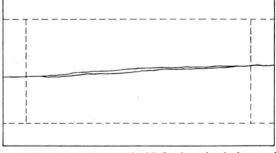

(b)

Figure 4. System of fixed mechanical restraint. Elastic and plastic strain caused by rigidly attached battens is demonstrated by behaviour of 16th century Venetian painting measuring about 66 × 95 × 1 cm. (*a*) Edge view showing concave warp. After removal of cross-battens panel resumed usual convex warp, showing that shear stresses between shrinking panel and rigid cross-battens must have been high, causing elastic yield of both panel and cross-battens. (*b*) Back of panel, showing battens. Note ruptures in lower part at different levels where tension stresses exceeded strength of the wood. (*c*) Front of panel, battens still attached, showing ruptures in wood, slight convex warp adjacent to ruptures, and no apparent rupture over regions supported by rigid battens. In these areas significant plastic strain must have occurred in addition to elastic strain already noted in (*a*). Negligible buckling of paint was observed, as might be expected in paint under tensile rather than compressive forces.

(By courtesy of the Fogg Museum of Art, Harvard University)

of three distinct mechanical systems will serve our purpose. These three systems may be specified by the measures taken to control warp.

Panels with no mechanical control

In the first group are panels with no mechanical restraint. Warp, if any, is accepted. In many cases the original panel has not been modified in any way. Neither has the frame been used as a restraining device by rigid mounting. By unlimited swelling and shrinking and by varying its warp without external control, the panel is free to adjust internal stresses arising from humidity variations. In many cases, provided the seasonal humidity variation is not extreme, the paint on unrestrained panels seems to tolerate the wood movement. Although buckling of paint and flat cleavage occur, there might be general agreement that the paint on unrestrained panels does not present the most desperate problems of conservation. For this reason, many prefer to avoid external interference with wood movement.

Panels with fixed mechanical control

The second group comprises panels with rigidly attached cross-members, such as adhered cross-battens or cross-grain panels in a built-up plywood type of construction (*Figure 4*). Attachment of battens by nails or screws is more common than by glue, but does not have quite the same mechanical effect because the attachment is intermittent. For conciseness in this discussion, intermittent attachment will not be considered.

Consider a panel with the back reinforced by rigidly adhered battens at all sides. This is a dangerous construction. Not only warping but shrinking and swelling are mechanically controlled. Although the normal shrinkage is impeded by the fixed battens, the panel is subjected to shrinkage stress. Under extreme stress the panel ruptures, and the stresses are relieved. I have had the opportunity of examining several panels split across in this way and have noticed an interesting peculiarity. In these cases, after the rigid battens were removed, it was not possible to fit the broken edges together again. When the parts were brought

Figure 5. Rupture in a panel with fixed mechanical control.

together, a good join was possible at the edges, the regions under direct restraint by the battens. But in the central part of the panel the wood had shrunk, so that there was an exasperating aperture between the broken parts (*Figure 5*). Such behaviour can be explained in this way: At the edges the battens opposed shrinkage continuously over the entire area of adhesion. The dimension of the panel must have been preserved by plastic yield in the wood. Both time and a slightly higher moisture content owing to the barrier effect of the batten provided conditions favouring deformation of the dashpot type. When the batten was removed there was negligible recovery of dimension. The wood had been stretched. This phenomenon has been demonstrated in the laboratory and is known as 'set in tension'[7]. In the centre of the panel the moisture content may have been lower, causing more tension than at the edges. Undoubtedly there was plastic deformation. But, lacking continuous support, certain regions of the wood capable of more than average elastic yield were allowed to move locally. Then, as a region of weakness developed, the yield must have been entirely elastic, so that after rupture there was an appreciable degree of elastic recovery. Here deformation was a combination of spring and dashpot types. Perhaps if the battens had covered the entire back of the panel, like the cross-grain core of plywood construction, even greater shrinkage stress might have been tolerated without rupture; but this is only speculation. Plywood construction does introduce another serious complication, however, that makes its use very questionable. The cross-grained core ply itself may tend to shrink. Then there are shrinkage forces at right angles. The shearing stresses often cause complex ploughshare twists and unusual warping that changes with varying humidity.

What is the effect of these tensions on the paint? The fact is that the wood has been almost completely stabilized dimensionally over the area reinforced by the adhered battens. While we cannot overlook the damage to paint caused by a split in the support, I think we would find that the occurrence of buckling and blind cleavage is low on these panels.

Panels with free mechanical control

The reference of this rather contradictory classification is to devices which control warp without direct rigid attachment. These devices include cradles (*Figure 6*) of all types, dovetailed battens, battens fixed with screws working in slots, and frames which are often used to hold a panel flat. The mechanical partner to such a device is a panel that is warped. If there is no inherent warp in the panel, the panel is mechanically relaxed and its behaviour is like that of the unrestrained panels, regardless of any external structure that may have been attached. There are many Northern European oak panels, particularly triptych wings painted on both sides, that appear to be relaxed in spite of the old engaged frames.

For discussion we refer to a warped panel flattened by a free mechanical control. The deceptive logic of this system is that linear swelling and shrinking are not restricted. The batten serves only to hold the panel flat. The warped panel may be flattened temporarily by swelling with moisture the partially collapsed wood on the back surface. It is at this stage that the controlling device may be attached. But when the wood dries, the panel may no longer return to its relaxed shape. It is under elastic strain just as a beam is strained when it is supported at each end and loaded in the middle. The panel may be regarded as composed of a number of transverse structural filaments, some of which are in tension, while others are under compression. A line near the centre of the panel keeps its original length and may be called the neutral axis. Because of the strain, the filaments on the back side of the neutral axis are lengthened and are in tension, while those on the front side are shortened and are under compression. The greater the distance of a filament from the neutral axis, the greater will be the filament

stress. This is a textbook analysis of elastic yield or strain. It is clear that the control device causes some compressive stress on the paint layers. Now, suppose that the humidity drops and the panel shrinks. A relaxed panel will shrink and the warp will tend to increase. With the free control device the normal shrinkage is not inhibited; but the increase in warp is restrained and translated into amplified compressive strains on the front sides, amplified tension on the back. We now have produced at the front of the panel compression that causes dangerous shear on the paint layers. The threshold of paint rupture may already have been exceeded. On the back surface of the panel, tension stresses may have equalled the breaking strength of the wood, causing checks and splits.

But wood is also subject to plastic deformation. If the stresses at the front side of the panel bring about plastic yield or cellular collapse, the shrinkage may exceed that of elastic strain alone. Therefore the stresses on the paint of a warped panel controlled by a free or movable mechanical device are equal to the sum of the normal stresses found in relaxed panels, plus the stress from elastic strain, plus the stress from plastic strain. The last two factors vary with the amount of restraining force applied.

Conclusions

We may compare these mechanical systems applied to warped panels as in *Table 1*.

Table 1

Comparison of mechanical systems applied to warped panels

Mechanical system	Security of paint	Security of panel	Appearance
No control	Fair—normal wood movement causes shear at low humidities	Good	Poor—warp is accepted
Fixed control	Good—panel mechanically stabilized, but with threat of rupture	Poor—tensions may cause open rupture	Good—barring panel rupture
Free control	Poor—shear from normal wood movement increased by elastic and plastic strain	Poor—stresses may cause cracks at the back, groins at the front	Good—barring panel rupture

Variants of these three mechanical systems underlie the treatment of a great many panel paintings. The analyses suggest the confusion of mechanical principles. The objectives of treatment have been ambiguous, with first attention given to reduction of warp. There is evidence that a wood panel and its associated paint have not consistently been regarded as parts of a single mechanical system in which each component presents problems that must be solved with reference to the other. Finally, we must admit that our knowledge of the mechanical behaviour of painted panels is still elementary.

Awareness of these shortcomings has directed some of us towards what may appear to be radical experimental treatment of panels[8]. In order to make a constructive suggestion I shall outline briefly an experimental direction that we have followed for a number of years. The purpose has been to improve the

Figure 6. System of free mechanical restraint. Elastic strain induced by a cradle is demonstrated, making use of a 13th century Italo-Byzantine painting measuring about 60 × 45 × 1 cm. (*a*) Cradled panel is loosely secured at left side against a flat board. The thread marks a warp about 1 mm deep. (*b*) Transverse cradle members are removed and elastic recovery is observed. Convex warp is now 5 mm. (*c*) Right side is loaded to bring warp back to 1 mm. Under humidity conditions prevailing at the time of demonstration the cradle appears to 'load' the panel by about 7·5 kg stress. This load may be assumed to increase or decrease inversely with variations of wood moisture content.

(By courtesy of the Fogg Museum of Art, Harvard University)

security of the paint without recourse to transfer or major alteration of the original panel. Not every panel painting is suitable. Structural defects in the paint layers must be traceable to the behaviour of the panel and not to weaknesses inherent in the paint. There must be a reasonable expectation that any loose paint can effectively be secured by treatment from the front of the panel. The warp, if any, must be moderate and not unacceptably disfiguring. After rejoining splits and checks, we try to establish a uniform moisture content of about 10 per cent. We then apply a layer of glass cloth in a solution of Saran resin, used both as an adhesive and as a moisture barrier. The glass cloth is one side of what is to be a supplementary skin-stressed panel. We next apply the bulk material of the panel. There are many light solid foams that might serve. We use balsa wood cut across the grain into manageable blocks. A wax-resin mortar is spooned onto a block which is set into place with hand pressure to extrude excess adhesive. No other heat or pressure is necessary. This bulking layer follows the warp of the original panel, and when finished the back is worked down to a flat surface. The layer may be 2 or 3 cm thick where the warp is deepest. The balsa wood is then covered with a strong fabric adhered with the wax-resin adhesive to complete the auxiliary panel. Panels of this type have been carefully measured in varying humidities and have been found to be quite inactive dimensionally.

In theory this treatment combines the favourable aspects of the relaxed panel with those of the system of fixed mechanical control. The supplementary panel contributes high moisture barrier efficiency to reduce the movement of the original support, and imposes some mechanical restraint to persistent swelling and shrinking. It stabilizes warp near the point of minimum normal strain. Although the applied panel has sufficient rigidity to serve its purpose, it possesses a degree of yield. The danger of panel rupture from the rigid control is not eliminated, though I believe it is not high. The paint on these partially stabilized panels has behaved well over periods ranging from 2 to 10 years. The treatment seems to show promise, but it is our conviction that it is an elementary exercise in picture mechanics, and that a higher degree of sophistication is possible.

The purpose of this paper is to emphasize the importance of the mechanical principles that control the behaviour of structures. Although mechanics is a venerable science, it is now being broadened and modified by such new branches as dynamics and rheology. Rheology, to which references have been made, is particularly appropriate in our study of the behaviour of liquids and solids. Consideration of the flow properties of materials and of the diffusion of gases and liquids through substances introduces another factor, time—time not measured in centuries, but in varying periods whose phases influence mechanical cause and effect in unexpected ways. If it is too early to make a rigid definition of picture mechanics, perhaps this discussion has presented some of its aspects. A deeper exploration of the field of picture mechanics should open the way to significant improvements in the conservation of many types of works of art.

References

[1] Barkas, W. W., *The Swelling of Wood under Stress*, H.M. Stationery Office, London, 1949.

[2] Rawlins, F. I. G., The rheology of painting, *Tech. Stud. fine Arts*, 10, No. 2 (1941) 59–72.

[3] Reiner, M., The flow of matter, *Sci. Amer.*, 20, No. 6 (1959) 122–138.

[4] Barkas W. W., reference 1, p. 57, Table 8.

[5] Tiemann, H. D., *Wood Technology*, Pitman Publishing Corporation, New York, 1944, p. 158.

[6] Buck, R. D., The use of moisture barriers on panel painting, *Stud. Conservation*, 6, No. 1 (1961) 9.

[7] Tiemann, H. D., reference 5, p. 161.

[8] Reduction of warp by plastic deformation is described in *Museum*, 8, No. 3 (1955) 158–9; also by J. Brachert, *Gemäldepflege*, Otto Maier Verlag, Ravensburg, 1955, pp. 12–13. What appears to be the intentional use of plastic rather than elastic deformation in reducing warp is a departure from traditional practice. Whether this method puts paint under less compression than the system of elastic deformation depends on the location of the neutral axis of stress within the panel.

Christian Wolters

TREATMENT OF WARPED WOOD PANELS BY PLASTIC DEFORMATION; MOISTURE BARRIERS; AND ELASTIC SUPPORT

It is well known that wood panels with severe permanent warping cannot be put in cradles. Up to now the only solution has been, as a last resort, to transfer the painting to a new support. We began experiments about seven years ago in the Doerner-Institut on swelling, impregnating and sealing the back of the panel (see *Museum*, 8, No. 3 (1955) 155–158). We paid particular attention to the extreme cases of excessive curvature which occur when, for reasons of conservation (blistering of the paint layer, splits in the support), old cradles have to be removed; that is, those in which a painting had been cradled in order to straighten a particularly severe permanent warp. After a series of experiments the methods described below at first proved successful.

Swelling in an approximately 7·5 per cent solution of shellac in equal parts of ethyl alcohol and ethylene glycol: The panels are coated repeatedly with this shellac solution on the concave reverse side over a period of days, and in many cases weeks, and covered with oiled paper* until a sufficiently stable degree of straightening is obtained. Generally an application of a 25–30 per cent shellac solution in ethyl alcohol is used as a moisture barrier.

It was found possible to improve cases which appeared hopeless to such an extent that the remaining curvature was tolerable. However, complete straightening was never achieved, but merely a permanent reduction of about 50–70 per cent in the curvature, as care was taken not to subject the panels to too great a strain. No changes in the ground and paint layers, such as blistering or a decrease in the adhesive strength, were observed. We started from the supposition that, in order to achieve permanent straightening by plastic deformation, a solid (such as a resin) should be introduced with the swelling agent. Excellent practical results at first appeared to confirm this idea. However, the following experiments show that this is not right.

Specimens of spruce and oak wood were treated with the above-mentioned shellac solution under the same conditions as wood panels. After splitting the 15-mm thick pieces of wood the average depth of penetration was found to be from 0·15 to 0·25 mm. No greater depth of penetration could be achieved with pure ethyl alcohol. Therefore swelling cannot be caused by direct infiltration of liquid into the wood, nor can such a thin layer of shellac hold the panel straight mechanically. It is, on the contrary, the vapour from the liquid which penetrates the microscopic and submicroscopic openings and capillaries in the wood and causes the cell walls to swell. Water and alcohol vapour are partly absorbed chemically and partly merely physically. However, the vapour can condense into liquid again in the capillaries (capillary condensation).

Healthy wood can normally absorb liquid only on the faces, along the vessels. However, wood that has been eaten away by pests or attacked by dry rot can easily absorb liquid and can

therefore be stabilized and even held straight by dissolved solids (synthetic resins, resins, waxes and plastics). It is therefore possible to separate the swelling process from the application of the moisture barrier. There would then be freedom of choice for swelling agents and insulating materials. Experiments in this direction indicate that the success of the straightening operation is dependent on the length of the swelling process. Wood specimens which were severely warped in a short time show a considerably more rapid correction of the curvature than specimens subjected to a slower swelling process. Wood may, of course, be deformed plastically as well as elastically. The plasticity of swollen wood is greater, and this quality plays a part in the industrial heat processing of wood. We do not yet know on what the effect of the time factor is dependent, but it is possible that during a swelling process lasting for a longer period there occur fatigue phenomena and permanent variations in form which could be used to advantage in straightening panels.

In *Studies in Conservation*, 6, No. 1 (1961) 9 ff., R. D. Buck reported on the use of moisture barriers on wood panel paintings. He showed that they neither prevent nor even reduce the shrinking and swelling of panel paintings, but that they considerably retard the rate of moisture transfer between wood and its surroundings; that is, the panels are well insulated against short variations in atmosphere lasting up to a few days, but not against longer ones.

He listed the following factors which influence the rate of moisture transfer:

1. The type of wood.
2. The ratio of the surface area of the wood exposed to the atmosphere to the volume of the wood—a thin panel is therefore more sensitive than a thicker one.
3. The temperature—the higher the temperature, the more rapid the rate of moisture transfer to the surroundings.
4. The extent of the variations in moisture in the air surrounding the panel—the greater the change in relative humidity, the more rapid the rate of moisture transfer.
5. The type of moisture barrier (the type of material coating or covering the panel, the way it is applied and the thickness of the layer).

Buck investigated the effectiveness of aluminium paint, a coat of wax solution, and wax applied hot and infused. We continued these experiments with some other materials.

Pieces of spruce and oak wood, 6·5 × 5 cm in size and 1·5 cm thick, were covered or coated all round, with the exception of the faces, with the materials listed in *Table 1*. The pieces of wood were weighed before and ten days after being coated (after this period the weight of the specimens was more or less constant). The difference between the two weighings gave the weight of the coating. The weight of the coating per square centimetre of surface area was calculated from the predetermined surface area of the wooden blocks and the weight of the

---

* This is to prevent the solution from evaporating too quickly.

Table 1
Weight increase of coated wooden blocks in humidity cabinet

	Weight of coating (after 10 days at 38% relative humidity) (mg/cm²)		Percentage weight increase after 2 days at 87% relative humidity	
	Spruce	Oak	Spruce	Oak
Beeswax introduced with infra-red lamps; surface cleaned with white spirit	4·1	4·5	0·5	0·5
Beeswax introduced with infra-red lamps; surface not cleaned	6·0	8·5	0·1	0·1
Beeswax ironed in; surface cleaned with white spirit	4·5	5·3	0·6	0·4
Beeswax ironed in; surface not cleaned	6·5	7·7	0·09	0·07
33% solution of beeswax in white spirit	0·1	0·1	0·3	0·4
33% solution of dammar in white spirit	0·7	0·7	0·9	0·8
Floor-sealing varnish (made by Messrs Flamuco)				
2 coats	2·7	2·8	0·3	0·3
4 coats	9·4	9·4	0·2	0·2
6 coats	15·1	13·8	0·1	0·1
Self-adhesive PVC foil, 0·08 mm	14·1	14·1	0·1	0·1
Impregnation with shellac solution	6·5	5·5	0·6	0·6
Impregnated and surface sealed with concentrated shellac solution	13·0	9·3	0·1	0·2
Impregnation with shellac solution: 3 weeks under ultra-violet light	7·0	7·0	5·5	3·8
Impregnation and surface sealed with concentrated shellac solution; 3 weeks under ultra-violet light	11·5	11·3	1·26	0·9
Linseed-oil varnish with drier	6·1	5·5	1·1	1·1
Linseed-oil varnish with drier and red lead	29·9	31·0	0·6	0·6
Linseed oil varnish with drier and red iron oxide	12·6	10·9	0·8	0·9
No coating			**6·1**	**4·4**

total coating. As the specific weights of the dry coatings were not known, the thickness of the layer could not be calculated, but this would in any case represent a purely theoretical value, since wood does not have as even a surface as glass, for example, and the coating material penetrates the surface to an irregular depth.

Once the wood was dry, the faces of the wooden blocks were sealed by being dipped in melted sealing-wax. The layer of sealing-wax was approximately 3 mm thick and covered the surface of the blocks for about 5 mm from the edge. Thus a transfer of moisture through the face of the wood was prevented to a large extent. The sealed blocks of wood, which had formerly been stored at 38 per cent relative humidity, were then weighed and placed in a humidity cabinet at 87 per cent relative humidity for two days (the temperature was maintained constant at 22°C).

As the above-mentioned factors 1–4, which influence the rate of moisture transfer, were kept constant and all specimens were kept in the humidity cabinet for the same length of time, i.e. 2 days, the weight increase of the blocks of wood gives a direct indication of the effectiveness of the coatings as moisture barriers. In *Table 1* the increase in weight is expressed as a percentage. It therefore follows that the greater the percentage increase in the weight of the wood, the less effective is the corresponding coating as a moisture barrier.

It can be seen that beeswax melted into the surface of the wood with infra-red lamps or with an iron, six coats of floor-sealing varnish, 0·08-mm thick PVC foil and resealing with concentrated shellac solution provide the most effective moisture barriers. If the surface of the wood coated with beeswax applied hot is washed with white spirit, the barrier effect is diminished about five or sixfold. Even a 33 per cent beeswax solution in white spirit applied to the wood proved only about one third as effective as beeswax applied hot and equalled approximately two coats of floor-sealing varnish. Coatings of unpigmented linseed-oil varnish, linseed-oil varnish with red lead, linseed-oil varnish with red iron oxide and a 33 per cent solution of dammar in white spirit let in 6–11 times more moisture in the same period as beeswax applied hot. Wax, shellac, floor-sealing varnish and PVC foil, the most effective barriers, reduce the transfer of moisture under the given experimental conditions, i.e. within the first two days, by 97–98 per cent in comparison with untreated wood.

As an elastic mechanical support for endangered panel paintings—particularly those pictures treated in accordance with the process described above—we use a type of frame support, as described in *Museum*, 8, No. 3 (1955) 178–179. According to the condition of the panel extra batten supports can be used, adapted to the curvature of the panel. This process, by means of a layer of synthetic foam and flexible steel springs, ensures that the panel has a limited elastic possibility of warping and full freedom to expand. An elastic frame support with corresponding mechanical supports, therefore, to a certain extent has the advantages of a cradle without its possible dangers.

A. W. Lucas

THE TRANSFER OF EASEL PAINTINGS

The transfer of a painting from its original support to a new one is not undertaken lightly at the National Gallery. Everything that can be done to make the transfer unnecessary is done or tried first.

Necessity for a transfer

There are four main maladies which necessitate the transfer of a painting from its original support:

1. Deterioration of the support itself.
2. Disintegration of one or all of the layers.
3. Lack of adhesion between the panel and ground or between the ground and support.
4. A badly designed wooden panel in which the grains of the wooden members are joined in such a way that they work against each other and crack.

Supports

The basic material of supports, until the recent introduction of man-made fibres, has been cellulose in some natural form. This cellulose is subject to deterioration resulting from attack by infestations of bacteria, fungi and vegetable parasites, insects and their works, and chemical rot such as deterioration with age. When the wooden supports are no longer strong enough to support the ground and paint it is best to transfer the painting to a new support, as the wood has usually been destroyed just underneath the ground by worm channelling or dry rot, or both acting together, although the exposed surface may appear to be in sound condition. Experience has shown that impregnating such panels with wax resin or lacquers is unsatisfactory because of poor penetration owing to airlocks in the worm cavities and poor wetting of the cement to the wood remains.

Canvas, when in a rotten state, absorbs adhesives and molten wax resins easily before lining so that its complete removal is not necessary in most cases. There is only the need to complete the removal of the original canvas when there is an objectionable layer between the paint film and the canvas, such as a thick layer of glue size which has become very brittle and is breaking up the paint film.

Grounds

The deterioration of grounds varies somewhat with the materials used. Aqueous glue grounds are attacked by bacteria which find sustenance from glue medium and chalk or gypsum fillers. Egg emulsion, egg and oil and aqueous glue with oil emulsion seem more susceptible to fungal attack.

Drying oil, drying oil plus resin and drying oil with siccatives break down chemically and become granular with age. Where white lead has been used as the basic filler and an excess of siccative added, the breaking down of the ground into a granular state is often quite rapid—within six to ten years. In oil grounds where a large proportion of ochre has been used to colour the ground, powdering of the ground takes place.

Lack of adhesion

Lack of adhesion between various layers is due to faulty technique or the application or use of unsuitable materials. A heavy layer of aqueous glue size presents an unsympathetic surface, as does an oil or resin varnish layer. The excessive use of saponifying agents produces a greasy surface which makes satisfactory adhesion impossible. Saponifying agents do not always prevent an oil ground from becoming granular.

Paint layer

All the various causes of the deterioration of grounds which have been mentioned can occur in the paint film. If deterioration has taken place in the upper paint layers it can be treated from the front but if deterioration has taken place in the layers near the ground a transfer is usually necessary in order to get at the offensive layer. If there is deterioration in all layers it must be considered that it is impossible to transfer the painting at all and it must be stored either on or off exhibition in such a way that the least harm can come to it through falling or loose paint. In any case it would be necessary to make some attempt to stick the upper layers together. The danger in attempting to transfer a painting where many layers of paint are detached from one another is that it is likely that some of the underlayers will be lost and this would affect the colours and design of the painting. Coloured grounds are fairly easily matched in colour but retouching under-painting accurately from the rear would be extremely difficult.

Cases of poor adhesion between the paint and the ground or the ground and support can often be improved by removing the ground and replacing it with one which is more compatible with the paint; for example, a hard aqueous glue ground with a greasy oil paint on it replaced with an oil lead ground. It is simply hydrophobic to hydrophobic and hydrophilic to hydrophilic in most cases. Washing exposed greasy surfaces with petroleum ether or similar fairly volatile degreasing agents helps to improve bonding. Where there is a hard aqueous glue film which is sticking well to the ground but not to the support it should be reduced in thickness by carefully washing with hot water; during the final washing calcium carbonate or fine pumice powder can be washed in to make a rough surface, to aid bonding with the new support.

Methods of transferring wood panels

The term 'transfer' should mean a complete removal of the original support and the paint or paint plus ground transferred to a new support; but semi-transfers, which we have found very satisfactory, can be carried out with wooden panels if they are of soft wood not less than 1 cm or of hard wood 5 mm or more and where the defects are only bad warping and cracking. This is best done by first flattening the panel by exposing the back of it to moisture from wet cloths. When flat, all objects which restrict the natural movement of the panel, such as cradles, cross-battens, keys and buttons, should be removed; the panel should be reduced by approximately one fifth of its thickness.

This removes the collapsed wood cells which are damaged beyond repair. The freshly exposed wood should be kept covered as much as possible; rubber mats are suitable for this purpose. Now a scrim (a coarse net-like material usually made of jute fibre) is stuck on with an adhesive composed of 3 parts dammar resin, 2 parts beeswax with a filler of 3 parts volume powdered chalk (calcium carbonate). Two layers of balsa wood about 8 to 10 mm thick, the first layer with the grain of the panel and the second layer across the grain at 90°, are stuck on with the same wax-resin-chalk cement.

The balsa wood is stuck down in individual strips about 1 m long and 10 cm wide by pouring sufficient molten wax-resin cement in the position where the balsa wood is to be fixed. The board is pressed into the hot wax resin, extruding the cement while holding it there until the cement sets, which takes about two or three minutes. The balsa is finally trimmed and covered with canvas stuck down with the same wax-resin cement. The side edges can be covered with thin strips of oak fastened by brass or copper screws into the balsa.

It is undesirable to reduce the original panel to less than 1 cm for soft woods and 5 mm for hard woods. The thinner a piece of wood is made the more active it becomes to relative humidity changes and age shrinkage; the likelihood of cracking becomes greater as it loses constructional strength at a greater rate relative to shrinking and swelling strength. If a panel has to be thinned within the limits of the dimensions stated it is better to remove the wood completely, as even the thinnest layer exerts considerable force with moisture changes.

Removal of wood from paint

Before work is started on the back of a panel all paint blisters must be secured down and the painted surface faced with a protecting temporary support.

Two types of facing can be used which vary in strength. Strongly sticking facings are not always necessary for minor work such as a semi-transfer or transfer of an early Italian School painting which would be on a thick gesso. Mulberry paper is used fixed down with a mixture of 3 parts dammar resin to 2 parts of beeswax dissolved in a second mixture of turpentine containing 50 per cent mastic. This mixture should form a thick cream at room temperature, but should brush out thinly. It can be applied onto the tissue paper and rubbed through to the varnish or painted surface of the picture. Two layers of tissue paper can be applied, but it is best to let the first layer dry for 24 hours before putting on the second. Another 24 hours will be needed for drying before work can be started. This facing will stand up to a considerable amount of heat—in fact, as much as most types of paint can stand.

A much stronger facing can be made by sticking the mulberry paper down with strong mastic varnish, 60 per cent mastic in turpentine with 5 per cent stand oil and 2 per cent beeswax. Mastic has extraordinary sticking power when a small amount of stand oil is added.

Both these facings can be removed easily without damaging natural varnishes if they are more than two years old. They withstand water if it is necessary to use it when scraping away a gesso ground or when using excessive moisture to flatten a warped wooden panel. They are extremely flexible and do not contract much on drying so that there is very little tension on the front of the painting. Aqueous glues tend to contract considerably on drying, so causing severe strain. When an oil painting is unvarnished and it is desirable to keep that appearance, most of the resin-wax facing can be easily removed with turpentine; the remains can be made to disappear by spraying on a thin coat of matt varnish, which will give some protection to the paint.

For facing a painting where the varnish would soak in and discolour the paint, the paint can be sealed first with thin coats of sodium carboxymethylcellulose; then the tissue can be stuck down with a weak solution of gelatine. Great care must be taken when removing the tissue if the paint is powdering. Some of the sodium carboxymethylcellulose can be left on as it has very little varnishing power (changing the tone values of darker paints and making them darker) and also affords the paint surface some protection.

Starch and dextrin adhesives stick very well, but they are very difficult to remove if the facing has been heated by ironing or by a hot table, especially if oil has been emulsified into it. The addition of sugar in some form improves the solubility after baking but weakens the facing when excessive moisture has to be used during the transferring operation. Polymethacrylates tend to shell off when moisture is used and when the paint surface is greasy, and have been found unreliable. Polyvinyl acetate is unreliable if greasiness is present and needs considerable amounts of solvent to wash it off; this also applies to the polymethacrylates.

Removal of wood

Orthodox methods are used when cutting away the wood. A power plane making 18,000 cuts per minute is used to cut down to within 5 mm of the ground. The vibration caused by the power plane seems to have very little effect on loose flaking paint if there is a satisfactory facing, especially if there is a thick layer of wax covering the facing. If the paint is extremely loose and fragile a thick layer of wax can be built up on a cold hot-table by brushing on hot wax, and with a similar layer on the facing the two wax surfaces are then pressed together when the hot-table is slightly heated to 10°C and then raised to 21°C for a short period to fuse the wax. The table is cooled and then the picture is well secured. Of course, to release the painting after the treatment the hot-table is quickly heated and when the wax is soft enough the painting can be slid off sideways.

The remaining 5 mm of wood are best taken away with gouges, cutting flutes with the grain; first with a 2-cm wide gouge cutting the deepest part of each flute to 3 mm in 4 or 5 cuts, then cutting away the highest parts of the flutes, levelling off so that the number of flutes is doubled and the cuts are shallower. The flutes are now deepened with a 1-cm gouge to about 1·5 mm; then again the highest parts are removed, doubling the flutes, leaving about 5 mm of wood. This operation is repeated again with a 5-mm gouge so that there is only a very thin veneer of wood and in the deepest part of the flutes the ground can be seen. The remaining wood can then be removed with a small gouge cutting at 30° obliquely to the flutes. The remaining wood fibres can be scraped away with a sharp knife after making the knife and the ground damp. It is important to keep the cutting even in depth and the fluting neat, and it is very important to keep the gouges as sharp as possible. In fact, one should not attempt to carry out a transfer until the tempering and sharpening of cutting tools has been mastered. With really sharp cutting tools very little downward pressure is required, none at all when cutting with the smallest gouges. There is also less likelihood of lifting out shakes and knots which have paint on them. Use of a mallet is unnecessary, as hammering sets up violent vibration strains.

The newly exposed wood and gesso surfaces should be prevented from curling up with loss of moisture by covering with thick rubber mats. It has been found unsatisfactory to increase the relative humidity of the workroom in order to prevent curling by loss of moisture from wood and gesso. To be successful the humidity has to be raised to 100 per cent at quite a high temperature, and this damages tools and equipment. On the other hand, the relative humidity should not be allowed to fall below 50 per cent at 65°F, or curling will start on the areas of wood or gesso exposed from the rubber mats for working on. Between 55 and 60 per cent relative humidity at 65°F seems quite satisfactory.

Removal of grounds

The various types of ground can be simply divided into oil and aqueous glue grounds. Oil grounds are rarely met with on old wood panels, but mostly on canvas, so that Italian gesso grounds are the commonest to be treated. The chalk grounds of the Northern Schools seem to have survived rather better, though they do need removing from time to time. The wood is, as a rule, oak for the Northern Schools and poplar for the Italian Schools. Oak, although much harder than poplar, cuts clean and is easier to control. Chalk grounds are very much thinner and harder in general than gesso but the method of removal is the same. The method of removing an aqueous glue ground is simple, but needs a certain amount of skill. Aqueous glue grounds become soft when made moist. If the ground is made slightly damp so that the moisture only penetrates a short distance below the surface—say, a fraction of a millimetre—this thin layer can be scraped off by holding the knife blade at 90° to the ground. The degree of damping controls the depth of the amount scraped away at one time. Chalk grounds tend to absorb more water, tending to blister up, but this can be controlled best by diluting the water in alcohol. Some practice should be gained on worthless samples or even on newly prepared grounds.

Oil grounds

Oil grounds are best left on if they are only loose in places, but if very loose they usually flake away in brittle sheets when a very thin-bladed knife is used. Where the ground is loose in places the loose parts can be stuck back to the back of the paint layer with weak gelatine solution, which can be soaked in more vigorously from the back. If the oil ground is a modern commercial undercoat paint which has become granular, lining wax-resin can be well ironed in and the painting secured to the new support with the same medium. In some experimental tests softening oil grounds with solvents was found to be too uncontrollable to warrant their use on actual paintings.

Regrounding paint films

The most successful method, both in practice and experiment, is to use a gesso-type ground secured to a ridged-type support with wax resin. The gesso ground, if properly prepared and applied, sticks well to all types of paint. Nearly all paint films, especially oil paints, are sensitive to heat buckling, wrinkling and folding, even when secured down well to a heavy facing. The regrounding with oil and lead, where oil is the principal binding medium, has the disadvantage of remaining in an unstable state for a long time. Wax-resin, used as a binding medium with fillers and colorants, usually must be applied at a temperature of at least 21°C for good adhesion, and this is above the temperature when oil paint starts to expand and cause trouble (about 25°C).

The process of repriming with gesso is as follows:

(a) Ensure that there is no layer of powdering ground or soft sludge left anywhere.

(b) Ensure that the back of the paint film is sound and not blistering or powdering, for it is much easier to treat from the back than from the front later, nor can it be expected that the

medium from the new ground will feed and overcome such defects.

(c) Apply a thin mixture of 10 per cent by weight of either dry gelatine or parchment glue dissolved in water plus 5 per cent calcium carbonate dihydrate and 5 per cent calcium carbonate (two inert fillers of different particle size to give a good key to the paint surface and to improve the wetting of the size layer). This mixture is applied very thinly at just above melting point. When just dry, thick cartridge paper is laid on and the rubber mats are replaced and left to dry for about 24 hours. Such glue films appear dry in a few minutes but are not hard dry until some hours have passed. When hard, the size takes up most of the moisture from the next thick coat of gesso, so easing the strain on the paint film.

(d) Apply the gesso. A gesso is made by mixing a solution of 15 per cent parchment of rabbit-skin glue dissolved in water plus calcium sulphate dihydrate pressed down tightly in a measuring vessel to make an equal volume to that of glue-water. This mixture should be made up at just about the melting point of the glue-water and a thin coat brushed on just sufficient to be opaque when dry. If the original ground was toned or had a coloured imprimature both the size layer and this opaque layer of gesso should be tinted to match. For a colour match between new and old gesso the new gesso has to match in its dry state.

The gesso mixture is kept constant throughout the five layers needed to build a thickness of 2·5 mm. After the third layer fine Terylene bolting cloth is laid onto the three coats and then the fourth coat is laid on through it to help stick and bed it down. The Terylene bolting does not distort very much when made wet and so does not wrinkle; it does, however, rise up in places and here the Terylene can be rubbed down with the finger into the setting gesso. If any blisters are found when the fourth layer of gesso has dried, a little wet gesso rubbed in quickly secures the loose places.

The fifth coat of gesso should cover the Terylene bolting cloth, so encasing it. Great care should be taken to keep all layers of gesso fairly smooth, though slight brush strokes do not matter. If the gesso becomes uneven through lack of skill in applying it, it can be sandpapered gently smooth, but the dust made must be wiped off with a damp cloth before proceeding with another coat of gesso. It is not necessary to put on a gesso grosso (hard gesso). Twenty-four hours at least should elapse between each layer, and each should be treated in the same way as for the sizing, using fresh or completely dry cartridge paper every time to absorb the excess moisture while the rubber mats are on.

The reinforced gesso, although brittle, will be a stronger bed for the paint layer and will withstand most glues, including the polyester resin types such as Araldite and phenol formaldehyde or polyurethane pastes, since active hardeners will not be able to penetrate through the gesso and dissolve the paint. Although these adhesives have been found to work very satisfactorily in tests, wax-resin cement has been used mostly in practice.

The support and the back of the new gesso are given a coat of wax-resin. Then these two surfaces are put together and ironed from the front, the paint films no longer being sensitive to heat once the gesso is on. This method seems to be the easiest in application, and the painting can easily be released from the support by the application of heat if necessary. The wax can be scraped from the gesso and the gesso can be washed off.

Supports

Because the main defect in paint which makes a transfer necessary is brittleness, a rigid support is more desirable than a flexible one like canvas. The rigid support gives great latitude in the harness of the paint film ground and prevents stress owing to lateral contraction.

A semi-hardboard made of oil-bound paper fibres such as 'Sundeala' board has been found satisfactory. It absorbs adhesives well and is soft enough to be cut away easily. It can be reinforced at the back with light bulk materials such as expanded paper or expanded polystyrene so that the boards can easily be joined for very large paintings and yet be very light in weight. At the National Gallery we have used 'Dufaylite', which is expanded paper sandwiched between the Sundeala and hardboard, all glued together with Araldite. Araldite contains about 15 per cent toluene, which facilitates the spreading of this glue. After using the Araldite plus toluene it must be left for an hour or so to allow the toluene to evaporate. The edges of such panels must be protected with well-seasoned hardwood about 1 cm thick; the hardboard and wood are then sealed with polyurethane paints and varnish.

Conclusion

In this paper I have described briefly a few of the methods used in the National Gallery over the last fifteen years. I am sure that colleagues who carry out this work use other methods and materials successfully. Skill of application and full understanding of the properties of the materials used are the most important factors for making a successful transfer. A survey of the 41 paintings which have been transferred in the National Gallery—some of them were treated more than 150 years ago—showed that some paintings have given constant trouble with flaking and blistering while others have remained remarkably stable; yet the materials and methods, as far as one can tell, have been the same. Thirty paintings have been transferred from wood to canvas using bone glue, starch paste and Venetian turpentine. There are two or three layers of canvas on most with heavy layers of the glue mixture between them, making a hard, stiff support which has, in most cases, buckled unevenly. Those which have been transferred onto a rigid support have a more natural appearance than those transferred onto canvas. Where paintings have had to be re-transferred, the removal of the thick hard glue has been a very long and tedious job. The need for re-transfer has been caused by the canvas and glue layer contracting by aging, so forcing the paint and ground away from the canvas. These serious defects in the aqueous glue and canvas method for transfer have encouraged experiments to evolve the methods described.

G. Urbani

LA CONSERVATION DES PEINTURES SUR PANNEAUX

Je voudrais tout d'abord exprimer mon admiration pour le rapport de M. Buck (voir p. 156); sa contribution à la connaissance des problèmes relatifs à la conservation des peintures sur panneaux me parait être de celles qui ne se limitent pas à des éclaircissements en marge de données techniques déjà connues, mais elle renouvelle radicalement le mode d'approche de la question.

Jusqu'ici la mécanique du bois n'avait jamais été étudiée et décrite avec la clarté de M. Buck, et il est facile de prévoir que dorénavant on ne pourra pas reconsidérer le problème autrement que sur la trace qu'il nous a donnée. C'est justement sur cette trace que je voudrais proposer quelques questions de détail et d'autres de caractère plus général, qui ne touchent pas à la substance de l'exposé de M. Buck, mais qui, d'une certaine façon, en cherchent les incidences concrètes qu'elle peut avoir sur le plan pratique.

La première conclusion à laquelle me semble conduire le complexe de notions nouvelles que nous devons à M. Buck est qu'une peinture sur panneau de bois, pour se conserver de la meilleure façon possible, devrait être placée dans les conditions d'immobilité quasi absolue. Comment ces conditions peuvent elles être réalisées? M. Buck nous propose un système, qui me semble être déduit de celui que j'ai vu appliqué en diverses occasions en Angleterre et même en Amérique, et dont M. Lucas (voir p. 165) nous a fait une minutieuse description.

Le système proposé par M. Lucas, bien qu'il l'appelle semi-transposition (semi-transfert), équivaut pratiquement à une transposition de couleur. Le panneau, réduit à une épaisseur minime, est isolé et en même temps soutenu par une structure qui ne ressent pas les variations d'humidité. Je n'ai rien à redire à la composition de cette structure et sur les résultats atteints. Je suis convaincu que la couleur resistera sur le nouveau support beaucoup mieux qu'avant. Je me demande seulement en quoi cette solution diffère d'une transposition, qui offrirait une garantie de réussite au moins égale, si non supérieure, du fait de la totale élimination du bois. Il est évident que dans le système proposé par M. Lucas ne jouent pas seulement des considérations techniques, qui porteraient, sans aucun doute, en théorie comme en pratique, à préférer la solution plus radicale de la transposition. Si donc on préfère une solution qui du point de vue technique est décidément ambigue, c'est parce qu'on attache à la conservation partielle du bois une valeur pour ainsi dire historique; valeur à sauvegarder même contre les exigences de la technique, comme témoin de ce qu'était la structure originelle du panneau. Du reste, quelque chose de ce genre transparait dans la forme même adoptée pour le nouveau support en balsa et résine. En volume et dimensions celui-ci equivaut exactement à un vieux support de bois, alors que pour la fonction qu'il remplit il aurait pu très bien se réduire à une mince plaque de résine. Je ne critiquerait certes pas le sain principe de respect qui, d'une façon pour ainsi quasi-inconsciente, a guidé ceux qui ont conçu ce type de support, me bornant seulement à constater qu'ils ont adopté un tel principe de manière plutôt formelle que technique. La faible épaisseur de bois ancien qui subsiste entre la couleur et le nouveau support est devenue, si vous me permettez

l'expression, une sorte de «corps mystique» ou une relique sans aucune fonction structurale; d'autre part, le nouveau support de balsa a une fonction en excès: celle de figurer comme un symbole du vieux support de bois.

Si nous passons du système Lucas au système Buck, nous voyons que le principe du respect du vieux support a acquis une majeure importance. Le bois conserve son épaisseur originelle mais il est complètement couvert et caché par la nouvelle structure de balsa. Celle-ci développe une fonction surtout isolante, car je crois, et nous le dirons plus avant, que la fonction de contrainte des mouvements du vieux bois est assez relative et en principe dangereuse. Du point de vue technique ce système remplit beaucoup mieux que le système Lucas la fonction de protéger et de conserver la structure originelle du support, mais il cache cette structure, il la rend invisible et surtout s'incorpore à elle d'une façon tellement stricte que, certes, on ne pourra plus le retirer ou substituer sans grave préjudice de l'intégrité du vieux bois.

Il me semble donc qu'une première conclusion devrait être claire: si nous attachons une valeur culturelle non seulement à l'oeuvre d'art en soi, mais également à sa structure originelle, il nous faut envisager le problème de la conservation de cette structure d'un point de vue strictement technique, et non idéaliste—comme il est un peu envisagé soit par M. Buck que par M. Lucas.

Quelle serait donc la solution rigoureusement technique? Elle est qu'il faut arriver (sauf dans les cas très rares qui rendent indispensable la transposition) à éliminer les dommages produits par le support original sur la couche picturale, en conservant ce support dans son intégrité, sans le détruire ou l'altérer, d'une façon qui pratiquement équivaudrait à une destruction.

Sans prétendre suggérer concrètement tous les procédés techniques que l'on peut adopter à cette fin, il me semble que l'on peut dès maintenant esquisser les différentes voies que notre recherche peut emprunter.

Tout d'abord le conditionnement de l'ambiance: Stabiliser, au niveau le plus convenable, l'humidité d'une ou de plusieurs salles d'un musée, n'est certes pas une entreprise difficile, et beaucoup moins coûteuse que d'en stabiliser la température.

Si un panneau est placé dans une ambiance adéquate, il restera parfaitement sain et immobile.

On peut également faire beaucoup dans le domaine des isolants. Mais il ne faut pas perdre de vue qu'à une matière qui pénètre trop dans le bois et soit difficile à enlever—comme c'est le cas, il me semble, du tissu de verre avec résine—est de loin préférable une matière qui constitue un tegument protectif elastique, faiblement adhésif et parfaitement imperméable, de manière à se superposer au bois comme une pellicule (film) si possible transparente et amovible à volonté.

Il ne faut pas oublier que si l'adhésion entre la couche picturale, la couche de préparation et le support de bois est bonne, il n'y a pas de raison de craindre que la couleur se soulève et tombe, même si le panneau est placé dans des conditions d'ambiance peu propices. Par contre, il se trouve que justement à ce problème d'adhésion entre les différentes couches on n'a pas accordé jusqu'à maintenant l'attention nécessaire et qu'il n'existe pas de technique de consolidation vraiment satisfaisante. J'attire l'attention sur ce point car il me semble de la plus grande importance et susceptible d'importantes recherches techniques. Le système belge, adopté pour la première fois sur l'Agneau Mystique, est certainement excellent mais il ne convient pas aux tableaux italiens, qui ont en général des préparations beaucoup plus épaisses.

J'ajouterai finalement que j'ai été un peu surpris du peu d'attention—et je dirai même de la méfiance—avec laquelle M. Buck considère les systèmes de parquetage mobile. Et j'ai été encore plus surpris de l'exemple qu'il a fait pour appuyer sa thèse; c'est à dire l'exemple des panneaux à chassis fixes, qui même s'ils se fendaient ne donneraient pas lieu aux soulèvements de la couleur. Je ne veux pas considérer maintenant ce qui est le plus grave, si un soulèvement de la couleur ou un éclatement du panneau. (Je crois que ce dernier est infiniment plus grave.) Mais j'attire tout de suite l'attention sur le fait que dans l'exemple de M. Buck la combinaison des deux éléments—chassis fixe et éclatement du panneau—équivaut pratiquement, mais d'une manière très rudimentaire et empirique, à un système de parquetage mobile. Le panneau reste plan parce qu'il y est contraint par le chassis fixe, mais peut développer ses mouvements parce qu'il est fendu. De la même façon un parquetage mobile empêche le panneau de s'incurver et lui permet de se mouvoir, sans toutefois qu'il doive pour autant se fendre. En réalité, si sur un panneau fendu il ne se produit plus de soulèvement de la couleur, c'est parce que le panneau ne fait plus système; c'est à dire, qu'il s'est fractionné en deux ou plusieurs fragments de surface réduite, qui bien qu'ils se meuvent dans toutes les directions possibles, n'enchaînent pas ces mouvements dans un seul système de sollicitations que forcément aurait une ampleur beaucoup plus grande, et en conséquence produirait des soulèvements de couleur.

Mais pour réduire l'ampleur des mouvements d'un panneau il n'est certes pas nécessaire de le fragmenter en plusieurs morceaux, ou bien, comme le propose M. Lucas, de réduire le panneau lui-même à une épaisseur minimum. Il suffit, comme il est courant de le faire à l'Istituto del Restauro, d'exécuter au dos du panneau, dans le sens de la veine du bois, de nombreuses incisions parallèles et peu éloignées l'une de l'autre, profondes de la moitié, à peu près, de l'épaisseur du panneau. De minces baguettes de bois y sont ensuite introduites et collées, de manière à reconstituer la continuité de la structure du panneau, que les incisions mentionnées ont rendu, par ailleurs, assez inerte. Ce système permet aussi de réduire sensiblement la courbe du panneau, sans emploie d'humidité. Quant aux parquetages mobiles, ils peuvent également être appliqués aux panneaux incurvés; il suffit à cette fin de donner une hauteur variable aux éléments en bois qui tiennent les éléments mobiles du parquetage.

Enfin nous ne considérons pas nos systèmes comme les seuls possibles et les seuls parfaits. A présent, à l'Istituto sont à l'étude plusieurs nouveaux systèmes de parquetage mobile. Nous croyons de ne devoir pas abandonner une technique qui a donné depuis longtemps des excellents résultats, et qui surtout permet de conserver la structure ancienne des panneaux dans son intégrité. Nous nous efforçons d'améliorer toujours plus cette technique, en évitant le plus possible que son intervention dans la matière de l'oeuvre d'art ne soit défigurante et irrémédiable pour toujours. Nous aussi nous sommes pour le progrès, comme d'ailleurs il est si facile de l'être, à notre époque; mais nous croyons que notre progrès à nous, à différence de ce qu'on dit de l'autre, ne veut pas des victimes.

Robert L. Feller

NEW SOLVENT-TYPE VARNISHES

Vinylacetate and butylmethacrylate polymers have been used in conservation for about twenty-five years. These and other synthetic resins are perhaps still not well known and may be considered to be 'new' in the sense that many conservators have had little experience with them. The types of synthetic thermo-plastic resins of special interest to conservators are limited and are much the same wherever in the world they are manufactured. Therefore, although these remarks will refer primarily to products sold in America, it is hoped that the examples will provide a general outline of the subject and its major problems. The pertinent material that has already appeared in the book *On Picture Varnishes and Their Solvents* will not be reviewed in detail, but will merely be referred to[1].

Picture varnish is of the solvent type, consisting simply of a volatile solvent and a non-volatile thermoplastic substance. A varnish may be 'new' with respect to either component.

Solvents

Only brief mention will be made of solvents. There is available a certain amount of new knowledge concerning 'solvent power' and the 'balance' of solvent properties which is of assistance in the selection of new solvents. The fundamental principles of solvent action have been reviewed by Stolow and applied in his detailed investigation of the action of solvents on oil paint[2].

New facts are known about the properties of petroleum. In the matter of new materials, it might be mentioned that, because of the variety of petroleum fractions available and the tendency of turpentine to oxidize, turpentine is becoming less frequently used in the conservation laboratory. The propellant-solvent methylene dichloride is now frequently encountered in the pressurized spray cans found in artists' supply stores[3].

Characterization of polymers

A statement of the chemical nature of a polymer is a key specification: polyethylene, poly(vinylchloride-acetate), poly-styrene. In addition, the essential properties of any resin may be characterized by specifying at least three parameters: average molecular weight, hardness and solubility type. It is obviously of importance to specify whether a resin is soluble in a 'strong' solvent or a 'mild' one*. Hardness, although poorly defined, appears to be related to Young's modulus[4] or to the stiffness of a film. The polymers of chief interest to the conservator are those that are internally plasticized (reference 1, p. 110); that is, the films do not need the addition of plasticizers such as dibutylphthalate to give them flexibility†.

A protective coating must have reasonable toughness in order to be successful. In other words, it must possess a certain minimum strength and it must be able to stretch somewhat

without cracking (reference 1, p. 135). It is known that, up to a certain point, increasing the average molecular weight of a polymer will increase the strength of the films and give them greater ability to elongate. Therefore, the characterization of polymers through some measurement that indicates the average molecular weight is an important specification.

The viscosity of a solution of resin at 20 per cent solids concentration in toluene has been taken as a rough indication

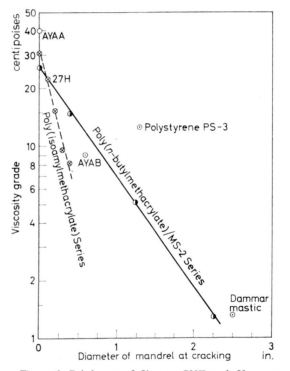

Figure 1. Brittleness of films at 70°F and 50 per cent relative humidity as a function of their viscosity grade (1·5-mil thick films on 1-mil aluminium foil).

of the average molecular weight. This measurement has been designated in our laboratory as the 'viscosity grade' of the resin (reference 1, p. 106). Data in *Table 1* show the relationship between viscosity grade and the brittleness of the baked-dry films as measured by the mandrel bending test. The data on mixtures of resin MS-2 (Howards of Ilford, Ltd) and the du Pont n-butylmethacrylate polymer 'Lucite' 44 illustrate the effect of adding the tough methacrylate polymer to the brittle MS-2.

The data in *Table 1* (with those in Table II, p. 108, of reference 1) are plotted in *Figure 1*. From consideration of this diagram, it is apparent that a resin, or mixture of resins, must have a viscosity grade of about 20 centipoises to produce films that are able to withstand a bend of 0·1 in. (2·54 mm) or less in this test. Many of the tough coatings used in commerce are

---

* In the case of methacrylate polymers, it has been found possible to define a precise scale of solubility grade (reference 1, p. 46).

† Plasticizers that are fluid, such as dibutylphthalate, have been avoided in picture varnishes primarily to guard against the possibility that the plasticizer might migrate into the paint and thereby soften or otherwise affect it.

171

based on resins of considerably higher viscosity grade than this (reference 1, p. 111).

The selection of suitable viscosity grades for the resin in solvent-type varnishes remains open to question and discussion.

Table 1

Viscosity grade vs. cracking of baked-dry films

Test conditions: 70°F, 50 per cent relative humidity

Resin formulation in film	Viscosity grade (centipoises)	Sward hard-ness*	Diameter of mandrel at cracking (in.)
Lucite 44	48	32	<0·1
Lucite 44/MS-2 80/20	26	53	<0·1
Lucite 44/MS-2 60/40	14·8	60	0·6
Lucite 44/MS-2 20/80	5·2	77	1·3
Lucite 44/MS-2 10/90	1·3	—	2·3
Lucite 44/AW-2 10/90	1·3	—	1·6
AW-2	1·2	91	4·0
Dammar, Mastic	1·5	81	2·5

* Hardness of windowglass base equals 100.

From an analysis of the data in *Figure 1*, however, it does not seem necessary to select grades much higher than 25 centipoises for most protective coatings. In our research, we have been especially interested in types between 9 and 25 centipoises.

Synthetic polymers in solvent-type varnishes

A brief history of the introduction of synthetic thermoplastics in conservation has been presented elsewhere (reference 1, p. 104). Polyvinyl acetate was described in the early 1930s by Stout and Gettens. In view of the importance of this polymer, the National Gallery of Art Research Project at Mellon Institute undertook the preparation of a list of the different molecular weight grades available in various countries (reference 1, p. 218). Lower molecular weight varieties, particularly resin AYAB, have been introduced in recent years in a number of applications where higher fluidity and gloss were desired*.

Because they are available as granular powders and because of their solubility in 'mild' solvents, the butylmethacrylate polymers from the du Pont company have attracted much attention: the n-butyl polymer, 'Lucite' 44†, the isobutyl, 'Lucite' 45, and the 50–50 copolymer of these, 'Lucite' 46. Most conservators have found it convenient to use mixtures of 'Lucite' 44 and 45, varied according to the need. 'Lucite' 44 is one of the toughest thermoplastic resins available: literature from the du Pont company states that test samples will stretch three times their original length before breaking. Poly(n-butylmethacrylate) is readily identified by its hardness and solubility characteristics‡.

Resin AW-2, a resin in the viscosity-grade class of dammar and mastic, has received considerable attention abroad and is now available in the solid form in America. The data in *Table 1* show that AW-2 is considerably brittle when used alone. A number of proprietary varnishes are said to be prepared with

* Polymer AYAB exhibits cold flow in bulk, but in thin films it seems to be satisfactory in tests thus far. If used as the final coating, it may have a slight tendency to become dirty, for the reasons noted (reference 1, p. 134) in the case of poly(n-butylmethacrylate).

† Bedacryl 112 X (Imperial Chemical Industries) is similar in viscosity grade (reference 1, p. 217).

‡ We have identified in proprietary varnishes a second variety of the n-butyl polymer, having a viscosity grade of 27 centipoises. This is supplied by an American manufacturer other than du Pont and is not available in the solid form.

resin AW-2 and additions of stand oil. Howards of Ilford (England) markets a variety of AW-2, designated as MS-2. They have also produced a fully hydrogenated type, MS-2A, which has been evaluated by G. Thomson (see p. 176) at the National Gallery, London. Resins AW-2 and MS-2A are of high quality, but the author has had little experience with them in comparison to polymers of higher molecular weight.

Artists' supply stores in America offer a variety of paints and varnishes put up in spray cans. Dammar resin is available in this form, but it is believed that most of the coatings are based on cellulose acetate-butyrate and the Rohm and Haas acrylate-methacrylate copolymer 'Acryloid' B-72 ('Paraloid' in Europe). These proprietary formulations are seldom used on fine paintings. Tests show, however, that many of them are based on excellent materials and have their use in the conservation laboratory. As mentioned above, the development of pressurized containers has introduced methylene dichloride and related solvents.

Table 2

Selected resins for solvent-type varnishes

In order of decreasing fluidity, brittleness and penetration in porous areas:

Resin	Viscosity grade	Sward hardness
AW-2	1·3	86
Dammar	1·4	81
Polyvinyl acetate AYAB	9·0	63
27H (experimental varnish)	23·0	49
Poly(n-butylmethacrylate)	27·0	25
Acryloid B-72	29·0	65
Lucite 44 poly(n-butylmethacrylate)	48·0	30
Lucite 46 (n-butyl/isobutylmethacrylate copolymer)	50·0	61
Polyvinyl acetate AYAF	80·0	63

In order of increasing strength of solvent needed to formulate the varnish:

Resin	Solubility grade*
27H (experimental varnish)	8
AW-2	10 (?)
Lucite 44, 45 and 46	25
Dammar	—†
Acryloid B-72	80
Polyvinyl acetate AYAF, AYAB	89

* Percentage toluene by weight in n-dodecane necessary to make a clear solution at 25°C.

† Soluble in 'mild' petroleum fractions when fresh, requires toluene or 'stronger' solvent when aged.

An experimental varnish known as 27H was developed at Mellon Institute in 1953*. This polymer was unique in that it was specially prepared with selected film strength, high resistance to yellowing and solubility in a petroleum solvent having no aromatic compounds (reference 1, p. 200). Extensive studies of this and related polymers led to the discovery and investigation of the tendency of thermoplastic polymers to cross-link under the effect of light, a problem of fundamental interest that will be discussed below.

Table 2 summarizes the properties of the resins of principal interest to conservators in America.

Application of varnish

A number of problems is associated with the introduction of new and unfamiliar materials. In the application of a varnish,

* Varnish 27H was made only in limited quantities in the laboratory at the time and samples are no longer available.

perhaps the central problem has been the selection of a solvent sufficiently 'mild' to be used with little danger of attacking the paint during application, and, at a later time, during the removal. The risk of attack, of course, depends on the character of the paint or other material directly beneath the varnish. In certain cases, the ability of the substrate to withstand solvents of the 'strength' of toluene and cellosolve ($C_2H_5O(CH_2)_2OH$) has made the application of polyvinyl acetate possible. The Rohm and Haas 'Acryloid' B-72 is also soluble in toluene and forms a slightly cloudy solution in xylene. The butyl-methacrylate polymers are soluble in turpentine and in petroleum fractions having about 25 to 35 per cent aromatics. The experimental polymer 27H was designed to be soluble in paraffin and cycloparaffin hydrocarbons. Resin AW-2 is soluble in similar solvents. *Table 2* lists these polymers in order of their solubility grade (reference 1, p. 45).

In our research, polymers that may be applied and removed in xylene have been sought as a standard of the maximum solubility parameter or 'strength' of solvent to be used. To establish such a specification, the investigator must bear in mind that stronger solvents are generally required to remove aged resins than to dissolve them originally. More information is needed on the removal of aged coatings before this question can be properly considered. Miss Elizabeth Jones' re-forming process, for example, represents one of the many facets of the problem that should be further explored. Certain new facts regarding the aging and removal of polymers are discussed below.

The polymers listed in *Table 2* require solvents no 'stronger' than toluene to dissolve them. Yet, having thus limited the number, one still has the problem of learning to apply these materials, particularly if their molecular weight is significantly higher than mastic, dammar and AW-2 resins (reference 1, p. 120). High viscosity grade is, of course, associated with the desirable properties of increased strength and reduced brittleness. In order to take full advantage of these properties, American conservators have learned to apply the coatings by spray application. A discussion of the relative merits of brushing and spraying will not be undertaken here. Suffice it to say that many conservators have found spraying to be highly satisfactory once they have learned the technique. The use of spraying equipment requires skill and experience, however, just as does successful brushing.

To furnish additional information concerning the application of these materials, the National Gallery of Art Research Project undertook a study of the relationship of viscosity grade to film-forming properties. This led to data of the type shown in *Figure 1*. Commercial resins of lower viscosity grade than those which were in general use in 1950 were also sought out. For example, the use of polyvinyl acetate AYAB, AYAA and several other polymers in the 20–30 centipoise range of viscosity grade has been suggested.

While the spraying of coatings has introduced problems in the selection of solvents, the desire to brush solutions of high polymers in certain applications has also required special consideration. A sound review of petroleum chemistry was required in order to select solvents of a given solubility parameter and with varying evaporation rate (reference 1, p. 17). This subject was briefly reviewed in the *Application of Science in the Examination of Works of Art*, Museum of Fine Arts, Boston, Mass., 1959, pp. 70–72. Attention has been drawn to the wide variety of proprietary solvents described in the *Petroleum Thinner Index* of the National Paint, Varnish, and Lacquer Association, Washington 5, D.C.

Problems in removal of coatings

A fundamental problem associated with materials used in conservation involves their ease of removal. The use of thermoplastic polymers in the viscosity-grade range of 9 to 80 centipoises has raised a problem of basic interest: among the ways that such a substance may become altered in time, one manner is through the formation of cross-links. Although this phenomenon is not of major importance with materials of the average molecular weight of dammar, mastic and AW-2 resins, it is one the chemist must face if he wishes to use thermoplastic polymers of much higher molecular weight. As has been pointed out, it does not take very many chemical cross-links to cause such a polymer to become insoluble (reference 1, p. 203).

The tendency for thermoplastic polymers to cross-link upon aging has been found to be more the general rule, and the lack of this tendency the exception, than one might at first expect. Activation of certain chemical bonds by light and heat imparts the tendency to form new chemical bonds. Bond formation, of course, may take place with neighbouring molecular chains in the polymer. If this proceeds, the chains may become so linked together that they eventually fail to be dispersed in solvents. Thus, our investigation of polymers of the higher alkylmethacrylate esters traced the tendency to lose solubility particularly to the presence of tertiary hydrogen atoms in the side-chain (reference 1, p. 152). The tendency to cross-link has also been observed in poly(vinylstearate-acetate) copolymers, poly(vinylbutyral) and cellulose acetate-butyrate.

Table 3

Average rate of cross-linking of poly(n-butylmethacrylate) and poly(isoamylmethacrylate) on aluminium foil, under various filters in the fadeometer at 62°C

Filter	Filter, wavelength at 50% transmission	Relative rate for films to reach 50% insolubility	Relative rate calculated by the equation
Corex D glass	305	1·0	0·97
Window glass	330	0·44	0·49
Uvinul M-40 filter	358	0·19	0·21
Plexiglas UF-1	396	0·05	0·05

The first phase of an extensive investigation of cross-linking was to determine the structures in the methacrylate side-chain that possessed the greatest tendency to become insoluble. This led to the conclusion just stated and to the selection of materials with a reduced tendency. The second phase was to determine the nature of the radiation that caused cross-linking. Data in *Table 3* demonstrate that ultra-violet radiation is primarily responsible. The influence of wavelength upon the rate is almost precisely that predicted by the probable damage factor for a given wavelength (D_λ), described in the Harrison report of the Metropolitan Museum of Art*. The rate at which the films reached 50 per cent insolubility was found to follow the equation

$$\text{Rate} = 1/T_{50} = 0.16D_\lambda - 0.05$$

where T_{50} is the time required to attain 50 per cent insolubility. Investigation also showed that an increase in the temperature of the samples increased the rate of cross-linking.

How important is this phenomenon under museum conditions? Most of the accelerated-aging tests first used to detect

* The results of these experiments were reported to The British Group, IIC, at their meeting of September 29, 1960.

and study the problem involved both elevated temperatures and ultra-violet radiation not normally encountered in a picture gallery. To minimize the effect of temperature, our laboratory conducted tests under 'daylight' fluorescent lamps in an air-conditioned room at 80°F and 50 per cent relative humidity. Under these conditions, the butylmethacrylate polymers from du Pont were found to develop 50 to 80 per cent insolubility in 8 to 10 million footcandle-hours of exposure. (After this exposure, the polymers could still be removed easily with toluene.) Such a degree of insolubility might be expected to develop in a matter of 50 to 100 years if the objects were to be

the polymers from a viscosity grade of 27 centipoises to about 10 centipoises. The possibility of inhibiting cross-linking has also been mentioned (reference 1, pp. 159 and 161).

To conclude these remarks, it should be said first that the problem of cross-linking is a general one in the aging of thermoplastic polymers of reasonably high molecular weight. Research has shown, however, that certain chemical structures have greater tendency than others and that ultra-violet radiations are primarily responsible for the phenomenon. Moreover, the ability of a film to swell, rather than the actual insoluble matter present, controls in large measure the ease of removal.

Table 4

Ease of removal of pairs of films in relationship to their ability to be swollen by toluene

Aged film	Percentage insoluble in toluene	Fadeometer exposure (hours)	Percentage gain in weight (absorbed toluene after 3 days)	Time (sec) required to remove film with swabs dipped in:	
				Toluene	Acetone
Isobutyl MA* polymer	89·1	111	598	105	65
n-Butyl MA* polymer	100	228	77·2	>180	220
1/1 AW-2/n-propyl MA* polymer	96·2	416	91·4	75	6
1/1 MS-2/n-propyl MA* polymer	95·0	416	43·3	>180	25

*MA = methacrylate

illuminated at a level of about 50 footcandles during the day. From this first estimate, we may conclude that the phenomenon is not one to cause immediate alarm. Nevertheless, cross-linking can take place during exposure in museums and the possibility warrants particular attention wherever ordinary fluorescent lamps are to be used without ultra-violet filters or wherever daylight enters through ordinary window glass*.

Since practically all films become more difficult to remove in time, the laboratory is prompted to return again to fundamental problems regarding the removal of films and the rate at which films, once soluble in solvents such as toluene, come to require 'stronger' solvents for removal. This led to studies which suggested that the ability of a film to swell under the action of solvents was important in facilitating its removal (reference 1, p. 200). Recent data, given in *Table 4*, demonstrate that the amount of insoluble material present in a film is not necessarily the major indication of its ability to be removed. Even though cross-linking may proceed to the extent that 50 to 95 per cent of the film becomes insoluble, this does not mean that the film cannot be removed with considerable ease as a soft swollen jelly. These preliminary findings concerning the role that swelling plays in removal draw special attention to the techniques used by Stolow in his studies of solvent action.

Polymers of low molecular weight might be expected to become insoluble at a lower rate. We have thus far found little benefit, however, in lowering the average molecular weight of

The investigations continue and new information is being gained about cross-linking. From what has been learned so far, however, the author believes that, with proper supervision and keeping of records, coatings such as poly(butylmethacrylate) may still be used in the conservation of many objects.

Polymers with little tendency to cross-link

The search for high polymers which have little or no tendency to cross-link continues. Polyvinyl acetate has an extremely low tendency to cross-link in the fadeometer and in sunlight, if it does so at all. This fact was first pointed out by Thomson and has been confirmed in our experiments. Polyvinyl acetate, therefore, retains its important place in the conservation laboratory.

Table 5

Percentage insolubility of Acryloid B-82 and Rhoplex AC-33 upon exposure on aluminium foil in fadeometer at 62°C

Insolubility in: Exposure time:	Toluene 394 h	Toluene 1045 h	Toluene 2027 h	Acetone 2027 h
B-82*	4·2	22·4	62·0	4·4
AC-33	10·6	43·8	77·4	4·8

* Rohm and Haas polymer similar to B-72.

Our search for structures in the methacrylate family that have little tendency to cross-link led us to the prediction that a copolymer of ethylmethacrylate and methylacrylate should possess this property. Tests in the fadeometer revealed that after 2000 hours on aluminium foil at 62°C such a polymer was still soluble in acetone to the extent of 95 per cent or better. This exposure is equivalent to over 40 million footcandle-hours. Although originally soluble in toluene, the polymer developed a certain degree of insolubility in this solvent as time went on. This change is apparently due to partial oxidation of the polymer and not to cross-linking, since otherwise the high solubility in acetone would not have occurred.

---

* There are ways of detecting the onset of cross-linking. Thomson's test is simple and highly sensitive (*Nature*, 178 (1956) 807; reference 1, p. 205). Measurements of the degree of soluble matter in samples picked up on a cotton swab have been used in our laboratory to follow the course of cross-linking in a quantitative way. A chromatographic leaching method has also been used (reference 1, p. 115). The conservator can detect the presence of cross-linked material by the tendency of a film to swell considerably under the action of solvents, and by the presence of a jelly-like mass. Such behaviour is considerably different from that observed when a fresh film of a polymer is dissolved with solvents.

Following these tests of durability, we have suggested the consideration of this type of copolymer for certain applications. Commercially available polymers that are similar are the Rohm and Haas resin 'Acryloid' B-72 and their emulsion of a related polymer, 'Rhoplex' AC-33. The results of the exposure of these proprietary polymers in the fadeometer are given in *Table 5*. The conclusions from these data are the same as those made concerning the behaviour of the related polymers prepared in the laboratory. 'Acryloid' B-72 may be applied in xylene; evaporation may be retarded by the addition of solvents such as diethylbenzene or all-aromatic petroleum fractions. Varnish formulated with these solvents is slightly cloudy, but the films are satisfactory in appearance*.

Conclusions

We have learned much about the properties of solvent-type coatings in recent years, yet much remains to be investigated.

---

* The use of 'Acryloid' B-72 in the conservation of metal objects dates back a number of years: See *Rohm and Haas Reporter*, 8, No. 3 (1950) 14.

Thus far, research has discovered two thermoplastic polymers of reasonably high molecular weight which are soluble in solvents as 'mild' as toluene and xylene, and which form films that remain strong, colourless and soluble for extremely long periods of time. It is hoped that ever-increasing experience with these polymers in applications where they are suitable will strengthen the conservator's confidence and satisfaction in their use. In the range of viscosity grade similar to dammar and mastic resins, resins AW-2 and MS-2A also appear to be sound additions to the conservator's stock of materials.

References

[1] FELLER, R. L., STOLOW, N. and JONES, E. H., *On Picture Varnishes and Their Solvents*, Intermuseum Conservation Association, Oberlin, Ohio, 1959.

[2] STOLOW, N., *J. Oil Col. Chem. Ass.*, 40 (1957) 337, 448; reference 1, p. 60.

[3] BROWN, J. A., *Paint Varn. Prod.*, 50 (1960) 86; SCIARRA, J. J., *ibid.*, 51 (1961) 3.

[4] INOUE, Y. and IKEDA, K., *Chem. High Polymers (Japan)*, 11 (1954) 409; *Chem. Abstr.*, 50 (1956) 6086.

Garry Thomson

NEW PICTURE VARNISHES

My object in this paper is to give a concise summary of the 'new picture varnish' situation as it appears to me today.

In one way the prospect is disappointing, since the ideal varnish is still nowhere in sight. On the other hand, our investigations on this particular problem have illuminated some important aspects of the use of synthetic resins in conservation. First of all, let us state two chemical principles of conservation practice, very obvious perhaps, but often not rigorously enforced owing to lack of adequate data or to other considerations.

(a) The principle of permanence: that any added conservation material in adhesive contact with a museum object should be at least as resistant to change as the original materials of the object.

(b) The principle of reversibility: that any added conservation material should be removable with safety at any future time.

Natural resin varnishes are notoriously inadequate under principle (a) and most new varnishes are to be suspected under principle (b) until proved innocent; that is to say, they may become insoluble with time. This is the varnish situation today in a nutshell.

The importance of these principles to conservators in general varies in proportion to the value of the object under treatment and also, in a less easily defined way, according to the nature of the adhesive contact. Here are three examples:

1. Treatment of a specimen of neolithic water-logged wood, using a resin which is allowed to diffuse into the wood and become cross-linked *in situ*. Such a process can be highly successful in stabilizing the wood, but is, by its nature, completely irreversible. One would therefore hesitate to use it on unique objects.

2. Repair of a valuable piece of pottery, using a well-proved thermosetting adhesive. This is justifiable in most cases, since the adhesive does not cover the surface and is confined to a thin glue-line. Even if it weakened subsequently, its failure would endanger the pot no more than that of an old-fashioned adhesive.

3. Varnishing a valuable painting. This is the extreme case, from most points of view. Firstly, a varnish covers the whole picture surface with an adhesive bond; secondly pictures are unique and of very high value and should not have to be disturbed at intervals. Both principles, those of permanence and reversibility, therefore, apply most strongly to picture varnishes.

Research on picture varnishes therefore means much more than ordering bottles of the latest resin, or of collecting the opinions of scientists in other fields. It requires work on problems which will most certainly not be tackled by any organization outside the field of conservation.

Permanence

Varnishes spend their lives spread out as thin films exposed to air, which is an oxidizing environment. The energy for the chemical reactions leading to oxidation is most likely to come from the light shining on the picture, whether natural or artificial. Thus deterioration of a varnish is mainly a matter of photochemical oxidation. The more stable a varnish is, the more likely this is to be true. Furthermore, only the shorter wavelengths of light at the blue and ultra-violet end of the spectrum will be sufficiently energetic to be useful in such photochemical reactions—at least for more reasonably stable varnishes.

Though there is no substitute for actual testing, we now know enough about photochemical oxidation to be wary of certain chemical groups, such as double bonds between carbon atoms, carbonyl groups in a carbon chain and tertiary hydrogen atoms (triple-branched carbon chains). Natural resins contain all three of these vulnerable points, and there seems little to be gained by attempts at chemically stabilizing them, e.g. by hydrogenation. The resins AW-2 and MS-2 contain carbonyl

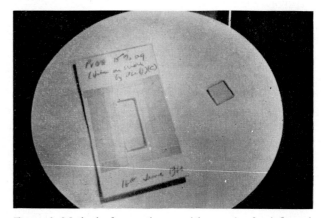

Figure 1. Method of mounting varnish samples for infra-red analysis. Where possible (e.g. polyvinyl acetate, butyral, alcohol) free films are mounted over windows cut in stiff card, using adhesive tape (*left*). Brittle films (dammar, mastic, AW-2, MS-2A) are dip-coated on a $1\frac{1}{4}$ cm wide sodium chloride crystal, which is transparent to infra-red light.

groups. These can be reduced to hydroxyl groups by a chemical reaction, giving the resin MS-2A, which is a decidedly more stable material (see Appendix 1). However, experience in the author's laboratory, and in that of R. L. Feller in America, as well as the accumulating experience of industry, seems to show that polyvinyl acetate and some of the acrylics are of a higher order of permanence as regards retention of strength and optical clarity.

In Appendix 2 the application of infra-red spectroscopy to the study of varnish deterioration is outlined (*Figure 1*).

Reversibility

Much has been written about the tendency to insolubility of certain synthetic varnishes. Sometimes the dangers have been minimized, sometimes unduly exaggerated. It cannot be denied, however, that a varnish which may become insoluble with time, however slowly, is far from being ideal. As Miss E. Jones has clearly demonstrated[1], all varnishes, natural and synthetic, tend slowly to become less soluble with time. This is not the same as cross-linking insolubility.

The processes tending to reduce solubility without leading to insolubility are twofold. Firstly, oxidation, which may do no more than reduce solubility in the original solvent. Dammar and mastic become sufficiently oxidized to be partly insoluble in petroleum solvents after a month or so, whereas after a few years they may be unaffected by toluene. Secondly, a slow process during which the individual molecules shift up against each other into, as it were, more 'comfortable' positions. Residual solvent escapes, molecules become more closely knit and polar attractions exert themselves, until the stage is ultimately reached in which all forces between atoms and molecules are in equilibrium. It can be readily imagined that all this settling down, decrease in internal energy, tendency to crystallization, or whatever one likes to call it, leads to a greater reluctance to be dispersed in a solvent, i.e. a decreased solubility. The 're-forming' technique developed by Miss Jones is an elegant way of allowing some untangling to take place before the varnish is removed, and therefore of increasing the solubility.

Neither of these processes leads to complete insolubility. This is a result of chemical links being formed between neighbouring molecules. If sufficient links are formed—and if the molecules are long, surprisingly few links are needed[2]—the whole varnish will become insoluble, since no solvent can break chemical links, though chemical reagents may do so. On the other hand, in the early stages of cross-linking the varnish will readily swell to form a weak jelly which can quite easily be removed. But as cross-linking proceeds swelling will decrease, until the varnish will not respond to even the most powerful solvent. Feller and Thomson have both developed methods for spotting a fall in solubility and the onset of cross-linking[3,4].

Published evidence is available that some of the methacrylates are likely to become cross-linked as varnishes[5,6]. Among the other synthetics suggested as varnishes it has been said that polyvinyl alcohol may become insoluble. In the author's experience this tendency is smaller than that noted for some methacrylates, but some cross-linking does appear to take place under the action of light (see *Figure 5*). There is no evidence that polyvinyl acetate is subject to cross-linking.

Mechanical, optical and chemical properties

Under this heading we are not likely to run into insuperable difficulties in choosing a picture varnish. Feller has made a detailed study of hardness, flexibility and solubility characteristics of picture varnishes[6]. Clearly some degree of flexibility greater than that found in the natural resins is desirable. Even if picture surfaces are never flexed during handling, changes in the moisture content of the support result in continual movement, and therefore continually varying stress on the varnish film. But two points should be remembered. Firstly, the craquelure on an old varnish is just as likely to be due to oxidative breakdown as to mechanical strain. Samples of natural resin on glass kept under constant temperature but strong light in the author's laboratory have developed extensive craquelure. Secondly, a varnish film can be too strong and flexible. A chance abrasion could catch a corner of the film and either pull a long strip off or, worse, pull some of the paint film off with it. The author has noted a case of an experimental picture with an unusually weak paint film which was literally pulled apart when the butyl methacrylate varnish was swollen in toluene.

Quite a large number of long-chain polymers would be perfectly adequate as picture varnishes from the point of view of mechanical properties. The resins AW-2, MS-2 and MS-2A are, however, inadequate in this respect, being a little too brittle and easily damaged.

The necessary optical properties are a potentially high gloss and transparency (which can be reduced as required) and a suitable refractive index. Few candidates fail on these grounds. However, those satisfied with natural-resin varnishes will be satisfied with less than the best optical qualities. For the discerning eye will have noticed that the refinements of a new coat of natural-resin varnish do not last more than a few weeks. Thereafter slight and uneven losses of gloss destroy the careful finish given by the restorer.

There remain the chemical properties, with the emphasis on solubility. The likelihood of reactivity between synthetic varnish and paint is small for pure polymers. Plasticizers could cause trouble, and, if an emulsion varnish is considered, all the emulsion additives should be examined for possible physical or chemical action on the paint film.

Solubility

Solubility of the varnish is a very important limiting factor, whether the varnish is going on or coming off. The most harmless solvents of all are the petroleum solvents (predominantly saturated aliphatic hydrocarbons) and water, which are chemically at opposite extremes, since the former are the most non-polar and the latter is the most highly polar of solvents. Strong points in favour of AW-2, MS-2, MS-2A and 27H (iso-amyl methacrylate) are their solubility in petroleum solvents. Next on the list of moderately harmless solvents come those typified by toluene and xylene. Polyvinyl acetate and the higher methacrylates are soluble in toluene. Alcohols, ketones and esters are strong solvents, and those polymers which prefer them, such as polyvinyl butyral, are at a very strong disadvantage as picture varnishes.

Handling qualities

Varnishing is one of the lesser skills of the picture restorer. Nevertheless, a varnish found to be unsatisfactory on drying may disturb months of retouching work by its removal. Varnish application, therefore, should be easily controllable for evenness of gloss. It should be possible to add or to thin varnish locally. All types of varnish, old and new, brushed or sprayed, have their advocates. The harassed scientist, faced with the imponderable qualities required by the restorer, should trust to his common-sense, with the certainty that a really good varnish will quickly be appreciated.

Permeability to gases

Permeability is a measure of the quantity of a gas passing through a film of the varnish when there is a specified excess of the gas on one side of the film. We are chiefly interested in the permeability to water, oxygen and the polluting gases (such as ammonia, sulphur dioxide, hydrogen sulphide) since all these are likely to affect the paint film.

Water: It is unlikely that we can slow down deterioration by using a varnish as a moisture barrier: sufficient water would still penetrate. On the other hand, a moisture barrier acts as a buffer against stresses and strains following changes in humidity, particularly in wood panels.

Oxygen: The effectiveness of a varnish as an oxygen barrier can be assessed by tests (see next section), but an explanation in chemical terms would be complicated.

Polluting gases: These are present in the atmosphere in relatively low concentration so that their reaction with a paint film is probably effectively reduced by most varnishes.

The comparative figures in *Tables 1* and *2* have been adapted by the author from a number of sources[7], and rounded off for the purposes of comparison. Although figures for pollutant gases

Table 1

Relative permeability to water vapour
Polythene = 100

Paraffin wax	2
Dammar, mastic (1 month)	17
Linseed oil (1–6 months)	
Polymethyl methacrylate	90–100
Polystyrene	
Iso-amyl methacrylate	130
n-butyl methacrylate	180
Polyvinyl acetate	200–600
Polyvinyl alcohol	very high

have not been collected for the common varnishes, sufficient can probably be deduced from the tables. For instance, films highly permeable to water will also be permeable to the water-soluble

Table 2

Permeability to gases at normal humidities
(around 60 per cent)

	Hydrogen	Oxygen	Hydrogen sulphide	Carbon dioxide
Polythene	2000	750	8000	3000
Polyvinyl alcohol	4	4	3	5·5 (r.h. = 0) 40,000 (r.h. = 100)

gases, ammonia and sulphur dioxide, and these will diffuse more rapidly at high relative humidities. But the same does not follow for such gases as oxygen and hydrogen sulphide. In fact, polyvinyl alcohol (soluble in water) probably has no rival for impermeability to oxygen.

Polyvinyl alcohol as an oxygen barrier

Simonds *et al.*[8] (1949) state that the resistance of polyvinyl alcohol 'to passage of oxygen is higher than the known value for any other commercial film'. It is possible that this may no longer be true, though polyvinyl alcohol must remain an unusually effective barrier to oxygen, and probably to other gases of low water solubility. The protective power of polyvinyl alcohol (PVOH) has been tested by the author over the last three years by partly coating an area of natural-resin varnish with PVOH and exposing it to strong light from daylight fluorescent tubes. Under these conditions the unprotected mastic has become clear yellow, while the PVOH has prevented all yellowing. This cannot, incidentally, be a light-filtering effect, since PVOH is transparent to the near ultra-violet.

Since the wrinkling of dammar, mastic, AW-2 and MS-2 is likely to be a direct result of oxidation, it is not surprising that this is also prevented by a coat of PVOH, applied after the film is approximately dry of solvent. In addition, a PVOH surface will not bloom. All these properties, and the added one that PVOH could be replaced by using water without in any way disturbing the paint layer, might seem to make PVOH an attractive proposition as a final varnish coat over AW-2. Because of the chance of cross-linking PVOH has always been tested by the author as a second layer over a white-spirit-soluble resin which will not cross-link. But the main disadvantage of this system is the lack of adhesion between the two. This need

not matter for a rough-surfaced picture, but on a glossy picture it is quite easy to pull a large strip of PVOH off by a chance scratch. Textile conservation experts have found that PVOH does indeed tend to become insoluble as a textile adhesive. It is possible that this may be partly or wholly an adsorption effect, as can be shown in the following manner.

A small fragment of fresh PVOH film is placed near a corner of a square of filter paper (about 15 × 15 cm) and stuck down with a drop of water. Water is then made to flow up the paper, as in chromatography. The PVOH is thus dissolved and carried along the paper in a long streak. The paper is dried at room temperature, turned through 90°, and the process repeated. This time PVOH is picked up from the streak and carried at right angles to it, close to the water front. But when the paper is finally dried and sprayed with an indicator, PVOH will be seen in two positions: remaining along the streak as well as at the water front. Thus PVOH which has just been demonstrated as fully soluble is immediately adsorbed by the cellulose when the paper is dried at room temperature, so that it cannot be dissolved. It is suggested that the same process happens to a large extent when PVOH is dried onto certain textiles.

The chemical process causing genuine insolubility must be a loss of water between adjacent chains, forming an ether link (*Figure 5*):

$$-CH_2-CH-CH_2- \qquad -CH_2-CH-CH_2-$$
$$\begin{array}{c} | \\ OH \end{array}$$
$$\rightarrow \qquad O \qquad + H_2O$$
$$\begin{array}{c} OH \\ | \end{array}$$
$$-CH_2-CH-CH_2- \qquad -CH_2-CH-CH_2-$$

Cross-linking should therefore be encouraged by low humidity. Three years' exposure (relative humidity less than 30 per cent, 7000 lux, about 35°C) gives a film with some cross-linking, but one which swells to such a weak gel in about 3 seconds that a test is needed to spot the insoluble portion. The possibility of insolubility should therefore be borne in mind by anyone using this material for conservation.

The two types of synthetic varnish

There are today two fairly distinct schools in the use of synthetic varnishes.

The first favours those synthetics similar in many ways to the natural resins, but more durable—AW-2, MS-2 and especially MS-2A. These resins are of much lower molecular weight than the normal thermoplastics. They form hard, brittle films from concentrated (50 per cent or more) solutions in very mild petroleum solvents. Their gloss can be controlled by adding small quantities of wax, and they can be readily manipulated to give the required finish. MS-2A is superior to AW-2 and MS-2 because of its higher permanence and greatly reduced tendency to matt or bloom.

The second school favours tough flexible films of high durability, which are usually sprayed on. These must be examined closely for their resistance to cross-linking, since they are all long-chain polymers. Feller has found, however, that polyvinyl acetate and Rohm and Haas Acryloid B-72 (see p. 174) are highly resistant to cross-linking. For permanence these materials are almost certainly superior to MS-2A. Their application requires slightly stronger solvents, such as toluene.

Unfortunately, all the possible materials fall into these two categories, whereas there would be much to be said for a varnish of intermediate properties.

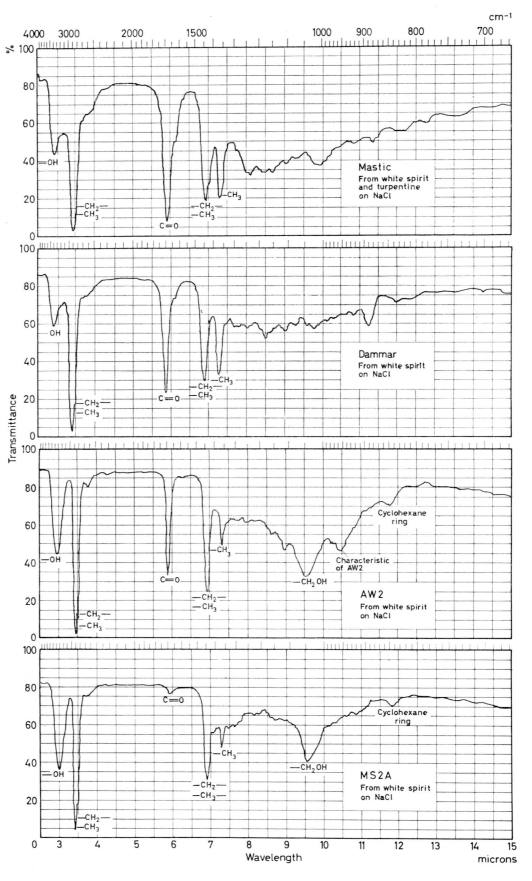

Figure 2. Infra-red spectra of mastic, dammar, AW-2 and MS-2A. In general, dips in the curve (absorptions) can be ascribed to definite chemical groups if they occur at wavelengths shorter than about 8 microns. At longer wavelengths there is less certainty, though the pattern is very useful for identification. All samples are mixtures (compare *Figure 3*), so that each curve is the result of several overlapping patterns and thus shows less detail. Note smaller amount of carbonyl (5·9 microns) in MS-2A compared with AW-2.

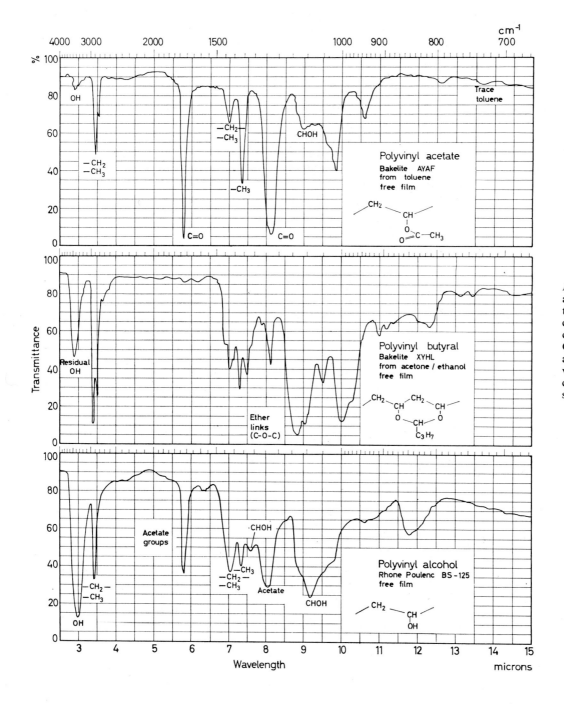

Figure 3. Both polyvinyl acetate and polyvinyl butyral contain polyvinyl alcohol groupings in their chains. Thus presence of OH groups is indicated on all three curves. Conversely, polyvinyl alcohols contain acetate groups—sample shown has about 20 per cent acetate.

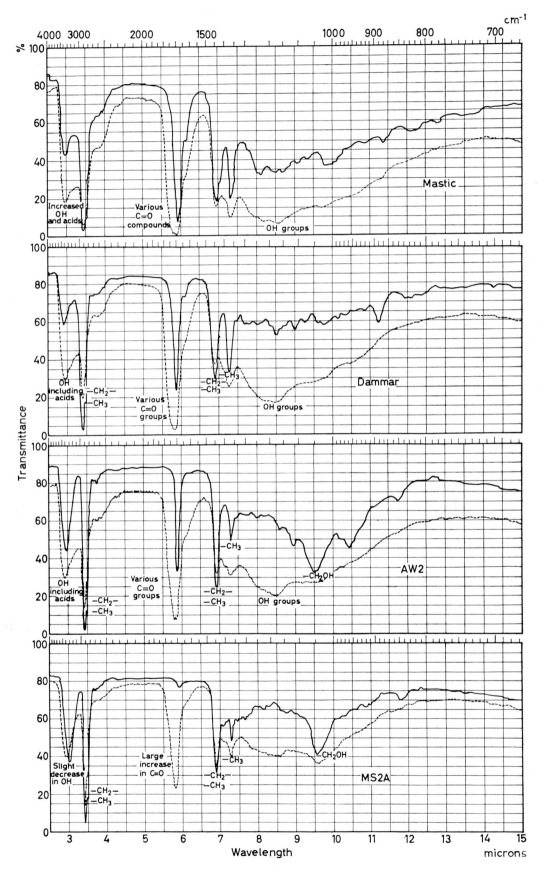

Figure 4. Lower, broken line shows effect of two months' exposure to ultraviolet fluorescent tubes (peak energy at 3500 Å). This exposure is closely equivalent to about a year under daylight fluorescent tubes at 7000 lux. General lowering of the line, especially around 5 microns, indicates loss of gloss. Lowering and loss of detail in 8–15 micron region indicate that variety of (oxidation) products is formed. Note superior stability of MS-2A, though the increase in its carbonyl groups (5·8 microns) is much greater than anything that has occurred in *Figure 5.*

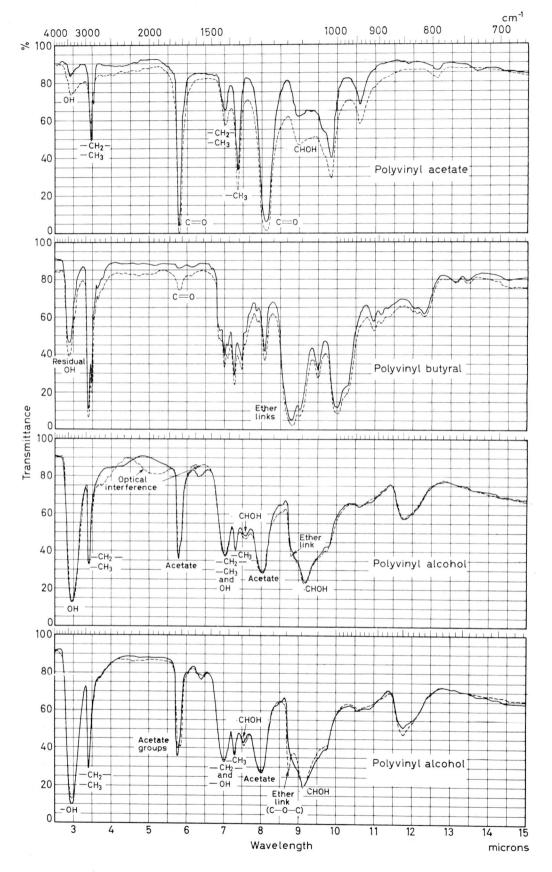

Figure 5. Top three curves: broken line shows effect of 2 months' ultraviolet exposure, as in *Figure 4.* Bottom curve: broken line shows effect of heat ($\frac{1}{2}$ hour at 135°C) on polyvinyl alcohol. Only small changes have occurred in these linear polymers. (Polyvinyl acetate has suffered from being too tightly stretched—resulting pinholes have caused loss of gloss.) Heat is known to cause insolubility in polyvinyl alcohol, and the new absorption in the bottom curve shows that this is due to ether-linking between chains. Slight ether-linking is also evident in ultraviolet - exposed polyvinyl alcohol (third curve).

Problems to be solved

Problem number one, to my mind, is this: To devise a sensitive analytical method of determining which way a varnish film is changing with time.

Without going into chemical complications, we may accept that the varnish is composed of molecular chains which can either break up or link together. If the chains break up (chain scission) the varnish will weaken and eventually disintegrate. If they cross-link, the varnish will become horny and insoluble. These reactions can proceed together.

What we need, therefore, is to be able to measure the balance between breaking and linking, or perhaps to form a 'solubility spectrum' of all the different molecular sizes and shapes in a varnish at any time. This can, of course, be done by long analysis with plenty of samples, but the Feller and Thomson methods, using paper strips, might form the basis for a more elegant method. Since all things change with time, we should probably end by selecting a varnish which showed a very slight drift towards increasing solubility with time. Since the drift must be very slight indeed, the test must be very sensitive.

Among the lesser problems waiting for investigation are the various possibilities for multi-layer systems. How much is one layer disturbed when another is put over it or comes off it? How to combine properties of two layers to their mutual advantage? As far as other properties go, we should also know a little more about how to ensure that a varnish protects the paint film chemically and mechanically, but never constrains it.

All these are analytical problems. Among the thousands of possible synthetic polymers, we only ever see those which (a) can be produced efficiently and (b) can be sold at a profit. Efficient production usually follows an estimate of profit, but the quantities we want are too small to warrant industrial research. There seems therefore no alternative but to do our own experimental syntheses. No one else is going to do them for us the way we want.

Appendix 1

Permanence comparisons at the National Gallery Laboratory, London

The tests from which the following permanence comparisons have been deduced were all made in one of two exposure cabinets containing fluorescent tubes: firstly, an almost closed box, temperature about 42°C (110°F), initial illumination 19,000 lux (but perhaps dropping to half this figure as the tubes aged); or, secondly, a cabinet open at the sides, temperature about 35°C (95°F), illumination 10,000 lux (initial), 6000 lux (after 2 years). In comparing these figures with conditions in a temperate-zone museum, it should be noted that a rise in temperature of the laboratory air, originally at, say, 20°C, 60 per cent relative humidity, to 35°C as it enters the cabinet will cause the relative humidity to drop below 30 per cent. Thus exposure takes place under very dry conditions. Other factors such as type and strength of illumination and temperature could, perhaps, be scaled to real conditions with some certainty but it is possible that the abnormally low humidity may change the course of certain reactions. This also applies to the infra-red spectral changes detailed in Appendix 2.

Under exposure in either of the two cabinets, the first visible signs of yellowing take place approximately as follows:

Dammar and mastic	8 days
AW-2	30 days
MS-2A	almost imperceptible after 3 years

(we can infer that MS-2 behaves like AW-2)

After 5 years in the first box, films of dammar, mastic and AW-2 show bad loss of gloss owing to surface attack, and much craquelure. Iso-amyl methacrylate (kindly supplied by the Mellon Institute) and polyvinyl acetate AYAF show no visible defects apart from dirt and dust after this time. MS-2A has only been tested for 3 years in box 2, but shows no loss of gloss or craquelure in this time.

Cautiously comparing these results with real life, we note that mastic starts to yellow after 8 days in the cabinets, whereas a similar sample on white glass in strong north light (say 2000 lux peak daylight, under glass) is likely to show the first signs of yellowing in about 1 month. On an average north wall in the National Gallery in well-diffused daylight (of perhaps 1/10th the above north light illumination), tests show that a similar stage is reached in a year or so. On this basis we can estimate an acceleration factor of about 50. Thus 5 years in an exposure cabinet is equivalent to about 250 years in a museum.

For a number of obvious reasons, this factor of 50 remains the crudest kind of approximation, though it appears to be in rough agreement with experience. Of somewhat greater value, bearing in mind the artificial conditions, especially the dryness, of exposure, are the following figures for comparative permanence, based on the same exposure tests:

Dammar, mastic	1
AW-2, MS-2	4
MS-2A	100
PVAc, iso-amyl methacrylate	200 at least

Published experience with outdoor paints would certainly add evidence for the extremely high mechanical and optical permanence of PVAc and the methacrylates, but I am a little doubtful that MS-2A has 100 times the expected life of the natural resins, from our infra-red data (see Appendix 2).

Appendix 2

The National Gallery Laboratory in London is using a Perkin-Elmer 'Infracord' infra-red spectrophotometer to gain information on the chemical changes which result in varnish deterioration.

The group of wavelengths lying beyond the red are called the infra-red. They are emitted by any strongly heated object, and the source of radiation in an infra-red spectrophotometer is a heated ceramic rod instead of a light source. Radiation from this source strikes a thin film of the specimen, and the instrument analyses the radiation that passes through, wavelength by wavelength, from just beyond the red to a wavelength of 15 microns. Just as a colour-filter absorbs part of the visible light that strikes it, so all organic materials absorb some wavelengths in the infra-red region. This information is plotted on a strip of graph paper, and from the resulting absorption pattern quite a lot about the chemical structure of the sample can be determined. The same varnish sample can be analysed at intervals, and the curves for each analysis superimposed on top of each other. Some examples of this are shown in *Figures 2–5*.

References

[1] Jones, E. H., in *On Picture Varnishes and their Solvents*, Feller, R. L., Stolow, N. and Jones, E. H. (Reports from a Seminar at Oberlin, Ohio, 1957), Intermuseum Conservation Association, Oberlin, 1959, pp. 166–198.

[2] Thomson, G., *Stud. Conservation*, 3 (1957) 75, note 1. For the same polymer, and presuming a constant cross-linking rate, the time for a given proportion of cross-linking to take place is inversely proportional to the degree of polymerization.

[3] FELLER, R. L., reference 1, pp. 155–63.

[4] THOMSON, G., *Nature*, 178 (1956) 807.

[5] THOMSON, G., reference 2, pp. 64–67.

[6] FELLER, R. L., Part 3 of *On Picture Varnishes and their Solvents;* and *Stud. Conservation*, 3 (1958) 162–174.

[7] Water-vapour permeability adapted from RENFREW, A. (ed.), *Polythene*, second edition, Iliffe, London, 1960, p. 253; FELLER, R. L., *On Picture Varnishes and their Solvents*, p. 144, Table II. Gas permeabilities adapted from SIMRIL, V. L. and HESHBERGER, A., *Mod. Plastics*, 27, No. 11 (1950) 95.

[8] SIMONDS, H. R., WEITH, A. J. and BIGELOW, M. H., *Handbook of Plastics*, second edition, Van Nostrand, New York, 1949, p. 576.

Agnes Geijer

PRESERVATION OF TEXTILE OBJECTS

The treatment of textile objects and fragments constitutes a very complex problem, too vast to be answered in one short paper. Emphasizing the precariousness of generalizations in this field, I shall try to present some points of principle that have to be kept in mind when dealing with precious old textiles. Some words concerning the background for these judgements may first be mentioned.

A remarkable quantity of ecclesiastic vestments, some dating back to the 13th century, has been preserved in Swedish churches. In order to save these historical treasures two leading Stockholm museum directors in 1908 established 'Pietas', a studio with the special purpose of textile conservation under scholarly control. This semi-official workshop subsequently developed into a kind of central institute for textile research and preservation, consulted by churches and museums all over the country as well as from abroad. Since 1930 'Pietas' has been under the direction of the present author, who was also attached to the Central Office and Museum of National Antiquities, into which the workshop was later formally incorporated. In 1938 'Pietas' was entrusted with the conservation of flags and banners belonging to the large collection of war trophies captured by the Swedish armies mostly during the 17th and early 18th centuries. For the methods developed for such objects see *Studies in Conservation*, 3 (1957) 1.

From the beginning every object has been analysed and photographed, thus making the 53 annual catalogues of 'Pietas' a rich archive, invaluable for students of textile art. Practical experience has subsequently developed a number of methods and procedures. Besides this work, in 1930–36 the writer was personally occupied with archaeological textiles belonging to the famous Viking burials of Birka (*ca* A.D. 800–975), which resulted in a combination of scholarly research and practical preparation work (published in 1938, 'Birka III'). The above-mentioned catalogues exemplify the very heterogeneous 'clientele' which can be received in our 'textile hospital'.

All organic material is subject to degradation caused by the oxidizing effects of the ambient air. Fragile textile material is easily affected, but the speed of this aging process also depends on the yarn and dyes used, which are differently affected when exposed to moisture, dryness, heat, light and other variations of local conditions.

Animal fibres—mainly wool and silk—are more resistant, whereas vegetable fibres (especially flax and cotton) rapidly moulder and decay in damp surroundings, which explains why these materials do not turn up in archaeological finds containing woollen material. As far as I know this is the case also in the famous 'deep-frozen' burials of Siberia and Greenland and in the peat finds of northern Europe, where objects of animal fibres, sealed off from the atmosphere and in constant contact with moisture—perhaps also because of the presence of methane—have been well protected against decomposition.

In some 'normal' archaeological finds the animal fibres have been conserved owing to the proximity of metallic objects containing copper, which, in contact with moisture, produces salts that act as disinfectant. But the best possible conditions for conservation of fragile organic materials are created by a constantly dry climate, such as that of Egypt, where even linen and cotton have been preserved. When not buried under the soil the textile fibres react somewhat differently. There is, however, hardly space to enter into the details of that question.

Storage and display

How are precious old textiles to be treated—the ones excavated and those never buried? To that question there are many different answers, but I dare say that the daily care, i.e. appropriate storage and display, should be given first consideration.

Light plays a predominant role. Particularly sunlight, but even ordinary daylight and artificial light are harmful. The damage caused by the various kinds of light varies according to the nature of the fibres and dyes. Light not only fades colours but also intensifies the oxidizing process in the fibres, thus promoting their destruction.

The preservation of colours raises very intricate problems. It is indeed difficult to reconcile the need for protection against the harmful effects of light with the legitimate desire of museums to exhibit the objects at their best to the public. Unfortunately the manner of displaying textiles in our museums often constitutes a direct danger to them.

Treatment for conservation

Now to the 'surgical operation' or active treatment generally called conservation. Its different measures may conveniently be grouped as follows:

1. As the composition of a garment or other textile unit can be of historical value, its parts should not be unnecessarily removed. Note that small details or joins may be of vital significance for the attribution. In all cases the original features must be carefully documented by descriptions and photographs.

Figure 1. Silk flag rinsed and laid flat to dry on specially constructed table. This has a raised strip along three edges. By adding a fourth strip the table is converted to a basin; by successively adding narrow tables the surface can be increased to 310 × 410 cm.

2. Cleaning, i.e. removal of those impurities which may damage the textile fibres and spoil the object's appearance, is an

(a)

(b)

Figure 2. Polish flag; 17th century intarsia work in silk taffetas, (*a*) before and (*b*) after conservation including water treatment as in *Figure 1*. Mounted between layers of silk veil, fixed with sparse sewing.

important measure, but it requires great knowledge and skill. Without that, cleaning may have disastrous results. Water may be used in most cases, but it ought to be soft and pure. Tap-water varies in quality and must be tested before being used. It is safest to use rainwater or distilled water. If the object is very dirty a synthetic detergent may be used, provided it does not contain any bleaching or optically active agents, like many of the detergents on the market. It may, however, be noted that some kinds of textile objects are damaged by water; among others painted silks, some dyes (especially 19th century) and padded material. In such cases some organic solvent (dry-cleaning) may be used.

A skilful water treatment (see *Figures 1* and *2*) can give astonishing results. It not only gets rid of the dirt but makes the fibres swell so that the threads straighten, become more flexible and also recover their natural sheen. Fabrics which have become crumpled or distorted regain their original shape and flatness without ironing, and this result will last if the fabric is left to dry against a smooth surface such as glass—the easily acquired effect of surface tension. When dried the fabric loosens spontaneously and can be easily removed.

This kind of treatment is to be recommended, in principle, for large objects as well as for tiny fragments, ranging from the scrupulous cleaning of excavated textiles—carried out with the help of a dropping-bottle, an aquarelle brush and blotting paper—to washing with a sponge in a large basin, the sponge partly replacing the dropping-bottle.

esthetic and practical standpoints. I shall return later to this matter.

It may be mentioned that in Stockholm we have made experiments with a water-soluble cellulose derivative, known as Modocoll E, to which are added a polyglycol and a fungicide†. This composition has been successfully tested for artificial aging. The first piece to be treated was a large Coptic tunic

Figure 3. Part of Coptic woollen tunic before (left) and after (right) conservation: consolidation with Modocoll-polyglycol and sparse sewing to a linen fabric.

Copyright Antiquarian Topographic Archives, Stockholm

3. In cases of more or less advanced deterioration, some kind of chemical impregnation may be desirable or even necessary. Fragments tending to harden and fall apart may need a fixative backing.

Various types of plastic (vinyl resins, etc.) have been used either for glueing or for impregnation; the result, unfortunately, is seldom quite satisfactory*. Plastics have a serious disadvantage: being hard to dissolve they can be removed only by means of solvents which may be harmful to the textile fibres. Furthermore, the treatment or glueing carried out with these products has the effect of depriving the fabrics of their flexibility and elasticity, which is a serious disadvantage from both the

(*Figure 3*) which badly needed a strengthening impregnation to stand the handling which was necessary for adapting a supporting fabric. Afterwards the Modocoll, used alone, appeared excellent also for other purposes, e.g. for saving various delicate remains during excavation work (*Figure 4*).

4. Very often a fragmentary piece has to be reinforced by, or fixed to, a foundation material. In discussions on practical methods of textile conservation the opinion has been put forward that a choice could, in theory, be made of either textile methods or chemical methods, i.e. between sewing and glueing. It has even been claimed that the latter method should be the new and only rational one. This is, indeed, an oversimplification.

---

* My criticisms of various methods of this type were published in *Svenska Museer*, 1959 (issued June 1960); a mimeographed English version is available from the Textile Department, Riksantikvarie-ämbetet, Stockholm. Part of the same paper was published in French in *Bulletin de Liaison du CIETA*, No. 13, Lyons, 1961.

† The Modocoll methods as hitherto practised are published in Swedish in *Svenska Museer*, 1961, p.1. A translation in English is available on request. Concerning the cellulose derivation itself, see *The Modocoll E Manual*, published by Mo och Domsjö AB, Sweden, 1960.

Sewing and glueing have been in use for a long time and both with bad results owing to defective knowledge, lack of consideration or—to put it more gracefully—excessive zeal.

It is, however, undeniable that both methods can produce good results when used in the correct manner. Which method to employ must, of course, be decided individually. If we

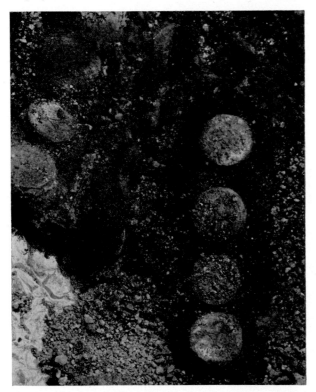

Figure 4. Portion of 6th century tomb. The bronze 'agraffes' are fastened to fine tablet braids, very much decayed. By spraying with a strong Modocoll solution fragments could be laid free and safely moved away. (Actual size)

accept the view that the principal task is to maintain the original nature of the object, and that, as far as possible, the door must be left open for the future, the conclusion is that irreversible steps must be avoided. Unfortunately, most of the glueing methods applied up to the present fall in this category.

Even textile methods, however, can be irreversible and thus inappropriate when the needle-work is too solid and too close to be removed without damaging the original. The universal rule, 'gently does it', is particularly applicable when dealing with fragile textiles. The sewing must be done with fine needles and supple yarn guided by a light hand, the stitches being sparse and fairly long. Excessively short stitches retaining a very limited number of threads subject the latter to strain and finally to breakage. It is to be regretted that many textiles have been damaged by sewing too much. Such examples do not, however, contradict the fact that sewing can give excellent results. I even venture to conclude that, in principle, the sewing needle, used alone or combined with some chemical treatment, is the instrument to be recommended. In this connection I must add that in several cases, especially small fragments, no fixing at all is necessary if the object is covered with a protective layer of glass, a plastic film or a silk veil (so-called crepeline).

5. The reinforcing work can often act as a reconstruction of the original form when filling gaps that are unpleasant to the

eye. But conflicts can also occur between these two opposite aims. The point to be emphasized in this connection is that remodelling of an old piece must not adversely affect its original qualities or modify its characteristics. The protection of the original nature of the piece is the essential objective. A skilful supplementary restoration may do much to give a true impression of an ancient object of art; an impression that the loose fragments would be unable to provide. Such restorations must, however, be made with the utmost tact and on the basis of specialized scientific knowledge.

Tapestry repair

As 'Tapestry repair' was included in the Rome Conference it may be appropriate to add a few words in this connection. Reweaving tapestries is a method which has been practised, I suppose, for about a hundred years. It has often caused irreparable and shocking damage, partly because the new yarn used was badly dyed but also because of unscrupulous reconstructions of missing sections of the design.

The eminent Swedish scholar John Böttiger, who saved the remains of the Royal Swedish collection of tapestries, considered this to be falsification. The method he introduced instead consists of filling the missing parts and reinforcing fragile sections by introducing from the back a special woven material dyed in a neutral or blending colour to which the loose threads are carefully sewn down; no fragments whatever are allowed to be removed, as is commonly done when reweaving.

This absolutely honest method often gives a good esthetic result, especially when an old tapestry is worn and faded. However, when comparing such a work with the magnificent Devonshire hunting tapestry in the Victoria and Albert Museum, London, recently restored by reweaving in the Haarlem workshop, I do not hesitate to say that this could not be improved upon esthetically because of the perfect execution—not because of the method itself. Nevertheless, it must be emphasized that, from the art historian's point of view, this piece is a less valuable document than it was before. It is no longer possible to be certain of what has remained of the original and what has been restored, what parts have been removed and rewoven, and what has been reconstructed by the restorers.

Reweaving tapestries is an extremely expensive process and this, of course, raises the question of economics: how much can one spend, and what is the piece worth? The latter question, at any rate, can only be answered by the art historians.

It is, however, obvious that such expensive methods cannot be commonly employed. The Stockholm method is less expensive. But as far as I can judge from Mr Beecher's paper (see p. 195) his second method may be another good (and less expensive) solution in many cases where damaged tapestries necessarily need a support. For esthetic reasons, where expense is an important factor, I dare say that so far I prefer the London method to the plastic impregnation method developed in Delft. I am basing my judgement regarding the latter on a sample shown in Lyons in 1959.

Conclusion

Although this type of object is not often handled in our workshop, I have chosen to speak at some length about tapestries because the problems they raise stress the necessity of estimating the historical and artistic value of the piece in question. The same view, however, and to the same degree, applies equally to numerous other textile objects. Here again I must emphasize that the art historian, and not the scientist, must make the final decision. It is my opinion that the decision should emanate from the historical-humanistic side, for the following reasons. Textile art belongs to this field of research, a field that will profit from the results of sound and careful conservation. It is the students in this field who supply the fundamental historic facts and the empiric knowledge of the extant material that should give the necessary background for estimating the artistic and scholarly value of the objects in question.

Familiarity with the historical and technical development and nature of textile art is an essential qualification for making a decision. The choice of a measure may be an irrevocable step which needs to be carefully considered by the person responsible. He should ask himself or another qualified person what the physical and chemical consequences may be, as far as possible, even including the long-term ones. He must take as many precautions as possible by the use of fully reversible methods in order to aid the application of improved measures in the future, as well as for further research.

It is a matter of course to investigate, often by scientific means, the material, the fibres and dyes, the weave, and other techniques; to judge the state of preservation or deterioration of the textile; and to tell which consolidation procedure may be possible. Here help is needed from the scientists. It is, however, no less important that the manual workers possess a high degree of knowledge concerning various textile techniques, as well as manual dexterity and special training in handling fragile objects.

I strongly emphasize the necessity of establishing an intense cooperation between different experts of the types mentioned, in the first place on the local level. The principal question is not always which method to choose but how the separate steps are to be practically executed.

I should like to mention one special point where we need biological research: that of damage caused by high temperatures. Swedish laboratory work concerning modern linen has established that the temperatures used should never exceed 80°C. During normal washing of white silk garments, the white easily turns yellowish, which may be a sign of weakening. The same is true of wool. But where do the dangerous temperatures begin, in case of modern textiles of different fibres as well as 'old' material? It is important to know this before one applies on ancient textiles the 'finishing' methods worked out for modern material. According to Dr Leene (p. 190) the latter are generally applied at high temperatures.

In this connection it might be stressed that the designation 'old' is a bit misleading because the 'aging' of textiles sometimes does not depend on the real age. There are, indeed, instances of textiles 3000 years old which are 'younger' than garments made only 300 years ago (*Figure 5*).

There is no doubt that workers in this field have much to learn from one another. Written evidence of experience in this

Figure 5. Piece of woollen material, showing its perfect preservation. Bog find from about 1500 B.C., dated by pollen analysis. (Actual size)

Copyright Antiquarian Topographic Archives, Stockholm

field is, of course, welcome, preferably information on procedures practised in single cases or for limited types, on technical observations and systematic research and on suitable implements and information material.

Summing up, I wish to emphasize the necessity of open and positive discussion, of a cooperation beyond professional and geographical frontiers. Of course, I agree with Dr Leene upon the need of fundamental research, though not only in the field of science, but also as a branch of the humanities.

Jentina E. Leene

RESTORATION AND PRESERVATION OF ANCIENT TEXTILES, AND NATURAL SCIENCE

Introduction

In our laboratory since 1953 we have been studying methods for the preservation of those ancient textiles which for several reasons cannot be restored by sewing and darning. As we only study chemical and physical problems, we have looked for a 'chemical' solution to the textile problems submitted to us by the directors of several Dutch museums.

This does not imply that we have a preference for 'chemical' treatment of ancient textiles. On the contrary, whenever possible, we advise the use of the other methods. This possibility, however, depends above all on circumstances (museum conditions, available credit for restoration purposes, etc.) which are outside our domain but which are the responsibility of the museum directors and conservators. However, since we do accept responsibility towards the object to be treated, we are always anxious to formulate the reasons that have led us to our advice and to mention the advantages as well as the disadvantages of a recommended treatment[1,2,3].

In practice restoring and preserving methods often coincide to a great extent; nevertheless, the concept 'restoration' is to be distinguished from the concept 'preservation'.

If restoration is defined as treatment with the purpose of restoring a former, better condition, then the concept of 'preservation' implies the maintaining of an existing condition or a condition created after restoration and, consequently, a check on further decay.

The objects put before the restorer generally require both treatments. They have already undergone the influence of the use for which they were intended; that is to say, they have suffered wear and tear. Moreover, they have been exposed to changeable climatological conditions (temperature, light, oxygen, humidity) by which they have aged. Micro-organisms, as well as foreign substances in the air (industrial fumes), dust, and sometimes wind and rain (weathering), have also contributed to the deterioration. In the case of textiles obtained from excavations, the possibility exists that composition, pH and moisture of the soil and micro-organisms, as well as remains of decomposed bodies, have had an effect on them. More often than not the condition of an object is dependent on the metal decorations found on it.

In the strict sense the restoration of a textile should be a putting back of the clock; namely, undoing the changes caused by the above-mentioned processes.

Many people have tried to achieve this by introducing new threads or new pieces of fabric made of comparable material and woven in the same pattern—often found only by comparison with other specimens, which were made after the same cartoon (tapestries)—or in a pattern thought to be correct.

It is evident that this is not a real restoration; the newly introduced material will always have a chemical and physical behaviour different from the ancient material, but it is a more or less esthetically satisfying kind of mending.

There is also a trend to the real restoration by using 'biochemical' or 'chemical' methods (both are neither further defined nor published by the research workers concerned), by which an attempt is made to restore the original physical properties such as elasticity, strength, handling, etc.

This is a very difficult problem, because during degradation by aging and weathering chemical reactions take place which are irreversible. The only thing that can be done, as far as I see at present, is to try out methods such as those used in the textile industry for improving the crease resistance and handling of fabrics and the permanence of pleats.

Most of these industrial processes require a treatment at temperatures above 100°C. If these temperatures are too high for application to ancient textiles, a search must be made for processes which proceed at distinctly lower temperatures or at room temperature.

Yet being careful about the temperature is not enough. When applying the methods mentioned the consequences are that in the fibres chemical reactions take place between, for example, the wool protein and the chemicals (e.g. formaldehyde). Moreover, there can be a cross-linking which changes the submicroscopic structure of the fibre. Here I must draw attention to a very important point: If there is a possibility of restoring the original 'appearance' of the material by changing the submicroscopic as well as the chemical structure as it is at the moment of treatment without actually restoring the original chemical structure, the question arises: 'Is this to be allowed?' I wish to emphasize that only in the case of an ideal success of the applied method will there be an advantage in restoring the original elasticity, suppleness, etc. There will, of course, always be the disadvantages that by the alteration in chemical structure it will not be possible in future to obtain reliable data on the original material, and that carbon dating and radiation dating will then also be impossible. These treatments cannot be undone, and therefore any future research on the structure of the ancient fibres will be hindered.

These remarks on the use of chemicals for irreversible restorations also hold good for preservation techniques.

It will be evident that, for an adequate treatment, the restorer has to know more about the chemical and physical properties of recent and ancient fibres than is generally the case. On recent fibres there are many good handbooks, but very little is known about ancient fibres and a systematic treatise is lacking.

This is a very unpleasant situation, for as long as this knowledge is lacking there is no possibility of good restoration and preservation. It will, moreover, be necessary to identify dyestuffs and to analyse soil and dirt, if present. Here also much remains to be done. Therefore we have to plan the cooperation of interested fibre scientists who should divide the work among themselves and start the desired research.

We have already studied degradation by light and atmospheric conditions (the results of which are not yet to be published) and we are planning research on ancient cellulose and protein fibres.

Preservation

In the meantime our ancient textiles need treatment, otherwise they will fall to dust. It is obvious then that we have to limit ourselves to reversible methods. If the methods mentioned by Geyer[4] and Greene[5] are not applicable the use of adhesives can be taken into consideration.

Starches have been used for many years for glueing fragile textiles onto supporting fabrics or pieces of cardboard. The results of these treatments are well known. There are good and bad ones, and, depending on the climate of the country concerned and the way of glueing the treatment lasts for a shorter or longer period[6,7]. Fortunately the starches are often totally removable by enzymes. During the last few years, since transparent adhesive tape has come on the market, many 'restorations'—or rather 'conservations'—have been performed by the lavish use of tapes across tears and worn spots. Their removal is extremely difficult and often causes an aggravation of the conditions. Furthermore, solvents are detrimental to certain dyestuffs, and therefore it cannot be too emphatically stated that the use of these tapes is absolutely forbidden. Also, there has of late been an increasing use of synthetic adhesives instead of starches and other natural adhesives. Research in our laboratory up to the present has been directed specially at this kind of adhesive, with which ancient textiles can be fixed on either a rigid support or a flexible support.

The adhesives which can be used for the purpose must satisfy certain conditions:

1. They must be completely transparent and colourless in order that the object that has to undergo treatment may retain its original appearance as far as possible.

2. They must have sufficient adhesive power, even after being exposed to atmospheric conditions for a considerable period.

3. They must not be subject to degradation and change of colour by the action of light and atmospheric conditions (industrial gases, etc.).

4. They must be free of elements which may be harmful to the fibres and the dyes.

5. They must be applicable at about room temperature.

6. They must change the properties of the surface of the textiles as little as possible.

7. They must be easy to remove in case this should prove necessary; for instance, for studying the weave, yarns, fibres, dyestuffs, etc.

8. They must not contain elements that will interfere with radiation dating and eventually carbon dating of textile materials.

We started with the use of polyvinyl alcohol (PVOH)[8,9]; this is soluble in water when in new condition, but after some time we discovered that it lost its solubility. The cause could be, among others, a substantial adhesion to the fibres, as well as mutual cross-linking of the PVOH molecules. This was later confirmed by the observation that a solution of PVOH which had stood during some three years became a solid mass that was totally insoluble.

The second adhesive we used was polyvinyl formal (PVF)[10], soluble in dioxane. This also gave reasonable results in some, but not all, cases. After application it is very difficult to remove because it goes into solution from the solid state via the gel phase. This gel phase dissolves only very slowly if stirring is not possible.

During the last two years we have made experiments with polyvinylbutyral (PVB)[11], soluble in ethyl alcohol (96 per cent), to which we added a certain percentage of a plasticizer. With this adhesive we obtained a good adhesion in many cases and a good flexibility so that it could be used with flexible supports, whereas the textile character of the surface is better maintained.

As far as we know at present neither the PVB nor the plasticizer contains elements harmful to the fibres. Its removability is much better, and from the literature we know that its light resistance is very good. Textiles stuck with this adhesive to a flexible support can be rolled, and hence the transfer is easier. Moreover, with a flexible support there are fewer limitations to the measurements than with a rigid one. It is possible to use fabrics of large widths (up to several metres), whereas the length is practically unlimited, or alternatively to sew or glue two or more fabrics of smaller widths to one another.

We have also tried Setamul N6525 (Vinamul N6525)*, a polyvinyl acetate internally plasticized with vinyl caprate, recommended by Mr Beecher (Victoria and Albert Museum, London)[12], with great success. It is applied as an emulsion in water. After the evaporation of the water it is soluble in ethyl alcohol (96 per cent). At the moment we do not know how its solubility is affected by time.

The next step will be to look for film-forming resins which, applied to curtains and tapestries hanging vertically, give them sufficient strength to be exposed without a support. Another problem is the preservation of laces, which are sometimes nearly dark brown and have little stiffness left, and linen fabrics (table-cloths, etc.). In these cases we use, if necessary, a very mild bleaching with sodium perborate at about 40°C, and stop as soon as the bleaching has gone far enough. It is not advisable to continue until the object has become really white[11]. If desired it is also possible to stiffen lace by impregnation with PVB. As this compound is not soluble in water, the lace can be washed at any time without effect on this treatment.

References

[1] GEYER, A., Bull. C.I.E.T.A., No. 13 (1961) 19–26.

[2] LEENE, J. E., Bull. C.I.E.T.A., No. 14 (1961) 16–20.

[3] GEYER, A., Bull. C.I.E.T.A., No. 14 (1961) 20–21.

[4] GEYER, A., Textilt Material i fynd och samlingar, Fornännen, 5–6 (1956) 267–282.

[5] GREENE, F. S., Workshop notes, Paper 1, The Textile Museum, Washington, D.C; Stud. Conservation, 2 (1955) 1–16.

[6] SEMENOVITCH, N. N., Restavratziyá i issledovaniye khoudogestvennych pamyatnikov, Musée de l'Ermitage, Moscow, 1955.

[7] LEENE, J. E., Bull. C.I.E.T.A., No. 14 (1961) 22–28.

[8] SIEDERS, R., UYTENBOGAART, J. W. H. and LEENE, J. E., Bull. Kon. Ned. Oudheidk. Bond, 6th Series, 9 (1956) 250–259.

[9] SIEDERS, R., UYTENBOGAART, J. W. H. and LEENE, J. E., Stud. Conservation, 2 (1956) 161–169.

[10] LODEWIJKS, J., Bull. C.I.E.T.A., No. 7 (1958) 20–23.

[11] LODEWIJKS, J., thesis to be published.

[12] BEECHER, E. R., Mus. J., 58 (1959) 234–235.

---

* This is a commercially available product. Vinamuls are produced by Vinyl Products, England; Setamul by Synthese NV, Katwijk aan Zee, the Netherlands.

Louisa Bellinger

BASIC HABITS OF TEXTILE FIBRES

At the Textile Museum in Washington, D.C., we deal to a great extent with fabrics made before the 10th century A.D., some of which go back as far as 2000 B.C. We have been making a study of such fabrics and their fibres for some years, not only with a view to conserving or restoring them but also to find out why the four main textile fibres—cotton, linen, silk and wool—were each used in a slightly different way. I realize that many of the fabrics preserved and exhibited in museums are very much younger than those I study habitually, but I think you will be interested, as we are, to see how much of the information we have tabulated is still applicable today. As there are no synthetic fibres in my field I shall only mention them occasionally, nor shall I expand on the microscopic or chemical study of fibres. There are good textbooks available for both these useful lines of research. We have organized our efforts on a slightly different but parallel line. We have tried to become acquainted with fibres and have noted the behaviour of the individual fibres as weavers long ago must have done, for when dealing with very old fabrics it is a great advantage to know how they will act under given circumstances. Our acquaintance does, of course, include magnification, but only low-power magnification in order to study a large enough area to see how numbers of fibres are grouped and how they behave in the situations man has contrived for them, for spinning and weaving are man-made crafts. Let us now explore some of the individual habits of the fibres and set out ways in which these data can be of use.

The natural fibres, cotton, linen, silk and wool, fall into two main categories. Cotton and linen are vegetable fibres; silk and wool are animal. Too many of us have forgotten that neither group was designed by nature to be made into fabrics. Wool and silk, to be sure, were created to protect living creatures, and cotton to protect the cotton seed, but linen had no such duty. Each fibre had specific functions to perform and the man-made crafts of spinning and weaving may hinder but do not entirely prohibit that performance. We must remember that there is nothing stable or permanent about a woven fabric. If it were to be ravelled and the yarns unwound, the separate fibres would be at liberty again unchanged.

Linen

Here are some of our data, starting with linen. Linen is a baste fibre, largely cellulose. In the growing plant groups of linen fibres hold flax stems upright and transmit moisture from the earth to the flower. They are sturdy fibres and smooth so that moisture can rise along their sides by capillary attraction. They lie closely together in a yarn as they did in the flax stem and the many points of contact make the yarn firm and tough. When linen fibres have been wet they rotate as they dry in the direction of the centre part of the letter S. (All vegetable fibres move as they dry.) The pre-Dynastic Egyptians apparently noted this habit and followed it when splicing linen fibres together, for the twist of the splice in the early yarns as well as the spin of the later ones, when they had learned to use a distaff, always lies in the S direction when made by an Egyptian craftsman. Thus they made long yarns for weaving which

would tighten or at least stay tight when washed. As we wash linens today, even though we follow good scientific rules and pick cleaning agents developed for washing cellulose, how many of us realize that if the yarns are S-spun they will tighten as they dry but if they are Z-spun they will unwind? Of course, they do not unwind all at once: linen fibres are 12 to 20 in. long. Still a linen canvas with single yarns Z-spun, no matter how tight it is stretched to begin with, will continue to loosen in a damp climate. We are sometimes annoyed to find that water spilled on a dyed linen fabric may shift the colour. In all fairness to the linen we should not be surprised, for the bundles of fibres in the spun yarns are only acting as they were designed to act in the flax stem. They are passing moisture along from one end to the other, the new supply propelling the old before it and incidentally taking the dye along too. There is evidence that Dynastic Egyptians tried to dye linen as the Greco-Roman world dyed wool but found that subsequent washings paled or entirely removed the colours. Whether this fact has always been known to weavers or whether it is rediscovered periodically I do not know, but I have found that most of the bright coloured stripes in modern linen dish towels are made with cotton yarns. In this instance man has been outmanoeuvered for a long time by an innate habit of a fibre.

Cotton

Cotton, the other vegetable fibre, is also cellulose; it is, however, not a baste fibre but a seed hair. Its function is to protect the cotton seed in its embryonic condition. It therefore does not transmit moisture, which might drown the seed, but seeks to isolate moisture or dry it. Cotton is a flat fibre with twists in it. It cannot be made into a smooth thread like linen because of the twists, so there is little capillary action in a cotton thread unless it has been Mercerized, a process which distends the fibre, making it round instead of flat. When cotton is drying each little fibre wriggles energetically, even when spun firmly and woven into a compact fabric. An example of this arose during the last war, when American troops in the South Pacific, where the climate is hot and humid, found that cotton gabardine uniforms itched unbearably, for every yarn in the close-packed fabric contained thousands of tiny fibres each wriggling to become dry. The Indians in a similar climate wear diaphanous fabrics which dry quickly: the British wear wool, which does not wriggle. Once more man is powerless against the habits of a fibre.

Cotton yarns from Asia in general and India in particular are Z-spun—the direction opposite to Egyptian spinning. We suppose the original users of cotton watched its habits and used it accordingly. The exception which proves this rule is the cotton from Meroë, which is S-spun. Apparently Nubians learned the Egyptian direction of spinning, which had been designed for linen, and applied it to their own vegetable fibre. Be that as it may, in our experience we have found that Z-spun cotton yarns tighten with washing whereas S-spun cotton yarns tend to pull apart if not handled very gently. After all, Near Eastern cotton measured only from $\frac{1}{8}$ to 1 in. long as against 12 to 20 in. for linen, so when Near Eastern cotton starts to unwind it does not have far to go. Western Hemisphere cotton is somewhat longer and is found spun in either direction, but New World yarns are apt to be plied as well as spun so that either the original spin or the ply is strengthened by the fibre movement while drying. Cotton, unlike linen, could be dyed easily and would hold the dye. It could be painted with dye or block-printed effectively. Reserve dyed and tie dyed patterns are common, and cotton could be gilded. Gold would not stick to the smooth surface of linen, but linen was an excellent base for painting with pigment, though it would not hold dye.

Wool and silk

Wool and silk, the protein fibres, were designed by nature to create an atmosphere for the creatures which lived or hibernated in their shade. Moisture does not make them move. Their part is to endure rather than to act. However, they do have to temper the climate to the unshorn lamb and silk worm, and to that end normally contained, and can also absorb, much more moisture than the vegetable fibres. The moisture content of air-dried linen is 5–8 per cent, of cotton 6–8 per cent, of wool 8–14 per cent and of silk 10–12 per cent of their respective weights. When the same fibres are exposed to an atmosphere saturated with moisture, linen absorbs 13 per cent of its weight, cotton 21 per cent and both wool and silk 30 per cent. The habitual moisture content of a fibre has a definite relationship to the amount of dry heat that fibre can stand. An iron cooler than 320°F will not take wrinkles out of silk, but one over 340°F will do appreciable damage to the fibres for it will dry up too much of the necessary moisture. Wool, which can have a moisture content 2 per cent lower than silk, should be ironed at a temperature between 350° and 370°F. The purpose of cotton, as we have seen, is to dry up moisture, so it can be ironed from 400° to 420°F. Linen, which passes moisture along without trying to retain it, can be ironed from 450° to 500°F. Rayon and nylon should be ironed below 300°F. This is not because of their moisture content but because they are apt to melt. When using a steam iron, the gauge should be set at the lowest point where water is turned to steam, for that temperature will produce the wettest steam. If an iron is hotter than that the wrinkles will not come out so well, for the steam will be dry and will merely act like hot air.

After this digression we return to wool. Wool fibres are covered with scales which vary in number and shape according to the breed of animal. Moisture can penetrate under the edges of the scales as under the ends of shingles on a roof, and the scales can catch scales on other fibres and felt together with them. Silk is a continuous filament—or rather a double filament—covered with gum sericin. The filaments, once the sericin is boiled off, are smooth and slippery. Neither wool nor silk has a preference as to direction of spin, though wool, being short, must be spun to make a yarn. As 400 to 1000 yards of continuous filament may be reeled from a cocoon, spinning is not necessary for silk, and was seldom practised in the Far East, where silk weaving began. Even in the Near East, where craftsmen were in the habit of spinning their yarns, the slight twist incident to reeling several cocoons together made a group of filaments into manageable weft yarns, though the weavers continued to spin their warp yarns as they did wool warps. Silk and wool differ in strength. Wool is only fairly strong and weakens when wet. Silk is very strong, its strength comparing favourably with a steel wire of the same size. The protein fibres are easy to dye. In the Near East wool was dyed in the pelt before spinning—in fact, the sheep themselves were occasionally dyed. Silk, like cotton, was dyed in the yarn, or patterns were applied to the finished cloth by printing, painting or reserve dyeing.

This information, as well as other data gathered mainly to help us place our textiles and crafts both geographically and in time, also serves to give us quite a new slant toward methods of handling fabrics while they are being cleaned and mounted.

Cleaning and mounting

Our object is to mount ancient textiles so that they may be studied and enjoyed without coming to harm. They cannot be studied easily if they are full of dust and dirt, nor can they be enjoyed to the full if they are crooked and wrinkled. A cleaning process is clearly necessary, not only to remove dust and dirt but also to relax the fabrics so they may be mounted with their warps straight as they were on the loom. This straightening of the warp brings the pattern back to where it was originally put by the weaver. In fact we do not like art historians to study early wool textiles that have not been cleaned and straightened, for we have found that when a textile was crooked or wrinkled there was a certain tendency to call it archaic or degenerate.

The first step in our cleaning process is dust removal. To the scientific cleaner dust and dirt are quite different. Dust consists of light, dry, loose particles of matter that may be removed by using the brush attachment of a vacuum cleaner, after putting screening over the fabric to protect it against the suction. This vacuuming is a must, for by putting a dusty fabric into a bath the dust may be turned into sticky dirt which will be harder to remove. Dust may be removed by suction irrespective of the type of fabric or fibres of which it is composed.

We shall not discuss here the processes of dry-cleaning or washing except to say that if both are necessary dry-cleaning should come first when working with old fabrics, as its possible drying effect will be counteracted by the washing. What I wish to speak of here is the behaviour of a textile while it is being processed.

As standard practice we always use Lumite screen under the fabric, and over it as well if it is to be turned. The screening allows dirt to fall away from the fabric and it supports the wet weight of the fabric. When the washing is finished the screen is lifted from the specimen. We do not lift the specimen from the screen. The foregoing data will give us a basis for making other preparations. In the Near East a great number of the yarns are singles, which means, in the case of vegetable fibres, that they will tighten or unwind according to their spin and the natural habit of turning of the fibre concerned. (When two or more singles are plied together the spin and ply more or less cancel each other, for one will be with the desire of the fibre, and the other against it.) Silk by itself will wash beautifully if the dye does not run. Dyes must be tested before washing with the soap or detergent to be used in the bath. If single yarns of a vegetable fibre are present, great care must be taken to keep them quiet if they are not spun according to their own preference. They may be covered with silk net inside the screening. If they are spun as they wish, the only particular care which must be taken is to see that their inevitable action does not interfere with any animal fibres which may also be present. For instance, if we have a cotton cloth embroidered with unspun silk, a combination often found in Asiatic 'tiraz' fabrics, we must be sure that the silk is protected against the strenuous efforts of the cotton to become dry. For if the silk has been weakened by sunlight and there is no spin to keep the filaments together or comparatively loose, the silk may crack off and be lost entirely. If there is any doubt of the durability of the silk, do not wash silk embroidery on cotton. However, if the silk yarn is spun and plied as it is in most Caucasian embroideries, the spin and ply give it elasticity enough for the action of the cotton to have little effect. Mulham cloth with fine silk warp ends and comparatively coarse cotton weft is a nuisance to dry, for the whole fabric tends to roll up diagonally as the cotton rolls. If preparations are made to keep all diagonally opposite points down there will be little trouble with the other corners, which will be trying to press down through the mount rather than to rise. Very sheer fabrics may be processed if this habit is taken into account. Where cotton is used in a textile with a wool warp, the warp usually has enough spin to be safe against the cotton. But if this textile has, beside the cotton weft, wool wefts with only a slight spin, the wriggling of the cotton may tend to crack off dry wool fibres.

The movements of linen are not so violent as those of cotton, but linen fibres are guaranteed to spread moisture. Preparations must be made to dry a linen fabric quickly if it is decorated with silk, which might bleed while drying slowly. It is not enough to dry the immediate area containing the silk as it would be if the fabric were cotton; it must not only be dried but it must be kept dry because the linen fibres, unless circumvented, will import moisture from those sections which are still wet. If this imported moisture reaches the silk it may still bleed. Cretan embroidery is worked in silk on a fabric with a linen warp and cotton weft, so both fibres must be dealt with.

Wool and linen may prove a tedious combination to manage, for wool is elastic and weakens with wetting, while linen is strong and inelastic. Such a fabric is apt to be relatively thick and if the yarns are closely packed as well, it is difficult to remove the dirt from the inner reaches of the weave. Tamping may be indicated to knock out the dirt or it may be better to use several baths, with intervening times for the fibres to dry, on the theory that when the outer layer of dirt is washed away it would allow inner dirt to loosen and prepare to depart in a second bath. Drying of a linen and wool fabric is somewhat of a problem as well, for saturated linen can only absorb 13 per cent of its weight in water while air-dried wool contains 8–14 per cent water. In this case the linen will continue to pull moisture from the wool and therefore it stays wet a long time.

Conclusion

These are some of the problems we are studying at the Textile Museum and a few examples that show how the knowledge we already have may be used to the best advantage to forestall mishap. We are continually undertaking new experiments and perfecting methods which let us process sheer as well as sturdy fabrics and may, we hope, give added life to tender as well as tough fibres. We believe that cleaning of ancient fabrics should be done by trained craftsmen and we are beginning to train apprentices.

In the near future we hope to start experiments to establish the humidity at which various fibres may best be dried. It is ironic that one of our chief concerns is not how to dry ancient fabrics but how to keep them moist enough.

E. R. Beecher

REINFORCING WEAKENED TEXTILES WITH SYNTHETIC-FIBRE NET

The purpose of this paper is to describe an extension of the method of reinforcing weakened textiles by sealing them to a supporting fabric of plastic net.

Originally, the procedure was designed to meet the problem presented by delicate silk fabrics that had lost their strength and were too tender to be held by sewing. The combination of lightness, strength and durability offered by a fabric of fine nylon net suggested that if this could be successfully laminated to fragile silk without significantly reducing its pliability, an acceptable method of reinforcement might be achieved.

In order to secure the maximum degree of contact between the fragile material and the supporting net, they are held together by a permanently flexible adhesive in the following manner. The filaments of the net are coated with an internally plasticized polyvinyl acetate emulsion (*Table 1*), which is allowed to dry; the weak fabric is then placed upon the net and light pressure with a heated iron causes it to adhere.

The question which naturally arises at this point—namely, the effect of heat upon old fabrics—is an important one. Some conservators take the view that contact with any significant

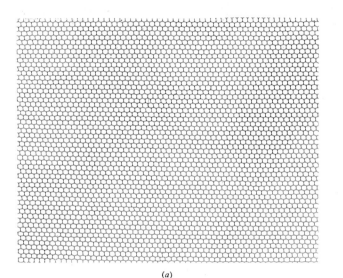

(a)

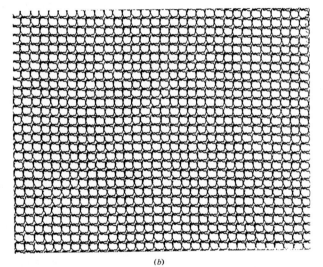

(b)

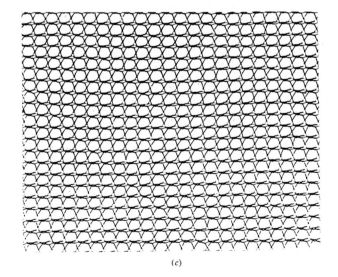

(c)

Figure 1. Nylon and Terylene supporting nets: (*a*) nylon tulle, 15 denier, 100 per cent bobbin; (*b*) filet mesh net, 125 denier Terylene warp, 140 denier nylon bobbin; (*c*) filet mesh net, 125 denier Terylene warp, 250 denier Terylene bobbin (all actual size).

degree of heat is not permissible. A reference to mounting a fragile textile by 'applying momentary heat which should not exceed 110°C' has attracted sharp criticism as being drastic and damaging. It is true, of course, that to expose textile fibres to excessive or prolonged heating must injure them; but it may be said with equal certainty that the majority of old fabrics has suffered much more damage from ordinary exposure to light

Table 1
Technical data on the internally plasticized vinyl
acetate–vinyl caprate copolymer* emulsions used

Total solids content (percentage)	55–57
Plasticizer (percentage on total copolymer)	15–25
Emulsion system	Anionic
Particle charge	Negative
Film properties	
Clarity (percentage of light transmitted through 0·1 mm film)	98–99
Heat discoloration (none = 0, severe = 100), 16 hours at 120°C	8

* Trade name: *Vinamul* 6525, made by Vinyl Products, Carshalton, Surrey.

than would be caused by momentary contact with a degree of heat a little above the temperature of boiling water. Happily, however, the degree of heat required to effect adhesion between the prepared tulle and the weak fabric is mild, and need be no more than about 70°C.

The particular advantages of this method of reinforcing fragile tissues are:

1. The pliancy of the textile is preserved.
2. The weave remains visible on both sides of the fabric.
3. The mounting operation is carried out without applying moisture or sticky substances.
4. It causes no staining or discoloration.
5. An indefinite amount of time can be spent arranging or straightening the specimen, but it can be fastened to the backing instantly.
6. It can be unmounted if necessary.

As a logical development of this manner of treating light-weight fabrics, the possibility of applying it to heavier materials was investigated and found to be feasible. In consequence, a

17th century tapestry (measuring 12 × 8 ft.) that was in a state of serious disrepair has been repaired by essentially the same method, modified in details of technique.

The backing material selected was a square-mesh net woven from filaments of nylon and Terylene, of less weight than the warp threads of the tapestry but considerably stronger. It is a sound principle in exercises of this kind that the reinforcing fabric should be lighter in weight, though possessing more strength, than the material it is to support.

Once the net had been prepared by coating its filaments with plasticized polyvinyl acetate emulsion, the tapestry was laid face down on a flat wood surface, like a table top, fitted with a flexible tube leading to a vacuum pump, after the pattern of a hot-table used for picture relining. The treated net was then spread over the back of the tapestry, the direction of least stretch being at right angles to the warp threads. Finally, a sheet of Melinex was placed over tapestry and net and sealed to the edges of the table top with adhesive strips. The vacuum pump, when put in operation, extracted air from the enclosure formed by the Melinex film, which in consequence was pressed by the atmosphere against the underlying net and tapestry and held them in intimate contact, the net accommodating itself to the minute ridges and contours of the tapestry. Radiant heat was then applied by means of an infra-red lamp, causing the polyvinyl acetate on the net to soften and adhere to the tapestry, thereby sealing them together.

A border of net was allowed to protrude beyond the top edge of the tapestry, and when the operation of sealing was completed this border was fastened to a batten, which was raised sufficiently to allow the tapestry to hang clear. It was allowed to remain suspended for several days. The purpose of this was to test the ability of the net fully to support the tapestry.

Net reinforcement attached in this manner does, to some degree, reduce the softness and pliability of the tapestry, but this is only noticeable when the textile is handled. There is no visual evidence of it, and when hung the fabric falls into its natural drape in an unrestricted manner.

Because it is economical in terms of time and labour involved, this technique for reinforcing deteriorated tapestry fabrics makes possible the preservation and display of examples that might otherwise be regarded as hopeless because their restoration by traditional methods is impracticable.

P. Rotondi

LA FORMATION DES CONSERVATEURS ET DES RESTAURATEURS

Le problème de la formation des conservateurs et des restaurateurs aurait dû avoir, pour l'Italie, un porte parole dont la préparation et l'expérience dépassent de loin la mienne. Il aurait dû être Cesare Brandi, qui a dû renoncer à participer à nos travaux. Nous avons ressenti sa présence lorsque nous avons visité l'Istituto Centrale del Restauro qui, depuis ses origines, l'a eu pour directeur et animateur, non seulement dans le domaine des recherches scientifiques et des réalisations pratiques, mais aussi dans celui de l'enseignement. C'est pourquoi je crois opportun de lui adresser une pensée toute spéciale, en ce moment où nous nous préparons à aborder un sujet aussi attachant: sujet qui, d'ailleurs, pourrait être traité de deux façons absolument différentes, selon que je laisse libre cours à ma fantaisie pour tenter d'imaginer ce que devrait être, dans tous ses aspects, la préparation idéale des conservateurs et des restaurateurs, ou que je m'attache au contraire à serrer de près ce qui, dans ce domaine, constitue la réalité effective qui m'entoure, et que je me limite à en faire le point pour en tirer les conséquences qui s'imposent.

Cette dernière voie me paraît, dans son réalisme, la plus juste et la plus utile. Je commencerai donc par me demander ce qui, en Italie, a été fait jusqu'ici et ce qu'on fait actuellement dans ce domaine.

Je dois tout d'abord attirer votre attention sur le fait que le «conservateur» d'une oeuvre d'art n'a pas partout dans le monde la même personnalité, les mêmes fonctions et les mêmes prérogatives. Dans bien de pays, par exemple, et notamment en Italie, le conservateur d'une église et des trésors d'art qu'elle contient, dont la valeur peut être immense, est en fait un prêtre, qui, presque toujours, manque de toute préparation technique et scientifique dans le domaine, non seulement de la restauration, mais même de la conservation courante des oeuvres d'art. De même les conservateurs de nombreuses et importantes galeries privées ne sont autres que leurs propriétaires respectifs, eux aussi dénués de toute préparation en fait de conservation.

Si j'ai voulu dès l'abord rappeler cette situation, c'est pour montrer combien il reste difficile de parler d'une manière générale de l'éducation et de la formation des conservateurs, et quel immense travail il reste à accomplir avant de pouvoir réaliser, je ne dis pas une préparation technique et scientifique, mais une simple prise de conscience du problème de la conservation de la part de personnes qui l'ignorent encore complètement.

En Italie, une loi spéciale a cherché à remédier aux dangers de cette situation en établissant qu'il est devoir de l'état d'intervenir, par des restaurations ou d'autres mesures, dans la conservation des oeuvres d'art qui sont propriété de l'église ou de personnes privées, en se substituant pratiquement à elles. Mais cette loi n'a réussi que dans une proportion minime à éviter le danger continuel de la mauvaise conservation, étant donné qu'il est bien difficile d'empêcher un propriétaire légitime de conserver, de la manière qui lui plaît, l'objet d'art qu'il possède. C'est pourquoi j'insiste sur la nécessité d'un travail assidu de divulgation auquel nous devons tous contribuer pour créer dans notre domaine une opinion publique consciente et active, et je suis convaincu que tout pourra être utile à la réalisation de ce but: un congrès, une campagne de presse, une conversation; mais surtout de bonnes restaurations, divulguées de manière à servir à tous d'exemple et de guide.

Naturellement, dans tous les pays où, comme en Italie, la loi est intervenue pour réglementer la conservation du patrimoine artistique, sont apparus des fonctionnaires publics que l'on ne peut pas appeler conservateurs au sens strict du mot, mais qui exercent cependant une activité très semblable à celle des conservateurs. Il s'agit des inspecteurs, des directeurs et des surintendants des Beaux-Arts, qui peuvent être en même temps directeurs des musées et des galeries de l'état. Voyons donc comment est organisée en Italie la préparation de ces fonctionnaires et quels sont ses rapports avec la préparation des restaurateurs.

Dans les universités italiennes, la seule Faculté de Lettres délivre les titres exigés de ces fonctionnaires pour qu'ils puissent entreprendre leur carrière, titres qui consistent dans le doctorat en lettres et le certificat de perfectionnement en histoire de l'art ou archéologie. Pour pouvoir obtenir ces titres, il faut fréquenter non seulement les cours fondamentaux de la Faculté de Lettres, mais encore des cours spéciaux qui, sous forme de perfectionnement, visent à affiner la préparation technique et scientifique des étudiants en leur fournissant, notamment, des notions théoriques sur la restauration des oeuvres d'art. Ces notions prennent parfois l'étendue d'un véritable cours, comme ce fut le cas au cours de ces dernières années à l'Université de Rome, où les étudiants qui se spécialisaient en histoire de l'art ont pu bénéficier des expériences réalisées à l'Istituto Centrale del Restauro.

Cependant, l'idée de créer une véritable faculté universitaire d'histoire de l'art, où les futurs fonctionnaires des Beaux-Arts trouveraient des cours particulièrement adaptés aux exigences de leur travail, fait son chemin. Une place fondamentale devrait y être accordée aux cours de muséographie et de science de la restauration, conçus naturellement de manière à permettre l'orientation des étudiants dans toutes les directions possibles.

L'idée de créer cette faculté universitaire est née de la conscience que les futurs fonctionnaires chargés de la conservation des oeuvres d'art doivent recevoir une formation plus efficace et plus spécialisée que celle qu'ils reçoivent actuellement; une formation qui les prépare à affronter, pendant leur carrière, n'importe quel problème (culturel, technique, scientifique) avec la compétence nécessaire. Cette compétence, tout en s'appliquant aux domaines les plus variés, doit avoir pour base une claire conscience historique et esthétique. En Italie, cette conception est considérée comme essentielle, et c'est pour cette raison que les études préparatoires auront toujours pour nous, comme point de départ, l'histoire et la critique d'art. Nous avons en effet la ferme conviction que dans notre domaine il n'est possible de concevoir aucune action de restauration, de conservation ou de présentation muséographique sans partir de l'appréciation critique de l'oeuvre qui doit être restaurée, conservée ou exposée.

C'est précisément cela, et cela seulement, qui constitue le terrain commun à la formation des futurs inspecteurs, directeurs ou surintendants des Beaux-Arts et à celle des futurs restaurateurs. Nous sommes convaincus, en Italie, que, une fois acquise une solide conscience historique et esthétique, les conservateurs et les restaurateurs pourront affronter sans craintes tous les autres domaines d'étude et de travail. On ne pourrait, en vérité, affirmer le contraire.

C'est pour cette raison que le programme suivi à l'Istituto Centrale del Restauro pour la formation des élèves donne la première place à l'histoire de l'art, avant toutes les autres matières. «L'enseignement de l'histoire de l'art», dit ce programme, «doit viser à la lecture de l'oeuvre d'art figurative, à fin d'apprendre à l'élève à se rendre compte des valeurs formelles qu'il est appelé à reconnaître et à respecter.»

L'étude de la chimie, de la physique, des sciences naturelles et de la technique de la restauration, de même que les travaux pratiques de radiographie, de spectrographie et de restauration, sont tous envisagés dans leurs rapports avec ce principe fondamental qui consiste, comme nous l'avons vu, en l'appréciation des valeurs formelles que la conservation et la restauration devront respecter.

Voilà ce qui, en Italie, est considéré comme le point névralgique de la formation des conservateurs et des restaurateurs.

Quand les uns et les autres auront atteint une capacité parfaite dans l'individualisation des valeurs formelles de l'oeuvre d'art, le reste ne sera plus qu'une question d'habilité technique et de réflexes—habilité technique et réflexes qui pourront être affinés par des années de pratique et d'expérience spécialisée, de recherches techniques et scientifiques, grâce à une étroite collaboration des restaurateurs, des gens de science et des critiques.

Le résultat de ce travail donnera naissance à son tour à des cours périodiques que les fonctionnaires et les restaurateurs des surintendances devront venir suivre à Rome à l'Istituto Centrale del Restauro. Ces cours, dont le projet est à l'étude, serviront à tenir chacun au courant des problèmes actuels et à susciter des échanges d'idées et d'expériences. L'idéal serait que quelque chose d'analogue puisse être réalisée également sur le plan international, non seulement par l'organisation de conférences comme celle-ci, mais encore en favorisant les stages et les cycles de travaux auprès des principaux laboratoires de restauration qui existent de par le monde. Nous ne devons jamais oublier que l'oeuvre d'art est un bien universel. Il est souhaitable que les principes et les modalités de sa conservation le deviennent aussi.

Sheldon Keck

TRAINING FOR ENGINEERS IN CONSERVATION

In a recent article[1] our colleague, Rutherford J. Gettens, very correctly observes that 'only a small portion of the riches of the past has survived. Much has been destroyed by fire, earthquakes, flood, war and rebellion. A small residue and a precious one is left, but that is threatened by the most inexorable agency of destruction of them all—time itself and slow decomposition. What disaster has spared time may eventually destroy.' Those of us who have worked in one museum for more than a quarter of a century, or who, like Ugo Procacci[2], have studied photographic records of the last half century, realize the truth of Gettens' statement and are well aware, from first-hand experience, that deterioration is a slow but inevitable occurrence, continuing day in and day out in our most precious artistic possessions. We believe, however, that though only a minute number of artifacts can escape forever, deterioration can be slowed, perhaps almost stopped. But we know that few people are conscious of the speed of this deterioration, fewer are interested in doing anything about it and fewer still know what to do.

As our artistic heritage decreases with age, however, the need for deeper knowledge of how to preserve it for the future has become more urgently apparent to those of us who are active in the field.

The responsibility for the conservation of our art extends to many people. In the museum everyone from the director to the guard who patrols the gallery has the duty of protecting works of art. Not only those who work in museums, but collectors, artists, government personnel and private citizens share this responsibility. All need to be better informed about the causes and rates of deterioration, as well as what should and can be done to preserve our art. An informed public, aware of the problems involved, will support research and will appreciate the results of a well-done restoration. Artists need, more and more, to be taught the principles and practice of sound construction to avoid 'inherent vice' in their creations. Collectors and curators need information on proper environment, as well as safer methods of handling, transporting and exhibiting works in their care. They also need to know what standards govern procedures for treating or restoring works of art.

Most of us are aware that, in spite of the richly informative publications of UNESCO, ICOM, the Rome Centre, IIC and others, much more remains to be done to educate museum personnel, collectors, dealers, art packers and carriers to put into effect the principles and standards for care and preservation already clearly delineated. Dramatic and graphic propaganda* is continuously needed until everyone involved in art is forced to realize the insidious action of 'time itself' and how persistent efforts are indispensable to counteract it.

While a programme of general education is extremely important, we recognize above all the urgent necessity for comprehensive education and practical training of the person who is entrusted with the actual preservative and restorative operation on a work of art. On him falls the ultimate responsibility for prolonging the existence of the work. If he is ignorant or inexperienced, his failure can result in damage or total loss. Primarily it is the training of this person, sometimes called 'restorer', sometimes 'conservator', that we are considering here.

Perhaps at this point a few definitions are in order to be sure we share a common understanding, especially since terms such as 'conservator' and 'restorer' have different meanings in various languages. The term 'conservation' is a broad one and certainly not a new one as applied to art*. It has already been defined in the Articles of Association of our organization†, but I think conservation may be more simply described as a concept including (a) 'preservation'—namely, action taken to prevent, stop or retard deterioration—and (b) 'restoration'—action taken to correct deterioration and alteration.

Preservation seeks to maintain an unchanging physical and chemical condition. It therefore stresses the scientific phase of conservation. It may involve only the continuous application of environmental controls or it may include treating the object with an additive or preservative. An apt comparison is furnished in the preservation of foods, accomplished by refrigeration, vacuum, dehydration or treatment with heat and additives which inhibit decay. One way provides a favourable environment, another produces a more stable chemical state.

Restoration is conceived as a more temporary operation, with a beginning and an end, completed when the structure has been returned, as nearly as circumstances permit, to what is considered its original physical and esthetic state. This includes rehabilitation of an already degraded structure, removal of deteriorated or later additions and compensation for losses. Restoration attempts to undo the alterations of time even to the extent of reversing chemical processes where possible. Restoration leans heavily on the critical judgement of the operator and stresses, therefore, both the esthetic and historical phases of conservation. But, if it relies entirely on esthetic criteria, the result may be, as it too often has been, a beauty treatment which neglects underlying and continuing disintegration.

The first question, perhaps the main one, which must be answered to our common satisfaction, is what kind of a position in the world of art and museums the student of conservation will occupy on completion of his education and training. Do we have a clear picture of the specific functions, professional or otherwise, for which the 'conservator' or 'restorer' who graduates from a training programme will be prepared? Is he

---

* Means to educate museum personnel as well as the public, for example, include exhibitions, motion pictures, demonstrations, lectures and posters concerning the care and handling of works of art.

* The term 'conservazione' applied to paintings appears as early as 1833 in an unpublished manuscript by Giovanni O'Kelly Edwards on the *History of the Restoration of the Pictures of Venice*, Academy of Fine Arts, Venice.

† *Articles of Association of the IIC*, London, 1950, p. 9. Conservation is defined as 'any action taken to determine the nature or properties of materials used in any kinds of cultural holdings or in their housing, handling or treatment, any action taken to understand and control the causes of deterioration and any action taken to better the condition of such holdings', and directly following is the statement that 'the word "conservator" shall be construed accordingly'.

to be just a highly skilled mechanic or will he be only a theoretician, a combination art historian and scientist, who directs technicians in a delicate operation on the complex body of a deteriorated and previously restored work of art?

Considering the variety of response to treatment that may unpredictably occur from area to area in the same work, especially in the field of painting, even after detailed examination, there seems little doubt that while the conservator must be a skilled craftsman, he must also have the initiative to act with authority on the basis of both wide practical experience and precise knowledge of materials and principles. Unless he is an expert operator himself he cannot with confidence direct the hands of others when a crisis demanding an immediate decision has occurred. As Stout[3] very aptly expressed it in 1950, 'The man who does the work is the man who must know what he is doing.' But what must he know, in order to know what he is doing? What must he know in order to fulfil his function as a conservator or restorer?

There is not, in my opinion, a danger that the restorer will be replaced by the art historian or scientist, or that he must protect himself from their encroachment into his domain. At the same time, Philippot[4] has noted that a number of forms of deterioration have been neglected or left without solution because they go beyond the competence of the restorer. The restorer then must cease to be trained only as a craftsman, artisan or artist. In order to progress technologically and to perform with esthetic judgement he must combine his craft with a knowledge of art history and an understanding of science.

If conservation includes preservation and restoration, then a 'conservator' is one who has mastered the knowledge and artistic skill needed for both of these areas of activity. A 'restorer' may be one who has mastered only the art of restoration, but since, today, an acceptable restoration includes physical rehabilitation as well, it seems essential that a well-trained restorer should also have mastered both phases of conservation. The product of today's training should qualify as an 'engineer in conservation' even though, in actuality, he is called a conservator or restorer. Primarily he must himself be able to perform the actual repair of a deteriorated work of art, because he knows its structure, understands the causes of alteration and is skilled in applying the indicated treatment. In order to complete the treatment with judgement and sensitivity, this engineer must have knowledge of art history, art technology and art criticism. Though not a scientist, he must be familiar with the scope, methods and applications of science. And though he may not be able to operate all of the specialized equipment used in examination and analysis, he must know what scientific instruments will give the particular information sought. He must be familiar with their limitations and with the significance of their results. Because his knowledge covers both art and science he will be able to act as the liaison between art historian, curator or art collector and the scientist who may make the analysis. He should be able to translate for him the findings of the scientist. In other words, in addition to his primary duties in conservation, the conservator-restorer has a secondary function* since, in our time, the scientific examination has become an essential part of the study of works of art, not only as an aid in treatment, but to reveal evidence of condition and authenticity to the art historian.

To achieve a high standard of professional competence, therefore, the student of conservation must first be trained in his craft. He must develop manual skill through continuous supervised practice. His eye must gain experience and his mind learn to interpret what the eye sees. Skills of this kind can be learned, but not taught, though guidance is essential in the process. Added to craftsmanship he must acquire a profound knowledge of materials, of environmental agents of deterioration and of the histories of art and technology. Involved in these subjects are principles of chemistry, physics, mechanics, history and art criticism. Where can he receive all this education? Who can teach him? And how long will it take him to become professionally trained? The questions of precisely what curriculum and how much time will produce a conservator remain open. It may take considerable experiment before a satisfactory working result is formulated. To gain the advantages of wide knowledge and experience so very important to the conservator requires a long time, but this can be shortened with teaching and guidance by experienced and communicative instructors.

Philippot[5] has concluded that instruction takes place either in small restoration studios or, more systematically, in art schools or institutes for conservation. In England, at the University of London's Courtauld Institute, the study has been placed on a university level. In the United States we have followed the British pattern with the establishment in 1959–60 of a Conservation Center at the Institute of Fine Arts, New York University*. Until then the only ways of learning the practice of conservation in the United States were through apprenticeship in small studios, self-teaching† or study in Europe. As practised in the United States, the apprenticeship system involves neither a system nor a binding contract, as it did in early times. The relationship of master to pupil follows no established tradition. It is often informal and haphazard, with no definite agreement regarding scope of curriculum, duration of training, costs or remuneration. For just these reasons, as well as for others, very few conservators in museums or in private practice have been willing to take the time or responsibility to train an apprentice. This method, together with self-training, has resulted in the widespread treatment of works of art by partially trained and inexperienced operators. It is hoped that the Center at New York University will eventually exert a potent influence in setting professional standards for enduring preservation and for ethical restoration practice in the United States.

It appears to me that training centres‡ which have emerged in

---

* Murray Pease of the Metropolitan Museum of Art presented this aspect of the conservator's role at a lecture entitled 'The conservator and the museum curator' at New York University, April 14, 1961.

* The Center was established through a grant of the Rockefeller Foundation, July 1959, and is housed in the Institute of Fine Arts, 1 East 78th Street, New York.

† A book on the restoration of paintings published in 1959 in the United States advertises itself as follows on the flyleaf: 'The artist who wishes to learn restoration will find this book an indispensable must. His income from a single restoration commission, which is usually easy to obtain, generally pays for the book more than ten times over.' The author proceeds in the book to explain how an artist may teach himself restoration.

‡ The Institut Royal du Patrimoine Artistique, Brussels; the Courtauld Institute, London; the Doerner Institut, Munich; the Istituto del Restauro, Rome; the Institut für Technologie der Malerei, Stuttgart; the Akademie der Bildenden Künste, Vienna; Conservation Center, Institute of Fine Arts, New York University, New York. All except the last are concerned mainly with the conservation of painting and sculpture. The programme of the New York University Center embraces broad principles governing the care of all the plastic and archaeological arts. This inclusive approach does not prevent eventual specialization which, in fact, is encouraged after the student has been introduced to the extensive variety of materials of all art forms and the problems of their preservation. Nevertheless, the aims and scope of education and training remain the same for all.

art schools, conservation institutes and universities since the original recommendations in *Mouseion* in 1932[6] can provide better than any other way facilities and faculties for the broad though specialized training modern conservation requires. Each of the three different types has advantages and disadvantages, but all, by their very nature, can more easily and more methodically expose the student to learned specialists in different fields, to various points of view about procedures and philosophy and to a broad vista of the problems to be solved than can the individual restorer in the small restoration studio. Most of the centres pursuing a planned and published curriculum allow three to four years* to give the student the necessary practical instruction and knowledge of art and science.

Because I feel they deserve much more penetrating study by a competent committee, I have not attempted in this paper to make any critical analyses or comparisons of current schools or training centres. For instance, I lack information on centres in Vienna, Lisbon and Barcelona, in all of which I believe teaching is done. Some others I know only from published brochures or brief visits. I would like, therefore, to direct attention to some areas which should be included in any detailed study:

1. At the Institut für Technologie der Malerei in Stuttgart, entrance requirements for students in restoration include one year of practice in a restorer's studio, plus a special aptitude test. In addition the first two semesters are considered probationary. Selection of students who have manual dexterity as well as intellectual ability, integrity, objectivity and patience is extremely important. Methods of selection cannot be too carefully formulated.

2. An analysis of the curriculum of the Istituto del Restauro, in Rome, shows that in their 3 to 4 year course about 79 per cent of the time is devoted to actual studio practice to gain skill and experience; 21 per cent is given to sciences, art history and theory of restoration. While this ratio may not be considered ideal by everyone, emphasis on the development of practical skills is essential to producing a high standard of practice after training is completed.

3. At the Doerner Institut in Munich certain advanced students are permitted to earn as they learn. Privately owned works of art are treated under supervision and students who need financial aid receive remuneration for what they do. Such a system may involve organizational, legal, ethical and practical difficulties, unless all aspects have been very carefully studied and are clearly delineated to everyone concerned. This method, however, may help the advanced student to prolong the duration of supervised study and to acquaint himself with professional practice.

4. The amount of time required to educate and train a conservator is considered to be about 3–4 years. Can a completely competent conservator be trained in this period or is an additional period of supervised practice needed, perhaps an internship with an established practitioner?

5. The Courtauld Institute and British Council in London have since 1956 presented a compressed two-week course on the conservation of paintings which is open to practising restorers as well as to others concerned with the preservation of paintings. In a less formal way, the Institut Royal du Patrimoine Artistique in Brussels has done similar educational work by inviting restorers from many parts of the world to spend as much time as they can in observing and practising with the staff of the institute. Refresher courses or highly specialized courses can be of great value and inspiration to older restorers who want to keep abreast of advances in the field.

6. In order to promote growth and progress, research and development of new materials and methods should be encouraged and undertaken in teaching centres as is presently done in Rome and Brussels.

7. The question of licensing remains a matter of the laws of individual countries, but should continue to be studied by educators in our field for the purposes of having as nearly as possible an international unity in requirements and standards.

The field of art conservation is composed of a small number of persons, compared, for instance, with those of medicine, law, architecture, creative art or art history: and it is an extremely specialized field. Since this is so, it seems logical that the very few educational centres now extant should cooperate in the teaching process by exchanging curricular ideas, students and teachers. Without loss of autonomy on the part of each centre, it might be possible for IIC and the Rome Centre to aid in this cooperation and to coordinate a kind of international training programme. Involved would be a thorough study of the present curriculum, teaching procedures and conservation processes in each of the present schools to make use of the strong points of each for the common benefit of all schools and students. Just as a start, centralization at the Rome Centre of information on all schools of conservation, including scope, aims, duration of courses, costs and requirements for admission, would simplify the present problem for young people seeking an education in this field. It might be feasible for IIC to have a standing committee of interested members from different countries which would work closely with the Rome Centre in studying means of education and training, set standards and suggest changes in present curriculi. Through international cooperation and through cooperation, in each country, of the teaching conservators with art historians and scientists, it should be possible to produce engineers in conservation who surpass in skill and knowledge those of us who are practising today. Only through progress in our field can we save our dwindling patrimony.

References

[1] GETTENS, R. J., Teaching and research in art conservation, *Science*, 133 (1961) 1212–1216.

[2] PROCACCI, U., Fresco crisis, *Connoisseur*, 142 (1958) 154–158.

[3] STOUT, G. L., The viewpoint of the conservator, *Alumni*, 19 (1950) 283.

[4] PHILIPPOT, P., Réflexions sur le problème de la formation des restaurateurs de peintures et de sculptures, *Stud. Conservation*, 5 (1960) 61–69.

[5] PHILIPPOT, P., reference 4, pp. 65–66.

[6] EIGENBERGER, R. *et al.*, Pour une éducation professionnelle des restaurateurs d'oeuvres d'art, *Mouseion*, 19 (1932) 83–85.

---

* Information on period of training, though incomplete for all centres listed in the previous footnote, is as follows:

Doerner Institut	3 years
Istituto del Restauro	3–4 years
Institut für Technologie der Malerei	6 semesters
Conservation Center, New York University	4 years

In Appendix V, pp. 27–29, of *The Conservation of English Wall-Paintings*, by the Wall-painting Committee, published by the Central Council for the Care of Churches, Aberdeen, 1959, a proposal is made for a three-year postgraduate course in the conservation of wall-paintings with possibly two additional years for advanced study.

Helmut Ruhemann

THE TRAINING OF RESTORERS

Introduction

From me no recent advance in restoration can be expected: I am a survival of the days of horse-drawn vehicles. My contribution would rather be a plea not to neglect tradition and accumulated experience in training future generations.

I hope I shall not be suspected of being a reactionary. From the outset I have eagerly availed myself of the aids that scientists offered to our profession and used them in teaching. Almost daily I profit by their advice. One can hardly know too much science, but, since a whole life is not long enough to learn restoring well, one can easily loose too much time in learning too many unnecessary details of science. Fortunately the physical and chemical side of conservation is now taken care of by those devoted scientists who have given up far more remunerative posts and prospects in order to work in our laboratories.

I want merely to recommend keeping the balance between the teaching of science on the one hand and that of aspects connected with art on the other. What little I have to contribute is all laid down in great detail in a book which is expected to come out in a year or so. This contribution is largely taken from its text, so I need not be exhaustive on my topic here.

Aims of restoring and training

The task of the restorer or conservator was agreed upon 31 years ago in this city: 'To preserve and to show to its best advantage every particle remaining of a painting'. We also laid down the main principle that should guide the restorer or conservator: 'Everything he does must be guided by the master's intention'. Thus he must study the master's intention and technique. That he can do only on perfectly clean pictures.

Taking for granted a thorough instruction in methods of consolidation, one of the first things he must be taught is therefore how to clean pictures thoroughly and safely.

Methods of teaching

At least as important as teaching safe practices is to instil the highest and soundest principles into the students and to teach them proper convictions and habits.

It would be tragic if remnants of 19th century errors and prejudices were propagated in training institutes. I am glad to say that there is now little danger left of this happening, since even in the institutions where the most conservative theories used to be proclaimed everything seems to be adjusting itself naturally.

I think I have shown in my book that the two quotations used in favour of incomplete cleaning are not valid; namely, Pliny's note on Appelles' 'black varnish with which he mitigated all too strident colours' and Baldinucci's remark that 'patina even suited certain pictures well'. The first is by a notoriously unreliable chronicler who lived 400 years after Appelles. The second may even be meant ironically. Neither is by a painter. On the other hand, we quote five or six great masters' own words which show unmistakably that they were anxious that the brightness and hue of their paint should not diminish and that they did not want their varnish to darken (Catalogue of Exhibition of Cleaned Pictures, National Gallery, London, 1946).

Patina

Patina may add charm to a building or a mediocre painting but it does nothing but detract from the quality of a fine one. The equivalent of a painting covered with patina or yellow varnish, however slight, is not a sculpture with patina, but a sculpture covered with enough mud to conceal its true form.

Semi-cleaning

In my book I show in great detail how the darkened varnishes and restorers' 'gravies' have fooled some of the foremost authorities and have caused their respect of 'patina'. Thus, teaching always to leave some of the dark varnish or dirt is utterly misleading and a pathetic waste of time. All my eminent colleagues who have tried it have admitted that it is very rarely possible to leave an even layer and that some must be painted back where too much has come off.

Above all, such half measures prevent the cleaner from learning his job properly and from making any progress in getting to know either the behaviour of original paint or the masters' methods or intentions, which must form the foundation of any restoration work on masterpieces.

Taste

That the cleaner should use his own taste instead of respecting that of the master is obviously wrong. It is equally erroneous to think that because a picture is old, dirt or darkened varnish must be left on it in order not to destroy the appearance of age. However much we may try we cannot remove the true signs of age intrinsic in the paint, fading or darkening of some colours, and cracking.

Moreover, if the practice of not cleaning right down to the original paint were general, none of the hundreds of discoveries would have been made (including signatures, reassessments and re-attributions) which are due to the removal of later overpainting.

Appearance of age

We are not interested in the appearance of age in a great painting (as in that of an antique chair), but in recovering as far as possible its original condition. What we must, however, teach young restorers is not to make an old picture look new by too much retouching and too shiny varnishing; this is where taste comes in. Looking at his finished retouching under ultra-violet light will give the beginner a salutary shock and will perhaps prevent him from ever repainting any spot unnecessarily.

Learning to clean

Of course he must be taught to leave a varnish which cannot be removed without harming the paint underneath. I have encountered about six such cases, either by Reynolds or by more modern painters who mixed soft resin with their paint.

The first cleaning experience the uninitiated should have is with a vulnerable resin painting of this type (any early 20th century picture will do). It would give him another salutary shock and prevent him from becoming overconfident.

Retarded progress

The old legend of Titian's and Rembrandt's vulnerable glazes has certainly served as a deterrent to the ignorant, but it has also retarded enlightenment and progress. The Titians and Rembrandts that I have cleaned are full of beautifully preserved transparent touches, known as glazes, which are delicate only in the esthetic sense. The only painting that I encountered in my 41 years of practice where in the test original paint came off with turpentine was a Stubbs of about 1800, which was obviously painted with a wax-resin medium. And even this picture I was able to clean completely and safely.

Creation of training centres

Ten years ago, Sir Philip Hendy wrote in *The Problems of Conservation* (Report on Progress in International Co-operation, International Council of Museums, 1950): 'The Commission . . . expressed the hope that in the future the greatest possible number of restorers would undergo systematic training and that the government of each country would establish travelling scholarships for this purpose at properly qualified schools of restoration. Also that, with the aid of bursaries, different countries should exchange restorers for training courses; so that knowledge of their different methods should be shared. . . .'

All these important suggestions of the ICOM Commission still await realization. Perhaps it is a matter for UNESCO or one of the large foundations to take in hand.

In some countries it will take time to overcome entirely the reluctance, still rife in at least one famous institution, to share unreservedly all the experience acquired in a lifetime.

Berenson once wrote: 'All restorers disagree.' It would be deplorable if the good ones agreed with the practice of the bad; and everywhere there are those who, however successful outwardly, envy and denigrate the better ones; but on a higher level there is agreement, collaboration and friendship.

Selecting candidates

From thirty years' teaching experience I have learnt that the greatest problem is how to select the most suitable recruits.

A training institute, particularly if it is attached to a university, should, of course, demand university entrance standard, but the many candidates who do not have it should also be catered for, at least for the present, while the dearth of qualified restorers lasts.

I do not agree with those of my colleagues in the USA who hold that anybody with an intelligence a little above average can be taught to be a good restorer. He can only be taught the teachable things, and talent, sensitivity, flair and a sharp eye are not among them. They can be developed, but only where they are inborn.

This brings us to the important question: should a picture restorer be an artist by nature and training? I have no doubt that he should, though several very successful restorers seem to have managed well without any apparent artistic talent or training, but these are exceptions. However, opinions on this point differ. Mr F. M. Kahn believes that a painter let loose on an old master's picture would paint too much on it. This could be true only of one without respect and understanding of great

art and without self-discipline. Mr Bazin, Curator of Paintings at the Louvre Museum, holds, in common with most curators I know, that 'restorers must be painters'.

It is not so much that the restorer must know how to paint retouchings, as that he must be able profoundly to identify himself with the old master and above all he must be thoroughly familiar with all the painter's materials, which only results from years of practical experience as a painter; and, in seeing a dirty, damaged and repainted picture, he must be able to visualize how it ought to look; how it will eventually look depends even more on his artistic feeling, taste and esthetic tact than on his mastery of the materials and the ways in which they have to be used.

Suggestions for a syllabus

Specialized craftsmen

Naturally a restorer who wants to specialize in the merely technical side of picture restoration, i.e. lining, woodwork, blister-laying, etc., does not need any artistic qualification except the necessary respect for the treasures he is to treat. Anybody with the technical gift of a good cabinet-maker or bookbinder can become an excellent preserver of paintings if he is taught by a conservator who masters all aspects of restoration.

I expect that, in a training course, those students whose bent and gifts make them more apt for this part of restoration work will soon sort themselves out and their further training is specialized accordingly. The minimum would probably be a three-year diploma course.

At a meeting of the United Kingdom Group of IIC, held at Stoke-on-Trent on July 4, 1961, complete agreement seems to have been reached on these main points: that training in art history and painting are more useful to a picture restorer than a scientific training, and that the specialist picture restorer must spend his whole time on pictures only.

If a student goes on overcleaning (on worthless trial pictures, of course) it may betray an incurable inadequacy of his character. If his retouching does not improve sufficiently (be it 'deceiving' or 'visible') it must be due to a lack of talent. In both cases he should be encouraged either to specialize in consolidation work or give up.

Test for talent

The first requirement for all persons concerned will always be integrity, and the second, talent. Both these evasive qualities should be tested by every available method, including graphology, before appointment or admission. For 'flair' and intelligence, a special test has proved most useful: I have 32 x-ray photographs, 16 of them from original Van Goghs and 16 from the forgeries made after these. I shuffle them together like a pack of cards and the candidate has to put the originals in one row and the imitations in another. Similar tests can easily be devised. Artistic gift should be judged from drawings. Those who do not pass these tests should from the outset be advised to train for preservation (consolidation) work only.

At one of the leading institutes the test for artistic qualification consists of nothing but an outline drawing from one or two pictures. In my opinion the candidate should at least be able to make a good drawing of a hand, and his eye for colour shades should be as carefully tested as his integrity of character.

The Louvre Museum has an excellent elaborate scheme for the entrance examination to its restoration studios, including a copy from an old master's painting and an art historical essay, but I suppose their candidates for apprenticeship have already gone through some previous training at an art college, which is preferable. A long trial period is, of course, imperative.

Restorers of objects

Should picture restorers be trained together with restorers of works of art and of archaeological treasures? My answer is that they should perhaps attend part of the science courses together, especially elementary ones, but there are so many things which only the one kind of specialist needs to know that it would be a great waste of time to make both groups partake in the parts of the training unnecessary to them.

Connoisseurship

A restorer who masters all the relevant science and uses all the scientific aids can still be the worst of his profession, whilst one with no scientific training can still be one of the best if his talent is great. He will, of course, have to be intelligent too and will therefore make use of every help he can get from scientific methods.

I find training in connoisseurship and in ethics of conservation most indispensable. A close contact and regular seminars with outstanding art historians will benefit both sides. Guided visits to galleries and picture sales should be on the syllabus as well as lectures on the methods of the old masters and on the detection of forgeries.

Commissions

Another point on which opinions differ is whether or not an official training centre should accept commissions to restore pictures. I am in favour of it, because no medical school can work without patients. If only the teachers work on the difficult and valuable cases, the risk would be negligible, as there would always be sufficient supervision. The fees for work done (e.g. for museums) would help to finance training institutes.

Languages

Another suggestion for the syllabus or examinations concerns languages. I have always found it most useful to know sufficient French, Italian and German to enable one to read all the relevant literature and to make travel more useful.

Postgraduate practices

After finishing three years or so at the training institute and passing a rigid final examination, the student should work another three years in the restoration department of a museum or with a freelance restorer of standing before he starts on his own and is entrusted with valuable pictures.

Volunteers

I have always been in favour of museums taking on 'volunteers', including those from other countries, perhaps on an exchange basis, and this system has worked most satisfactorily at museums in Berlin, Munich and other places. The authorities of the London National Gallery object to it, mainly because of the difficulty of solving the problem of responsibility in case of an accident. It should not be too difficult to solve this problem and others that have been mentioned, such as the possible moral obligation on the part of the gallery to reward the volunteer for the help he is giving and the difficulty of avoiding a conflict with regulations forbidding unpaid employment of apprentices.

Importance of the teacher

I should like also to stress that in our field, even more than in an ordinary school, not only the success of tuition but also the design of the syllabus will to some extent depend on the teachers available. Apart from the elementary ones, certain subjects will occupy a larger place in the programme if prominent specialists are at hand, at least until sufficient teachers emerge from the younger restorers.

The services of the older restorers of world renown in Amsterdam, Boston, Brussels, Florence, Munich, New York, Oberlin, Rome, Vienna, Warsaw and Zurich, to name only those I know personally, should be secured for training the younger generation.

Part of the syllabus could be covered by part-time teachers or by visiting lecturers employed elsewhere. The international composition of both the body of pupils and the teaching staff would help enormously in spreading international cooperation and that spirit of comradeship which is so admirable among North American restorers.

The principal

Whatever the syllabus and staff of any new training institute for restorers, it should have generous funds and be run by a picture restorer who has greatly excelled in his profession (if he has some command of science, all the better) or by an art historian administrator with long experience in restorers' studios.

National differences

It goes almost without saying that the syllabus of a training institute will vary greatly in the different countries, though they should be catering for international attendance. In Italy the emphasis will naturally be on frescoes, in Holland on Dutch paintings, etc.

Varying emphasis

Emphasis on either aspect of conservation will vary. In France and England the accumulation of darkened and tinted varnishes on the masterpieces during the 19th and 20th centuries reached appalling proportions. The material deterioration was comparatively slow and unspectacular. By contrast in the USA nearly all the paintings arrived from Europe already looking their best. The question of cleaning was no special problem. The extremes of climate and over-heating made the consolidation side of conserving all-important and with their technical bent American restorers soon improved consolidation methods considerably. To this day they have little time for anything else and only a few of them are interested in careful 're-integration' or 'in-painting'. In Italy, though there are not nearly enough conservators to deal with the vast destruction caused by war and insects, an admirably large proportion of their efforts is directed to exemplary cleaning and admirable visible (*striato*) retouching.

Similarly the balance will be different in other countries. Some will need more preservers, some a greater number of 'artistic' conservators (I cannot bring myself to use this word 'artistic' without inverted commas in connection with restoration). Several American museum directors to whom the eventual appearance of a painting matters as much as its preservation are looking with nostalgia across the ocean, and are trying to recruit their restorers from people trained in the European tradition, where connoisseurship, though waning, still plays a great part.

Matching 'compensation'

The discipline of matching retouchings should be rigorously taught in every restoration school; it has been the foundation of a practical and factual probing of the masters' techniques. Several wrong guesses published in textbooks will be disproved by this new kind of investigation, which has been helped by the physicists and chemists specializing on paintings; they in turn are assisted in their invaluable research by findings we have made. The experience gained in thorough cleaning and close retouching provides indispensable guidance for cleaning and restoring methods.

Many mistakes made in earlier restorations would have been avoided if this knowledge of the masters' methods and intentions, acquired through restoration, had been known and taught. I, for one, could have avoided my early mistakes if I had known then what complete retouching and complete cleaning have taught me. It was not the slipping of a scalpel or too strong a solvent that caused those mistakes, but the lack of understanding of the masters' methods. If well-matched retouching were to go out of fashion, I should not be surprised if the connoisseur-restorer disappeared at the same time.

Unmatched retouching, like incomplete cleaning, encourages an attitude of being satisfied with imperfection. It can be carried out by craftsmen who are not sensitive artists by nature; there is certainly no more exacting way of testing a restorer candidate for his general capacity of living up to the old masters than by closely matched retouching (which includes first-rate *striato*).

In this brief survey of my approach to teaching problems, I have deliberately set very high standards, though we may rarely achieve them.

Appendixes

Advice to young restorers

Wherever paintings of value are concerned:
Before touching the picture have photographs made;
Try to ascribe the picture to a definite school or master and to value it;
Try to ascertain and note the method and the various layers of the painting;
Report in writing on the condition of the painting and on suggested treatment. Give a written estimate, with wide margins between minimum and maximum cost;
Make minute cleaning tests on all colours;

Make the safety margin test;
Record these tests, if possible on standard forms (*Table 1*);
Test many cleaning solvents on trial pictures, but study one cleaning agent particularly well;
Paint out samples of every new substance you use on glass and old pictures;
Do not leave dirt in the depressions of the surface texture;
Do not accept commissions on the sale of paintings;
Avoid retouching forgeries and doubtful signatures.

Test for a restorer's diploma

(Answer any four questions, one of which must be No. 5 or No. 6. Time allowed, two hours.)

1. Describe either (a) Rubens' panel technique or (b) the primitive Italian technique with green underpaint.
2. Describe the treatment to be adopted for blisters and flaking paint.
3. Describe the safety-margin cleaning test.
4. Give an account of the technique of retouching.
5. What is the significance of the refractive index of the pigment and the medium?
6. Give as many examples as you can of pigments introduced since 1700. Name some historically important pigments which are now considered to be obsolete.
7. Name some typically heavy and typically light pigments.
8. What is the main use for restoration purposes of: (a) ultra-violet; (b) infra-red; (c) x-rays?
9. What are the ideal aims of the restorer?
10. Should losses in paintings be completely disguised by retouching or left visible? Give reasons.
11. Describe the disadvantages of cradling.
12. Describe the significance in restoring of the 'law of the turbid medium'.

Déon: 'De la conservation et restauration des tableaux', Paris, 1851

p. 55: 'It is understandable that the romantic amateur loves the rust and haze of the varnish, for it has become a veil behind which he can see whatever he desires: . . . "Under this smoky and grimy crust I shall perhaps find a masterpiece." How can one resist such a lure? How can one not prefer the deceptive hope of a treasure to a cold and mediocre reality?

'But in a museum like ours*, the finest in the world, the pictures must be shown sincerely, clean and in full light: Show them openly, that is how you will confound those scholars, clever with words, but less erudite than skilful in usurping other people's knowledge.

'Yes, we repeat, our pictures can bear the full light of day, and we must add that the duty of their curators is to show them to us with all their qualities, without heeding the clamours of ignorance.

'We must even say that it is a necessity to put the pictures right, for this museum, created for study, is today disastrous to young artists who go there seeking inspiration.'

_____
* The Louvre.

Table 1

Cleaning tests

ARTIST OR SCHOOL (signed?) PERIOD (dated?)	OWNER	DATE OF TESTS EXAMINED BY	
TITLE OR SUBJECT	PREVIOUS CLEANING	PHOTOGRAPHS	
CONDITION	CLEANING TESTS Varnish yields to . . . . vols. acetone . . . . vols. white spirit Paint resists . . . . vols. acetone . . . . vols. white spirit Vulnerable colours . . . . yield to . . . . vols. acetone . . . . vols. white spirit	SURFACE DIRT REMOVED WITH CLEANING CARRIED OUT WITH . . . . vols. acetone . . . . vols. white spirit METHOD USED FOR CLEANING Wiping . . . . Rolling	
PERIOD OR DATE	MEDIUM	IMPERVIOUS TO	CLEANED WITH	SAFETY MARGIN (yes or no)

Bohdan Marconi

PROGRAMME OF THE FACULTY OF CONSERVATION AT THE ACADEMY OF FINE ARTS IN WARSAW

Introduction

Because of the immense destruction of works of art during the Second World War and the insufficient number of highly qualified conservator-restorers, I was entrusted with the preparation of a programme for training conservator-restorers at the Academy of Fine Arts in Warsaw. In 1947, in collaboration with the then existing Head Office of Museums and the Protection of Historical Monuments at the Ministry of Culture and Art, the first Faculty of Conservation in Poland was organized at the Academy of Fine Arts in Warsaw.

During the years 1947–1959 this programme was subject to numerous changes with regard to the number of years of specialization and conditions of admission—after obtaining a degree at the Academy, or after the first, second or third year of studies at the Academy. With experience the scope of theoretical courses was enlarged.

At the beginning the programme included the conservation of paintings, murals, polychromes, sculptures (in stone), decorative arts, drawings, prints and ancient books. Archaeological objects were not and are not included. Esthetic conservation problems in this field are rare and rather simple. It seems, therefore, that the conservation of archaeological objects can be done by highly qualified laboratory workers under the supervision of scientists (chemists, physicists, biologists, etc.) familiar with esthetic and museum problems, and archaeologists. The training of laboratory workers for this purpose should be effected by special training courses designed to acquaint them with the latest methods and means.

The conservation of sculpture was discontinued, since under the conditions prevailing after the war the problem consisted merely of joining broken fragments or of reconstructing missing parts or even copying architectural sculptures. The essential problems connected with the conservation of stone are being solved on a world scale, but no solution has yet been reached.

The training of conservator-restorers of drawings, prints and ancient books at the Faculty of Conservation is reasonable in principle and it should train artists able to take care of objects having an artistic value. Large collections of prints and drawings, as well as libraries, need a large number of laboratory workers to make repairs and take care of the storage conditions. This should be done under the supervision of scientists (chemists, biologists, specialists on paper and leather) as well as those familiar with the problems of conservation from the artistic point of view.

At present the conservation of drawings, prints and books, which has existed since 1950, is temporarily separated from the Faculty and is controlled directly by the Rector of the Academy.

The aim of the studies is to train artist-conservators well acquainted with the problems of modern conservation, both artistic and technical, in the history of painting techniques, technology, chemistry and physics to the extent that they may require this, and also photography for conservation purposes.

The history of art, which the students study for four years, beginning with the first year of their studies, is completed with lectures and practice in special museum problems such as cataloguing, methodology of attributions, study of costume, heraldry, palaeography, etc.

In view of the necessity for the cooperation of conservators with specialists in chemistry, physics and biology, as well as having lectures and practice within the framework of the programme, the Faculty of Conservation cooperates with a number of scientific institutes, with the university, the polytechnic (spectrography), the High School of Agriculture (fungi, moulds and insects), etc.

Organization of the faculty

The students are admitted to the Faculty of Conservation after completing three years at the Painting Faculty of the Academy. Two lectures on conservation (three hours each, with slides) are given to all third-year students in order to interest the eventual candidates and to explain to all students that the ability to paint is not sufficient by itself for modern conservation.

Academy graduates can also be admitted, but then they are not entitled to scholarships and to student homes.

The studies last three years (fourth, fifth and sixth year), of which the sixth is devoted to the diploma thesis. Some delay in submitting the thesis may be allowed if there is difficulty in obtaining an object which is suitable for the diploma work or if difficulties arise during the conservation.

Detailed programme

During the fourth year the students are informed on all problems of conservation, which will enable them to make some scientific researches, some training exercises on objects available to the faculty, and practical training, beginning with the most simple treatments.

During the fifth year theoretical and practical training is enlarged.

The faculty trains students in the conservation of paintings, murals and polychrome sculpture (Prof. Bohdan Marconi).

The problems of conservation of such materials as wood, textiles, metals and gildings are included in the programme. The knowledge of the more complicated and delicate problems of conservation of paintings, both from the technical point of view and from the esthetic one, enables the graduate to specialize further in the conservation of objects of decorative art.

The workshop of the conservation of paintings and decorative art and the main laboratory of the State Conservation Laboratories at the Ministry of Culture and Art are used in training the students. In agreement with the Academy of Fine Arts and State Laboratories and Workshops the students can use for their training a number of objects sent in by the Ministry of Culture and Art and district conservators and museums (murals, altars, paintings, sculptures, stalls, etc.).

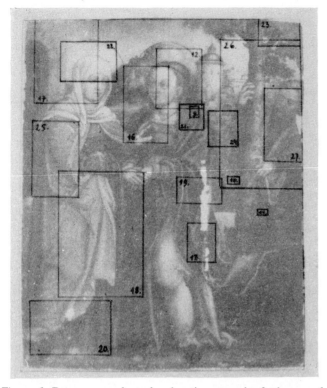

Figure 1. Boguszyce polyptych: location record of photographs taken from the front side.

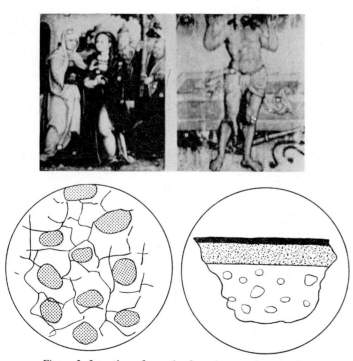

Figure 2. Location of samples for microscopic and micro-chemical analysis, taken from both sides of the treated fragment, and records of cross-sections and surface.

Figure 3. Microphotographs of white lead and chalk from ground.

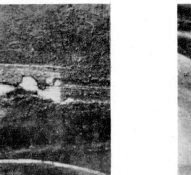

Figure 5. Macrophotographs taken during the removal of the oil layer.

Figure 4. Fluorescence in ultra-violet light, before and after removal of a recent thick layer of oil.

Figure 6. After conservation, mounted in the reconstructed wing of the polyptych.

Figure 7. Copy of the treated fragment.

After the fourth year the students are obliged to have 1–2 months' practical training during the vacation period, and after the fifth year, 4 months of practical training before they start on their thesis. This training normally consists of the conservation of murals. The practical training takes place under the supervision of the professor and assistant professors of the Faculty of Conservation, Academy of Fine Arts.

Lectures: Lectures are held—with the demonstration of researches and treatment, when necessary—on the following subjects:

1. History of conservation and modern principles.
2. Esthetics and ethics of conservation.
3. History of painting techniques.
4. State of conservation, depending on the structure, conditions and former restorations. Symptoms of normal and premature aging. Illnesses of different structural elements; influence of surrounding conditions (humidity, temperature, light). Noxious organisms (mould, fungi, insects) and their destruction and prevention. Handling of objects, storing and transportation.
5. Scientific methods and the history of their application: radiology, ultra-violet rays and fluorescence, infra-red, spectrography, magnifying lenses, the microscope and microchemical analyses (in connection with the lectures in chemistry).
6. Documentation. Description of the state of conservation: photography (simple, colour and in various lights), radiographs, recording of microscope and microchemical analyses, designs (plans, structures).

7. Forgeries and copies: history, esthetic analysis, scientific and technical research.
8. Technical methods of modern conservation.

Practical training: Handling of works of art. Treatment, beginning with the most simple procedures, depending on the objects available, preceded by a careful study of each object.

Schedule of lectures and practical training
(in hours per week)

Subject	4th year	5th year
Theory of conservation	3	3
Practical training	10	10
Technology and practical training on the conservation of murals	5	5
Chemistry and laboratory training, photography	3	3
Special museum problems	3	3
Painting, copying, drawing	14	14
	—	—
	38	38

Chemistry: Theory to the extent needed for a conservator. Microchemical analyses and technology of structural materials of objects of art and of materials for conservation (artificial materials included). Photography for conservation (half a year). Practical training in chemistry (analyses) and photography in the laboratory.

Figure 8. The Rosary Madonna before conservation: 17th or early 18th century repaintings are evident.

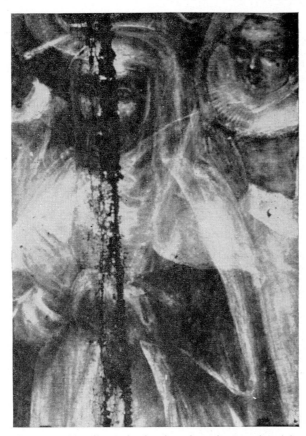

Figure 9. X-radiograph showing the saint on the right (56 kV, 10 mA, 8 sec, 85 cm focal distance).

Figure 10. The Rosary Madonna after cleaning, before restoration.

History of art: Special museum problems: cataloguing, methodology of attributions, history of costume, heraldry, palaeography. Practical training in museums and libraries, seminar.

Technology: Training in the technology of the conservation of murals. Practical training with painting materials. Making of copies or compositions in mural techniques. Intentional damaging, covering with plaster, repainting in order to make injections, reinforcements, cleaning of whitewash or repaintings, transfer, conservation and retouching.

Practical painting techniques: Painting from nature in different techniques. Copies in the technique of the original (half a year). Drawing (in the evenings).

Thesis

(a) Conservation of a painting or a fragment of a mural done independently by the student in consultation with the professor and his assistant as well as the lecturer in chemistry. Scientific documentation, including the description of the state of conservation, the result of studies (radiography, fluorescence in ultra-violet rays, ultra-violet reflection, infra-red, microchemical analysis; eventually also spectrography, photographs before, during and after treatment, macro- and microphotographs, structure drawings, drawings of changes in colours and diagrams). The description of treatment applied, its motivation and esthetic solutions.

(b) Attribution from the point of view of the history of art: description of the artist, school and period, giving comparative and bibliographical data.

(c) Copy of an easel painting or of a fragment of a large picture or a fragment of mural painting done in the techniques of the original.

After graduation the graduate obtains a diploma as an artist in conservation.

In the years 1947–1959 fifty diplomas were awarded; most of these were for conservation of paintings, three for conservation of objects of decorative art, three for conservation of drawings, prints and ancient books, and one for conservation of sculptures. Nearly all graduates, with very few exceptions (notably women, because of family reasons), work in their profession in museums and state laboratories, and very few work privately.

Figures 1–10 give a selection from the photographic documentation in diploma theses presented at the Warsaw Academy of Fine Arts. The first seven refer to the left wing of a polyptych in a wooden church at Boguszyce, Polish School, Jantas from Warsaw, 1558. The last three concern a Polish School Rosary Madonna of 1599 from St James Church, Sandomierz.

Henry Hodges

AN *AB INITIO* COURSE IN THE CONSERVATION OF ANTIQUITIES

The following observations are intended to do no more than to summarize the present position of the course in the conservation of antiquities given at the London University Institute of Archaeology, to which are appended a few pious hopes for the future.

The course was originally intended for the enlightenment of students taking the Post-Graduate Diploma in Archaeology on the principle that those wishing to go into the administrative side of the museum world, or intending to excavate, should at least have some inkling about the well-being of the antiquities in their care. Indeed all students taking this diploma are still required to attend the first year of this course and complete a limited number of laboratory hours.

In the immediate pre-war and post-war periods the curators of a number of museums sent members of their junior technical staffs to attend this course on conservation. This was a frank admission that the apprentice system in the museums was not really working out; indeed, far too often there were apprentices taken on with no one qualified in the museum to instruct them. The final demand for an *ab initio* training came, in fact, from a number of curators of Empire and Commonwealth museums who were only too painfully aware that if their technical staff were to receive any training at all it had to come from outside their own countries. At that time, in the immediate post-war period, students could seldom be spared for more than a year, and in that period they were often expected to learn the rudiments of other things besides conservation—for example, display and excavation techniques. The situation was thus far from ideal, and one must confess to too high a proportion of students whose training fell short of even the basic requirements. An examination of these failures invariably showed that the trouble lay in an inability to grasp the simple scientific principles underlying all conservation work. Clearly, when the opportunity arose, three things had to be done:

1. A greater emphasis had to be laid on the teaching of elementary physics and chemistry.
2. All teaching not directly connected with conservation had to be ruthlessly pruned.
3. The length of the course had to be increased to at least two academic years.

These conditions were realized when, four years ago, the Institute moved to a new building, and the Conservation Department was thus endowed with a new laboratory designed especially with teaching in view.

General scheme

Allowing a course of two years, what should we attempt to teach? The answer is surely extremely simple:

1. The nature of the archaeological materials themselves;
2. The causes of their deterioration;
3. The prevention or cure of that deterioration.

Laboratory work must occupy a large part of the student's working day, for manual dexterity and a working knowledge of tools and materials can be acquired only by constant practice. Added to this there are some ancillary techniques which, while not directly connected with conservation, are nonetheless vital to the work of a conservation laboratory, principally photography and draughtsmanship. The problem thus resolves itself into one of arriving at workable proportions of lecture time/laboratory time/ancillary subject time. In my opinion at least half the students' time should be spent in the conservation laboratory, and our final solution, working a seven-hour day through a five-day week (35 hours a week), which is about all the staff can tolerate even if the students could stand more, looks like this:

Laboratory work	17 hours
Formal lectures	8 hours
Photography	7 hours
Draughtsmanship	3 hours
	35 hours

Lecture programme

The first student year is seen as one in which a basic groundwork is acquired, the second as one of increasing specialization. But what is basic to the conservation of antiquities? The foundation stones on which we have decided to build are elementary chemistry and physics on the one hand, and the study of technology (materials and techniques of early man) on the other. The chemistry and physics look something like the subjects generally taught at school, but even at this stage the emphasis is put on what is vital to conservation, while some aspects, because of the shortage of time, have to be omitted. Thus, for example, silicon and the silicates are given far more emphasis than in any school textbook, while the commercial production methods of most compounds have to be omitted. The course is thus more than a revision of those things learnt at school for students fortunate enough to have taken these subjects before they came to us. I should add that some laboratory time is devoted to practical work on these subjects.

Technology is not envisaged as the history of technology. It is quite simply a study of the materials available to early man and the methods he used to work them, as well as the interreaction of materials and techniques. The lectures have to be curiously basic at times, for it is dangerous to assume that the modern student, for all his apparent sophistication, has any first-hand knowledge of even the simplest craft-processes. Thus, of a group of twenty British students only two had ever seen a blacksmith at work, and they had only seen horses being shod, while the assistant curator of a major provincial (African) museum had never seen pottery being made, although he had a most imposing list of examination successes. This being the case, a part of the course is devoted to pottery-making and some aspects of metal-working. In parentheses I must add that some students have taken outside classes in ceramics. From our point of view they seem to be virtually useless. Using prepared clays, electric wheels and commercially formulated glazes, the students may eventually produce a passable ashtray;

about making pottery from the raw materials they seem to learn next to nothing.

By careful dove-tailing of the courses it is naturally possible to begin teaching conservation concurrently. Thus, once the student has learnt the fundamentals of the crystallization of soluble salts, the effects of crystallization within a ceramic body can be appreciated, and the cure put into practice. The chief difficulty here is to keep all three courses in step. From our experience it is almost always fatal to cover any aspect of conservation before the physical and chemical background has been adequately prepared.

What I have termed the ancillary subjects, photography and draughtsmanship, are not taught in the Conservation Department, but in the respective departments within the Institute. I hope I do not need to emphasize the importance of these subjects as they affect the keeping of decent laboratory records. Needless to say, teaching follows the same lines as in our department: no student, for example, touches a camera until he has acquired a reasonable theoretical background.

I have left until last any mention of a formal course in archaeology. I confess I hold heretical views on this matter. I, personally, feel that the history of science and technology would be the most suitable subject for our students. Be this as it may, our students do take a short course on general archaeology—omitting, I am sorry to say, the New World and the Far Orient. From it at least they may learn what the archaeologist expects of them, and vice versa.

In the second year, in place of general physics and chemistry, we aim to cover very limited fields of a wide variety of sciences:

Botany: The structure of wood (but not identification); the structure of plant fibres used in textile making.

Zoology: The structure of skin, connective tissue and bone; the identification of the bones of the commoner domesticated and wild animals.

Chemistry: A rather summary survey of the commoner organic compounds, particularly polymers; the simpler spot tests for radicals; some aspects of metallography.

Physics: The behaviour of light, x-rays and ultra-violet (including some practice in the use of radiography and ultra-violet); simple circuit electricity.

The aim of this course is self-evident: it attempts to familiarize the student with the fundamental techniques of examining artifacts from a material point of view. Remembering that many of the students may end up in laboratories not over-endowed with money or equipment, the object is to make the student as self-reliant as possible.

Also in the second year the students are given a course on the care of pictures. We are, naturally, not attempting to turn them into picture restorers, yet, at the same time, many combined museums and art galleries, while having a conservator to deal with the archaeological collection, have no one to care for the pictures. Any well-trained conservator, we feel, should at least be able to look at a picture and decide whether it requires attention or not.

Laboratory work

Laboratory work is graded to the ability of the individual student. Every student begins with a very simple job and is given a progressively more difficult task after each is completed.

Despite what we believe to be very careful selection, the rate of progress of the individual student varies enormously. But speed and well-finished work are not our only criteria of good laboratory students. Our insistence on the keeping of clear and accurate laboratory records often appears to the students almost maniacal. Why it should be so difficult to get the

average student to keep a record of his work I cannot imagine, although nearly all of them see at some time in the laboratory objects that have been treated in the past, and the further treatment of which would be greatly expedited if only one knew what had been done to them.

We endeavour to give our students as wide a range of materials to deal with as possible: pottery in various stages of decay; objects of bronze, iron, lead and silver; wood that is worm-eaten, suffering from dry-rot and water-logged; leather suffering from physical or chemical decay; and, when the opportunity arises, glass and fabrics. Much of our material comes from excavations carried out by the staff of the Institute, the rest from smaller museums in south-east England. Materials are accepted for treatment only on the understanding that the work will be undertaken as it suits our teaching programme, and we have found it prudent never to specify a date at which any particular job will be finished. Apart from the difficulty of estimating the time required to carry out any piece of work, an epidemic—even the common cold—among the students can wreak havoc upon the best-planned schedule.

We have always adopted the policy of giving our students antiquities to work on from the very outset of the course. It might seem simpler to use what is expendable. This, I think, would be bad training. On the whole, students are quick to evaluate, and should they realize that what they are working on is frankly rubbish, I have no doubt that their work would suffer accordingly.

In their second year of laboratory work we also aim to give our students a grounding in casting techniques, using not only the older plaster and gelatine moulds but also natural latex, synthetic rubbers and polyvinyl chloride. Casting materials include polyesters and acrylates, while each student is expected to make a number of copper electrotypes.

Selection of students

From all that has been said it must be clear that the type of student we would like to encourage is the one who already has had a fairly good scientific grounding at school. As things are in Britain today, and I suspect elsewhere, any student who shows a competence in science subjects at school will normally go on to a university, where he will take a degree, and thence be scooped up by some industrial organization. We are thus faced with the almost inescapable fact that for some years to come our students will have had little or no previous scientific training; and from what I have seen of students from other countries, the same is true there. It is no good bemoaning this state of affairs; one simply has to accept the situation as it is, but it does make the selection of suitable students difficult. On the whole we tend to examine the hobbies and pastimes of prospective students as much as their academic records; any hobby that requires a certain amount of manual dexterity and a curiosity about what makes things work suggests a suitable type of personality.

A certain amount of artistic talent in the student is clearly to be preferred, but one must remember that one is looking as much for the copyist as the creative artist. I regret to say that in our experience students who have spent any appreciable time in an art school are generally most unsatisfactory. This may not be true elsewhere, but we have found that on the whole the cult of 'artistic temperament' amounts to little more than a total lack of self-discipline and responsible behaviour, both of which are insupportable in a laboratory.

Future prospects

At the moment our students receive no official recognition

of their ability other than our own internal certificate, and the validity of this depends only upon the esteem in which we are held by others. This may seem rather harsh treatment for those who are successful, and indeed I feel it to be so; but it must be remembered that the course has been in existence in its present shape for only four years. To redress this state of affairs two alternatives seem possible:

1. To persuade the authorities of the University that the course is eligible for degree status.

2. To persuade the museum authorities (the Museum Association) that the course is eligible for diploma status.

The first alternative would mean that the course would have to be extended by another year, and would equally have to include a wider range of subjects. For the immediate future we have so tailored the course to suit the requirements of the museums that we feel that it is to the Museums Association that we must look for help and advice; on this score the omens are at present good.

INDEX

A-J-K dough, 134
Abrasion,
  effects, 35
  protection from, 142
Acetates, polyvinyl (*see* Polyvinyl acetate)
Acetone,
  leaching by, 85
  solubility, 80, 81, 82
  swelling power, 86
Acidity, degree of, 68
Acids
  paper deterioration, 40
  stripping reagents, 109
Acrostalagmus koningi, 67
Acrylate-methacrylate, 172
Acrylates, 144
  casting, 212
Acrylic resins, fixatives, 119, 121, 122
Acrylics, 176
Acryloid, 119, 172, 173, 175
  cross-linking, 178
  insolubility, 174
Actinomycetes, 57
Adhesion, 140–144
  forces of, 141
Adhesives, 141, 142
  aqueous, 144
  classification, 143
  glass restoration, 155
  supporting nets, 195
  textiles preservation, 191
  thermosetting, 176
  wax-resin, 162
Aerogels, silica, 48, 52, 59
Aerosols, poisoning following inhalation, 52
Afnor standards, 65, 66
Age of objects, 113
Aging, 209
  accelerated, tests, 173
  appearance of age, 202
  artificial, 67
  bacterial, 7
  decomposition products, 85
  ease of solubility of certain resins, 79–83
  effects, 80
  fungi causing, 7
  investigations into nature of, 82
  materials, 7–8
  murals, 123
  re-forming, 80
  textiles, 185, 190
  varnish degradation, 82
Agneau Mystique, 170
Agritol, 48
Air
  bubbles and canvasses, 119, 121
  impurities, purification, 15
  pollution, paper deterioration, 41
  transportation by, 15
Air-conditioning (*see also* Atmosphere,
      Environment, Humidity, Temperature),
      58
  chambers, 78
Alcohol, 176
  diacetone, 82, 83
  diffusion of solvents, 87
  paint films, danger to, 84
  polyvinyl (*see* Polyvinyl alcohol)
  solubility, 177
Alcohol-ether-resin process, consolidation of
      water-logged wood, 125
Aldrin, 49, 50, 52
Alexandrian mosaic plaques, 145, 146, 147
Alizarin, fungal activity, 76
Algae, 62
Alkali carbonates, 90
Alkaline sequestering agents, 109
Alkalis, paper deterioration, 40
Alkyd resins, 75
Alkyl methacrylates, 173
Alum process, consolidation of fragile
      objects, 125
Alum solution, adhesives, 144

Aluminium
  concentration in glass, 148
  inclusions in glass, 150
  paint, effectiveness, 163
Alvar, 80, 81, 129
American colonial glasses, 146
Ammonia,
  quaternary salts of, 67, 68, 71
  solvents, permeability, 177, 178
Ammonium lauryl dimethylcarboxymethyl
      bromide, 67, 71, 72
Analysing crystals,
  lithium fluoride, 36
  mica, 36
Analysis, 19–38
  archaeological research, 33–38
  chemical, 21
  chromatographic, 21
  destructive methods, 20, 21
  electrolytic, 21
  fluorescence, 112, 113
  handbook, 26–28
  inter-element effects, 34
  methods of, 19–25
  microchemical, 21
    antiquities, 19–25, 29–32
    paintings, 29–32
  non-destructive, 20–22, 30, 31, 33–38,
      111–117
  physical techniques of, 112
    antiquities, 29–32
    paintings 29–32
  pigments, 36
  polarographic, 21
  quantitative, 35
  sample size, 34
  specimen holder, 34
  spectro-chemical, 36
  spectrographic, 21, 113
  superficial, 113
  type required, 31
  X-ray diffraction, 112, 113
  X-ray fluorescence, 113, 115
Ancient glass,
  microanalysis, 145–151
  repair, 152–155
  reproduction, 152–155
  textiles (*see* Textiles)
Anglesite, 91
Animal fibres, 192
  degradation, 185
Annealing, 148, 151
Anobidae, 56, 59
Anobium punctuatum, 73
Anobium striatum, 56
Antibiotics
  fungicides, as, 48
  toxicity, 49
Antichlors, 76, 77, 78
Antifungicides, 71
Antimony, 114
  concentration in glass, 147
  glass colouring agents, 147
  inclusions in glass, 150
Antioxidant inhibitors, 81
Antiparasitic compounds, 48
Antique glass, restoration, 152
Antiquities
  analysis methods, 19–25, 29–32
  bronze
    cross sections, 105, 107
    examination and treatment, 104–110
  conservation
    ab initio course, 211–213
    degree status, 213
    diploma status, 213
    diplomas, 211
    draughtmanship, 211, 212
    photography, 211, 212
  deterioration
    causes, 211
    prevention, 211
  France, 93–96

Antiquities—*continued*
  laboratory work, courses, 211
  lecture programme, 211
  metallic, 93, 95
  methods of analysis, 19
  national, 93
Antlerite, 91
Apothecium, 64
Araldite, 126, 130, 133, 134, 167, 168
Archaeology,
  courses, 212
  metal objects, examination, 101–103
Archimedes method, 113
Archival material,
  conservation methods, 39–47
  decay, causes, 40
  deterioration factors, isolation, 40
  insect attack, 39
Archives, biological agents damaging paper,
      55–61
Argentine, 91
Arigal C process, wood consolidation, 126
Arnegonde ring, 112
Arsenic, 114
Art
  collectors, 200
  history, 197, 198, 200, 203, 206, 210
Artists
  materials, tropical conditions, influence, 74
  signatures, authenticating, 37
Ascomycetes, 70
Ascomyceti, 57
Aspergillus, 57, 63, 70
Aspergillus niger, 10
Atacamite, 90, 108
Atmosphere,
  changes, paper deterioration, 41
  protection from, 140
Atmospheric moisture, canvasses, 75
Atmospheric pollution, 50, 76
Atomic density, 35
Atomic number, electron-beam probe
      analysis, 146
Atomic piles, 23
Atropus pulsatorium, 56
Attribution, 206, 210
Australia
  aborigine paintings, 74
  conservation of works of art, 73
Autoclave, 71
AW-2 resin, 172, 173, 174, 176
  infra-red spectra, 180
  picture varnishes, 177
  ultra-violet exposure, 182
  viscosity, 175
  wrinkling, 178
AYAA, 173
AYAB, 172, 173
Azurite, 108
  crystalline, 90

Bacillus thurigensis, 48
Bacteria, 62, 64
  aging caused by, 7
  cellulose deterioration, 165
Bacteriological cabinet, 71
Bakelite mounting, 146
Balsa, 157, 162, 166, 169
Banners, conservation, 185
Barrow method (deacidification), 67
Basidiomycetes, 70
Baste fibre, 75, 192
Bedacryl, 129, 172
Beeswax, 98, 136, 140, 164, 166
Bentonite, 15
Benzotriazole, 109
Benzoyl peroxide, 134
Beta rays, 23
Betilidi, 56
Bibliographical data, 210
Biotrol, 48
Bird, bronze, 137, 138

215

Birdlip bronze bowl, 132
Birka, 185
Bismuth, 113
Black beetles, 56
Blatta, 56
Bleaching methods, tests, 78
Blind cleavage of paint, 156, 160
Boats, consolidation, 125, 126
Boguszyce polyptych, 207
Bond formation, 173
Bondafiller, 129, 134
Bone
  analysis of, 25
  mineralized, 130
  ornamental, 31
  patina, 89, 108, 109
  relief, mineralized, 129
  restoration and conservation, 97–100
  sheet, photography, 104, 105
  small objects, 139
  stripping reagents, 109
  taper section, examination, 105, 106, 108
  weapons, 31
Bookbindings, durability, 41
Bookclasp, gilt copper, examination, 107
Books
  ancient, programme of Academy of Arts, Warsaw, 206
  biological agents causing damage, 57
  dusting, 59
  fumigation, 78
  leather bindings, 40, 41
  lice, 56, 59
Borers, Australia, 73
Bornite, 90
Boron, organic compounds of, 71
Botallacite, 91
Braconidi, 56
Bragg law, 33
Brochantite, 91
Bronze, 94
  ancient, 89, 135–139
  antique, 137
  antiquities, 104–110
    cross sections, 105, 107
    grinding and polishing, 105
    low magnification, examination, 104
    naked eye examination, 104
  bandeau, 130, 131
  boiling in distilled water, 109
  bowl, consolidation, 132
  chinese, 31
  cleavage, plane of, 105
  corrosion layers, 108
  cuprous chloride removal, 109
  disease, 107, 108, 129, 130, 135, 139
  epoxy resin application, 132
  hanging bowl, 137, 138
  metallurgical examination, 101
Buffering solutions, 78
Buffers, 10
Bullae, leaden, 131, 132
Butanol, tertiary, 125
Butylmethacrylate, 172, 173
Butylmethacrylate polymers, 171, 174
n-butylmethacrylate, 80, 81, 141, 171
  murals, paint film consolidation, 120
  permeability to water, 143
  permeability to water vapour, 178
Butyral, 143, 176

^{14}C, 21, 23, 48, 113, 143
Cadmium sulphide cells, 4, 5
Caequartyl BE, 67, 68
Calcium, 113
  carbonate, 77, 166
    regrounding paint films, 167
    washing easel paintings, 165
  caseinate, 123
    fixing of detached murals, 119, 120, 121
  chloride, 59
  glass colouring agents, 147
  inclusions in glass, 150
  silicate, precipitation, 125
Calcton, 143
Calgon, 109
  consolidation, 126
Calotermes flavicollis, 55, 56
Cameras, 104
  stands, 105
Cannon barrels, 137

Canvasses
  Australia, 73
  cotton, 119
  facing, mural removal, 119, 120
  flax, 75
  hemp, 119, 122
  jute, 75
  photochemical effects of light, 75
  ramic fibres, 75
  shrinkage, 121
  sisal, 75
  transfer of easel paintings, 165
  tropical conditions, 74, 75
Carbon,
  dating, 190, 191
  dioxide, 135
    solvent permeability, 178
  radioactive, 21
Carbon blacks, fungal activity, 76
Carbon-carbon bond, 8
Carbonates,
  copper, 89, 108
  lead, 91, 131
Carbonyl groups,
  MS2A, 182
  photochemical reactions, 176
Carbowax (*see also* Polyethyleneglycol), 126
Carboxymethycellulose, 166
Cartridge paper, regrounding paint films, 167
Casein,
  fixatives, 119, 120
  paints
    mould growth, 75
    resistance, 75
Cassiterite, 91
Casting techniques, 212
Cataloguing, 206
Cathodic reduction, 109, 131
Caucasian embroideries, 193
Cellfalcicula, 57
Cellosolve, 82, 83, 86, 173
Cellulose, 8
  acetate, 66, 67, 68
    paper reinforcement, 65
  acetate-butyrate, 172, 173
  adhesives, 119
  degradation, 58
  deterioration, 165
  fibres, 192
  lacquer, patina stabilization, 110
  light effects, metallic oxides as barrier, 44
  methyl, 144
  molecular breakdown, 42
  nitrate, 142
  supports in tropics, 74
Cellulosic structure, 142
Cellvibrio, 57
Cement, wax-resin, 166
Cephalosporium, 63
Ceramics,
  analysis, 32
  crystallization effects, 212
  examination of, 24
  lecture programme, 211
  surface contamination, 32
  surface enrichment, 32
Cerargyrite, 91, 92
Cerussite, 89, 91
Chaetomium, 57, 70
  globosum, 66
Chain polymers, 7
Chalcocite, 90
Chalconatronite, 90
Chalcopyrite, 90
Chalk
  fillers, 165, 166
  grounds, 167
Chemical cleaning, 135
Chemical methods of conservation of archival materials, 39–47
Chemistry, 198, 209, 212
  lecture programme, 211
Chinese bronzes, 31
  adze, examination, 105, 106
Chinese coins, 89
Chloramine-T, 43, 76, 77, 78
Chlorbenzide, toxicity, 49
Chlordane
  maximum atmospheric concentration, 50
  toxicity, 49
  treatment following poisoning, 52

Chlorides
  copper, 90, 92, 108, 109
  cuprous, mineralized bronze, 130
  lead, 91
  silver, 91
Chlorine
  dioxide, 44
  oxidation caused by, 143
Chlorophyceae, 62
Chlorthion, toxicity, 49
Chromatographic leaching, 174
Chromium, 114
  binary systems, 35
Chrysocolla, 90
Citric acid, 77
Cleaning, 203
  chemical, 135
  electrochemical, 135
  methods, 79–88
  systematic, 94
Climate, 71
  canvasses, 75
  microbial damage and, 57
Clips, rust, prevention, 44
Closed package, relative humidity, 13–15
Cloths,
  analysis of, 25
  packing, 14
Coatings, 79
  aged, removal, 173
  impermeable, 135
  protective, 79
  removal, 79
  surface, 135
  varnish, function, 84
Cobalt-60, 48
Cobalt oxide, glass colouring agents, 147
Coccus, 64
Cockroaches, 59
  insecticides, 48
Cohesion, fragile objects, 140
Cohesive strength, 142
Coins
  analysis methods, 31
  chinese, 89
  roman, examination, 106
  surface composition, 31
Coleoptera, 56
Collections,
  inventories, 94
  presentation of, 93
Colophory, mould growth resistance, 75
Colours,
  fading, 202
  transfer of, 169
Concentration gradients in glass, 151
Condensation, 14
  corrosion caused by, 13
  moisture, 11, 136
Conservation,
  diplomas, 210
  esthetics, 200, 209
  ethics, 209
  history, 209
  principles, 176
  programme at Academy of Fine Arts in Warsaw, 206–210
  thesis, 210
Conservators, training of, 197
Consolidants, classification, 143
Consolidation
  fragile and metal objects, 125–144
  friable paints, 144
Copals,
  coatings, 81
  resin mould growth resistance, 75
  varnish, 80
Copies, 209
Copolymers, 175
Copper, 113, 114
  alloys, hard solder joints, 105
  binary systems, 35
  carbonates, 108
  chlorides, 135
  compounds, toxicity, 49
  corrosion, 91
  electrotypes, 212
  glass colouring agents, 147, 148
  inclusions in glass, 150
  mineral alteration products, 89–91
  oxides, 99, 108
  ternary systems, 35

Copper-based pigments, 31
Copper-iron, interaction, 35
Copper-lead alloys, inclusions in glass, 150
Coptic woollen tubic, 187
Corex D glass, 173
Corinth, medieval glass, 146, 147, 148, 149, 150
Corrodentia, 56
Corrosion, 94, 128
  condensation causing, 13
  copper, 91
  crusts, 89
  Egyptian statuettes, 139
  fragile objects, 140
  glasses, 150
  layers on bronze, 108
  metals, 135
  mineralized products, 135
  paper, 67
  products, 31
    polarity, 142
  recurring, 99
Cosmolloid, 128, 132, 134
Costume, study, 206
Cotton
  Asian, 192
  basic habits, 192
  canvasses, tropical conditions, 75
  degradation, 185
  elasticity, 194
  fungi attack, 59
  gabardine, 192
  Indian, 192
  mercerized, 192
  New World yarns, 193
  packing, 14
  reserve dyed, 193
  tie dyed, 193
  tropical conditions, influence, 74
  Western Hemisphere yarns, 193
Cotunnite, 91
Coulomb-Hvoslef's equation, 140
Counting techniques, glass, 151
Cradles, 160, 161, 163, 165
Craquelure, 156, 177
Cretan embroidery, 194
Crosslinking, 142, 143, 173, 174, 176, 178,
  179, 190, 191
Crustose, 64
Ctenolepisma targionii, 55, 56
Cumengite, 91
Cupric carbonate, 137
Cupric irons, glass colouring agents, 147
Cuprite, 90, 108, 137, 138
Cuprous chloride, 135
Cuprous nickel, 135
Cuprous oxide, glass colouring agents, 147,
  148
Curators, 200
Curved-crystal optics, 35, 36
Cutting tools, sharpening, 166
Cyclohexanone, swelling power, 86
Cytophaga, 57

Damage
  permissible, 31
  photochemical, 1–6
Dammar, 79, 80, 173, 176, 177
  infra-red spectra, 180
  mould growth resistance, 75
  permeability to water, 143
  permeability to water vapour, 178
  removal, 81, 82
  transfer of paintings, 166
  ultra-violet exposure, 182
  viscosity grade, 175
    vs cracking, 172
  wrinkling, 178
Dampness, books storage, 58
Dark field illumination, 107
Daylight
  controlling, 1–6
  fluorescent lamps, 174
  photography, 104
DDD, toxicity, 49
DDT, 59
  maximum atmospheric concentration, 50
  toxicity, 49
  treatment following poisoning, 52
De-acidification,
  non-aqueous, of delicate documents, 44
  stability of documents, 42

Decomposition products, glass, 150
Decorative arts, programme at Academy of
  Fine Arts, Warsaw, 206
Deep-frozen burials, 185
Deformation of overheated metal, 99
Degreasing agents, 165
De-humidification, 59
Dehumidifier, silica-gel, 11, 12
Dehumidifying cabinets, 77
Delos, 114
Dematiaceae, 63
Demeton
  toxicity, 49
  treatment following poisoning, 52
Dendrochronology, 23
Density, determination of, 113
Dental wax, 132
Depolymerization, 7, 8, 143
Desiccation, 9
Detarol, 109
Deterioration, environmental agents, 200
Deuteromiceti, 57
Devitrification, 148
Dewpoint, 11, 12
Dextrin,
  adhesives, 65, 66, 144, 166
  paste, 77
  silking, 42
Diatrete from Niederemmel, 154, 155
Diazinon
  blood cholinesterase of workers, 50
  toxicity, 49
Dibutyl phthalate, 134
p-Dichlorobenzene, 59
Dieldrin
  lethal dosage, 49
  maximum atmospheric concentration, 50
  toxicity, 49
  treatment following poisoning, 52
Diethylbenzene, 175
Diffraction, x-ray, 26, 29, 33, 34, 91
Diffusion of solvents
  Fick's law, 87
  film thickness effects, 87
  temperature changes, 87
Dilan, treatment following poisoning, 52
Dimefox, toxicity, 49
Dinitrobutylphenol, toxicity, 49
Dinitrocresol, toxicity, 49
Dinitrophenol, treatment following poisoning,
  52
Diopside, 148, 149
Dioxide, lead, 91
Dipterex, toxicity, 49
Dirt, protection from, 142
Disinfectants
  cutaneous absorption, 49
  toxicity, 49
Disinfection, 59, 60
  books, 71
  depots, 71
  parchment, 71
  pastel drawings, 71
  preventive, 72
  vacuum autoclaving, 71
Disinfestation, 59, 60
  poisoning risks, 49
  preparation before, 51
Distacco method of mural removal, 118, 119,
  121
  adhesive, 119, 120
Dithiocarbamates, toxicity, 49
DNC, toxicity, 49
Documentation, 209
  scientific, 210
Documents
  Australia, 73
  curative treatment of, 70, 71
  disinfection of, 71
  dusting, 59
  effect of fungus, 65
  effect of insects, 65
  fumigation, 78
  harmful biological agents, 65
  mould on, 70–72
  preventive treatment of, 70
  protection against further attack, 72
  protection against humidity, 65
  protection against insects, 65
  reinforcing of, 65–68
  resistance to fungi, 66
  resistance to micro-organisms, 65–68

Dolomite, source of lime in glass, 148, 149
Double bonds, photochemical reaction, 176
Draughtsmanship, 212
Drawings,
  Australia, 73
  fumigation, 78
  programme at Academy of Fine Arts,
    Warsaw, 206
Dry rot, 165
Drying agents, packaging, 13
Drying oil, chemical breakdown, 165
Dryness, textiles, 185
Dufaylite, 168
Dusting, 59

Earthenware, unglazed, consolidation, 127
Easel paintings
  adhesion, lack of, 165
  copy, 210
  deterioration of support, 165
  grounds, deterioration, 165
  lack of adhesion to support, 165
  tansfer, 165–168
Ecclesiastical vestments, preservation, 185
Education and Training 197–213
Efflorescence, calcium carbonate, 121
Egg tempera, mould growth resistance, 75
Egg white, 79, 119
Egyptian glasses, 147
Egyptian statuettes, 139
El Amarna glasses, 146, 147, 148, 149
Elastic modulus, 140
Elastic mould materials, glass restoration, 153
Elastic support, treatment of warped wood
  panels, 163–164
Electricity, simple circuit, 212
Electrochemical cleaning, 135
Electrolysis, 135
  silver, 92
Electrolytic consolidation, 131
Electrolytic polishing, 102
Electrolytic process, wood consolidation, 125
Electromagnetic lenses, 145
Electromagnetic spectrum, 33
Electron-beam probe
  microanalysis, 30, 31, 32, 33–38, 113,
    145–151
Electrons, beam, 145
Electro-osmosis, consolidation of wood, 125
Emesa helmet, silver, 133
Empiricism, 19
Emission lines, 33
Emission spectrometry, 29, 31, 32, 34
Emulsion, 144
Enamels, examination of, 24
Encapsulation, 128, 130, 132
Endrin, toxicity, 49
Energy, requirements to break bonds in
  silicones and fluorocarbons, 143
Engineers, training in conservation, 199
Environment, information on (*see also* Air-
  conditioning, Atmosphere, Humidity,
  Temperature), 199
Environmental chamber, 9, 11
Epoxy resin, 130, 131, 134, 144
  adhesion to metal, 132
  consolidation of water-logged wood, 126
  glass restoration, 155
Equilibrium moisture content, 9–12
Esthetic analysis, 209
Etching, spot, 102
Eternit, 122
Ethanol, 79
^{14}C, 82
Ethyl alcohol, coloured, 163
Ethylene
  dichloride, solubility, 80, 81
  oxide, 71, 72
Ethyl methacrylate, 174
Etruscan period,
  metal objects, 91, 101
  mirror, bronze, 137, 138
Eubacterii, 57
Examination, non-destructive, 113
Exhibitions, travelling, 9, 113

Fabrication, method of, 112
Fadeometer exposure, 174
Faience, electron beam analysis, 37
Ferric chloride, indications, 128

Fibre-board, packing, 9, 10, 11, 12
Fibrenyle, 129
Fibres
  animal, 192
  moisture content, 193
  protein, 193
  spinning, 192
  textile, basic habits, 192–194
  vegetable, 192, 193
  weaving, 192
Films (see also Oil, Paint, Tempera and
    Varnishes)
  paint, mould growth, 75
  removal, 174
  thickness gauge, 84
Filters (see also Ultra-violet),
  neutral density, 4, 5
Fire, protection of patrimony during, 95
First aid measures, 51, 52
Flags, conservation, 185, 186
Flamuco varnish, 164
Flat cleavage of paint, 156, 159
Flat-crystal optics, 36
Flaws, 116
Flax, 192
  canvasses, tropical conditions, 75
  degradation, 185
Flexometry, 23
Fluorescence, 34, 35, 112, 114, 116, 146, 209,
    210
Fluorescent analysers
  emission spectrograph, 34
  trace elements, 34
  wet chemistry, 34
Fluorescent lamps, 174
Fluorescent spectrometry, 29
Fluorescent tubes
  daylight, 182
  exposure of polyvinyl alcohol, 178
  ultra-violet, 182
Fluorine/phosphorus ratio, in bone, 23
Fluoroacetamide, toxicity, 49
Foam-rubber packing, 17
Forgeries, 209
Formaldehyde, 71, 72
Foxing, paper, 58
Fragile objects
  consolidation, 125–144
    continuous phase, 140
    discontinuous phase, 140
    new methods, 140–144
Fragile tissues, reinforcement, 196
France
  archaeological collections in, 93
  museums in, 93
  problems of conservation, 93
Freeze-drying process, water-logged wood,
    125
Frescoes, 118–124
  cut away, 118
  damage from minor shocks, 124
  ethylene oxide, use, 63
  microbiological changes, 62–64
  restoration, 62
  stains, 62
Friable paints, penetration, 144
Friction, removal of coating, 79
Fumigants, 48
  toxic residues, 50
Fumigation, 60, 78
  thymol cabinet, 77
  vacuum, precautions, 51
Fungi, 62, 64, 72, 73
  aging caused by, 7
  attacks in tropics, 75
  cellulose deterioration, 165
  development of, 70
  paper, 57, 70
  pigments secreted by, 58
Fungicidal solutions, 76
Fungicides, 39–78
  development, possible, 43
  impregnation of, 67
  leather, effects on, 42
  pulverized, 71, 72
  research, 44
  sprayed, 71
  textile preservation, 187
  toxicity, 49
Furniture beetle, 73
Fusarium, 70
Gadrallus immarginatus, 56

Galena, 91
Galleries, window-lighted, 1–6
Gallic period, examination of metal objects,
    101
Gallium–copper alloy, 133, 134
Gamma rays, 23
  spectrometry, 31, 32, 111
Gammexane
  paper damage, 42
  toxicity, 49
  treatment following poisoning, 52
Gas chromatography, 88
Gas-flow proportional counter, 30
Gases
  frescoes, conditioning of, 63, 64
  pollutant, 178
  protection from, 142
  toxic, 50
    fumigation precautions, 51
Geiger-counter spectrometer, 33
Geiger-Müller tube, 33, 36
Gel material, 157
Gelatine
  oil grounds, 167
  painting, facing, 166
Gems, analysis of, 25
Germination of spores, 70
Gesso, 166
  application, 167
  exposure, 166, 167
  grounds, 167
  reinforced, 167
Glass, 145–155
  analysis, 32
  ancient,
    microanalysis, 145–151
    repair and reproduction, 152–155
  annealing, 148, 151
  colouring agents, 147
  concentration gradients, 146, 151
  corrosion, 150
  decomposition, 151
    products, 150
  Eighteenth Dynasty, 146, 147, 148, 149
  electron beam analysis, 37
  examination of, 24
  fragment from medieval factory, 146, 147,
      148, 149, 150
  instabilities, 148
  lead, 146, 147, 150
  metallic inclusions, 149–150
  opacifying agents, 146, 147, 148–149
  plug formation, 146
  submersion in salt water, 151
  synthetic, 147
  vacuum deposition, 146
  weathering crusts, 146, 150–151
Glazes
  analysis, 32
  electron beam analysis, 37
  vulnerable, 203
Glueing, textiles, 187, 188
Glues, 79, 144
  aqueous, 166, 168
  bone, 168
  consolidation of fragile objects, 140
  contraction, 119
  grounds, attack by bacteria, 165
  insect damage, 56
  mural detachment, 119, 120, 121, 122
  parchment, regrounding paint films, 167
  rabbit skin, 167
Goethite, 92
Gold, 94, 112
  beaded wire decorations, 105, 106
  coins, 112
Gold-silver-copper system, 112, 113
Gouache, 75
  mould growth, 75
Gouges, wood removal, 166
Green efflorescence, 110
Grey tin, 91
Grounds
  aqueous glue, 167
  chalk, 167
  deterioration, 165
  Italian gesso, 167
  oil, 167
  removal, 167
Gums, 79
Guthion, toxicity, 49
Gypsum fillers, 165

Gyrophana lacrymans, 70

27H (see Iso-amyl methacrylate)
Hair thermohygrograph, 9
Halogen compounds, organic, 48
Handbook on analysis, 26–28
Hanging bowl, bronze, 137, 138
Haplographium, 57
Hardeners, 144
Hardwoods, panelling, 166
Hazardous radiation, 2
Heat
  effect on old fabrics, 195–196
  radiant, textile reinforcement, 196
  textiles, 185
Heptaclor, toxicity, 49
Heraldry, 206
Herculaneum papyri, 39, 40
Hexachlorocyclohexane, 67
History of art, 197, 198, 200, 203, 206, 210
Horn silver, 92, 110
Hot table heating, 166
Hot wax, wood panelling removal, 166
Humidity (see also Air-conditioning, Atmo-
    sphere, Environment, Water), 70, 95, 99,
    170
  absolute, 13
  cabinet, 65
    tests, 75
  calcium caseinate, 120
  chamber, 76
  consolidation of fragile objects, 140
  controlled atmospheres, 9
  mural decay, 120
  paper coloration, 58
  relative, 59, 108, 110
    closed package, 13–15
    desiccation of oils, 73
    mitigating variations, 13
    moisture loss from wood in workroom,
        166, 167
    mould growth, 76
    paper deterioration, 40
    permeability of films, 178
    wood panels, 163, 166
  variations of, 169
    murals, 123
Hydrocarbons
  paraffinic, swelling action, 86
  solubility, 177
Hydrocerussite, 91
Hydrochloric acid, patina stabilization, 110
Hydrogen
  atoms, tertiary, 173, 176
  peroxide, 8
  solvent permeability, 178
  sulphate, 143
  sulphide, solvent permeability, 177, 178
Hydrogenation, 176
Hydrolysis, degree of, 68
Hydrophobic properties, 136
Hydrophobization, 44
Hydroxy groups, 176
Hydrozincite, 92
Hygrometers, paper, 77
Hyphae, 64
'Hypo' photographic, 110
Hypochlorites, 76, 78
  watercolour restorations, 77, 78
Hysteresis, 15

Illumination, 1–6 (see also Light and
    Lighting)
  levels, 4
Impasto, heavy, paint films, 75
Impermeabilization, 135
Impermeable coatings, 135
Impregnants, 140–141, 144
Impregnation, 135, 136, 137, 139, 140, 141
Infracord infra-red spectrometer, 179
Infra-red, 198
  analysis, 176
  drying, 103
  lamps, 164
    textile reinforcement, 196
  light, 136, 137
  radiation, 21, 22
  spectrography, 209, 210
  spectrometer, 179
  spectrophotometry, 81, 82
  spectroscopy, 88, 176

Ink
  microanalysis, 44
  revival methods, 44
Insecticides, 39–78
  chemical composition, 51
  clothes contamination, 49
  concentrated, 49
  contact, 48, 59
  development, possible, 43
  evaporation of mixtures, 50
  gaseous, 60
  ingestion, of, 48
  labelling, 51, 52
  maximum atmospheric concentrations, 50
  microbial, 48
  poisoning caused by, 48–55
  research, 44
  resin, 52
  respiratory, 48
  toxic residues, 48–61
  toxicity, 49, 51
  use on occupied premises, 48–61
  W.H.O. regulations, 51
Insects
  depredations, 73, 74
  functional characteristics, 55
  morphological characteristics, 55
  paper deterioration, 41
  sterilization by isotopes, 48
  xylophagous, 60
Insolubility, solvents, 178
Instability, glass, 148
Insulation, fibre-board, 11
Intarsia work, 186
Interaction, effects, 35
Inter-elemental effects, 35
Internal pressures, fragile objects, 140, 142
Intonaco, 118, 119, 120, 121
  cohesion, degree of, 123
  defective, 119
Iron, 94, 113
  gallotannate, ink revival, 44
  inclusions in glass, 150
  mineral alteration products, 92
  oxide, 128, 164
    cracked, 128
  oxidized fittings on wooden beam, 128
  rust, 89, 92
  sulphurized, 140
Iron-copper, interaction, 35
Iron-manganese, interaction, 35
Isis, statuette the, of, 137, 138
Iso-amyl methacrylate, 143, 177, 178
  permeability to water vapour, 178
Isoptera, 55, 56
Isotopes, radioactive, 21, 23, 48
Italian School painting, transfer, 166
Ivory
  analysis of, 25
  consolidation, 125, 126

Jewellery, metal, analysis, 31
Jute
  canvasses, tropical conditions, 75
  fibres, 129, 134

K radiation, 34
'Kaken gel', 14, 15
Kanta sword, 133
Kaolin, 129, 134
Ketones, solubility, 177
Kraft paper, 9

Laboratory
  analysis, 25
  treatment, 94
  work, courses, 212
  workers, training, 206
Lacquers, impregnation of panels, 165
Lamination, 65, 67
  materials, 41
  present studies, 44
  silk and plastic, 44
Latex rubber, 128
Laurium Mines (Greece), 114
Leaching process,
  ancient glass, 151
  chromatographic, 174
Lead, 114–116
  arsenate, toxicity, 49

Lead—continued
  binary systems, 35
  carbonate, 131
  cerussite, 89
  concentration in glass, 147, 148
  glasses, 146, 147, 150
  litharge, 89
  mineral alteration products, 91
  mineralized,
    cathodic reduction, 131
    consolidation, 131
  oxide, 91
  sulphides, substituted by iron gallotannate, 44
  ternary systems, 35
  white, 85
Leaden bullae, 131, 132
Leather, 70–72
  book bindings, damage caused by gas lights, 40
  consolidation, 125
  desiccation, 126
  fungi, 59, 70
  fungicides, 42
  insect damage, 56
Lectures, schedules, 209
Legislation
  affecting conservation, 197
  church properties, 197
Lepismatidae, 55, 56
Libraries, biological agents damaging paper, 55–61
Lichens, 62
Lictids, 59
Light
  behaviour, 212
  controller, 4
  influence on museum objects, 7–8
  intensity, 8
  paper deterioration, 40
  photochemical effects in tropics, 74
  Planck constant, 7
  quanta, 7
  textiles, 185
  visible, 8
  wavelength, 7
Lighting, 59
  bronze antiquities, examination, 104
Ligneous fibres, supports in tropics, 74
Lime, dolomite as source in glasses, 148, 149
Limestone, consolidation, 127
Limonite, 92
Lindane
  lethal dosage, 49
  maximum atmospheric concentration, 50
Linear polymers, deterioration, 143
Linen
  basic habits, 192
  moisture content, 193
  movements of, 194
  S-spun, 192
  Z-spun, 192
Linseed oil, 79
  dried films, 85
  leather consolidation, 126
  mould growth resistance, 75
  permeability to water, 143
  permeability to water vapour, 178
  solvent action studies, 84–88
  varnish, 164
Liposcelidi, 56
Litharge, 89, 91
Lucite, 171, 172
Lyctidae, 56

Macrochemistry, wet, 29
Macrophotographs, oil layer removal, 208
Magnesium, 113
  concentration in glass, 147, 148
Magnetism, residual, 113
Magnetite, 92
Malachite, 89, 108
Malathion
  maximum atmospheric concentration, 50
  toxicity, 49
Man, damage by, 57
Mandrel bending test, 171
Manganese
  concentration in glass, 147
  inclusions in glass, 150
Manganese—iron interaction, 35

Manuscripts
  flaking, consolidation, 127
  parchment, 44
  sulphides, application, 39
  tannins, application, 39
Maranyl nylon, 127, 128, 130, 134
Masonite Tempered Preswood, 75
  panels, 75
  support for detached murals, 119, 121, 122
Massicot, 91
Mastic, 79, 80, 173, 176, 177
  infra-red spectra, 180
  mould growth resistance, 75
  panel facings, 166
  permeability to water, 143
  permeability to water vapour, 178
  solubility, 81, 82
  ultra-violet exposure, 182
  viscosity grade, 175
    vs cracking, 172
Materials
  aging, 7–8
  insoluble, 174
  knowledge of, 200
  paintings, analysis, 26–28
Matrix absorption, electron-beam probe, 146
Maxwell body, 157
Mechanics, application to treatment of panel paintings, 156–162
Medieval period,
  glass fragments, 146–150
  metal objects, examination, 101
Melaconite, 89
Melamine formaldehydes, 144
Melinex, 196
Melitite, 149
Mercuric acetate, 67
Mercury compounds, organic, toxicity, 49
Mercury-vapour, lamps, 22
Mesopotamian glasses, 147
Metal-working, 211
Metallic inclusions in ancient glass, 149–150
Metallic objects (see also Metals), 89–117
  encapsulation, 128, 132
  examination of, 24
  fragile
    consolidation, 128–134
    cracked, 132
    encapsulation, 128
    strengthening methods, 128
  inclusions in glass, 146
  metallurgical examination, 101–103
  mineral alteration products, 89–92
  patina, consolidation, 127
  polished, photography, 104
  sampling, 101
  stripping, 135
Metallographical examination, 101
Metallography, 113, 212
Metallurgical examination of metal objects, 101–103
Metallurgy, non-destructive methods in, 111–117
Metals (see also Metallic objects),
  analysis methods, 31
  antiquities, conservation of, 93–96
  heavy, 113
  mineralized, 128
  moisture and corrosion, 135
  weakened, disintegration, 135
Methacrylate, 132, 134, 143, 174, 177
  encapsulation of bronze, 130
  glass restoration, 152, 155
  resistance to solvent action, 81
  side chain, 173
Methanol
  leaching by, 85
  solubility, 80
Methoxychlor,
  maximum atmospheric concentration, 50
  toxicity, 49
Methyl bromide, 48, 71
  fumigation precautions, 51
Methyl cellulose, 144
Methyl methacrylate polymer, 143
Methylene dichloride, 171, 172
Methylparathion, toxicity, 49
Mice, damage by, 57
Micro techniques, 21
Microanalyser, electron-probe, 30, 31, 32
Microanalysis,
  ink, 44

Microanalysis—*continued*
  electron-beam probe, 145–151
Microbeam probe in non-destructive testing, 33–38
Microbiological changes in frescoes, 62–64
Microchemical analysis, 29–32, 207, 209, 210
  materials of paintings, 26
Microcrystalline wax, 136
Microfilms, permanancy, 44
Microflora, heterotrophic, 63
Micro-organisms
  frescoes, changes on, 62
  paper, damage, 57
  paper deterioration, 41
  resistance of documents to, 65
Microphotography, 21, 207
Micro-sampling technique for examination of metal objects, 101
Microscope, 209
  electron, 113
  optic, 113
  projection, 104, 105
Microscopy, 21, 111
Miersite, 92
Millefiori fragment (glass) 146, 147, 148
Mineral alteration products on metal products, 89–92
Mineral oils, toxicity, 49
Mineral plus metal, 131
Mineralization, 128, 132
  examination results, 107
Mineralized corrosion products, 135
Minerals
  corrosion layers on bronze, 108
  differentiation, 107
Miniatures, consolidation, 44
Minium, 91
Modern period, metal objects, examination, 101
Modocoll E, 187, 188
Modulus, elasticity, of, 141
Moisture, 13–15
  barriers, treatment of warped wood panels, 163–164
  condensation, 11, 136
  content, equilibrium, 9–12
  films, 135
  metals and, 135
  paper aging, 42
  paper coloration, 58
  paper deterioration, 41
  textiles, 185
Molecular
  distribution, 141
  ranges, 142
Molecules, 7
  forces acting between, 141
Monomer molecules, 7
  glass restoration, 152
Mould, 70–72
  development of, 70
  generation, 13
  growth, 10, 14
    discoloration and disintegration, 76
    monsoonal conditions, 73
    oxidation, 77, 78
    paint binders, resistance, 75
    paint films, 75
    paper, 77
    pigments, 75
    resistance to mould growth, 75
    tropics, 74
    waterstains, 77
  infection, air-conditioning, 76
MS-2A, 172, 176
  infra-red spectra, 180
  picture varnishes, 177
  ultra-violet exposure, 182
  viscosity, 175
  wrinkling, 178
Mulberry paper, 166
Mulham cloth, 194
Murals, 23
  aging tests, 123
  atmospheric agencies, 123
  chemical analysis, 123
  conservation, 209
  damp sites, 118, 119, 120
  decay, 120
  detaching
    Italian methods, 118–122
    metal mesh support, 119, 122
  deterioration, 123

Murals—*continued*
  humidity, 123
  isolation of paint layer, 120
  lime bonding, 118
  observations, 123–124
  paint
    adhesion with plaster, 118
    film consolidation, 120
    flaking, 118
  plastic backing, 124
  programme at Academy of Fine Arts, Warsaw, 206
  restoration, 123
  support of detached, 124
  supports, attachment, 123
  temperature variations, 123
  transfer, 123
Museum climate, 1–18
Museums
  environment, 9
  inspectors, 94
  inventories, 93
  photographic service, 94
  objects, influence of light, 7–8
  reserves, 94
Mycelia, 57, 63, 70–72, 76
Mycosis, 58
Myrothecium verrucaria, 68
Myxobacteria, 57
Myxotrichum, 57

Naftoflex, 152
Nantokite, 90, 108
Naphtha, solubility, 80
Naphthaline, toxicity, 49
Natural resins, 140, 177
Natural varnishes, solubility, 177
Nets, supporting, 195
Neutrons, 23
  generators, 31
    portable, 31
New South Wales, 74
Nickel, 113, 114
  binary systems, 35
Nicobium castaneum, 56
Niederemmel diatrete, 154, 155
Niello inlay, 132
Nijmegen mirror, 132
Nishapur glass fragment, 146, 147, 148
Nitrates, copper, 90
Nitrocellulose, 143
  lacquer, glass restoration, 152
Non-destructive analysis (*see* Analysis)
Non-polar substances, 141, 142
Nylon
  maranyl, 127, 128, 130, 134
  modified, 143
  moisture content, 193
  soluble, 127
  supporting nets, 195, 196

Oak panels, 163, 166, 167
Observation,
  magnetic, 112
  techniques of, 111
  visual, 111
Oil (*see also* Films)
  emulsion, fungal attack, 165
  film, solubility, 85
  grounds, powdering, 165
  paint
    analysis, 37
    mould growth, 75
    protective coatings, 79
    solvents, action of, 171
Oiled paper, 163
Oils (*see also* Oil paints) Indonesian artists, 74
Opacifying agents, 147, 148–149
Opacity, degree of, 68
Opaque glass, 150
Optical spectroscopy, 33
Optics
  curved-crystal, 35, 36
  flat-crystal, 36
Overcast sky, radiation hazard, 2
Overcleaning, 84
Oxidation, 143, 176
  ambient air, 185
  photochemical, 176
  varnishes, 177
  wrinkling caused by, 178

Oxides
  copper, 90–91, 107, 108
  iron, 92, 128
    cracked, 128
    fungal activity, 75
  lead, 91
  silver
    method of disease spot treatment, 129
    patina stabilization, 110
  tin, 91, 108
  zinc, fungal activity, 75
Oxidizing agents, paper deterioration, 40
Oxygen, 135, 143
  barrier, 177
  paper aging, 42
  solvents, permeability, 177, 178
  water vapour and, 8
Ozone, oxidation caused by, 143

Pacatien statue, 97–99
Packing
  relative humidity, 13–15
  Victoria and Albert Museum, methods, 16–18
Paecilomyces, 57
Paint (*see also*, Films, Oil, Tempera)
  adhesive strength, 157
  aluminium, 163
  binders, mould growth resistance, 75
  blister, 157, 163, 166
  buckled, 156, 159, 160
  buckling, 157, 167, 170
  changes in frescoes, 62
  crackle, 156, 157
  cupped, 156
  curled, 156
  decreased cohesion of layers, 63
  defects, on panels, 156
  elasticity, 157
  films
    Australia, 73
    heavy impasto, 75
    linseed-oil, 75
    mould growth, 75
    raw linseed oil, 75
  flaking
    reattachment, 127
    vibration by power plane, 166
  flat cleavage, 157
  layers, 165
    adhesion of, 169, 170
    Belgian system, 170
    consolidation of, 170
    loosening of, 169
  mould growth on films, 75
  panels, security, 160
  rupture, 157
  surfaces, blanched, 88
  swelling of drying-off, 79
  wrinkling, 167
Paintings
  analysis methods, 29–32
  blistering, 168
  cleaning, "swab" method, 84
  coating removal by naphtha, 81
  easel, transfer, 165–168
  examination of, 23
  handbook on analysis of materials, 26–28
  history of techniques, 206, 209
  identification of pigments and inerts, 26
  movable support, 23
  mural, 23
    detachment, 118–122
    observations, 123
  panel, *see* Panel paintings
  programme at Academy of Fine Arts, Warsaw, 206
  protective coatings, 79
  shipment,
    during winter, 9
    tropical countries, 10
  techniques, 210
  wall, consolidation, 127
Paladon, glass restoration, 152
Palaeography, 206
Palavit, glass restoration, 152
Palimpsests, deciphering, 40
Panel paintings (*see also* Panels *and* Wood), 156–170
  battens, 164, 170
  dovetailed, 160

Panel paintings—*continued*
  blind cleavage, 160
  buckling, 159, 160, 170
  checks, 160, 162
  concave warp, 159
  convex warp, 159, 161
  cracking of, 170
  cradles, 160, 161, 163, 165
  cross-battens, 159, 165
  dimensionally inactive, 162
  elastic mechanical support, 164
  elastic strain, 161
  elastic yield, 159, 160
  flat cleavage, 159
  free mechanical control of panels, 160, 161
  grounds, removal, 167
  mechanical control of panels, 159
  mechanical restraint, 162
  moisture barrier, 162
  moisture content, 162
      wood, 160
  neutral axis of panels, 160
  no mechanical control, 159
  paint rupture, 160
  panels, 159
  plastic deformation, 160
  plastic yield, 160
  relaxed panels, 160
  ruptures in wood, 159
  Saran resin, 162
  security, 160
  set in tension, 160
  shrinkage and swelling, 160, 163
      linear, 160
  splits, 160, 162
      support, 163
  stabilized panels, 162
  supports, 167
  swelling, 163
  transfer, 163
  treatment, 156–162
  warp, 159, 162
  wax-resin adhesive, 162
  wood removal, 166
Panels (*see also* Panel paintings *and* Wood),
    atmospheric sensitivity, 163
  cracking, 165, 166
  facings, 166
  flattening, 165
  flexible steel springs, 164
  impregnation, 163, 165
  lacquers, 165
  moisture barriers, 163–4
  moisture loss, prevention, 166
  moisture transfer, 163
  permanent warping, 163
  swelling, 163
  synthetic foam layers, 164
  synthetic resins, 163
  warped, 160, 163, 165
      treatment, 163–164
  wax resins, 165
  waxes, 163
  wood
      stabilization, 163
      transfer methods, 165
Paper, 72
  acidity, 40
      coloration and, 58
  aging, procedures for, 42
  artificial aging, 41
  biological agents damaging, 55–61
  biological attack, 40
  bleaching, 39
  bleaching of pulps, 44
  bursting strengths, 78
  calcium, addition of, 42
  cellulose acetate, 66
  chelating agents, 78
  chemical properties, 42
  chloramine-T as bleach, 43
  chlorites for cleaning, 42
  cleaning, 42
  coated, restoration of, 44
  coloration, 58
  corrosion, 67
  de-acidified documents, stability, 42
  decay, investigations, 41
  deterioration, 40
  dextrine
      deterioration, 42
      pastes, 43

Paper—*continued*
  discoloration, 76
  durability, 42
  examination of, 24
  expanded, 168
  experimental data, 78
  folding
      endurance, 42
      resistance, 68
  fungi, 57, 68, 70
  gammexane causing damage, 42
  hygrometers, 77
  insects damaging, 55–61
  irradiation tests, 43
  laminated, 65, 66, 68
      stability, 42
  low-grade, 76
  magnesium carbonates, addition of, 42
  mechanical properties, 42
  microbial damage, 57
      resistance to, 58
  Mylar, 66
  optical properties, 42
  oxidative degradation, 40
  packing, 14, 16
  permanence, factors affecting, 41
  pH of, 41, 65, 68
  physicochemical resistance, 68
  preservation, 78
  reinforcement
      dextrine, 65
      silk, 65
  resin alum size, 77
  resistance to fungi, 68
  restoration of, 65
  rodents, damage, 57
  silk, 65, 66
  sizing, 42, 77
  stains, 57, 58
  stretching resistance, 68
  tearing resistance, 68
  tissue, 17
      specifications, 43
  types, resistance to microbial damage, 58
  waterstains, 77
  wood pulp, 77
Papyri and cedarwood oil, 39
Parachlorometacresol, 67
Paradichlorbenzene, toxicity, 49
Paraffin, 136
  hydrocarbons, 173
  wax, 110, 129, 134, 136, 143, 178
Paraloid (*see* Acryloid)
Paratacamite, 90, 108
Parathion
  inhalation by workers, 50
  maximum atmospheric concentration, 50
  treatment following poisoning, 52
Parchment, 70, 72
  examination of, 24
  glue, regrounding paint films, 167
  insect damage, 56
  manuscripts,
      sulphides, application, 39
      tannins, application, 39
  miniatures on, consolidation, 44
  rodents, damage, 57
  strengthening, 44
Patina, 89, 98, 202
  atmospheric moisture and oxygen, reaction,
      108
  cassiterite, 91
  consolidation, 127
  examination, 105
  sections through, 108
  stabilization, 108, 109
      dry method, 110
      wet method, 110
  study, results, 108
  water, 91
Patination, 135
Penetration power of materials, 136
Penicillium, 57, 63, 67, 70
Pentachlorophenol, 71, 75
  spray, 10
Perithecia, 63, 64
Permanence, 176
Permeability, 142, 143
  film, 142
  water, to, 143
Perspex, 132
  glass restoration, 152

Pesticides, 48
  labelling, 51, 52
  W.H.O. regulations, 51
Pétri dishes, 71
Petroleum, 173
  all-aromatic, 175
  properties, 171
  solvent, 172, 177
Pettenkofer process for regeneration of
      varnish films, 84
Phenkoptone, toxicity, 49
Phenol formaldehyde, 167
Phosdrin, toxicity, 49
Phosgenite, 91
Phosphates, 92
Phosphorus compounds, organic, 48
Photocells, 4, 5
Photochemical reactions, 176
Photocontrollers, 6
Photo-flood illumination, 104
Photography, 21, 22, 111, 212
  bronze antiquities, 104
  conservation uses, 205, 206, 207, 209, 210,
      211, 212
  infra-red, 22
  lighting, 104
Photolysis, 8
Photo-oxidation, 8
Physical analysis, 29–32
Physical decay, 8
Physical methods of conservation, archival
      materials, 39–47
Physics, 212
  lecture programme, 211
Picture, mechanics, 162
Pictures
  cleaning, 84
      leaching, 88
  linseed oil, cleaning, 87
  pigment, investigation, 31, 32
  restoration, 203
  restorers, 212
  varnishes, new, 176–184
Pigments
  analysis, 36
  copper-based, 31
  data for proposed handbook, 26
  equipment for analysis, 27
  fading, 76
  fugitive, 76
  identification, 26
  mould growth, 75
  picture, 32
Pins, bronze, mineralized, 129
Planck constant, 7
Plant ash, concentration in glass, 147,
      148
Plaster of Paris, 128, 134
Plastic deformation, treatment of warped
      wood panels, 163–164
Plastic resins, 99
Plasticine, 129
Plasticizers, 142, 171, 177
  lamination, 43
  textiles, preservation, 187
  wood stabilization, 163
Plattnerite, 91
Plexiglas, 1, 2, 3, 4, 173
  glass restoration, 152
Plumbsol, 133
Plywood, tropical conditions, 75
Poisoning
  disinfestation risks, 49
  insecticides causing, 48–55
  precautions, 52
  prevention, 48
  skin contamination by insecticides, 49
  urgent measures after, 52
Polar substances, 142
Polarity of bonded surface, 141
Polishing
  electrolytic, 102
  local, 113
Polyamide, hardeners, 130
Poly(butylmethacrylate), 141, 174
  cross-linking, 173
  mould growth resistance, 75
Polychromes, programme at Academy of
      Fine Arts, Warsaw, 206
Polyesters, 66, 99, 100, 134
  casting, 212
  glass restoration, 155

Polyethylene
  misuse of, 10
  packing, 10
  permeability to water, 143
Polyethylene glycol process, wood consolidation, 126
Polyglycol, 144, 187
Poly(iso-amyl methacrylate) cross-linking, 173
Polymeric films, solvent action, 84
Polymerization, 144
  degree of, 68, 142
  glass restoration, 152
Polymers (see also Resins)
  bond formation, 173
  chain, breakdown, 88
  characterization, 171
  cross-linkage, 142, 143, 174, 178
  durability, 175
  high molecular grade, 174
  internally plasticized, 171
  low molecular weight, 174
  molecules, 7
    chains, 173
  reactivity, 177
  solvent action, 86
  synthetic, 179
  thermoplastic, 173, 175
  viscosity grade, 174
Polymethacrylates (see also Acrylics)
  consolidation of fragile objects, 127
  transfer operations, 166
Polymethyl methacrylate, permeability to water vapour, 178
Poly-n-propyl methacrylate, 80, 81
Polystyrene, 131
  expanded, 168
  permeability to water, 143
  permeability to water vapour, 178
Polythene wax, 136
Polyurethane pastes, 167
Polyvinyl acetal, 80, 81, 129, 134
Polyvinyl acetate, 79, 80, 81, 132, 144, 172, 173, 176, 191
  consolidation of fragile objects, 127
  cross-linking, 174, 178
  infra-red spectra, 180
  mould growth resistance, 75
  permeability to water, 143
  permeability to water vapour, 178
  reliability, 166
  supporting nets, 195
  ultra-violet exposure, 183
Polyvinyl alcohol, 67, 144, 152, 177, 191
  glass restoration, 152
  infra-red spectra, 180
  oxygen barrier, use, 178
  permeability to water vapour, 178
  ultra-violet exposure, 183
Polyvinyl butyral, 173, 193
  infra-red spectra, 180
  solubility, 177
  ultra-violet exposure, 183
Polyvinyl chloride, 212
Polyvinyl chloride acetate, polyvinyl chloroacetate, 80, 81, 143
Polyvinyl formal, 191
Polyvinylidene chloride, permeability to water, 143
Poly(vinylstearate-acetate), 173
Poplar panels, 167
Porosity of surfaces, 141
Potash
  concentration in glass, 147
  inclusions in glass, 150
Potash alum, consolidation of water-logged wood, 125
Potassium
  concentration in glass, 147, 148
  inclusions in glass, 150
  permanganate, 77
Pottery-making, 211
  courses, 212
Prepolymers, glass restoration, 152
Preservation
  archival materials, early attempts, 39
  training for engineers, 199
Pressurized spray cans, 171
Prints
  foxed, 76
  fumigation, 77
  programme at Academy of Fine Arts, Warsaw, 206

n-Propyl methacrylate, 80, 81
Protection of works of art during travel, 9–12
Protective clothing, 49
Protective lacquer, 135
Protein fibres, 193
Psocus domesticus, 56
Psocus venosus, 56
Public buildings, insecticides, 48
Pumice powder, washing easel paintings, 165
Purite, 92
PVC foil, 164
PVOH (see Polyvinyl alcohol)
Pycnidia, 63, 64
Pyrethrine, toxicity, 49

Radiation
  fluorescence, 34
  hazards, 1–6
  luminous, 2
  monochromatic, 22
  nuclear, effects on documents, 41
  paper deterioration, 40
  spectral, hazards, 1–6
  ultra-violet, 1–6, 8
Radioactive isotopes, 48
Radioactivity, 23
  artificial, 21
Radiography, 22, 111, 116, 198
  electron emission, 22
Radiology, 209
Radioscopy, 22
Ramie fibres, canvasses, 75
Rayon
  insect damage, 56
  moisture content, 193
Red lead, 164
Reforming, 173
  ease of solubility of certain resins, 79–83
  effect, 81
  investigations into nature of, 82
  propanol solution, 80
  technique, 177
Refractive index, 21, 177
Refractometer, 21
Regrounding paint films, 167
Reinforced documents, biological resistance, 65–68
Relative humidity (see Humidity, relative)
Reliefs, bronze, support of mineralized, 129
Rembrandt's glazes, 203
Repellants, toxicity, 49
Replica technique, 112
  local, 113
  metallurgical examination, 103
Researches, scientific, 206
Resins (see also Polymers), 169
  aging, effects, 79–83
  foam-forming, 124
  hardness, 171
  molecular weight, 171
  natural, 140, 177
  plastic, 99
  polyester, 66, 99
  soft, mixed with paint, 202
  solubility, 171
  synthetic, 80, 171
    bonding, 75
    fixing of detached murals, 120
  thermosetting, 79
  varnishes, natural, 176
  viscosity grades, 172
  viscosity of a solution, 171
Resistance, biological, 65
Restoration
  aims, 202
  archival materials, 39
  cleaning, 203
    tests, 205
  in-painting, 204
  laboratories, 198
  matching retouchings, 204, 205
  overcleaning, 203
  re-intergation, 204
  semi-cleaning, 202
  soft resin mixed with paint, 202
  solvents, 205
  teachers, importance of, 204
  teaching methods, 202
  techniques, 198
  training centres, 203
  training for engineers, 199

Restoration—continued
  volunteers, 204
  x-ray photographs, 203
Restorers, 200
  connoisseurship, 204
  syllabus, suggestions, 203
  test for diploma, 205
  training, 197, 202
Reticulitermes lucifigus, 55, 56
Reversibility, 176
Reweaving of tapestries, 188
Rheology, 157, 162
Rhizopus nigricans, 10
Rhoplex, 174, 175
Rodents, damage by, 57
Roman period
  coins, examination, 106, 109
  glass dish, restoration, 153, 155
  glasses, 147
  metal objects, examination, 101
  Millefiori fragment, 146, 147, 148
  silver bronze coins, 109
Rosary Madonna, 209, 210
Retenone, toxicity, 49
Roux boxes, 65
Rubber mats
  panel covers, 166
  regrounding paint films, 167
Rubbers, synthetic, casting, 212
Rust prevention in metal clips, 44

Salt water, glass submerged in, 151
Salts
  humidity-storing, 12
  soluble, crystallization, 212
Sandarac, 79
Saponifying agents, 165
Saran, 162
  permeability to water, 143
Sarcino lutea, 62
Scabbard, silver, 133
Schizomyceti, 57
Schradan, toxicity, 49
Science and art, collaboration, 19
Scientific instruments, 200
Scientists, supervision, 206
Scintillation counters, 30, 112
Scrim, 166
Sculptures, programme at Academy of Fine Arts, Warsaw, 206
Scunthorpe bowl, 132
Sealing wax as moisture barrier, 164
Semi-transfer, 169
Senlis bronze pedestal, 97, 98
Sequestering agents, 109
Sericin, gum, 193
Setamul N6525, 191, 196
Shale, consolidation of materials, 127
Shellac, 129, 132, 164
  fixatives, 119, 120
  mould growth resistance, 75
Shipment, canvas paintings during winter, 9
Shirlan, 77
Shrinkage
  glass restoration, 152
  panel paintings, 160
  wood, 156–175
Siderite, 92
Sidotrepa panicea, 56
Silica, 148
  aerogels, 48, 52, 59
  consolidation of fragile objects, 125
Silica-gel, 11, 12, 15, 59, 77, 129
Silicates, 142
  copper, 90
Siliceous materials, consolidation, 127
Silicone rubber, glass restoration, 152, 153, 155
Silk
  basic habits, 192, 193
  degradation, 185
  irradiation tests, 43
  paper reinforced by, 65, 66
  spin, direction of, 193
  sunlight weakening, 193
  supporting nets, 195
Silver, 112
  coins, 109, 112
  disc brooch, 132
  Emesa helmet, 133
  gauze as reinforcement, 133

Silver—*continued*
  horn, 110
  mineral alteration products, 91–92
  oxide, 110, 129
    method of bronze disease treatment, 129
  scabbard, 133
  tarnish, 89, 91
Silver-copper alloy, consolidation, 131
Silverfish, 55, 56, 59
Sinopia, loss of, 119
Sisal canvasses, tropical conditions, 75
Sizes, 78
Size
  microbial resistance, 58
  resin alum, 77
Skins
  insecticide contamination, 49
  rodents, damage, 57
Smalt, 79
Soaking, prolonged, 135
Soda, concentration in glass, 147
Sodium
  carboxymethyl cellulose, 166
  chlorite, 44
  disilicate, 148, 149
  electron-beam probe analysis, 146
  perborate, 44
  sesquicarbonate, patina stabilization, 110
Soft woods, panelling, 166
Soil water in glass, 151
"Solar Gray" glass, 1, 3, 4
Soldering, Pacatien statue, 98; Vix vase, 97
Solidity, increase, 140
Solubility
  aging and reforming, 79–83
  parameter tables, 87
  solvents, 177
Solvents, 171
  action, 84–88, 171
  brittleness of films, 171
  brushing, 173
  chemical links, breakage, 177
  chemical properties, 177
  diffusion, 87
  flexibility, 177
  handling qualities, 177
  hardness, 177
  high viscosity grade, 173
  leaching, 84–85
  loss, classification for adhesives, 143
  mechanical properties, 177
  mild, 171, 172
  mixtures, 84
  optical properties, 177
  permeability to gases, 177, 178
  solubility, 80, 177
    parameter, 173
  spraying, 173
  strength, 173
  strong, 171
  swelling action, 83, 84–85
  vapours, 84
Spectral internal transmittance, 3
Spectral irradiance, 2
Spectro-chemical analysis, 36
Spectrographic analysis, 26
Spectrography (*see* Spectrometry)
Spectrometry
  emission
    optical, 29, 31, 32, 113–116
  fluorescent
    visible, 21
    X-ray, 29–37, 112–118, 145
  gamma-ray, 30–32
  Geiger counter, 33
  infra-red, 81, 82, 88, 176, 179–183
  optical (*see* Spectrometry, emission)
  X-ray (*see* Spectrometry, fluorescent)
Spectrophotometry (*see* Spectrometry)
Spectroscopy, 21, 23, 24, 113, 198
Spinning, fibres, 192
Spirits of wine, 79
Sporotrichum, 57
Spot etching, 102
Spring wood, 157
Spruce panels, 163
Stability, chemical, 136
Stabilization, treatment, 140
Stachybotrys, 57, 66
Stand oil film (*see also* Films, Oil, Paint), 84, 85
Stannic oxides, 91

Stannous oxides, 91
Starch
  adhesives, 144, 166
  enzymes, removal by, 191
  paste, 168
Statuary, 91
Steam
  adhesive removal, 120
  iron, use, 193
Steels, microstructure, 103
Stereography, 111
Stereoradiography, 22
Stereoscope, 22
Stomphilium, 57
Stones
  conservation, 206
  inclusions in glass, 146
    analysis, 148
Strappo method of mural removal, 118, 119, 120
  adhesives, 121
Streptomyces, 62, 64
Striato, 204
Stripping, metals, 135
Stroma, 63, 64
Stromeyerite, 91
Strontium, 114
Students, selection, 203, 212
Studio for restoration, 25
Sub-tropics, conservation of works of art, 73–78
Sugar, solubility, improvement, 166
Sulphates, copper, 91
Sulphides,
  copper, 90
  lead, 91
  silver, 91
Sulphodex, toxicity, 49
Sulphur dioxide, 8
  oxidation caused by, 143
  paper deterioration, 40
  solvents, permeability, 177, 178
Sulphuric acid, paper deterioration, 40
Sulphurized iron, 140
Sulphuryl fluoride, 48
Summer wood, 157
Sundeala, 168
Sunlight, 1–6
  automatic control, 6
  deterioration of archival materials, 40
  paper deterioration, 41
  silk, weakening, 193
Surface bonding, 141
Surface coatings, 135
Surface tension, 141
Swelling
  degree, 85, 86, 88
  measurement gauge, 84
  wood, 156–175
'Swing-fog', 71
Sword of Kanta, 133
Synthetic fibre net, 195–6
Synthetic glasses, 147
Synthetic materials (*see* Polymers *and* Resins)
  solvent-type varnishes, 172
Synthetic resins, 75, 80, 120, 153, 163, 171, 176
Synthetic varnish, 177, 178

Tannates, iron, 92
Tapestries, 185–196
  blending colours, 188
  neutral colour, 188
  repair, 188
    plastic impregnation method, 188
  reweaving, 188
Technology, 210
  history, 200
  lecture programme, 211
Technovit, 132, 134
  glass restoration, 152, 155
Tempera (*see also* Paint)
  analysis, 37
  mould growth, 75
    resistance, 75
  protective coatings, 79
  washing, 119
Temperate zone, transport through, 13
Temperature (*see also* Air-conditioning, Environment), 9–12
  change, classification of adhesives, 143

Temperature—*continued*
  consolidation of fragile objects, 140
  controlled atmospheres, 9
  elevated, ultra-violet radiation, 174
  high, textiles, damage, 189
  mould growth, 76
  paper deterioration, 40
  variation, 13
    murals, 123
Tenorite, 89
Tensile strength of film, 141
Tensol, 130, 131, 132, 134
TEPP
  maximum atmospheric concentration, 50
  toxicity, 49
Termites
  Australia, 73
  control, 53
  drywood, insecticides, 48
  paper damaged by, 55, 56
Terylene
  bolting cloth, 167
  supporting nets, 195, 196
Tests
  chemical, 68
  optic, 67
  physical, 67
Tetraethyl pyrophosphate, treatment following poisoning, 52
Tetrahedrite, 90
Textiles, 185–196
  adhesives, 191
    cross-linking, 190, 191
    textile degradation, 191
  aging, 185, 190
  basic habits of fibres, 192–194
  chemical impregnation, 187
  chemical reactions in fibres, 190
  cleaning, 185, 193, 194
  climatological conditions, 190
  consolidation procedure, 189
  darning, 190
  degradation, 185, 190
  detergents, use, 186
  dirt removal, 193
  dry cleaning, 186, 193
  dryness, 185
  dust removal, 193
  elasticity after backing, 187
  fixative backing, 187
  flexibility after backing, 187
  glueing, 187, 188
  heat, 185
  high temperatures, damage, 189
  industrial processes, 190
  irreversible restoration, 190
  light, 185
  lumite screen, 193
  moisture, 185
  mounting, 193
  needle-work, 188
  old, 185
  oxidizing effects of ambient air, 185
  Pietas, 185
  plastic film protection, 188
  preservation, 185–191
  radiation, 190
  reinforcement, 195–196
  restoration, 190–191
  reversible methods of preservation, 189
  sewing, 188, 190
  silk veil protection, 188
  storage, 185
  structure of fibres, 212
  supporting fabrics, 191
  synthetic-fibre net reinforcement, 195–196
  washing, 193
  water soluble cellulose derivative as fixative, 187
  weathering, 190
Thermohygrograph, 9
Thermoplastics, 141, 142, 171, 173, 175
Thermosetting adhesive, 176
Thermosetting plastics (*see* Thermosetting resins)
Thermosetting resins, 141, 142, 144
Thuricide, 48
Thysanura, 55, 56
Tin, 114
  binary systems, 35
  grey, 91
  mineral alteration products, 91

Tin—*continued*
oxide, 91, 108
ternary systems, 35
white, 91
"Tin pest", 91
Tiraz fabrics, 193
Titanium, white, 75
Titian's glazes, 203
T. L. Tubes, 8
TMTD, toxicity, 49
Toluene, 173, 177
film swelling, 174
leaching by, 85
solubility, 81, 82, 177
ease of, 80
Toxaphene, 52
toxicity, 49
Toxic residues, 50
problems, 52
Training, 197–213
centres, 200–201
programme, 199
restorers, 202
Transfer of easel paintings, 165–168
Transportation
air, 15
protection during, 9–12
Travel, protection of works of art, 9–12
Trennlack, glass restoration, 152
Trichloroethylene, swelling power, 86
Trichoderma, 57
Triethanolammonium diborolactate, 71
Triglycerides, polymeric, 85
Trimethyl carbinol, wood consolidation, 125
Tropical countries,
conservation of works of art, 73–78
shipment of paintings, 10
transport through, 13
Turkey red oil, leather consolidation, 126
Turpentine, 84, 173
oxidation, 171

Ultrasonics, 59, 113
Ultra-violet
absorbers, 8, 81
behaviour, 212
cut-off, 3
filters, 174
light, 59, 164
appearance of age, 202
fluorescence in, 208
fluorescent tubes, 182
paper aging, 42
PVOH transparency, 178
radiation, 1–6, 8, 21, 22, 173
elevated temperatures and, 174
probable damage factor, 173
rays, 209, 210
spectrum, 176
Universities, Italian, 197
Urea formaldehyde, 144
Uvinul M-40 filter, 173

Vacuum deposition, 146
Vapour, barriers, 143
Varnishes (*see also* Films), 171–184
aging and re-forming, 80
application, 172
black, 202
chemical structure, 179
crazing, 79
cross-linking, 179
insolubility, 176
darkened, 204
degradation, 82
deterioration, 176
experimental, 172
function of coating, 84
gloss, 177
mechanical strain, 177
molecular chains, 179

Varnishes—*continued*
multi-layer systems, 179
nitrocellulosic, 111
optical properties, 177
oxidation, 176, 177
oxidative breakdown, 177
permanence, 176
picture, 176–184
preparation, 79
refractive index, 177
regeneration, 84
removal, 83
old films, 88
reversibility, 176
solubility, 177
solvent-type, 171–175
synthetic, 178
tinted, 204
transparency, 177
Varnishing, panel paintings, 157
Vegetable fibres, 192, 193
dampness, 185
Vegetable parasites, cellulose deterioration, 165
Venetian glasses, restoration, 152
Venetian turpentine, 168
Ventilation, 59
lack of, 70
Victoria and Albert Museum, packing methods, 16–18
Viking burials of Birka, 185
Vinamul N6525, 191
Vinyl acetate (*see* Polyvinyl acetate)
Vinylite, 80, 81
Viscosity, adhesive, 141
Vitrification, fragile objects, 140
Vivianite, 92
Vix vase, 97–99
Volatile material, 144

Wall-paintings, consolidation, 127
War, protection of patrimony during, 95
Washing
intensive, 109
tempera, 119
Water (*see also* Humidity)
absorption, change in, 14
carbon dioxide in, 91
electrical conductivity, 109
evaporation from wood, 14
glasses attacked by, 151
permeability to, 143
speed of absorption, 14
sulphur-bearing, 91
vapour, 136, 143
oxygen and, 8
weight, 13
Watercolours
Australia, 73
mould growth, 75, 77
Wax
impregnation, 128
insecticidal and fungicidal, 72
microcrystalline, 128
wood stabilization, 163
Wax-resin adhesive, 162
cement, 166
impregnation of panels, 165
lining for panels, 167
Waxed paper, 14
Weapons, bronze, 31
Weathering, glass, 146, 150–151
Weaving, fibres, 192
Wet-rot, 70, 71
Wettability of liquids, 141
White lead, 85
filler, 165
fungal activity and, 75
White spirit, 164
White tin, 91
Window glass, 173, 174
Window-lighted galleries, 1–6
Winter, shipment of canvas paintings, 9
Wollastonite, 148, 149

Wood (*see also* Panel paintings) *and* Panels
basic material, 157
cellular structure, 157
collapsed cells, 166
compression shrinkage, 158
convex warp, 158, 159
cracking, 125
density, 157
dimensional stability of dried, 125
elasticity, 157, 160
examination, 24
glass cloth, 162
insect damage, 56
mechanical properties, 157
mechanics of, 169
moisture barrier, 158, 162
moisture content, 158, 160, 161, 162
moisture transfer, 164
panels
paint defects, 156
shear stress, 156
permanent warp, 158, 163
plastic yield, 158, 160
plasticity, 157
prehistoric, 126
reactions to temperature and humidity changes, 13
removal, 166
shrinkage, 156–175
forces, 157
stabilization, 163
stress-strain behaviour, 157
structure, 212
swelling and shrinking, 156–175
warping, 125, 156, 158, 159, 165
water evaporation, 14
water-logged, 125–126, 144, 176
Wood-wool, 17
Woodworm, 56, 59
Wool
basic habits, 192, 193
degradation, 185
dyeing, 193
pelt dyeing, 193
protein, chemical reactions, 190
spin, direction of, 193
yarn dyeing, 193
Works of Art
destruction during War, 206
examination of, 19
methods of analysis, 19
protection during travel, 9–12
Worm channelling, 165
Wrapping, objects, 17

X-radiography, 210
behaviour, 212
X-ray diffraction, 26, 29, 33, 34, 91, 112, 113
emission, 116
fluorescence, 23, 31, 32, 33, 34, 113, 145
fluorescent, 29, 30, 37
intensity, 146
micro, non-destructive analysis, 33–38
powder techniques, 148
spectrometer, 145
X-rays, 21, 22, 25, 33–38, 112
Xylene, 84, 173
solubility, 177

Yarns, single, 193
spinning, 193
Yellow ochre, 129
Young's modulus, 171

Zaponecht pigments, 152
Zenith sky, radiation hazard, 2
Zinc, 114
chlorides, 135
mineral alteration products, 92
oxide, fungal activity and, 75
Zoology, 212